Lt. Pat O'Brien

Kevin McNulty, Sr.

DEDICATION

To the memory of my granddaughter

June Elise Markelz

CONTENTS

****

NOTE FROM THE AUTHOR

The story you are about to read is the most fantastic tale I have ever experienced in my lifetime. It is certainly a story of an American hero. But it is also the story of America's transition from a raw isolated frontier to the industrialized power it became in the 20th Century. You will experience the new American Century through the lives of the O'Briens of Momence, Illinois who offered up their son as the quintessential American hero. Born in the old with a vision of the future, Lt. Pat O'Brien is an iconic American figure for all time.

ACKNOWLEDGEMENTS

Rex Rowe, for his service to our country, our community, and for insisting we honor Pat O'Brien. Marcia Tedford, for bringing me this project and for her friendship, support and tireless commitment to telling Pat's story. Jean Stetson, Director, Edward Chipman Library, for her enthusiasm, knowledge and for her professional advice. Vic Johnson, for his lifetime of inspiration and commitment to Kankakee County history. Mike Jenkins, my mentor, for his wisdom, military knowledge and unwavering support. Marikae Tischler, for her pure reactions to the book and confirmation of our efforts. Jo McNulty, my wife, and our family for letting me go off on another venture and telling me to rewrite the beginning. John Grech, Researcher and Historian for the 66th Squadron, Royal Flying Corps in England for all his work and clarity. Geoff Zokal and Michelle Chaney for their diligent editing of the final manuscript. My grandparents for coming to Kankakee County.

WE ALSO THANK

Lowell Library, Kankakee Library, Edward Chipman Library, Newton County Indiana Recorder of Deeds, Smithsonian National Air and Space Museum, Ralph Cooper, Larry O'Brien, Gerald and Marggie Petro, Carla Petro Smith, Judy Hoffman, Elaine O'Brien Saindon, Robert Widener, Virginia Diane Fontaine, Les Laskey, James Chen, Gary Carruthers, Marty McNulty, the late Kay Hess for her inspiration.

SPECIAL THANK YOU

We'd like to thank Lori Floto and Leslie Jacobs of Nevada who found us three years into our project. Without them a significant portion of Pat's story would be missing. They are the previously unknown granddaughters of Pat O'Brien and Agnes MacMillan and daughters of Carol who you will read about in this book.

Lt. Pat O'Brien
Royal Flying Corps

PART ONE

FRONTIER AMERICA

CHAPTER 1

Martin O'Brien

The arrival of the white man in America and his relentless movement across the continent is a story of freedom loving risk takers running headlong into a proud, settled and undisturbed native population. The stories of violent confrontation between European settlers and Indian nations so dominate America's frontier history, that little is known of the more peaceful friendships between these two proud peoples. Not all relationships between native Indians and their European neighbors were violent.

Such was the case between the great Potawatomi Indians who populated the entire northeastern area of Illinois and the area's earliest European settlers. Known as the Kankakee Potawatomi, these Native Americans were equal partners in the development of frontier Momence, Illinois and in areas to its east and west.

The very names of towns, townships, streets and geographical points of interest would become monuments to the great Indian people of the Kankakee River. Momence itself was named after a local Potawatomi, Isadore Moness. They lived from the Rock Creek area of Shaw-waw-nas-see near Bourbonnais, to the Momence limestone shelf at "the lower crossing" and further east still, through the Great Kankakee Marsh and the Yellow River as far as Plymouth, Indiana. The "Yellow" was designated so by the Indians as a result of its soft limestone granular mix which hued the river year round.

In the late spring of 1833, one of the area's first settlers, William Parish drove his flatbed wagon across the north bridge of Momence after which he squared it again rolling up Range Street. As he crossed River Street, he gently urged his white horse by stirring the reins a bit, more right-to-left this time, so as not to increase his speed too much. His eight year old daughter Carrie Marie rode on his left.

Parish proceeded passed the corner grocer, agriculture implement store and the unique art gallery that had a large painted watch on its marquis sign that extended over the wooden walk. This morning, oddly enough, the frozen watch face on the gallery marquis seemed to be right. Indeed, to Parish, time felt frozen in Momence on this sad day. Curious, he lifted his pocket watch from his vest checking the accuracy of his impression. The two times matched.

Pushing the gold chained time piece back into his pocket with his thumb, he cautioned the white mare to halt in a tone much lower than his usual commanding voice. His destination was the U.S. Post Office next to the gallery where he had slowed significantly to put his buggy to rest. Parish was meeting Sid Vail at the post office where they would pick up papers directing them to witness the departure of their friends. It was a time known as the Indian "removal period." W.W. Parish, a native of Naples, New York and early Momence settler, was to be one of three men from Momence to escort the final group of Potawatomi Indians out of the luscious Kankakee Valley on that day.

"Daddy, you are usually so talkative when we come to the stores," Carrie said. "Did your oats not agree with you this morning?" she asked with a sweet admiring voice.

"No, Carrie," he said. "You know you make the best oat breakfast of any young girl in Momence, and I love you for it!" He lifted his eyes up to the northeastern sky. "But today your father has a most unpleasant task to perform. Our friends are leaving us."

Carrie's brow lowered. "Who, father? Not Abigail!" said the concerned young girl.

Parish stepped off and his seat spring elevated, jostling Carrie a bit. As he planted his boot onto the dusty road bed he gasped. "No, Carrie. Today, all of our Indian friends will move far away from us - to the west." He reached for her. "To Iowa," he said in a guttural tone as he lifted her out. Carrie was capable of climbing down herself but Parish instinctively gave her aid, his mind being somewhere else.

Carrie Marie Parish couldn't quite register the Potawatomi as friends of hers. But she was genuinely concerned because she could tell that her father was burdened by the day's prospects. When she heard talk of Indians, her thoughts always settled on that scary day when two young boys ventured inside the white picket fence that surrounded the Parish house situated along the south bank. She had just entered the front room holding her doll when she looked up and saw two red faces staring in at her through the window. She dropped her doll and opened her mouth to scream but didn't make a sound! Her petrified stare caused the two "neighbors" to flee.

[12]

"Good morning, Sid" said Parish as he held the door open for his young daughter. Parish and his fellow escort Sid Vail spoke of their general sadness at the departure of the peaceful Pottawatomi. As part of the Treaty of Tippecanoe, three chiefs had signed a treaty with the U.S. government agreeing that all Potawatomi would move west of the Mississippi River within two years.

The opening of the Illinois territory to European claimants made the Kankakee Valley a magnet for white settlers. It would take fourteen years following their official removal before the Potawatomi could not be found in Illinois. Eventually, Momence would no longer be a frontier town. It would begin to change. People were coming, many people. They would claim land once held sacred to the Potawatomi. The indigenous nomadic Indians of the entire Kankakee Valley would be replaced by thousands of transplanted, determined, and anchored people from the European continent.

Martin O'Brien would be one such arrival to Momence, though he didn't know it yet as he drifted down the St. Lawrence River toward Quebec in 1830. He knew little of Illinois, of Yellowhead Township or the available land that once belonged to the great Pottawatomi. He had traveled sixty days from Cork, Ireland to North America to find a new life. Like many Irish, he took the most affordable route to the U.S. through Canada, where he could buy a cheap boat ride from Montreal to the south bank of the St. Lawrence, or cheaper yet, land at Saint-Lambert on the south shore and walk to the U.S. border. As his wooden ship slowed into Quebec City, O'Brien gazed south at the many islands that filled the St. Lawrence River while thinking he was facing north.

"Is that Quebec?" he asked a fellow passenger who had joined him along the rail as the ship drew close to port.

"No, in fact, that… my Irish brethren…that is practically America. The city is behind you", stated the fair haired Irish farmer sporting his blistering red forehead. The sun had beaten down on the two Irish lads the entire way down the St. Lawrence. Not far from the southern shore of the river was the State of New York, well within a day's walk.

Martin did a quick look over his shoulder, then gazed back toward the south. "Well, that's were I'll be goin' then," stated O'Brien with an affirmative nod. "To the States!" he said.

"Martin O'Brien," putting out his hand, introduced himself. "Seamus Flaherty," was the response of the red head. It had crossed Martin's mind that he might need to know how best to traverse the "Lawrence" once they reached Quebec. "So tell me Seamus, how would I achieve the crossing of this swift stream once we land at Quebec? Mind you … get to other side!"

"Oh, you don't do that here. You need to get downstream to Montreal. The French take a local steamship line from Quebec to Montreal, then cross again by boat to Saint-Lambert," said Flaherty. "But you can take a small river boat from Quebec and get off directly at Saint Lambert like the rest of us Irish scum rather than be forced to occupy a ship full of Frenchmen," he said with a laugh at the end. "From there you simply walk south to the States." Both men chuckled further at the jab given to the French.

O'Brien knew of Saint-Lambert but was uncertain just how long a walk it was to the American border.

"How long of a walk is it, Seamus? To the States I mean" asked Martin.

"Merely 230 kilometer, likely a half day's trip," said the experienced Irish traveler.

"So you've made the trip across the big sea before?" O'Brien asked.

"Why sure, me family has found a home in Quebec. For me, I go home at regular intervals," assured Flaherty. "Too many French here you know! They never change. And I refuse to learn French," he stated with another hearty laugh. Martin belted one himself and at the same time.

Martin O'Brien was a good looking and likable fellow. He was considered handsome by the young lasses back home and had a zest for adventure. He had a broad and infectious smile and had no reservation about engaging perfect strangers. In pubs he was often the center of attention and regularly held court. His Ulster pals had laughed to their toes when he told them he was leaving for America. To no one's surprise however, he announced his future one night causing his former school chums to raise large mugs of local brew and see him off the next day. The prospects of coming to America stirred him greatly and he planned to see the country before settling down, as his mother had so aptly advised.

"So, O'Brien, I don't imagine you'll head to Saint-Lambert today, will you? asked Flaherty.

"Well, no, I had hoped to find a haunt to wet the back of my throat with a more lively liquid than the ration of water we experienced over these last sixty days," Martin said.

"Why of course, man! It'll be a stop at the Neptune for you my thirsty friend," stated Flaherty with a familiar confidence. "The fine Neptune is where all Irish lads begin their first day in this new land," he said. The Neptune was one of the more popular eating and drinking establishments of the early 1800's in Quebec. It was a favorite spot of Irish Sea captains passing through the port. Seamus had first been introduced to the Neptune by members of the crew he befriended on his first trip to Quebec some seven years previous.

Once their ship docked, O'Brien and the skinny, deliberate Flaherty walked to the Corner of Côte de la Montagne and rue Sault au Matelot where they found the famous Neptune. The two made a contribution to its long lasting reputation well into the night.

The next day, Martin O'Brien stood on the dock at Quebec and shook the hand of his new friend. Seamus Flaherty had helped him get his bearings and had secured him a pass at no cost on the Malsham steamship which would take him down the St. Lawrence. At the Neptune the night before, Seamus had drawn a rough map of the New England landscape and showed Martin how he could head straight south from Saint-Lambert, board a second steamship at Fort Miller, then travel down the Hudson River to New York City.

O'Brien was ecstatic and smiling broadly as he thanked Seamus for his help. The two men shook hands as if two soldiers going off to different battles, first grasping right hands then slapping the left over their tight grip in a double hand shake. O'Brien made friends easily but in this case was especially appreciative of the friendly assistance he had received from Flaherty.

By the afternoon, as Martin O'Brien opened a brisk walk south out of Saint-Lambert, he took his first steps towards America, towards his future and his legacy. He would never return to Canada again. But in eighty-five years, Martin's grandson Alva would reenter Canada and it would be significant.

Martin O'Brien's first step onto American soil, though uneventful and surely unnoticed by Martin himself, had been duplicated that day a thousand times. On the day he entered the United States, thousands of other freedom loving risk takers took their first steps into America through various routes. No one single crossing into this beautiful land of opportunity could be considered dramatic in and of itself. But the mundane existence of the European immigrant became irrelevant once he entered the American Frontier. Whatever new life lie ahead would become part of their final epitaph. In exchange, America would acquire its soul from these people.

O'Brien's path was typical of so many immigrants in the years prior to the Civil War of 1861. He would walk, ride horseback, flatboat, steamship and wagon to unknown places down the eastern shores of New England. He would walk to Maryland, Washington DC and cross the Potomac into Virginia. He'd push inward and away from the established "thirteen" down the great Ohio River, America's true and natural north-south dividing line. Then South on a beacon to the Mississippi and the most mysterious city of New Orleans which seemed to be an eclectic imposter placed ashore before even British-born hearts stirred in Boston and formed a definable country in the new world.

For nearly two years, Martin O'Brien would be on the move. New York, Baltimore, and Cincinnati were mere shadows of the cities they would be someday. America was a pathway to prosperity but not without risk. Logic told O'Brien there would be work in cities and there was. But work would only serve as a means to his next destination. It was in O'Brien's nature not to be shackled by an extended plan but driven by continuous action. Unmindful of his next destination, he would travel continuously getting introduced to new and exciting opportunities. Not until he arrived in New Orleans, nearly two years later, would he pause and consider his sense of place and begin to think as men do when they leave their youth behind and begin to embrace their legacy.

His trip began on a steamboat down the Hudson River.

"So your name is O'Leary, is it?" barked a thin middle aged man holding a tin cup with ale. Martin dropped his cup away from his lip interrupting his first sip. They stood on the steamboat deck heading South on the Hudson.

"No, it's" pausing to sip, "O'Brien." I'm traveling to…"

The man cut him off. "Well, O'Brien, whether it's O'Leary, O'Brien or O'Malley, it still got an "O" in front of it and you know what that means do you not young lad," he said in an imitative Gaelic brogue.

"I can't say that I follow you," said Martin, finally swallowing his first sip.

"If you're going to New York and you've just come off the boat, there's really only one place for you to start and I'm afraid it's not the most accommodating landing," the abrasive but sophisticated man said. Louis Tappan spoke rapidly with the confidence of an experienced urban dweller. It struck Martin how direct he was and made him wonder what on God's green earth motivated this snappy dresser to help him!

"Look young fellow, you're Irish, you're not carrying any possessions, and you're obviously without a developed trade. I'm afraid your place to start in New York City is non-other than Chatham Square." He looked directly into Martin's blank stare. "I mean "The Points," man!" Martin smiled but wrinkled his brow not being familiar with anything the man said. "Five Points, that is. Do you know it?" he asked.

Martin shook his head as he lowered for a second sip of ale. Suddenly the steamboat jarred and they both grabbed the side. The boat slowed, drawing a bead on one of many crude docks along Manhattan's western shore.

Stable again, the stranger continued. "I'm Tappan, Louis Tappan. Proprietor, instigator, and anarchist to some," he said with a convincing grin. "I'll take you there O'Brien. I'll show you Five Points. You'll be my guest once we come ashore. My brother and I are always looking for young, eager workers." Knowing little else, Martin agreed as they downed the last of their ale.

The boat docked quickly and passengers jumped past Martin and Tappan who were stepping more carefully onto shore. As they walked toward New York's capital of vice and crime, Tappan gestured wildly as he described Five Points' sordid reputation.

Louis Tappan, an abolitionist do-gooder who regularly recruited young immigrants to join him. He was one of the few around the parameter of Five Points that capitalized on its energy yet avoided being drawn in. Many a wide-eyed new arrival had been swallowed up by its lure. The Irish, with nothing in their pockets and fewer prospects were often led to Five Points by people like Tappan. Opportunities included working the slaughterhouses or one the few remaining tanneries that inhabited the mosquito infested swamp. Tappan planned to introduce Martin to the Chatham Theatre on the edge of Five Points. Here political rallies were staged which regularly spilled into the streets resulting in extended bare-fisted fights and knife wielding brawls.

They stopped at the Bowery Theater first to hear a speaker assail New York politicians for ignoring the "lowly low." They never made it to the Chatham spending the remainder of the evening and early morning in local pubs. Martin got the full flavor of urban life. He spent the next morning sleeping in the hot dormer attic of Tappan's two-and-a-half flat. Waking up at noon with a throbbing head ache, he fought off mosquitoes who were taking aim at his exposed skin. They were truly the majority population of the Five Points, he thought.

Realizing Tappan was seeking only his volunteer help, Martin took a job in a local slaughter house the following week where he dragged the inner remains of freshly split sows hanging from hooks, shoveled the loose remains into a shoot that dumped into an awaiting wooden cart. The prize was then hauled away by Negros who dumped it in a slough near the old Collect Lake. As part of their meager pay the Negros were allowed to pull "usable parts" from the mush before dumping.

Martin O'Brien had no future in New York. One month to the day, after paying all his back rent to Tappan, he announced his departure. "I appreciate your help, Louis," said Martin as the two shook hands after settling up. "You know where to find me," Tappan stated. Quickly the two men parted ways. There were plenty of other Irish with less insight than Martin that he could assist.

O'Brien headed toward Baltimore where there were jobs loading ships. It was merely 170 miles away and he got there in two weeks, sleeping in the peaceful woods and bathing in pristine streams along the way.

His time in Baltimore would be much more lucrative. He worked the docks and secured his first amount of savings. The people were pleasant and dock workers banned together to share housing close to the docks. Martin's goal was to save enough money to go west, away from the ocean. His conversations with former steamship operators in Baltimore taught him that the only way west was to embark on the great Ohio River. His dock experience would come in handy if he could connect with a shipping company. He'd save till spring and depart once the thaw came. He wanted to see more of his newfound country.

In May of the following year, birds, flowers and the youth of Baltimore signaled that spring would once again rejuvenate them all after a long, harsh winter. Martin's purse felt weighty enough to sustain him on his trip of greatest distance since arriving from Ireland. The spring air and his unbridled enthusiasm convinced him it was time to move on and he was ready to discover new things. Men like Martin O'Brien were made for America's opportunities.

[18]

Martin glanced at a rough map given to him by his Baltimore dock boss, himself a former steamboat captain on the Ohio. "How big this country must be. Even when I get to Cincinnati I'll be well short of the Mississippi," he thought."

Martin had a sense of Ireland's size having traveled much of it before he left. He found the massive openness of America overwhelming and it stirred in him a feeling of exuberance and liberty. With so few people in such a large country his head spun to think of the choices he now had. His spirits soared at the prospects of living in America. "There can't be a happier man alive as I," Martin said aloud to himself as he made his way out of the port city of Baltimore.

Chapter 2

Ohio

Martin O'Brien turned and waved to his fellow dockworkers. He began his walk toward a large two story barn located at the edge of the shipyard where he planned to rent a horse. He'd had enough of ships and steamboats and the loading docks of Brown's Wharf for a while. Having farmed in Ireland as a boy, he longed to travel over solid ground and was happy to be heading west from Baltimore.

A total of seven turnpikes projected north and west from Baltimore in 1831. One in particular was the sixty-two mile Frederick Town Turnpike which was the first leg of a highway running westward to Cumberland, Maryland. From there Martin could connect to the new National Road. Baltimore was the only eastern seaport connected to America's first National Road. It was established as a result of a bill signed into law in 1806 by Thomas Jefferson himself. It would provide him a route to Wheeling, Virginia where he would again board a steamship and travel down the legendary Ohio River to his next destination, Cincinnati.

"Now I suggest you take this mare sir," stated Walter Grumish the stout German immigrant who operated a very successful horse and carriage rental facility at the edge of the Baltimore port. "She's not been out for three days and will provide you with solid service to the other end." He stated this as he kicked open the swing gate allowing the mare to step out.

"Why, that will be just fine," stated O'Brien. "Now, how does this work? I pay you and ride the mare straight though to Wheeling?"

Grumish waved him off, "Nein! Nein! Nein!"Vemember, I told you, see my partner at Coomberlond. His name is Friedrich Auch." He stated this while raising his brow, assuring Martin understood. "I have sent word with him that a tall, dark haired Irishman named O'Brien shall arrive in two to three days with de mare," he said raising his voice. "And he is to svitch de mare for a colt and send you on your vay," Grumish lowered his tone again creating an up and down sliding sound to the two part sentence.

O'Brien responded by nodding and taking the reins in his hand. "And I pay you for the entire thing, correct Mr. Grumish?" Martin said as he opened his leather pouch. He was pinching coins one at a time with his thumb and forefinger then flipping each coin to the back of his hand while he reached for another until the amount needed was firmly in his grip.

In a proper German way, Grumish stood leaning forward a bit but with his hands clasps behind his back. Not until Martin extended the cluster of coins did Grumish release his right hand, leaving the left behind and mouthing the count silently as O'Brien counted out his fee.

"Sixty-five, seventy, seventy-five, eighty, eighty-five. That should do it!" Martin snapped.

"Vielen Dahr! Herr Brien. Thank you very much," stated the smiling German, skipping the "O" this time in Martin's name. "Now, Veemember! You vill get back 10 cents from Mr. Auch. As long as you arrive safely with de mare," he said.

O'Brien shook the German's hand and tipped his hat. Then placing his boot in the left stirrup, swung his long right leg over top and squared himself into the saddle.

"What a comforting thing to be riding a horse once again," he thought. "It reminds me of home." Martin kicked and the mare bolted forward. His trip west had begun.

He rode up the turnpike for three days to Boonesboro, Maryland then picked-up the National Road on to Cumberland. The exchange at Cumberland went smoothly and after paying an additional fee to Auch, O'Brien rented a second horse and headed for Wheeling, Virginia and the Ohio River.

Martin was astounded when he crossed the Allegheny Mountains. He had not seen such beauty since leaving Ireland. It made him think about home and for the first time he felt pride as an American as well. His throat tightened and he felt his eyes begin to swell. After a short pause, he glanced off to the left in a mental gesture that removed his emotions.

Martin was experiencing what so many new Americans felt, time and time again, in the early frontier days. Generations of Americans, particularly those with memories of the old country, would always live in two places. This would also always be part of the American fabric. It's why Americans refer to themselves as Irish-American, German-American or African-American. This was the first time Martin *felt* American.

Traveling across southwestern Pennsylvania he reached Wheeling, Virginia on the Ohio River in three days. His back side told him he was ready to board a ship once again. Cincinnati by steam boat was 376 miles from Wheeling. He connected with the Velociped Steamer, a 109 ton ship that ran between Pittsburgh and Louisville.

"If you will unload the cotton and the sugar, I can exchange a fare to Cincinnati," said Ezra Johnson, who was hiring help at the Wheeling Port for the Velociped.

"Does that include food and drink?" asked Martin.

"You eat with the crew. If we dock for any reason, you're on your own," said Johnson.

"Sounds like a fair deal. I'd like to tie on with you," Martin responded.

Martin exchanged a fare for unloading cotton and sugar at Wheeling's port and for agreeing to load tobacco at Cincinnati on the other end upon arrival.

The trip to Cincinnati took over three weeks as the ship had engine problems at Portsmouth and spent five days in repair. Martin spent more than he desired while the ship was repaired. When he finally arrived, the hot muggy air of this rapidly growing river town was clear evidence that he had not only distanced himself from the ocean but had made a relentless drift to the south where the heat of summer was well underway in June. Unfortunately, the five day delay forced Martin to find work in Cincinnati and build back his reserves.

Steamboat manufacturing and repair was a major industry in the city, so Martin took a job in the steamship industry. Despite his intrigue for engines and all things mechanical, he stayed current with agriculture by talking with farmers who brought harvests from north and south each day to be sent down the Ohio and Mississippi Rivers. Most of his friends at work were farm boys themselves but like Martin found wages better in the steamboat industry. Still, they often talked about farming again one day.

One evening during dinner and drinks, Martin proposed an idea to his friends. "Boys, I say we take a ride to the country and away from this hog town," he said to his three chums at the Foss Schneider Pub.

"But Martin, it's near mid-night and where might we be getting horses now?" was the heavily Gaelic response of John Shea who was always the most pragmatic of the group.

"I'm not talking about now, you daft man!" Martin belted. "I mean, we're all farm boys are we not? Let's take what we've stowed away, tell the boss man we're through and rent us some horses to go north! I'm sick of ships. How 'bout it boys? Let's take a ride up the Miami to the fertile ground. We may find nothin'. We may find land. Heck, we may even find women!"

The whole table roared as Martin was always the one to get his buddies charged up. The last round of drinks included a bond by all four. They'd go together in a week's time on pay day. "It's set then?" Martin asked. "Indeed!" they all shouted. At that point, the proprietor shouted, "Let's go, boys! Enough dreamin' for one night!"

All the way home each man speculated on the milk and honey to be found north of Cincinnati. They would arrange to sleep in barns and sheds owned by the many farmers they had met over the season. They'd ride to Dayton, Monroe and finally Troy, Ohio. Perhaps they'd find land and start their life's existence. This "fools spirit" was another requirement in the new world. Young men all over the frontier exercised it many times. It was a necessary ritual required to turn a dream into action. Martin was one of the few that needed little prodding.

Martin O'Brien was a natural leader of men. He had just begun to see that in himself and only since he came ashore at Quebec. It seemed as though he was always the man others turned to when circumstances paralyzed their actions. Martin could decide and as result he'd often decided for the whole lot of them.

They were all Irish boys and frankly had had their fill of mosquitoes, river mud and long days. But were it not for O'Brien's prodding they would have likely drank themselves into few plans.

All but Martin were reaching their mid-twenties and none of them had a sliver of spare time to enjoy the fruits of their labor. They worked every hour offered to them. And they had little time for the women of Cincinnati. Martin, the oldest of the group, had initiated the plan and would go with them. But his motivation was to weigh the merits of anchoring roots in Ohio or taking a run at the Mississippi, New Orleans and the Gulf of Mexico itself. He wanted to feel how it all connected. He'd come so far since Quebec. Only by taking the entire route south to New Orleans would he have a real sense of the breadth and size of his new found land and he wanted to embrace it all.

Martin and his friends took their last pay and rode north along the old Indian trail that hugged the Great Miami River. As they rode north, O'Brien felt he had nothing to lose. America was again offering him such vast choices. His trip to Troy would not be his final stop. But it would be a fateful trip and not his last visit to Miami County.

English, French, Irish, and Scottish immigrants, whether arriving via the Ohio River, the Great Lakes, or Canada, brought fifes, drums, fiddles, and footwork to the fur-trade, military posts, lumber camps, farms, and small towns of frontier America. Brisk marches and "fiddle tunes," jigs and reels were part of community socials all over the Midwest and Ohio in particular.

On the night that Martin and his friends arrived in Troy, Ohio, noted fiddler Daniel Emmett and his talented quartet, were scheduled to perform in Adam Brookhart's two-story pole barn at the edge of town. A dance was planned each year in either Piqua or Troy. This year was Troy's turn to host and the evening held good promise for the four young Irish lads eager for a weekend's rest from their long trip north. The foursome got to town around three-o'clock in the afternoon and proceeded to the Anderson Inn for a hot meal and a few mugs to wet their dry throats.

"Business seems to be slow today, hey," proclaimed Martin to the mustached bartender. The owner of the bar was placing mugs in front of each weary traveler while he responded.

"Oh, well today, yes! You see everyone is working through the day. The big doin's are tonight." Finished, he wiped both hands on his long white apron. "Doins?" John Shea asked with an Irish lilt to his voice as he pulled the mug away from his lips.

"Why, yes, tonight is the Pique-Troy Community Reel," said the busy man. He walked left and right as he continued to talk. "Brookhart's barn will be spilling over with young and old alike. It's a big dance and everyone will be there. Just hope you boys aren't plannin' any ruckus," he said as he eyed Martin. "You boys from Piqua?"

O'Brien stood up. "Why, no, we're from Cincinnati!" Now the bartender looked truly concerned. "Oh, a bunch of river rats, are yah?" he stated.

"We're just on a bit of short trip off that muggy river. Out to see the country, you know? And looking for some good clean fun, as well" They looked friendly and harmless to the bartender. He believed O'Brien who was experienced at giving convincing speeches to strangers on a regular basis.

"Well, boys, I'd say we've stumbled into the right place. Looks like we'll be goin' to a dance tonight. Yah do dance now don't yah, John," asked O'Brien. The group roared with laughter since Shea was the most reserved. Shea grinned and went back to work on his mug without responding.

Chip O'Bannon, a third member of the party, joined in and said to the bar attendant, "Well, even if we don't dance, I'm sure there'll be a good number of fine young ladies from the surroundings, might there not?" For his part, O'Bannon was as spry as Martin but always played second fiddle so as to give the group the advantage of the best leader.

The boys enjoyed a good meal of boiled beef, white potatoes, and lima beans from local fields. It was a meal only an Irishman could love. They washed it down with healthy refills of the local brew and spent three hours in celebration of their first visit to Troy. After a half day's worth of conversation with the bartender, it was time to head to the barn. They flipped a healthy tip to the bartender, shook his hand, and went off to enjoy an evening of fun.

"Good Lord, listen too 'um!", stated Turf Brogan. Turf was his nickname. His real name was Ethan Brogan but he got the name "Turf" as a result of constantly talking of the old peat bogs back home in Ireland. The others heard about it daily as they toiled in the ship building trade in Cincinnati and pinned the name on him.

Turf was right. The barn roared with fiddle music and hand clapping. It was spring and the rafters of two story barn were near empty of hay and other winter provisions. The three fiddles, the hand tambour and clap-clap rhythm of the town's folk was amplified by empty barn, cascading out upper hay doors. Dan Emmett and his fiddle band, some of the best the boys had ever heard, had the locals clapping in unison so loud that they could hear the ruckus half-mile down the road. Emmett would become known to many in the frontier. He would later write lasting American favorites such as "Turkey in the Straw," "Old Dan Tucker," and "Dixie."

When the boys entered they were immediately awash in sound and motion as a full-scale reel swung by them like a horse race. Martin almost collided with a few. Turf jumped into the reel, leaving the other three standing with dropped jaws. John Shea and Chip O'Bannon joined the herd next, leaving Martin holding his position watching.

The ladies were dressed in long frilly dresses never worn during field work. Each one seemed to have her hair pushed up in a way reserved for some refined French ball. Almost as soon as the Irish lads had stepped inside, Martin became affixed on a twirling red head and her partner that nearly ran him down, causing him to step back. He locked his eyes on the couple. Watching the young lass appear and disappear on opposite sides of her twirling partner.

"Was this her beau?" he thought. "Couldn't be a husband, he's too young and so is she," he observed. O'Brien was struck by the young red-headed flower who seemed to standout above all others in the room. The roar of the reel itself was no longer present in his head. The dance went on agonizingly long until Emmett's crew slapped a final "shave and a haircut" ending on it and the barn roared with approval.

"How about a drink, O.B.?" Brogan asked. It snapped Martin out of his daze. "Sure, Turf, sure," When Martin responded he flicked his head right toward Turf, as if being awoken from a sudden day dream. They walked across the barn to the refreshment table where town girls, too young to participate, were thrilled to be serving the punch. They were catching their first glimpse of more mature girls who were bold enough to talk with boys and weren't afraid to flirt.

As Martin and Turf approached the refreshment table, two of the pigtailed school girls giggled well into their words asking, ""Would you like refreshments?" Martin was still glancing over his shoulder at the distant red head and answered a bit tardy following Turf's positive response.

Now Martin and Turf were good looking young lads. Martin was particularly striking to the young girls due to his height, his dark Irish features, and shoulders of a young man bearing months of ship loading at Baltimore. Turf was a flirt and winked back at the girls. The young girls extended the giggling session well past the official conversation. Once the two men were served and some safe distance away, they huddled like a swarm of bees to discuss their chance encounter.

A brisk waltz had ensued. John Shea had found a fairly rotund but pretty farm girl. They were measuring their steps around the parameter of the dusty dance floor. Chip O'Bannon was equally successful and was still with the pretty blond German girl he had grabbed during the first dance. He was now following her waltz steps with a much more studied look on his face.

Turf was rapidly expressing his pleasure at the "quality" of the event, talking like a young kid who just caught his first fish, when he turned and realized Martin had cut away. He had taken aim for the red head, not bothering to signal Turf of his departure. Undisturbed, Turf lifted his eyes to survey his chances at finding a willing partner.

O'Brien was focused. With a broad smile he walked directly toward Amy Hurley. Miss Hurly was a young but "of age" lass standing with her girlfriend and chipping off a small partial of a sugar cookie she had just taken from to bakery table. Seeing O'Brien move so directly at them, her girlfriend Mary, nudged her with an elbow and Amy looked up. Whether it was the directness of Martin's gate or the suddenness of Mary's nudge, Amy was not sure. But her hands lowered and separated and she let go of the sugar cookie. It rolled down a pleat in her dress and landed silently issuing a puff of dust off the dirt floor

.

"Hello, madam," he said to her with a quick, shot nod of his head.

"Hello," she said.

"My name is Martin O'Brien. Do you have a partner for this dance?" Martin was nervous for the first time in his life. She smiled and assured him she did not. "Excuse us miss," Martin said to Mary on Amy's right.

He extended his hand and walked her to a convenient space in the floor. Some instinct having taken over Martin, he bowed first. Not a deep obvious bow but a slight one that seemed to be what you did before taking your partner. It had roots in most of Western European countries. Even though he had never danced formally, he was somehow familiar with this classic ritual.

It struck Amy. "How dignified," she thought. She stepped forward, raising her right hand palm up to meet his and she placed her left on his right shoulder. She was immediately struck at how solid it felt. Martin hardly noticed their right hands touching for he was nervously anticipating how it would feel to place his right hand round her small waist. It is always the more anticipated element of a man's first dance with a lady. It crossed a line of intimacy that clasping hands did not.

Martin could not describe it but he found the feel of her waist unnerving. The extended separation between them and stillness of his extended right arm made this embrace much different than a warm goodbye hug with your mother or aunt. Regulated as it was, it amplified the moment. He was glad to take their first steps to his left so they could both concentrate on their feet and avoid the tension of their first extended embrace.

Martin O'Brien and Amy Hurley spent the rest of the dance together. O'Brien's buddies were equally engaged other than Turf, who moved from one lady to another. The boys had a great time and the celebration went well into the evening. Martin and Amy skipped a few dances and sat on hay bales placed along the wall of the barn away from the whirling dance floor.

He relayed his entire story since leaving Ireland.

Amy revealed her upbringing, family, friends, and one other important piece of information. She told him where she lived. Martin, an instinctively smooth talker, asked enough deflecting questions that Amy fell into a longwinded and detailed word map that told Martin exactly how to find her family farm. Toward the end of her informative verbal romp she suddenly realized how revealing she had been. She slowed her pace, eased the enthusiasm in her voice, and slowly detailed the final leg of the journey to her family farm. In the end, she was glad she did but she didn't want to appear to be too enthused. After all, her mother had taught her to maintain her dignity when dealing with the young men at dances.

They had some good talks. Interspersed with a dance or two, both became relaxed and felt the ease that couples do when they meet for the first time yet feel they've know the other for the entire lives. In a word, they clicked.

"Will you travel back to Cincinnati tomorrow?" asked Amy with a hesitation in her voice. "No we plan to leave first thing Monday morning," responded Martin.

After a long silence he stated quietly, "I thoroughly enjoyed my evening tonight Amy." She looked directly into his eyes and realized again how stunning they were and almost forgot to speak, "So did I, Mr. O'Brien."

"Hey O.B.! Let's go!" Turf shouted who had seen his dance partner off a few minutes early. "Sure, Turf," Martin shouted back. "I have to go now. Thanks, Amy," he said to her. Frozen in the moment, Amy didn't ask nor did she think to ask if she might see Martin O'Brien again. Had it come to her, her reserved nature or perhaps the instructions of her mother would not have let her ask.

"Good night, Mr. O'Brien," He nodded, smiled, and turned in the direction of Turf. He headed back to town with his three buddies, giving one last look back when he met the pack. Amy had already turned towards home. He could just see the hem of her dress flicker as she entered the darkness of nigh

Chapter 3

Storms on the Mississippi

On the Monday following the big dance, Martin and his friends headed home. They traveled the same pathway along the Miami & Erie Canal. It seemed to be a longer trip even though it was the same route.

"Is it me or is it taking longer to get back on this road?" Martin said to Turf.

"Well, we're not working the horses as hard and don't forget we've already made three stops," Turf replied. "Besides, I don't think any of us are in a big hurry to get back, are we?"

"That's true for sure, Turf," replied Martin. "I guess we should pick things up a bit or we'll never get back to Cincinnati." The four kicked the sides of their horses and their paced quickened. Twenty miles later it had slowed again as interest waned. Martin's thoughts drifted again to his weekend meeting Amy.

Martin was reliving his conversations with Amy and her seductive expressions. His associates noticed that he was particularly pensive and asked about his health a few times, implicating he may have had too much to drink. But the shrewd Irishman did not let on. Though he was clearly struck by cupid at Troy, his mind was also in full debate. He was measuring his elation about Amy Hurly and his temptation to turn back against the nagging allure of the Mississippi River which had plagued him since leaving Wheeling, Virginia.

Steamboat workers viewed the Mississippi as psychologically superior to the Ohio River. They spoke of it in reverent tones and felt drawn to its strong resolve. At its terminus was New Orleans, a city full of mystery and temptation. Farmers, who never stepped foot on a steam boat, also viewed the river as more than a transportation route. They paid homage with the harvests of grain and tightly bound bundles of shag every day, imagining what they might see were they brave enough to join their cargo on deck and escort it to the Gulf.

New Orleans was just too attractive and mysterious to be missed, particularly for a man with hunger for the unknown like Martin. As his horse completed the final leg of his trip from Troy, O'Brian decided. He'd sign on to a crew and head south. "With a little luck, I'll return to Troy someday," he thought.

Like generations of Irish before him, Martin would place his fate in the hands of the mystics. The Irish always maintained the ability to assign their fate to the whims of Irish mystics who could bring luck one day and be blamed for calamity the next.

When Martin and his associates arrived back in Cincinnati they sold their horses and sought work again. Martin announced his intent to sign on with a steamship operator and head down the Ohio and Mississippi to the big city of the south. "Well, O.B.," Turf murmured, "we're going to miss you."

"You know me. No grass grows beneath my feet," Martin said

Martin then offered a friendly gesture, knowing they would not take him up on it. "Why don't one of you come with me? It will be grand fun!" He had a broad grin on his face and his infectious smile almost convinced Turf. Even John Shea almost jumped at the chance but then caught himself.

"No, Martin, I think ye go on this one by yourself," said Shea. "Taking a two-day horse ride to meet a bunch of young lasses is one thing now – but floating down the Mississippi," he stated as he raised the pitch of his voice in a questioning manner, "Now that's a whole different story!" They all laughed for it seemed that the quiet John Shea was clearly terrified at the prospects.

Turf had plans and Chip O'Bannon only wanted to return to his old job at the shipyard. Chip worked strictly to support the frivolity of the weekend and wanted nothing to interrupt his supply of cash. A strong bond had formed between these men who worked long, hard days on the banks of the Ohio River. They were all sorry to see Martin leave. After a final toast that evening they parted ways.

The next morning, Martin O'Brien walked to the boat docks along Cincinnati's bank to find his contact. He had been told by a shipyard chum that the best steamship captain on the river was Henry Shreve of the Monongahela Steam Navigation Company. Shreve was famous along the entire waterway from Pittsburgh to New Orleans.

Docked at Cincinnati was Shreve's current ship, the Washington. She was a gigantic float of some 211 tons, length of 136 feet, breadth of 21 feet and the first boat with two decks, a predecessor to the showboats of the mid-1800's. Her boilers were on the first deck rather than in the hold. Her main cabin was sixty feet; she had three handsome private rooms besides a bar-room. She was the invention of Shreve himself.

"What luck!" thought O'Brien. "None other than the best Captain on the Ohio and the ship he entrusts to himself alone." As Martin approached the yard, the monster could be seen docked and steady alongside the woodened structure holding numerous steamships fast.

"Might you be Captain Shreve, sir?" He instinctively saluted, but not being a military man previously, he caught himself in mid-salute and executed somewhat irreverent half wave.

"I'm Shreve," said the stalwart man. "What can I help you with young man?"

"I'm looking to sign-on with an operator Captain," said O'Brien. "A good one!"

"Well, do you think you've found one?" smiled Shreve as he continued to wrap a thick roped around its mooring on shore.

"I'm told you're one of the best, sir," Martin retorted. And I want to see the Mississippi.

Shreve stood up, arching his back with an ache as he had done so many times before. "Well, you look strong enough. Have yah' ever been on a boat yourself, young man?" he asked.

"Only as a passenger but I've built them here in Cincinnati for two years," said O'Brien with good confidence. "I know every part of this ship, I'd say. I'd be a good maintenance man what with knowing how she's put together from the keel up!"

"That you might," was the Captains response. "I could use a good hand with an equally experienced mind to keep her afloat. Can you leave tomorrow?"

"Indeed I can, Sir!" Martin was thrilled and Shreve directed him to meet at the office of James V. Hickmeyer, Shreve's attorney, in one hour and they'd sign papers. Martin was about to work for a legendary captain and finally see the city that everyone boatman spoke of since he put in at Wheeling months ago. Two days later the Washington was moving south out of Cincinnati under Shreve with a crew that included steamboat worker Martin O'Brien.

"You've never been farther south than Cincinnati?" said Shreve to O'Brien. "No, I've been working in the yards my entire time there, short of a quick trip north to Miami County," Martin said. It had been the first time since coming aboard that O'Brien had flashed back to Amy and the barn dance.

"Miami?" questioned Shreve as he pulled the ship's wheel directing it west. Being a lifelong river boat captain, he had no idea of such places so distant from the river bank. Martin told him of his trip with his buddies. Shreve listened politely, though distant, as one does when hearing a tale of no significance.

"I was able to sell my horse and I also met a fine young lady there who…." Martin was cut off.

"You know, O'Brien, you're fortunate to have come this way during modern times. In the earlier days, the rapids could add two to three days to the journey, should there be a number of us making the run," said Shreve. "Now that the canal is complete we're able to skirt past them. We'll be on the muddy in no time." The muddy, of course, was the Mississippi and it caught Martin's attention.

Shreve's boat was well past Louisville and was making good time. From the wheelhouse, he could now see the bluffs at Golconda, Illinois in front of him and knew he was approaching the final three bends of the Ohio that would deposit the Washington onto the Mississippi. The Ohio turned sharply south at Golconda toward a second bend that welcomed the Tennessee River pouring in from the left bank. Shreve pulled the wheel hard this time. The tip of the jackstaff, a steamboat's directional focus, swung away from Golconda and the big steamer turned to port in a southerly direction.

As he headed south, the entire western sky was heavily laden with dark clouds harboring a major fall rain storm. Though it was approximately four in the afternoon, it was so dark that one could hardly see more than one hundred yards downstream. Were it not for the few craft entering the Ohio from the mouth of the Tennessee, Shreve would not be able to see his reference point for the next turn west.

In the Midwest, hot muggy days often give way to a single rolling cold front that enters from the west in the late afternoon. Just prior to turning at Golconda, Shreve had noticed a light breeze and could see the small vegetation along the bank flipping in the wind. Such an advanced breeze was a common calling card of severe storms that appeared approximately a half-hour ahead of the front. Shreve was timing his options like a master considering the wind, sky, river, speed, direction, and his keen navigational sense honed over many years.

At the mouth of the Tennessee he swung the steamship starboard ninety degrees toward the west and into the approaching storm. It had gained on him and the corners of his eyes seemed to pull back as the full horizon and the size of the front became readily apparent.

"Check the cabin deck one last time, O'Brien," he ordered. "There's a storm coming and I don't want to lose a spare bucket when this wind kicks up. Make sure everyone is inside." O'Brien turned and walked briskly aft along the starboard side. He had an admiring grin on his face, still marveling at how much detail an experienced Captain like Shreve displayed. "All I can think about right now is getting to the Mississippi and he's insuring our inventory of spare buckets," he chuckled to himself. Men like Shreve were admirable for their sense of mission, their ability to monitor multiple conditions and their attention to detail.

As O'Brien worked quickly, all passengers were scurrying inside, heeding the crew's commands. A small child, wrenching his arm in the grasp his mother's hand, glanced up at him with a concerned look. Martin thought well enough to smile back at the boy and the youngster grinned back as if to say, "He doesn't look worried, so I won't fret." Martin remembered the Captain's words that a good crew should project calm despite the urgency of the moment.

The distinct line between dark and white clouds was clearly dividing the western sky just above the horizon. A fifteen degree drop in air temperature was racing across a final stretch of Missouri real estate and would soon roll over the Mississippi and run headlong into the Washington and its crew. Henry Shreve estimated that wind and rain would arrive at some point past Metropolis, Illinois which was now on his right. He felt he had time. Through this odd twisting pathway of the Ohio River at the bottom of Illinois he turned north past Metropolis for a short run then another hard turn to port that had the boat almost due south. He was losing time.

Finally, he could see Cache Island on the left and the mouth of the Cash pouring in from the right bank at Cairo. He slid the steamboat along the west bank where a natural dyke lay just short of the Cash River. Here he would ride out the storm.

He accelerated. "I want to tuck this boat along the starboard side at Cairo," shouted Shreve. "We'll dock there until she blows over. Get me three crewmen on the main deck and check the loads!"

Like other steamships of its day, every square inch of the main deck space was weighed down with cargo. The Washington had cotton bales stem to stern along the main deck except for a section of fifteen shipping crates full of chickens along the edge of the deck on the port side. Near the boilers the crew had stacked some large cargo, tied four full sized steers to the mooring post and fourteen pigs were corralled inside hay bales. O'Brien stacked an additional height of bales to the makeshift pig pen and quickly laced additional rope through all the bales holding it firm.

Suddenly, a temperature drop washed over Martin and members of the crew still on deck. The boat was a hundred yards from shore. Martin and two other crewmembers, assured that all passengers and were safely inside and made their way back into the wheelhouse. As they pulled alongside the boatswain and his crew jumped onto the dock and secured the vessel. Just then it hit.

A rapid and sudden down draft pulled at the just secured ropes holding the Washington fast to shore. It was torrent of water and wind not unlike a slamming door. The very edge of definable front pealed back the thick layer of humidity that canvassed the entire Ohio River Valley.

A shrill of high register altissimo could be heard splashing against the surface of the river. Martin, Shreve and the remaining crew got inside just as a simultaneous crack and bright bolt of lightning struck the ship with a stunning explosion that jolted every man on board including Shreve himself. It was the worst storm he had seen on the river in thirty years. "Thank God we got her tied down," he thought.

The initial onslaught went on for a hard twenty minutes, a long time for such storms. The front had obviously paused, wreaking havoc over the 211 ton vessel and its surroundings. The burst finally gave way to a long sustained rain that had equal volumes of water but lacked the violent scream of the storm's entrance.

Typical of such storms there was a soothing quality about the dense cool rain that followed and Martin took a walk along the portside to inspect the damage. He was bathed as if swimming the Ohio itself, working his way aft and back again. He found the whole experience somehow beautiful and powerful at the same time. The ship had held fast and with the exception of a few startled and saturated chickens, all was fine. The cattle stood as stoically as they had the whole trip dripping streams of water down the crevices of the layered muscle destined for the New Orleans slaughter house. The pigs were still screeching, reporting to each other in a way not unlike the human cargo that was finally breathing a sigh of relief inside.

The Washington spent the night docked. Even Shreve had lost his motivation to take on the Mississippi after such a hard afternoon. The crew and passengers had a wonderful meal together on board prepared in the galley and served in the large room where the shipmates had freed every opening to let the cool moist breeze cool down the ship without the presence of bugs that had been washed away for a short spell following the storm.

The next morning they got away, made the final turn west past Cairo and were in an obvious southward flow on the greatest river in North America. Once they made the turn and Shreve was satisfied they had found the proper channel, Martin had time to pause and take in his surroundings.

The Mississippi was certainly wider and had a majestic quality. It had purpose and was carrying a powerful energy that pulled hundreds of boats each day to the big city of the south. Martin was reflecting on the many descriptions of New Orleans he had received from Cincinnati folks who'd been there when his peaceful moment was interrupted. "What the hell?" muttered Shreve, almost under his breath.

A skiff ferry-boat containing Johannes Clay and his family was making a crossing from the Missouri to the Tennessee. On board were his two sons and daughters-in-law, along with seven children between them. His younger children Katherine, Jessie, John, Wendell, and May were also on board. There were also five Negros, three grown and two children, plus six horses and all their provisions and belongings.

They were crossing the Mississippi at Missouri's Bootheel area at Fort La Petit Prairie near the mounds area of the Osage. An eddy of swirling current suddenly held their ferry fast. The ferry turned and lay directly in the path of the approaching steamer.

"Damn it!" burst Captain Shreve, who prided himself on being able to anticipating such things. "He's too heavy. He can't bring her straight" Martin was within ear shot of the barking captain and snapped his eyes up and forward toward the impending calamity that would drive the steamer head long into the side of the passing transport in their path. The captain slowed and began a process to reverse but there was no hope. The iron vessel slammed into the mid-section of the ferry and split it in two. The steamer rocked and jarred causing everyone on board to anchor their positions to avoid being tossed about but little damage was thrust upon the Washington.

The ferry was no match for Shreve's powerful steamer. In the confusion that ensued, horses aboard the ferry became frightened and leaped from their section of the boat which was pitching up away from their weighted end. It was slicing beneath the water's service taking with it the younger children. The front of the ferry had taken on a gush of water and was sinking rapidly as it held the bulk of heavier provisions.

Martin's body froze for only an instant as his eyes penetrated the scene. Then he bolted past Shreve and was on his way to jumping ship to save who he could. "O'Brien!" Captain Shreve shouted. "I need you here. They can't' be saved! You'll go down with them."

The swirl was swallowing up the last remains of the mortally wounded ferry boat and its precious youthful passengers. Martin's chest hallowed as he saw a flash of a bright petticoat flip above the surface followed by a clear view of little girl's stockings and wet brown shoes accompanying the innocent victim to the muddy bottom of the relentless monstrous river. His head and throat exploded and tears filled his eyes. He froze for a second time, then turned away to look behind the ship.

By this time O'Brien and other crew were looking aft. The force of the steamboat cut right through and beyond the impact point. Ships the size and weight of the Washington were incapable of stopping quickly, even after slicing through a small wooden ferry boat.

The horses had swum to shore, but all persons aboard were drowned, with the exception of Clay's oldest son who dived three times to rescue the children to no avail. A young boy about twelve had surfaced and could be seen swimming toward shore giving everyone aboard the Washington hope. Suddenly he too was overcome with fatigue and could be seen going below the surface a mere thirty yards from shore. Martin again felt the anguish of this terrible event and wondered if all river boat life had such traumatic events as he had experienced in the last three weeks.

They continued on. Shreve would report the details of the incident at Memphis so as to complete an official record. Martin and other crew members also gave their account as dock officials made notes. Two days later, the boat was on its way again, less than four hundred miles from New Orleans, Louisiana. As the steamer worked its way south, it was the first time Martin had time to reflect on the accident. The trauma of the moment had him suspended emotionally until now. He relived the experience a few more times during their first day out of Memphis.

The Mississippi then became what old timers called "old-age," entering a wide low valley that was once the embayment of the Gulf of Mexico itself. Sediment filled this area which over the centuries had extended the mouth of the river to its present location. This lower part of the Mississippi's course was contained by natural levees formed by flood-deposited sediments. Beyond the levees lay low floodplains often at a lower elevation than the river itself.

Another feature of the river was its meandering. The channel route from Cairo to New Orleans was almost three times as long as the valley. There were times when Martin felt they were taking an east-west route as much as a southerly one. And many times they were. Many of the river's bends were littered with the remains of steamboats captained by someone much less experienced the great Captain Shreve. Martin reflected on his fortunes to be traveling to New Orleans under such an experienced steamboat master.

Once near Helena, Arkansas, a developing steamboat port in its own right, they seemed to take a more direct route south. At Greenville they were a mere three-hundred miles from New Orleans. The steamer pulled aside at Vicksburg for supplies and a maintenance check. It was at this point that Martin witnessed the largest confluence of steamers since entering the river. Here he could see the teeming nature of commerce on the powerful waterway. While most towns along the Mississippi were born from steamboat landings in these days, Vicksburg was rapidly becoming a major stop. Here too, Martin saw the largest collection of steamboats dedicated to freight alone as the bounty of America's cotton churned its way north. Martin could feel the heat and the culture of the great south washing over his physical and psychological being.

For the first time since entering America, he felt a chapter of his live would close with his arrival in New Orleans. Had he now traversed the roads and waterways of America since stepping on her soil at St Lawrence? "For the love of God, I'll be glad to be off this stinking steamer boat," he thought. It was late fall in 1831 and the steamer would be in New Orleans for the winter months. "Perhaps I'll spend the winter in New Orleans and consider at my situation next spring," he said to himself with a deliberate nod.

It was this conversation with himself, posed against the image of Shreve shouting orders and pulling on the big wheel to traverse yet another turn, that caused Martin to realize that he was a man of the land, not of the water. Save for a few crazy men of the sea, was not all of the Irish race an agrarian lot, he thought. Young men often find their place through circumstance or such realizations that arrive after long periods of mindless adventure. It is how men learn where they should be. They learn it when they are not "at home" with their surroundings. Though he spent time in Cincinnati, his life was not at the docks. He felt like a "river rat" and longed for a place to be on solid ground. Perhaps New Orleans would be that place. He would soon find out.

At Pinckneyville, Mississippi the steamer did nearly a complete u-turn. Again, just prior to St. Francisville, a clear northward direction was taken. The river seemed to lack direction, purpose, or plan. Martin wondered if he'd ever see New Orleans. The meandering only added to Martin's own personal encumbrances. While his physical destination was defined, his pathway had not yet revealed itself. Shreve seemed to take the constant change in direction in stride, having made the trip a number of times and having committed himself to life on the river long ago.

"Aren't we heading due north Captain?" said Martin to the occupied man at the helm. "Oh, hell yes O'Brien," he said. "And this won't be the last," he chuckled. It takes forever to get the last hundred miles of this ditch to pass under a boat's hull. A few jogs past Baton Rouge and we'll hit the straits, then New Orleans will be on our left," he said.

"See you Irish potato farmers like a nice boat ride on Sundays but yah' just can't wait to get dirt between your toes again, hey, O'Brien," Shreve had a sympathetic ring to his voice but ended it with a quizzical look and extended laugh and shaking head.

Martin heard Shreve's words again in his head. What he said had such an impact on him that it seemed to bring clarity to his previously drifting intentions. "I'll stay in New Orleans for the winter," he thought, "then I'll head back. I've had enough boats."

They hit the straights past Assumption, then New Orleans was clearly visible on the left. At this point the steamboat was heading due east as the sun sank behind them and they approached the dock. New Orleans handled huge quantities of commodities for export from the interior and imported goods from other countries, which were warehoused and then transferred in New Orleans to smaller vessels and distributed the length and breadth of the vast Mississippi River watershed. The docks were teeming with cargo, bails, men, ropes, anchored ships, steamers and a mist that had settled in at dusk, covered the entire scene.

The economic rhythm of New Orleans during this time of the year, revolved around cotton. It was picked and baled from September to December. Shipments into the city built from September, peaking in January. The timing of all this played into Martin's plan quite well. He'd hibernate for the winter then load cotton in the spring to support his trip back north. Henry Shreve would head back in two weeks. Martin had informed him that he would be staying in New Orleans so Shreve set out to replace a percentage of his crew and aided Martin in finding work with a steamboat company as a dock worker.

"You've been a good worker, O'Brien," said Shreve as he and his departing crew toasted the few that would stay behind. "I won't say that our trip was without hardship but we made good time, maintained ourselves. I hope you all enjoy your next engagement," he said. "Here's to you all!"

Shreve had put a capstone on Martin O'Brien's life as a riverman. Henry Shreve would go on to be recognized by many along the river as a pioneer in steamboat trafficking. He would make significant improvements to the steamboat and the steam engine, such as separate boilers to power side paddlewheels independently, horizontal cylinders, and multiple decks to allow for passengers and entertainment. His biggest contribution would be the creation of a "snagboat" that kept the Mississippi free of dead wood and the many other restrictions that were part of the Mississippi's. The town of Shreveport, Louisiana would eventually honor him by taking his name.

Martin and Henry Shreve caught eyes during the toast offering broad smiles as the glasses were raised. Smiles broaden as the small jiggers were elevated a bit more before each man downed the ceremonial vile, which Martin felt, ended his initiation into his new home, America.

Chapter 4

Martin & Amy O'Brien

Martin walked down a narrow New Orleans street looking for a joint called Jean Lafitte's Blacksmith Shop. He reached Bourbon Street, turned right and glanced down at the note handed him by a dockworker. "Lafitte's, 941 Bourbon" he read aloud. He arrived at a small local tavern on the corner with a sign above the door marked "Créé en 1772." Hanging from the sign was a parchment that read, "Canal labor registered here." Lafitte's had recently become one of many places where Irish immigrants could get information about working on the canal to Lake Pontchartrain.

Construction of new Basin Canal was well underway. Thousands of Irish and German immigrants were digging the channel by hand through alligator and snake-infested swamps. It was being built to serve as a transport route between downtown New Orleans and Lake Pontchartrain. Canal workers died of mosquito-borne illnesses, creating a need for the continuous recruitment of labor. Agents working for the Orleans Navigation Company recruited workers near the docks and in local establishments where new arrivals frequently stopped.

Martin walked in to Lafitte's and could barely get to the bar. It was a typical French Quarter pub, barely large enough to hold twenty patrons but filled with nearly fifty, all drinking mightily.

"Is this where a fellow signs to work the canal?" Martin asked of the bartender.

"You need to see Captain Grummer down there," the bartender replied pointing to the end of the bar.

"Captain?" O'Brien asked

"He's not a real captain. Just a Hun who thinks he's a captain," responded Jacques Martin. "He's the one, alright. He's the one you see if you want to work on the dig."

Martin walked to the end of the bar and met the stout German who gave a quick thirty-second orientation to the job. "So if you want to work," Grummer began," yah shows up tomorrow morning at 6:00 a.m. with others. They'll explain everything there. Just print your name and sign here so you're on my list. I'll make sure they know who you are."

In fact, all Grummer did was deliver his short speech, get a signature from as many eager immigrants as he could and claim his small fee for all those that showed up.

"If you last a full week, I get paid," Grummer said. "If you don't, then I get nothin."

Martin felt uneasy about the way Grummer said "last a full week." So he asked the obvious question. "Do a lot of men quit?" he asked.

"Quit! Why sure, but more of them die working," Grummer responded coldly. "If I'm lucky enough to sign one that works a full month I get a hardy bonus. But that's no guarantee."

After signing Grummer's list, Pat turned to canvas the bar and then decided to order a drink. Three Irishmen, who had been in New Orleans since the canal project started, noticed his pouch of coins and further the change he received from the bartender. This was no Irishman just off the boat, they thought. Knowing that so many Irish would be sent to their death working on the canal, the three made it a practice to syphon off nearly fifty-percent of the Irish that signed the "dumb Hun's" list each day.

Taking his first sip of beer, Martin peered over the edge his glass and could see the three waving him over to their table. He lowered his glass and made his way through the crowded tavern.

"Join us, will you?" said Sean MacAleese, gesturing to the empty chair at their table.

"Thank you, I'm Martin O'Brien," Martin said while pulling back his chair. "I just got here."

"Yeah, we know," responded Matt Coughlin. "We seen yah come in." The other two chuckled.

"No, I mean I just arrived in New Orleans," Martin said. "I've been working docks in Cincinnati and thought I'd try my luck in New Orleans."

"We know that too, young lad," said Sean. "Otherwise, why would you be signing up for canal work?" Pausing to take a sip of his drink, he went on. "Only the most deprived need work on the canal. Hell, the Orleans Navigation Company won't even use slaves. They're too valuable. Instead they recruit unknowing Irish lads like you and work them to death. No, it's not meant for a fellow like you."

"You don't want to work in that hell," said Pat Driscoll. "You'd be better off working the docks where ye came from young Martin." The three related all they'd seen happen to those unfortunate enough to sign on with the canal. They visited for an hour talking about their experiences in America and their homes back in Ireland. Martin thanked them for the advice, shaking each man's hand as he departed. He also got a tip on where he might be able to find a room in town.

Martin did not report for canal work the next day. He returned to the docks and signed on as a stevedore with a dock company. Shreve had already headed back at dawn.

Martin spent the winter of 1831-32 loading and unloading ships, much as he had done in Cincinnati. He decided he would return to Ohio once the weather warmed up in the north. His decision to leave was fortunate as cholera would kill over 6,000 people in New Orleans including Driscoll, MacAleese, and Coughlin. During the same time, nearly 8,000 Irish would lose their lives working on the canal. Fortunately for Martin, he would escape some of the worst times ever known to New Orleans.

In March he headed north, never to return to New Orleans again. The spring of 1832 was particularly warm in central Ohio. Man and beast alike were toiling in warm and humid weather more similar to Georgia than the Ohio Valley. Martin stepped off his last steamboat at Cincinnati and after buying a horse he began his trip north to Troy. He hoped the weather would finally cool as he traveled north. It did not.

Six hours into his trip, Martin dosed off while riding. He was slouched over, his head bobbing in time with his mare's steady step. A mile or so into his nap the sound of rhythmic clips-clop penetrated his consciousness and he slowly awoke out of a deep sleep, forfeiting a dream about the wreck on the Mississippi. His dream always ended with the petticoat and wet brown shoes of the little girl disappearing below the muddy surface of the great Mississippi.

This time however, the story was cut short when the mare increased her gait. She had turned toward the Miami River a few yards on their right where a clearing had appeared, exposing the soft muddy bank that was likely a natural spot for embarking canoes.

The mare was eager to take a sip from the clear, clean river. "What's the matter, you thirsty gal?" O'Brien asked as he lightly shook the reins, giving her permission to leave the deliberate pathway of the old Indian trail. As the mare drank, Martin pulled back his arms and stretched deeply, arching his back and placing each vertebra into its original position. "You know I just don't remember this route taking so long," he said to the mare. "We can't be far now, perhaps another quarter-day's ride."

Martin took a moment to look up at the clear, flowing waterway. He felt independent and renewed. He had a horse, sufficient money to sustain him for a spell and all the possibilities of his choosing. A sense of pride came over him that many men experienced in America in the early days. It was a deep sense of freedom that energized the spirit of a man and motivated him to take great risks for even greater rewards. "There's no place on earth like this land, old girl," he said to his mare, which had lifted her head up hearing his voice, water dripping from the end of its nose.

Having taken her fill of water, the mare turned on her own and they proceeded on their way. After another four hours, Martin arrived at Troy. He immediately saw the Anderson Inn once again and the taste of boiled beef washed over him. Tying his horse, he pushed through the swing doors and saw the mustached bartender was still there, washing down his bar top.

"Good afternoon, sir," Martin spoke in his remaining Irish brogue. "Hello," was the quick response from the busy garcon who did not at first recognize O'Brien.

Martin ordered a tall ale, an order of beef, lima beans and potatoes. The two men talked for some time and eventually the bartender recalled the day Martin and his buddies had come into the tavern. Conversation eventually got around to O'Brien's interest in finding some work and a place to lay his head. The owner of the tavern had rooms upstairs and Martin handed him a full week's board at the end of his hearty meal.

"You know, O'Brien," Anderson said, "I hear the German Rheinschmidt is clearing nearly 10 acres of land just north of his holdings half way between here and Piqua. He might be in need of a strong young lad such as you. I'd take a ride up there in the morning and see if you might latch on with him."

Martin thanked his new landlord and took his small cloth bag containing his belongings with him up the interior stairs to the second floor of the inn. The long ride north had taken away three days of energy and Martin decided to call it a day. He found his assigned room, inserted his key, entered, and kicked off his boots. He laid prone on what was his first real bedding since leaving New Orleans.

[43]

Martin slept well. Though a fairly boisterous gathering of locals had spent the bulk of the evening drinking, playing cards and otherwise tossing a continuous waft of laughter to the second floor, Martin heard none of it. The next morning he felt rested, took a walk down the stairs and filled his wash basin from a pump against the west exterior of the building. He returned to his room where he freshened up but then realized his mare was still tied to the post out front.

"Oh, damn," he said to himself. "I'm certain she's lookin' for some water by now." He hurried his pace and combed quickly through his full head of hair with both hands as he peered into the small mirror above the sink. It had a crack across its diagonal and he paused a second. He looked older, he thought.

Sure enough when he got outside two barefoot boys with round hats were jostling with a wood bucket as the mare jammed its snoot deep inside for the last drop of water.

"This your horse, Mister?" asked the young chap.

"Yes, boys," said Martin. "Thanks so much for taking care of her. We had a long ride yesterday and I'll be darned if I didn't forget to water her down."

"She's a fine horse," said the older boy who was about ten.

"That she is, young man," Martin responded. Seeing the two boys made him think of his home in Ireland and his brother.

"Here boys!" Martin extended his arm squeezing two red copper cents between his thumb and index finger. They looked in amazement but didn't reach. "Take 'um lads," he said with a broad grin. The older put his palm out with his chin tucked but the younger couldn't resist a grin and Martin grinned himself. "Thanks mister," said the younger boy with a bit of a lisp.

As Martin rode off the two boys stood, staring admiringly till he was out of site. Martin had a character reserved for only a few. He was the type of individual that young boys sensed was exactly the way they hoped to be once they were men. Given any clarity of thought, both boys would have likely stated such but as Martin turned north out of sight, their frozen frame said just as much.

Martin rode north toward Piqua. He recalled the night he met Amy Hurley as he passed the big pole barn about a mile north of town. After another thirty minute ride he came to the grove of trees that marked the Rheinschmidt farm as Anderson had told. There was a tall Arian man standing at the road loading wood. Martin introduced himself and expressed interest in a job.

"Well, I do indeed need as much help as I can muster," said the lanky German as he shook O'Brien's hand. "It's late spring and I still have hopes of getting a crop in before it's too late. I need a man to drive an ox and chain to pull a final batch of stumps I've got laying along my northern most acre. Think you can work an ox and rope man?" Rheinschmidt asked. Martin affirmed and they shook hands agreeing on fifteen dollars a week. Martin began work that afternoon. He took a long walk to the northern acres and found an ox already tied to a post, along with rope and a few hand saws left there by Rheinschmidt.

Nearly twenty days went by and Martin completed the clearing of Rheinschmidt's north acres. He converted his rope rig to a single blade plow and started to plant. One day, as he was approaching a turn near a row end, he heard a familiar voice behind him say, "Good afternoon, Mr. O'Brien." It was Amy. She'd walked up the grassy dry creek that ran along side the German's property. She had heard in town that a young man, believed to be named O'Brien, was working for the Hun they all called "Rhinie."

"Why, Amy, how are you?" O'Brien asked. "How did you know I was here?"

"I didn't," she said, looking down in somewhat of a shy way. "I heard 'Rhinie' had a new hand and my friend Mary told me she heard his name might be O'Brien and I was walking near here and was just curious how much the new hand might get in a month and…" She paused, realizing that she just unleashed a torrent of nervous chattering. Martin stood grinning with both fists closed on his waist, one holding the reins. "Amy, I had no idea you had such a curious interest in agriculture," he blasted with a laugh. Amy blushed and laughed as well.

Martin dropped the reins and walked toward her. "How have you been, Miss Hurley?" he asked "It's been a while." "It's been a long while, indeed" she said. The two walked a bit up the grassy creek bottom and caught up on all that had transpired since their last meeting. Finding a bit of a rise along the creek's edge, they both sat down in fresh grass exchanging tales of their days since Piqua. Martin relayed in great detail his trip down the Mississippi, the accident, New Orleans and the great Shreve who showed him the ways of a steamboat captain.

"Perhaps you'll captain a boat yourself someday, hey Martin?" she stated with an encouraging tone. Martin quickly discounted it, much to Amy's excitement which she carefully concealed. He told her how he learned from his long trip that he much preferred land over stream and that like most Irish, he felt more at home "tuning over dirt than slicing a wake on a river's face." Amy related how her father was slowing and how many of the men in Troy who first settled the farms were getting to the age where they needed help. "They still believe they're young men," she pointed out. Amy had not married and was eighteen. Having mostly sisters, they were all helping on the family farm. She prided herself that she could handle any task given her at such an early age. They spoke for nearly an hour then went back to their work.

In the weeks ahead, Martin and Amy saw each other regularly. As it turned out the two farms were merely a mile apart and the Hurley farm lay between Troy and the Rheinschmidt land. Martin often met Amy halfway for a picnic lunch during the warm days. They'd eat along the dry creek bed which was fully concealed in long green grass. Martin began to help the Hurley's as well and between the two farms he learned all that entailed a self-sustaining family farm.

During the winter of 1832-1833, work slowed but when spring arrived Martin was flush with activity between the Hurly and Rheinschmidt farms. Work seemed more pressing to Martin this year since he had a full awareness of what needed to be done and by when. Amy and her sisters were also gearing up for what promised to be a fruitful year. The old timers had commented all winter how cold months with ample snow would result with a near perfect growing season.

Once the crops were in, Martin and Amy sat down alone for a picnic in the dry creek bed one day for the first time since the previous summer. Amy was quiet. Martin was rattling off a review of the past months activities as if logging in with Amy to explain his inattentive nature since spring had arrived. He paused and noticed Amy on his left taking a bite from a small scraping of cheese she had wrapped in a cotton cloth for the picnic. His heart suddenly swelled as he was overcome by how much he had missed his time at the dry creek with her. Dispensed from the grind of the last two months, he suddenly lunged to her, pressing his lips to hers as she lay back against the grassy growth that served as their love seat.

In the days ahead, they would talk of their love for each other and their strong desire to marry. Following the harvest that fall the Hurley's were hosting a Sunday brunch for family members and all hands that had worked on both farms. Martin rose during coffee to announce that he, "and the lovely Hurley lass named Amy," would plan to marry the following spring. Much to the delight of all present they celebrated with additional helpings of chocolate brownie cake that had been brought over by Mrs. Rheinschmidt herself.

Martin O'Brien and Amy Hurley were married in 1834 as planned. Shortly after the wedding, Thomas Hurley announced he was making plans to move further west to Illinois and sell the farm to Rheinschmidt. A portion of the sale would be given Martin and his new bride, which pleased the young couple.

"But how soon will you leave, papa?" asked a bewildered Amy, suddenly showing the nervous insecurity of a nineteen year-old.

"Oh, not for a spell my dear Amy," he said. "The opportunities in the Illinois Territory are said to be grand and the land is good quality. We'll help you get adjusted and perhaps you and Martin can join us there next year."

"Oh, if it would be so, I'd be so pleased, Martin," she said to her new husband with an accompanying pleading face. Martin smiled and replied, "Aw, ye do put a heavily laden pleading on a man, dear Amy." Martin could disarm any situation with his broad grin and the endearing Irish brogue.

Thomas had heard word that, with the Indians now removed west of the Mississippi, government land located in Northeastern Illinois was selling for one dollar and twenty-five cents per acre. Many immigrants from the east were moving west to settle on land located either side of the fur trading pathway called Vincennes Trail where it intersected the primary east west waterway in the area called the Kankakee. The river flowed from a tiny spring in northern Indiana, expanded into a mammoth marsh that was fifteen by twelve miles in size, then narrowed at the Illinois boarder before evolving into a single, shallow stream at Vincennes Trail.

Martin had his sights set on moving West as well, though he had not mentioned it to Amy or the others. Shortly after Thomas Hurley's departure, Martin learned of an opportunity to buy land himself in the area west of Fort Wayne, Indiana. Great Forests and rich soil were drawing Europeans to northeast Indiana since the removal of the great Miami tribes. As would be said by those that knew him, the grass did not grow long under the leather sole of Martin O'Brien, for he was a man of decision, of action and he sensed opportunities before most others.

In the late spring of 1835, Thomas Hurley left Ohio for Illinois. He took the National Road to Indianapolis. At Indianapolis he took the Michigan Road north which was originally surveyed to go straight to Fort Dearborn. The Great Kankakee Marsh made a direct route impossible so the road ran straight north to the South Bend Post then west into Illinois where it linked with Sauk Trail. Sauk Trail intersected the Vincennes Trail thirty miles south of Fort Dearborn. Hurley turned south on the Vincennes Trail toward the Kankakee River and Yellowhead Township.

Yellowhead area was named for the local Pottawatomi chief who was taken away a few years before. The Yellowhead area was five miles north of the Kankakee River along Vincennes Trail. It was hilly by local standards with a blend of prairie and wooded oak. Like all of the earliest pioneers, Hurley made use of his wagon for shelter when he first arrived. He cut big oaks adjacent to the prairie grass and built a more permanent shelter. In 1835, few crops were harvested in the whole of Yellowhead. New arrivals were busy building homes.

Hurley selected a spot at the edge of a large woods. He would clear most of the nearby trees and grow fine quality wheat. Water for the crops was furnished by three streams, the Bull, Pike and Trim Creeks. The very productive soil was dark loam, with a clay sub soil. At the time of Thomas' arrival, the Kankakee River area still had a few Indians but they were very friendly towards arriving white families. They occupied no particular section of the country, but would spend part of their time on the Kankakee River in the area near the crossings.

The first identifiable village in Yellowhead sat at the far end of a large six-mile long grove that was yet to fall victim to the axe and plow. Sherburnville, as it was referred to, was situated on land that seemed to be kneaded by the Good Lord himself, creating knobs, hills and hummocks through which flowed three nourishing streams. It was a meeting place as much as anything but it had a name, at least.

In 1833 Five miles South at the river, William Lacy had built a log cabin at what was being called "upper crossing" or Westport. A year later, Asher Sargeant built the first habitation a mile west of Lacy that would be anchor of the first city in northeast Illinois. It would become known as Momence.

Chapter 5

Yellowhead

By the time Martin and Amy O'Brien followed the Hurleys to Illinois in 1836, the migration of Europeans to the Kankakee River basin was beginning to pick up steam. Martin had taken the same route to Illinois as his father-in-law and they were approaching the intersection of the Vincennes Trail and Sauk Trail. Since 1833, Adam and Phoebe Brown operated a general store and inn on the northwest corner of the intersection of the two trails. Thomas Hurley had tied his rig there and was standing with his hands on his hips looking east to see if the approaching frontier wagon might indeed be his sweet daughter and her husband.

"Poppa!" Amy shouted as she caught sight of her father awaiting their arrival at Brown's Inn. "Oh, look Martin, its father. He's come to meet us," she said, leaping from the wagon. As Martin pulled his wagon adjacent to Hurley's, Amy and her father were still in a deep embrace. It was then that Martin realized how much he and Amy had missed the family.

"Ah, its' so good to see you Amy dear," Thomas Hurley said fighting back tears. "How are you son?" He shook Martin's hand with a strong and aggressive grip. The two men were genuinely quite pleased to see each other again. Thomas had missed Martin's energy and zest for life. Martin longed for their extensive conversations about the prospects of the frontier and for America. They hooked their rigs together so all could sit together in one wagon and talk during the final twenty-mile leg of the journey down Vincennes Trail.

"My, it was such a long trip father," said Amy.

"And beautiful the whole way," Martin added.

"Martin did so well. It wasn't half as tough as the trip down the Mississippi, was it dear?" Amy asked.

"We had nice weather and the nights avoided a fall chill," he said. "All and all, 'twas the good Lord that provided us a clear path," said Martin.

Thomas laughed, "Lord sakes O'Brien, I'd forgotten the thickness of your speech. I don't think it's thinned a bit since you stepped off the boat, has it boy?" They both had a hearty laugh and Martin ripped off some native Gaelic twist that had little meaning to Amy or Thomas but was a clear bit of Irish humor and a fateful foreboding. It launched a hearty well-turned wail that sliced the prairie air in every direction as the wagons rolled south.

"Mother has spent all day preparing a wonderful meal, Amy," said Hurley. "She'll be so pleased to see you once again." Amy was clearly moved to think of seeing her mother again. "Oh father, I've tried not to think of our meeting till now. I feared it would double the length of our trip should I think of her so," she said.

The Hurleys and O'Briens were together once again. Their separation nurtured a bond not realized in Ohio. This was Martin's family now too. He and Amy would take residence with the in-laws at Yellowhead until Martin could develop his own acres. Martin and Amy's young lives were just beginning and they knew little of the joys and pains that would come in the days ahead. Yellowhead, Momence, and the Kankakee Valley would shape their lives for certain but the O'Brien's would also leave their mark. The O'Brien name would someday be known around the world.

"Amy, my dearest, sweet girl!" were the words that greeted Amy O'Brien as her mother rushed out the front door of the meager Hurley cabin to greet her family. Martin and Thomas were unloading the wagon as Amy and her mother walked to the cabin holding each other around the waist. They instantly launched into rapid fire chatter as if a deadline had been placed on their "catch-up" conversation.

"Amy really missed you both, Thomas," Martin said as he lifted the largest chest over the wagon's side. Thomas, looking up with an obvious mist in his eyes on seeing Amy and his wife embrace said, "We'll be all together again, Martin. And you will love the people around here. They really take you in as their own."

Indeed the Hurley's and O'Brien's had settled in an area ripe with excitement for new arrivals. Martin and Thomas worked hard and built a strong farm operation in their new home. Martin and Amy's life together would be woven into the fabric of the Kankakee River basin, particularly in the area five miles south that was growing rapidly into Momence, Illinois. As the summer of 1838 approached, Amy was expecting her first child.

"Mista Hurly, Mista Brien," said the young freckled-face Nichols boy. "Hurry Mista's! It's the bee-bee. Iths-a commin!" Thomas and Martin were working in the farthest corner of the freshly plowed turf which was about to take on its first planting. Despite the young lad's developing speech, they fully understood his message and bolted across the knobby field toward the cabin being careful not to twist an ankle in the grotty terrain that was, as yet, untouched. The two men attempted to squeeze into the door simultaneously. Both laughed and Thomas gave deference to the father.

Amy had given birth to her first child. They would name him James. Martin never felt as complete a man as he did that day. It was a deep joy to the O'Brien's and Hurley's alike. Martin walked out of the cabin with his father-in-law after peeking in at the new mother and bright blue buddle beside her. He teared-up looking at the setting sun in the western sky, turning away from Thomas so as not to feel less honorable.

From the hills of Yellowhead one could see miles and miles of flatland as far west as the eye could focus. In the distance, well to the south, Martin's eye followed a dark green line framing the far southern extremes of the large prairie land before him. It was the Kankakee River. While hills, rivers and mountains in America are certainly inspiring, there was something about the flatlands of Illinois that gives one a sense of reach and the real possibility that all you can see can be yours.

This was a moment for Martin, common to men, when they feel cushioned between the humble earth and the extension of God's hand. When life's events and the wonder of nature's beauty cross, reflective men like Martin often feel like God's designated annotator, prodded to tell all of the goodness of life. Martin smiled to himself and wiped his brow with his forearm as any hard-working farmer would at the end of the day. His method was designed to deceive Thomas by the slightly lowering the path of his cuff, brushing droplets off his lashes.

The following year, a second boy was born but did not survive childbirth. In 1840, a girl named Rhoda was born, followed by another in '41 that died at birth. This was common during the hard times of frontier life. In 1843 Amy gave birth to Thomas and the next year Jefferson was born. Then, following a three year abeyance, Daniel O'Brien was born in the same Yellowhead cabin as the others.

Daniel was a happy and good natured baby and was keenly aware of Martin's presence as early as five months. As Daniel approached his second year of life, he could often be seen grasping the hem of Amy's long white apron which was draped over a dusty cotton dress worn to work the fields. Daniel loved to spend summer afternoons with his momma. He seemed fully satisfied carrying on the business of the day in the immediate parameter of the cabin.

Unlike four year old Jefferson and six year old Thomas, he was not yet old enough, or curious enough to run off in pursuit of their hero, the oldest brother James. After all, James was all of eight. During the summer Daniel was fond of pulling the "tiny weeds" around the cabin as instructed by his loving mother. Daniel's closeness to the ground made it easier for Amy to clear her bountiful garden of small invaders. She was in her final month of what had been, to date, her most difficult pregnancy. Daniel was a credible aide possessing what old Irish tillers liked to call "affection for soil."

After the harvest of 1848, Amy felt odd about her expected baby. It had laid in her differently than any of the others and did not seem to have the lively activity of the others. Short of the small newborn boy that died in '39 and the girl that had died of undeveloped lungs in '41, this baby was not like an O'Brien child. Her children were not ones to wait patiently prior to their first breath of earth's fresh air.

It was apparent that something was terribly wrong one night in late November. The child would not pass and Amy had been in labor since early that morning. Mrs. William Nichols joined Mrs. Hurley in attending to Amy through the night. Around two in the morning, the baby was making progress. Young James was awake with the adults, running to Bull Creek every thirty minutes to get fresh water. Finally at dawn, the long awaited baby was separated from its mother. It had been a full twenty-four hours of difficult labor. Poor James, all of ten years old, stood hovering over the bed half smiling, half crying and particularly confused by the state of his young momma. As the rising sun pierced through an exterior wall of the cabin he noticed how much older she seemed to look.

The men were out front on the garden bench postponing their day's work and heavily concerned about Amy. They were keeping an eye on Daniel who was already busily pulling the pesky "tiny weeds." Martin's heart sank as his mother-in-law and Mrs. Nichols approach the two men from the cabin.

Mrs. Hurley was dragging a stained cotton cloth she had failed to release when her daughter took her final breath. Amy had not survived the devastation overnight and it wracked Irene Hurley's entire soul so heavily that she had not unclenched her fist from the white cotton towel.

Mrs. Nichols spoke first, blending her first words with the unmistakable choke of a deep sob, "It's a boy Martin but Amy has not survived." The men froze in stunned disbelief. Neither had risen from their bench to greet the women due to the startling and uncharacteristic gate the women displayed coming from the house. Martin and Thomas knew that the women had bad news and both assumed the new baby had not survived.
Neither man imagined that it would be Amy who would be lost. "Look, Da Da," said young Daniel, as he held up a fist full of dandelion weeds. "Yes Danny son," were Martin's words as he once again looked left to the western horizon. This time he did not try to hide his tears. His vision was fully unblocked as he gazed over to his father-in-law Thomas who was bent at the waste and sobbing into both hands.

It was a long, sad winter that tested the inherent good nature of the entire family. Daniel was young enough to enjoy the world that a two-year old experiences each day regardless of tragic events. He and his new baby brother Merwin were now the all-encompassing duty of Irene Hurley. Young Jefferson moved in with local neighbor Ansil Chipman. He would live there the rest of his youth. Young Daniel possessed little memory of that horrible day and only a faint memory of his loving young mother. Daniel's older siblings James, Rhonda, and Thomas stayed with various friends and family members in order to help Martin hold his family together. The new baby, Merwin, was adopted by Russell Seager of Grant Park.

During the subsequent summer, Martin married thirty-three year old Sarah Ruggles on August 15, 1849. Their first child William O'Brien was born in 1850. Sarah was from Green County, Ohio and had migrated to Illinois a few years earlier. Those on the frontier would have fully understood and embraced such a quick marriage for Martin, father of so many young children.

That same year, Martin moved from Yellowhead to Momence Township establishing a new farm closer to the burgeoning village on the Kankakee River. The move was a logical one. The upper and lower crossings at the Kankakee River were attracting the increasing numbers to the valley. Yellowhead remained rural and sparsely populated due to the size of acreage purchased by farmers there.

The upper crossing featured Hill's Tavern on the south side of the river. It was the main stop for all traders crossing the river. The tavern was so popular that fur trappers and traders of the Chicago-Vincennes trail called the upper crossing "Hill's Crossing." Travelers regularly timed their trip so they could spend time at "Hill's." Robert and "Ma" Hill were genial, Southern types with a talent for hospitality and good cheer.

The lower crossing, one mile west, now had more structures than the area around Hill's Tavern. Locals could see the potential for the lower crossing becoming the population center of the area if for no other reason than it was less chaotic than the upper crossing which featured a continuous stream of travelers with short term needs. If a business center was to form serving the locals, it would likely be the lower crossing

Martin felt moving his family closer to the river, with its concentrated population, would provide more convenience and security for the family than the open rural area of Yellowhead Township.

Four years after marrying Sarah Ruggles, Martin O'Brien, like many men of the Momence area, was stirred by the discovery of gold on January 24, 1848. The Gold Rush was drawing thousands to seek their fortune out West. In the fall of 1853, Martin O'Brien decided to leave his family and head west to California for gold. Martin's spirit to travel had been stirred again. In truth, despite his deep love for his children, his marriage to Sarah Ruggles was one of necessity rather than love, freeing his spirit to leave, as he did.

Daniel O'Brien knew his daddy as "the big man that came to visit him at grandma's house." The young lad eagerly sought the company of his big brother James, now fourteen. Daniel also enjoyed babysitting little Merwin on visits to the Seagers. Merwin never knew his mother and was just getting to know his father.

The night before Martin and the group of Momence hopefuls left for California, the entire town came out to Hills Tavern to celebrate the daring detachment of men. There was a huge crowd in attendance at this function and the fun was fast and furious lasting until the break of day.

The next day, Captain Worcester and the men from Momence set forth on horseback toward the American trail that extended more than half-way across the continent. Worcester, Martin O'Brien and the group of notables started down Lynn's Lane from the upper crossing and headed west. Lion's Lane, as it was also called by locals, was a muddy path that ran along the southern bank of the Kankakee. The group would branch off at the old Rice Cemetery and progress to Bourbonnais, Wilmington, and then Galesburg. From there they would travel south to Memphis and eventually to St. Joe, Missouri where westward caravans took the overland route to the Rockies.

Each man looked down at his family from his horse with a pack animal in tow. Family members, including Sarah, Daniel and the other siblings walked along side for the first leg. The entire population watched the cavalcade pull away as the townsfolk paused at the lower crossing, waving hats and white kerchiefs moist with their salty tears.

Daniel could feel a cool breeze in his face as he stared west to see his daddy in the distance. It would be a hard winter. Daniel O'Brien now had neither a mother nor a father, but the extended family and friends that populated Momence and his surroundings would have to do. Young Daniel, now seven years old, felt sad at this departing. No doubt it was the sobs of young James holding his hand as they turned and walked back toward Hill's that also made him cry.

Daniel would learn to farm under the guidance of his brothers and grandfather. As he reached his early teens, Momence, Illinois had ripened into a hard-nosed town. Daniel spent most of his days on the farm and only on occasion did he "go to town" with grandpa or his big brother Jimmy in the buggy. He remained a home-loving peaceful boy, unaffected by the daily chaos generated in the wide open town of Momence.

His father would not return to Momence for five years. Like so many of the nearly 300,000 people that flocked to California to find gold, Martin O'Brien had meager success and even less enthusiasm upon his return home. The long separation took its toll on Martin. It was the first time he was separated from his children. And though their courtship and marriage was brief, Sarah was also on his mind. He was very excited when the meager band from Illinois re-entered Illinois crossing the Mississippi via ferry boat, this time at Davenport. He couldn't help staring the whole time to the south, imagining how New Orleans and villages south were faring these days.

The route home was changed to the western portion of Sauk Trail. Once across the Mississippi, he arrived at Vincennes Trail from the west in five days. The last twenty miles seemed like an eternity. When he finally arrived at Momence, his entire family was there having gotten word of his arrival from earlier arrivals. It was a joyful homecoming.

A few summers later, Sarah was expecting another child when Martin heard a young distant voice in the fields one afternoon. "Father, Father, come!" yelled young William. Thomas, Jefferson, and Daniel were urging on their huge ox straining to remove large oak stump from O'Brien's land. "It's mother, I can't wake her," he cried in a terrified voice. Martin once again felt the merging of emotion and physical pain as he dropped the reins and turned running toward the boy. It was two in the afternoon and "not waking" could only mean one thing. The rare summer flu had kept Sarah in bed for two weeks.

"Not again," he said under his breath as he lurched to a stop at the door, seeing his second wife in bed with her head back and mouth wide open. "I'm sorry, dear Sarah," he moaned as he reached her bed. "I should have been here for you." Daniel had entered by now and placed his hand on his father's shoulder who was kneeling and sobbing into the down cover Sarah had made for their bed. The young lad demonstrated a sense of calm. It would become part of his make-up for years to come. It was 1859. October was entering its third week. It was a cold overcast Monday in the Kankakee Valley and winter was showing its early signs.

Martin O'Brien and his sons smoothed black dirt over Sarah's final resting place near the back acres. From the small bench near the cabin, William could see his father and half-brothers brushing the Valley's finest soil over mother's grave. There was a natural grace to their movement. Being men of the plow they looked at ease in their graceful articulation of Sarah's final cover. William wiped his eyes as Martin had at the time of Amy's passing.

On the same afternoon Martin buried his second wife, hundreds of miles to the east, President James Buchanan was ordering a detachment of U.S. Marines to march on Harpers Ferry under the command of Robert E. Lee. Overnight, John Brown and a collection of associates had detached a party to capture Colonel Lewis Washington, great grandnephew of George Washington. They would free a small group of slaves, take two relics of George Washington including a sword presented to him by Frederick the Great and two pistols from LaFayette.

Unknown to most of the nation that day, the raid would create a spark pressurizing the entire nation and leading to a national rupture. It would not leave the O'Brien's untouched. As Martin and his sons wrapped their arms around young William and turned toward the house, none of them were cognizant of events back east. No one in the country knew. But the rupture would come. It would march from the Atlantic to the Mississippi and engulf everyone in its wake. The O'Brien's would be drawn into the melee in less than two years.

PART TWO

MOMENCE

Chapter 6

Insurrection

Martin married again in January 16, 1860. His new wife Louisa had two sons, Sam and George, by her previous marriage. The two families merged and nearly everyone would need to bring in the bountiful harvest of 1860. Like other farms in the area, acreage increased as families grew. But it would be the last great harvest for some time for the O'Briens and the other farmers of the Kankakee Valley. Americans were about to be ripped apart by war.

It rained nearly the entire spring of 1861 in the Kankakee Valley. Martin and his sons were hard pressed to get the crop in, but fields were still too wet in April. Finally, the rain stopped.

"Do you think we can plant yet, father?" Daniel asked, always eager to discuss strategy as well as take on the work.

"Well, the ground is better than last week," stated Martin as he pushed his heel into the dark black earth. "Yes, I think by tomorrow we can start, and none too soon. This damn weather is the wettest I've seen in ten years but there's still time. We'll get it in."

On the morning of April 12, 1861, at the very moment Martin O'Brien and his son Daniel were discussing the moisture content of the O'Brien farm, Southern artillery batteries opened fire on Fort Sumter at Charleston, South Carolina. The Civil War in the United States was beginning. Saturation would not become the biggest threat to O'Brien's summer's crop. The insurrection would take Martin's boys from him.

The following Saturday, Martin and Jefferson could hear the stirring inside Worcester's store. The two had jumped in their wagon and rode to Momence to get word of the latest stirrings since Sumter. The younger O'Briens wanted to go to town too but this visit was not for the young ones. At the outbreak of war, Jefferson was 17, prime age to volunteer though he planned to lie about his age and state he was 18. The wave that sweeps across a young man's soul at the sound of "War!" is like no other. What eighteen-year old does not desire to be instantly catapulted into manhood by going off to war?

"Why those southern bastards," was the sound that jumped out at Jefferson as he and Martin stepped up onto the board sidewalk in front of Worcheser's Emporium, Momence's central gathering place on Front street. Worcester dispensed drugs, medicines and plasters to alleviate man's ills, often making them worse. The store, and particularly the wood stove inside, was the central location for those who enjoyed divergent views and argumentative politics. As was the practice in spring, today's conversation was being held on steps out front, filling the entire boardwalk with speculators.

"I heard that Lincoln's lookin' to call up as many as 300,000 in six short months," stated Mark Atherton. Atherton ran the local hardware store and like most proprietors that Saturday morning, decided that the news of war was more important than the occasional customer that might walk into their store on this exhilarating morning. Everyone was at Worchester's that morning, including every potential customer in town. Most proprietors hung a "be right back" sign in their window and joined the crowd at Worchester's.

"So how the hell will Mr. Lincoln gather so many men in such a short spell?" whispered young W.P. Watson to Jefferson. The Watson's were old neighbors from Yellowhead and young Jefferson often played with W.P when the O'Brien's lived on the old farm. "Heck if I know, W.P., but I know I'm goin', retorted young Jefferson. The young men were wide-eyed as they watched nearly two dozen men argue back and forth over the means and ways of pushing the southern insurrectionist back to old Dixie. And doing so "and damn quick" was the notion of all those present.

Just then a rough looking bearded fellow who was identifiable to everyone in Momence spoke up. "I'll be gall dang if I'd leave the comfort of me cabin on the river to go chase off a bunch of varmints just because Abraham Lincoln don't particularly care for their company and asked me to."

"Ah shut up your crazy old loon! You're nuts in the head," retorted trapper Billy Allgood.

The contradictory bearded fellow was none other than "Crazy" Dan Parmalee. Poor Dan had gone a bit goofy ever since he was struck firm on the skull during a scuffle one year before. Allgood was no less tidy than Dan but sane nonetheless. Both were trappers who only came to town for provisions and generally were considered "river rats" by the more "sophisticated" residents of town.

"Ah, leave him' alone Billy. You know he's all but half himself now," shunned William Parish. Parish was one of the first citizens of Momence, along with A.S. Vail. Both were noted and respected members of the community. Though educated and of a different class than that of a Parmalee or Allgood, they were down to earth, worthy men who paid no mind to mixing with either the refined folks from the east or the skilled trapper from the marsh. Parish had even attended the convention that nominated Abraham Lincoln to the Presidency in '59 so news of war drew him to the store that morning. Parish and Vail were equally spellbound though cautious as were most of the older men.

Like Martin's sons, many of the sons of these pioneer families who would go to war would not only abandon their father's farm but would be leaving home for the first time in their lives. None of them knew what to expect. They had never been mustered into crowded encampments or seen much of the country their father's had when they came from the East. The routine of their new life in the Army would be an awakening for them all.

Within two weeks after the fall of Sumter, recruiting stations sprang up throughout the county. President Lincoln's call for volunteers was heard by Kankakee Valley men as an intense wave of excitement washed over the North.

"I'm signing up, pop," were Jefferson's words to his father as they traveled back to the farm.

"I know son, I figured you would," stated Martin. "I know you're full of excitement and fury right now but don't let all that stirring in town deceive you, boy. War is not all shiny buttons and brand new rifles. It's marching, killin' and lots of pain and suffering," said the concerned father.

Jefferson was quiet but after a respectful pause, he stated, "I know, pop, but I just gotta go. My buddies are goin' and gosh if Mr. Lincoln don't get the troops he needs, no telling how soon those southern boys might show up on our farm itself!"

Martin knew the young boy was right but it pained him no less. "Alright boy, I'll sign for yah!" We'll go to town on Monday. Mr. Vail tells me the recruiters will be there from Douglas by noon. We'll go together."

On recruitment day, Momence was as jovial as a late Saturday night when most of its patrons have had too much to drink. Fifers, fiddlers and drummers, more accustomed to entertaining at Hill's Tavern and the other local gin mills, played martial music down Range Street. 'The National Anthem' was played by the local lads on lutes, matched by whistling youths who also hammered tin pans in time with the two boy drummers from town. Young men talked bravely as the officers from Chicago were seen coming down Range Street to sign recruits at the post office. Momence was not without its "swooning damsels" either. Unaware of the true calamities of war, they were just as wide-eyed as the young male volunteers betting on their own personal glory.

"Who will come up and sign the roll?" shouted the officers.

A wall of young men stepped forward showing a great display of enthusiasm. Their fathers lingered on the parameter wishing they were young enough to go to war in their son's place. The older men in town, many of whom were grandfathers of young enthusiastic boys, stood watching from across the street. Their conversation was more reserved. Years of experience and fear for the young unsuspecting lads created mixed emotions in them.

Young men enlisted for all kinds of reasons. Some felt it was the right thing to do so as not to let down their family and friends. Others felt they might miss all the fun and glory. Still others feared being branded a coward. Some young men enlisted because they simply wanted a change. The Army was something different from trudging at the plow. War would be the great adventure of their lives.

The overwhelming number of new recruits came from American farms. The pay for a Union Private was not particularly generous, just $13 per month, but it beat working the family farm where little money actually landed in the pockets of young sons assisting their fathers. Most of the men from the Kankakee Valley mustered out of Camp Douglas, a huge new military installation just outside of Chicago. Camp Butler in Springfield staged most Illinois companies before they departed for the South. Both camps became primary holding areas for Confederate prisoners during the war.

Cairo and Mound City at Illinois' southern tip became major military depots. Cairo served as the Western Army's base of operations, ferrying rations, ammunition and other supplies downstream to troops in the field.

The area around Mound City, where Martin O'Brien had experienced the ferry boat tragedy during his days with Shreve, hosted a large contingent of the Union Navy. Steamboats were being converted into gunboats all along the Ohio and Mississippi rivers

.At the outbreak of war, Martin O'Brien had seven sons and two step sons. James was the oldest at twenty-three in 1861 and did not serve. Thomas, Jefferson and Daniel would all serve, but the rest were too young including William, Sarah O'Brien's boy, and Mulligan, son of Martin and Louisa, his third wife.

Twenty-one year old Thomas O'Brien and his "eighteen year old brother" Jefferson enlisted in Company D of the Forty-Second Infantry. The majority of men in Company D were area boys, led by Lieutenant B.F. Gray from Momence. They mustered out of Camp Douglas then reported to Springfield where most Illinois troops were dispatched before heading south.

Fighting began in earnest for the O'Brien brothers on the morning of September 19, 1863 at Chickamauga, Tennessee where the first push to Atlanta by the Union Army was abruptly halted by the South. At Chickamauga, the North suffered casualties second only to Gettysburg. In a hurried retreat toward Chattanooga, Company D was crossing a clearing when it was ambushed by Confederate Troops.

"Get to the woods!" shouted Lt Gray. "Find cover!" he shouted again, waving the men north while he peered back at the wall of fire that came unexpectedly from the rear. The Rebs had been trailing Gray's men for two miles. Knowing the territory, they waited until the clearing, and then opened fire.

The entire company sprinted for the woods. Jefferson was twenty yards ahead of his brother when the shots rang out. He dove behind a large ash tree and looked back for his brother. Men were charging into the woods but over half were dropping to the ground. Jefferson did not see Thomas. He looked left and then right but still no sign of him.

Some bodies were as still as a stone but others were still moving and many cried out. Jefferson could not see Thomas, nor did he recognize any of the chilling cries from those about to die in the field. The Yanks returned fire from the woods and pulled back. What was left of the Yankee Army was finally on high ground again and each company made its casualty assessment.

At dusk, the dead were recovered from the clearing. Thomas was there, lying face down in a field of tall grass. When the detail returned, Jefferson asked the officer in charge if he could see his brother. After walking between rows of bodies, he finally came upon his brother. He'd been shot in the back and Jefferson could see the rip through the front of Thomas' coat. He'd been shot through the heart. It struck Jefferson cold and he held his breath. He stooped down and squeezed the tip of Thomas' boot, sliding his fingers off the toe in an instinctively affectionate touch.

Three days later, as the 42nd was making its way south again with reinforcements, Momence native Lt. Gray recorded events in his diary. "Cold last night, and poor show for sleep. We stayed all day where we camped last night at the cross roads. We built some breastworks. The Rebs fell at our lines on the left but did not break them. Twelve more of our boys came in today, making it up to 21. Graham, T. O'Brien, Watson, and Dutcher are reported killed."

Martin's second son Thomas died in the service of his county on a hot September day in 1863 on the outskirts of Chattanooga, Tennessee. There was no time for Jefferson to mourn his brother or see he had a proper burial. The Army would arrange for that. Jefferson and the 42nd were already making plans for a second advance on Georgia. They would move at night. As Jefferson and Company D walked over the Alexander Bridge at midnight, the sound of men's boots hitting the wooden deck of the bridge somehow stirred his emotions and he began to cry silently in the dark. Tom's boots would not sound on the bridge with the others again. Jefferson would fight at the Battle of Mission Ridge under Grant and Sherman. He fought well into 1864 and all the way to Atlanta in the battles of Kennesaw Mountain, Peach Tree Creek and Jonesboro. He entered Atlanta with Sherman on July 22. Atlanta finally fell on September 2.

Meanwhile, Daniel did not know his brother had died. He had enlisted in Company K of the 113th Volunteer Infantry at Camp Douglas in the spring of 1864 before word reached Momence of Thomas' death. Daniel was eighteen and his departure took Martin O'Brien's right hand man off the farm. While his brothers served the eastern theatre of the war in the direction of Atlanta, Daniel's battles were along the Mississippi, near Vicksburg and near the Tennessee and Yazoo Rivers. He was not far from the banks of the Mississippi where Martin had made his way to New Orleans.

Daniel was first assigned to guard Confederate prisoners held at Springfield, Illinois. He first saw action in June of 1864 where 8,500 union troops, under General Samuel Sturgis, fought at the Battle of Brice Crossroads in Lee County Mississippi against the infamous Confederate commander Nathan Bedford Forrest and his 3,500 men. Nathan Forrest was a plantation owner before war and would later become the first Grand Wizard of the Klu Klux Klan. Sherman had once stated that Forrest needed to be stopped if it took 10,000 union troops to do so. He was a vaunted enemy.

For Daniel O'Brien, the physical demands of war went well beyond the labors of the plow. In addition to weakening his strong physique, the stress, destruction, and slaughter of the war grated at Daniel's spiritual make-up and persistent composition.

The war finally ended on April, 18 1865. When news of the surrender reached Jefferson and Daniel's respective camps some of the men cheered, others fired their rifles in the air to celebrate. Jefferson thought of his brother. Daniel pictured the farm. Most of the soldiers met the news solemnly and with relief. They were simply glad they had won and wanted to go home. Daniel felt he needed to spend time alone before returning home. He needed to rest his body and his soul before returning to civilian life.

Jefferson mustered out at Springfield, Illinois. He had served four years, five months and three days. The long process of bringing the men home on trains and ships began, with extensive delays caused by the paperwork for payrolls and final discharge. Soon the trains and boats of the south, along with the roads, were teeming with tens of thousands of blue clad soldiers on their way home. The joy of peace quickened their step north.

The landscape of America had changed in many ways. Most notable was the proliferation of rail lines which laced the countryside, replacing Indian trails and steamboat laden tributaries as the primary means of travel. The Civil War had ushered out Martin O'Brien's era of Indian pathways and steamboats and began the deployment of rail throughout America. Rail would open the west and would be an integral part of the O'Brien family history in the years to come.

Daniel O'Brien did not return home immediately. Following his honorable discharge at Camp Douglas, he stopped at Momence and announced he would spend some time on his own to "work the war out of his bones." Daniel had a good natured heart and the calamity of the Civil War had unnerved him. He planned to work as a laborer on various farms in Indiana. Two summers later, Daniel was ready to come home.

On the day Daniel made his way home, a mist-laden Kankakee Marsh was greeting the sunrise of another hot summer morning. Millions of frogs were ending their nightly serenade and smallmouth bass could be heard leaping above the water's limits to capture the first unsuspecting lacewing of the day. A lone American bald eagle began his pre-dawn flight at the marshland's eastern edge in Indiana. It flew west and surveyed the entire marsh below.

On a parallel path along the marsh's southern parameter was Daniel O'Brien, returning to Momence, this time, for good. He had spent time in the areas of Evansville, Crawfordsville, and Terre Haute. There were good opportunities for a young man with his farm experience to be "hired on" following the war. Returning farmer veterans were bringing their dormant land back to life. For a short time he also worked for Indiana's first rail line, the Evansville and Crawfordsville Railroad Company repairing track. Daniel had taken his time and reestablished his equilibrium.

Like the eagle, he was witnessing the day's earliest light and had traveled all night. Pushing through the night had been a good idea. He was arriving at the start of the day - able to purchase necessary provisions in town before riding to the O'Brien farm. Though he could not see the end of the marsh in front of him, he knew he was getting fairly close to Momence since his path was gradually drifting north. The marsh had begun to narrow in its formation of the Kankakee River.

He noticed tightness in his neck and realized he'd been looking to the right for some time, watching what seemed like the only bird in the sky towering over the tall trees of the great marsh. It was graceful and obviously large. Its flight was broad, purposeful and possessed a force as it descended below the trees. Thousands of fish in backwaters and small streams provided a daily feast for the great massive bird.

"Now that's a big one," Daniel said to himself as he rubbed his sore neck. "Must be that old Springfield that kicked back at me all the way through the rebellion," he said with a grin. Though Daniel was tired and little sore from his last two weeks of work, he felt relaxed and confident that he had finally put enough time between the war and a normal life. He was looking forward to being home once again.

Daniel returned his attention to the eagle. It dove to the left, then elevated again and sliced right. After a minute or so the great bird burst above the tree line. Daniel stopped his wagon to take one last look. The eagle took a hard right loop to the rear. He had escorted O'Brien for fourteen miles and was now turning back.

Daniel had come north on the Michigan Trail, turning west before the marsh on a simple path that bordered the entire southern edge of the marsh. He had yet to encounter a north-south intersection. But one mile from Momence he finally saw a pathway crossing his west-bound trek.

"It must be the trail," he thought. He was speaking of the Chicago Vincennes Trail now called "Hubbard's." Down a piece to the right were the Upper Crossing and the remains of Hill's Tavern. The old tavern had been moved to the corner of Market and River after Robert Hill died in 1853.

As he approached the intersection, a wooden cart, loaded down with rough timber pulled by two oxen, made its way south crossing his path. By the looks of the load, a barn or perhaps a large farm house awaited the arrival of freshly cut timber processed at a lumber mill in town.

The rutted and tramped crossing road of the old Hubbard Trail ran from Vermilion County in the south to Chicago. While the early commerce along this trail was limited to fur pelts, lumbering mills, tanneries, hay presses, brick kilns, coal yards, ice houses and other industries, were becoming prominent in the area of Momence.

As O'Brien passed over the old trail, he snapped his head to the right, focusing as far north as he could see. Suddenly, his wagon took a jarring from wheel ruts that had created a washboard effect for carts crossing the old trail's path. Dangling out the backend of his wagon were a few tin pans that clapped against each other like a ringing coda at the end of barn dance reel. Once recovered, Daniel remembered the last time he walked this trail. It was the same path that he and James had walked to see their father off to California almost twenty years before during Gold Rush days. It was good to be home.

A mile past Hubbard's, Daniel turned north and could see ahead of him the two bridges at the "lower crossing." The bridges were anchored in the middle by a narrow island between channels. The entire width of the island was no more than three hundred feet wide but it extended a good mile up river to the east. During dry days, the north branch looked like its marshy brother upstream. It was often referred to by the barefoot kids of town as the "frog pond" since they could walk in its midst, stepping on one grass clump to the next that dotted its crossing.

Daniel approached the southern "gateway" into Momence. "Ha! Look at that. A free bridge," he said seeing the newly posted sign. "Now that tells yah' something! The town looks bigger." River Street followed the curved pattern on its banks and an assortment of growing businesses backed up to the river. The town now extended seven blocks north of the river and homes existed on both sides of Range Street.

Once Daniel crossed, he could see the fronts of buildings that had exposed their backs to him as he crossed the bridge. There was the J.J. Moggs Lumber and Coal Company on the right along with the Melby & Hanson Tannery. To the left was L.A. Walker Blacksmith & Wagon Maker along with Brown's Cider Mill already utilizing the rapid flow of water rushing downstream.

The first block of Range included a furniture store, restaurant, meat shop, barber, Masonic Hall, billiard hall, large three-story hotel, and to the amazement of everyone including Daniel, a sign on the second floor of a grocery which read "painless dentist!" "Oh Christ," he said humorously, nearly mimicking Martin's authentic brogue that showed up when Daniel said certain words.

This was quite a little city. It had everything one needed. It was not a typical farm town where grain mills and hay presses dominated the central business district.

Daniel continued up Range Street. "Clump, chump, clump, chump," echoed off the face of store fronts along Range as he drove his wagon north. As Daniel approached the intersection of Front Street he suddenly took notice of another creature in step with the chomping hooves of his muscular colt. She was walking briskly up the wooden side walk at the same pace as his colt. "Well, I'll be," he said to himself under his breath.

He pulled hard on the reins and his horse immediately cut its gate in half. He watched the young lass double the tempo of his colt, twitching her waistline side to side in the original tempo of his horse's trot. This caused a tugging on the skirt hem in synch with her hips and her brown laced boots popped out from under the hem in similar synchronized fashion. Daniel was focused on this welcomed sight.

It was nineteen year old Margaret Hathaway on her way to Astle's Hardware Store. She had a brisk confident walk but was graceful nonetheless. Her hair looked light brown Daniel thought. He was not sure since only a few wisps showed under her plum-colored bonnet.

Daniel pulled his rig over to the right along wooden walk.

Chapter 7

Margaret Hathaway

"Hello Ma'am," Daniel said as he tipped his hat, having caught up with Margaret. She was returning from Astle's Hardware Store and stepping up on to the boardwalk at the southeast corner of Range and Front Streets.

"Good Morning," stated the young woman with a confident tone.

"I wonder ma'am, could you direct me to the emporium in town," asked Daniel trying to extend their conversation. He realized how funny he sounded and quickly thought, "Why did I ask her that? I know where it is. Why am I talking so stiff?"

"I would think you'll find all that you need at Worcheser's just up the street," Margaret said pointing east up Front Street.

"Thank you ma'am," Daniel responded with a second tip of his hat. Margaret took a step south and Daniel east, down Front Street. They separated precisely. Having caught a close-up glimpse of the handsome young Irish lad, Margaret smiled a bit once she was out of his site. He was a bit older than her and she attempted to calculate his age. He looked quite healthy and strong and had a great smile. Margaret suddenly arrived at River Street. "Who is that man?" she asked herself.

Daniel clearly knew where the emporium in town was. He'd been there many times before the war. "Such a blunder," Daniel thought. "She is charming and even more attractive up close. I could have thought of a more appropriate thing to ask. I wonder if she knew I was putting up to her? No, it was a simple enough question. And after all, I'm an honest looking fellow and how else is a young man, who's been away for some time, supposed to act?" he questioned. Clearly, Daniel reacted as most men do when they are struck by the beauty and presence of women with dramatic flair. This despite his war experience and regained confidence over the past few years in Indiana,

Gaining his purpose once again, Daniel found himself at the entrance of Cooke's Drugs. Margaret had indicated the store, located half-way down Front Street, and was Worchester's. In fact, the business had been sold to Civil War Veteran Edward S. Cooke a few years before. Margaret had demonstrated a common small town tendency to call things as they were originally christened despite a change of name or ownership. Worchester's was Cooke's. Being a savvy young man and desiring some reason to talk to Margaret Hathaway again, Daniel logged Margaret's faux pas in his mind. "I'll give her tease over this," he thought smiling at the pure genius of his plot.

After selecting a few items, he went on to Jacob Ruger's harness shop. Ruger, a German immigrant, had established his business at the corner of Front and Locust Streets. He was a veteran. Daniel was planning on purchasing some fresh leather straps, a saddle, saddler's hammer, and a pick iron. The saddle was a gift to his father.

"Why Daniel O'Brien, what a great day! You're home!" Ruger exclaimed. "Dan!" came a shout from behind the cork barrels. It was Jacob Ruger's son Jon who was learning the trade from his father. Dan was thrilled to see Jacob.

"My God man!" Dan yelled. "This can't be the same Jacob Ruger that left for Texas in '62. I heard you were dead!" Both men laughed and embraced. Jacob was also a fellow veteran. The natural bond between veterans instantly took hold. Ruger had enlisted and participated in many battles until his discharge at Galveston, Texas. He had proven his bravery many times in the field and was promoted to lieutenant and then captain very quickly.

"No, I survived, but many did not as I'm sure you've heard," Jacob said. "Blakeley was hell and it cost us many good men. I swore I'd never see the inside of this old harness shop again, but I'm here." He had that intense look of men who have seen the drama of war at its worse. Though he was looking squarely at Daniel O'Brien, his gaze seemed to view the war's image all over again.

"It's good to see you O'Brien," he said. "Jefferson told me you'd be coming soon. He had quite a campaign himself, and poor Thomas."

"Yes," said Daniel. "It was Chickamauga. A hell of a fight. I guess it was just Tom's time, hey Jake?"

"That it was. It's a damn tragedy," Jacob responded.

The two men had been clasping each other's forearms the whole time. First, as the closing of their initial embrace then, clearly, as a means of support while they relived a short portion of the horrific war as only two men of experience can do.

Jacob guided Daniel through the saddle section of the store and Jon was excited to recommend his best tools and leather. A final healthy hand shake between Daniel and Jacob ended their visit. Suddenly, as he walked out the door, O'Brien stopped, turned and gave an instinctive salute to Jacob. Once outside, he gave a hearty handshake to Jon who had just finished loading the new saddle.

On his way back to his wagon, Daniel stopped at Astle's Hardware for a few smaller items. He then made his way north to the farm. The clean fresh air of the Kankakee Valley filled his lungs once again. His new start as a farmer filled his spirits with life's exuberance. "It's good to be living again," he said to himself.

"Jefferson! Jeff! He's here," Martin shouted as Daniel moved up the O'Brien lane. They were thrilled to see him home. "Danny," was all the elder kept repeating in the same affectionate tone he had deployed when young Daniel was pulling those "tiny weeds" from beloved Amy's garden. In an instant, Martin whisked past every memory of Daniel as only a father can when his children live to a certain age.

"Here father, it's for you," Daniel said as he presented Ruger's finest leather saddle to Martin. It was a warm and sentimental homecoming that Martin cherished. As many men do, he broke the moment with humor. "Where ya' been Danny Boy, we've got a huge overrun of the "little weeds" out behind the house."

"Ha, I'll bet you do," Daniel said.

"Come on Daniel, the weeds can wait. Let's get a taste of this prime old whiskey. Pop has been keeping it from me for two years," was Jefferson's response.

In the weeks ahead, Daniel had occasion to pass Margaret Hathaway numerous times in town. Each time, he'd tip his hat and greet her in a formal way quite uncharacteristic of most young men in Momence. No one seemed to be puzzled by Dan's exceptional willingness to run to town for items Martin, Jefferson or even the neighbor needed. It was his excuse to see Margaret.

Toward the end of summer, Daniel was purchasing lumber from Bill Strunk at the Patterson's mill. Jefferson, who had married Luisa Burns on April 15, 1866, was making plans for his own place and the men of the family were all pitching in to get him established.

"You know Daniel, that Hathaway girl's been asking about you," said Strunk. Dan ignored him as they loaded the wagon. "Why sure, my gal tells me she's just waiting for you to have more than a five minute conversation with her," he went on.

"Thanks Bill," Daniel stated in a plain voice, obviously thanking him for the help in loading and not the personal advice. He climbed up into his spring seat, smiled and saluted his trusted friend and yelped a quick, "git-up" to his towing horse. He thought about a strategy all the way home. He'd make a point to engage Miss Hathaway a bit more. "Can't hurt," he said under his breath, offering himself some personal counsel.

It was one week prior to the 4th of July and Momence never missed the chance to chase a greased pig, run barefoot against any foe or tie opposite ankles together in a three-legged race. Despite the reserved nature of some Momence folks from New England in "the big houses," the slung back quality of town laborers from Tennessee or the somewhat out of place ruffian from the eastern marsh, these distinctly different classes of people all celebrated together. Revelry forged a fragile unity among the inhabitants of Momence and it became a quality of the town early on.

There were 116 families in Momence in 1872 and a total population of 956. It seemed that nearly everyone in town, plus folks from the county, were on hand for the Fourth of July. Daniel and a number of his veteran pals were slugging through the opposition's pitchers with ease. The east end of the Island was full of kids sneaking cookies, old men sharing jokes and women preparing lunch, swooshing flies and keeping their eyes on the river bank where their young'uns were wading in the shallow south branch, reaching for tadpoles.

"Hi Margaret," Daniel said tapping her shoulder from behind. They were on a first name basis now and had entered that playful period that develops just prior to courtship.

"Daniel O'Brien! You scared the bejesus out of me," laughed Margaret. Not only was Margaret a sweet gal but she was regularly disarmed by this handsome young Irishman with the broad smile. Like Martin, Daniel had a natural charm and Irish smile to boot but he was more subtle and a bit shyer than his father who had swooped young Amy off her feet at Troy with outgoing charm.

[74]

"What are ya' makin' there young lady?" Being a single man, he had packed a modest picnic and was hoping he'd find a nugget or two in Margaret's basket.

"You'll soon find out," Margaret said in a make-believe "put off" tone. "I took care of you. Just like a farmer. You know how to grow it but God forbid you'd prepare enough to eat," she said. Daniel loved the "scolding."

"I'll be right back," he said. "I'm batting next."

"It's almost ready," shouted back Margaret as the athletic Daniel was well beyond earshot already. Margaret had prepared corn bread, turkey and some goose. There was corn "cut away" and pudding, her specialty.

Within ten minutes Daniel was back. In fact the game was put on hold while nearly every wife, sister, mother and girlfriend had called out that food was "ready!" Daniel settled down on the blanket Margaret had spread under one of the large oaks.

"It looks grand Margaret," said Daniel. "It was nice of you to plan such a swell lunch. I just love these picnics, don't you?" They chatted through lunch oblivious to others around them. People were observing them, however. They were the "new courting couple" in town and nothing stirred chatter like an unmarried couple sharing a picnic blanket at the park.

Conversations in Momence always contained a healthy mixture of gossip, praise and otherwise small talk about everybody else. More than other towns, with populations often more homogeneous, Momence was a divergent mix. Talking about others was what people did.

"Margaret," Daniel said. "Seems only fair that since you've gone through all the trouble to provide me with such a fine lunch that - it only seems right - that I do the same for you, does it not?"

"Oh, that doesn't matter Dan," she said. "I enjoyed it." Margaret wasn't making small talk. She really did enjoy it. Daniel admired how much Margaret liked doing things for others. She was genuine and had a keen sense of what was right but she was never intolerant of others who might still be learning their way. Though he was not conscious of it, Daniel had fallen in love with Margaret Hathaway over the summer of 1872.

"I'd like to take you to dinner at the Columbia House next Sunday, Maggie," he said.

The Columbia House was near the train depot and was the favorite overnight stay or dinner stop for travelers and engineers alike on the new railroad through town. Townsfolk went there regularly but only for special occasions. After all, the owner Mr. Drayer provided some of the finest "inn food" in town.

Margaret felt her cheeks warm and tried to hide her blush. "I'd love to go with you O'Brien," she said looking directly at him, then lowered her eyes as she took a nibble from her corn bread which helped them both break the tension and excitement of the moment.

The following Sunday, Daniel picked Maggie up in his best rig. He had hitched his "town horse" to the buggy rather than one of the big stomping work horses used to pull his grain wagon or haul provisions. Daniel dressed up just a bit and Margaret was dressed appropriately. Their portions for dinner were a bit more in keeping with an indoor meal and were served on nice plates with shiny silver. Tea was served in nice crystal. There was even a flower on the table. Daniel had asked Drayer to "do something nice with the table and fixins'."

Following dinner, Daniel nervously arranged his silver in its original place. Margaret noticed and smiled at his odd behavior though Daniel didn't see her reaction.

"Maggie," Daniel began, "my brother Jeff always says I'm slow to conclude about things. He often teases me about the time it took me to come home from the war," he said with a smile and a nervous chuckle. "But Maggie, when I saw you for the first time walking down the street the day I came home, I made the quickest decision of my life," he paused again. "I knew that day Maggie, that somehow I would find a way to make you my girl. Today Maggie, I want to ask you to be my wife."

Margaret was very pleased and smiled but mentioned how short a time they had known each other. "Ah, heck, Maggie," he said. "I knew I wanted to marry you the first time we met when I nearly tripped looking back at you on my way to Cooke's drugs." He spoke somewhat shyly out of heartfelt respect for her.

"I too, Obrien," she said, then paused and looked directly at him. "I'd be pleased to marry you Daniel."

They spent the remainder of dinner, synchronizing a smile and glance with each nibble of vanilla pudding, consumed in a regular rhythm, without a word. Feeling obligated to break the silence after a time, Daniel said, "It's a nice pudding Maggie, but it's not as good as yours." She smiled as she pulled away the spoon between her lips completing another morsel.

Maggie and Daniel's spoons clinked at the bottom of their respective glass pudding bowls, finishing at the same time. Maggie subtly moved her white gloves to the other side of her dish where she then laid her hand slightly forward on the table. Daniel's hand was already in place, opposite hers. The two touched fingertips in such a way that few would have considered it holding hands. But it was an electrifying to both of them. It was a quiet, solitary moment that washed away the hovering world outside.

After a full summer of continuous "dizziness" between them, the wedding day was suddenly a week away. Mrs. J. Wheeler had undoubtedly the largest stock of ladies' wear in the entire county. Her Millinery Store at the southwest corner of Range and Front streets sold hats, curls, flowers, laces, velvets, beads, and fringes. Goods at thirty cents a yard included silk, cotton and woolen floss, zephyrs and chenilles. There were hoops skirts, panniers and everything feminine. Wheeler's Millinery was the focus of Margaret O'Brien and her closest friends two weeks prior to the wedding. They were making final selections around the large table in Mrs. Wheeler's shop. Margaret's thoughts kept jutting back and forth between the excitement of the moment, the pending arrival of her family from LaPorte and her fiancé Daniel whom she felt closer to everyday. It was an exciting time.

It was here in Momence that Margaret "Maggie" Hathaway, a caring girl of nineteen, would find her life. She and her new husband would raise their family here. She would experience the great joy that all mothers receive watching their children grow up. She would also experience great personal hardship when some would be taken from her before her death. Margaret could not see all that lie before her. She was the happiest she had been her entire young life. Like all young brides, her thoughts were captured in the present. What was ahead had no relevancy to her now. She'd be married soon.

The next morning Maggie's parents, Perry and Mary Hathaway, and the rest of the Hathaway family were ten miles south of the old Sauk Trail making their way toward Momence on the Vincennes. Just before dawn they had stopped at Johnson Inn for a few last minute items including a warm sweet cake that Mary planned to bring to Louisa O'Brien, Martin's third wife.

Martin's second marriage to Sarah Ruggles, with its short courtship and Martin's almost simultaneous departure for California, had not worked out. While Daniel's mother was Amy, Louisa would serve as mother of the groom. In addition, it was good practice to bring a gift to the lady of the house who would host the Hathaways during the wedding.

Maggie's little sister, five year old Hattie Belle Hathaway, was the only one actually sleeping as they moved closer to their destination. Mary Hathaway was awake and leaning up against the wagon's back flap looking over her right shoulder to the northwest. She marveled at the miles of golden wheat that was catching the morning's first sun. Hattie awoke due to the increased activity in their wagon.

"Are we getting closer mommy?" asked Hattie. "Not far Hattie. It won't take much longer," Mary said reassuringly. "Are you eager to see your big sister, dear?" Little Hattie Belle, the youngest of the five Hathaway's, nodded, smiled and snuggled next to her mother.

John Hathaway, Margaret's brother who was one year older, was sitting next to Perry Hathaway as they rode south toward Momence. In addition to little Hattie, there was Arleta who at the age of thirteen adored her sister Maggie, and young Jeremiah, age eleven. The Hathaway's were a bit younger than Martin O'Brien and his third wife Louisa. Perry and Mary Hathaway were forty-six and forty-three respectively. Martin O'Brien and his wife were approaching sixty.

"We're close now, John," Perry said as they passed the area of Yellowhead. "Why don't you get the others set and make sure we're ready to unload." John traded places with young Jeremiah who was thrilled to get the chance to ride into town with dad as the family wagon approached Momence.

"Ha! Look at that, Pop," said Jeremiah. "Is that the court house?" Jeremiah could see the new three-story Union School towering over the rest of town. "No son, that's their new school," Hathaway answered. Momence had constructed an iconic three-story school building one year previous. It had all the amenities of a "modern" school including a stage and auditorium on the third floor. The steel fence surrounded the building had gates such that they allowed children in but kept the frequently roaming livestock out.

"Golly, they must have a lot of kids in Maggie's town, hey Pop?" the boy said.

"That they do boy, that they do," Perry said.

The Hathaways, arriving on September 2, would spend the week getting to know the O'Brien's and enjoying the amenities of Momence. Daniel and Margaret were to be married on Monday, September 9, 1872.

On the day of the wedding, Justice of the Peace, Rodney Ashley, administered the wedding vows in Kankakee. The ceremony was brief but touched everyone in attendance. The bride and groom were two good, hardworking young people who were well respected beyond their years. Those present sensed that few bonds ever pledged could have a greater chance of lasting a lifetime. White kerchiefs drifted regularly under the hats of ladies from both families and Perry Hathaway gave a solid wink to Martin O'Brien as the two men turned, escorting their wives out of the door following the ceremony. The Hathaways and O'Briens had also merged that day.

A large public celebration, befitting of the grandest tradition of Momence ensued that afternoon. Hathaway, a noted veteran himself, felt quite at home meeting many of Daniel's and Jefferson's friends from the war. It was a memorable wedding and celebration for everyone. It would also inspire the Hathaways to relocate to Momence nine years later.

Both families rode wagons to Martin O'Brien's farm following the public reception. It was a typical warm "Indian Summer" day and no one wore coats or covers except the ladies who wore their wraps for the sake of fashion. A few had begun to remove their millinery-made hats as the wagons drew some distance from town. It was appropriate to maintain full fashion within the public portion of the day's events.

The extended celebration at Martin's home allowed the O'Briens and Hathaways to get to know each other further. There were a lot of people to meet. Daniel was reflective and deeply moved seeing the two families meld as a result of his marriage to Margaret. He always had a strong sense of family linkage and, more than most, he seemed to observe the broader meanings of life's routine and daily events.

Emma Hurley, fourteen year old daughter of Louise O'Brien from her previous marriage, had spent the bulk of the day with thirteen year old Arleta Cecilia Hathaway. They were seated on the old garden bench discussing their eminent entry into the sorority of womanhood when they too would be able to wear big hats like the older girls. Her brother, fifteen year old George Hurley was showing young Jeremiah Hathaway, now eleven, how to properly sling small pebbles at small dried oak cuts atop the split rail fence.

While Martin and Louisa performed the duties of hosts, Daniel observed that his father was the oldest of all those present and somehow, today, he observed Martin's profile and the timelines that adhered to his father's sunken cheekbone and brow. To Daniel, Martin's Irish roots, his time on steamboats, the Gold Rush days, and the hardy living Martin did among the men who muscled the American frontier, appeared for the first time. Martin's youthful slate-black hair had started to give way to silver. Today, Daniel sensed his own entry into adulthood as never before.

The wedding celebration extended well past sundown. Martin lit six oil-filled lamps and spaced them along the top of his split rail fence. Each beacon illuminated the warm September night and unintentionally created a tabernacle-like setting first recognized by Daniel. As he looked to the west, through the fire, past the lamps and into the dark night of the prairie, Daniel's vision took in the O'Briens and Hathaways in full animated conversation around the warm fire.

The family had gathered on chairs, stumps and the old garden bench that had witnessed the death of Amy O'Brien years before at Yellowhead. The youngsters were sitting on blankets and all were munching on Mary Hathaway's sweet cake which Louisa had saved for the family gathering. Hathaway surprised and pleased all the men by revealing a fresh bottle of whiskey he had picked up at the Johnson Inn.

Perry Hathaway, a former member of the 113th Indiana Volunteers, was in deep conversation with Jefferson O'Brien, then twenty-eight and James O'Brien thirty-four. Hathaway was scripting every detail of how his regiment had turned back the Confederate spy Thomas Hines. Hines led a detail of men into Indiana in '63 known as Hine's raids. Hathaway and his company confronted the incursion at Alton, Tobinsport, and Derby just south of French Lick, Indiana.

"Why that son-of-a-bitch looked just like John Wilkes Booth himself," barked Hathaway with his leg perched atop O'Brien's split rail fence. "Why sure. You heard, dint-cha, that he had to flee for his life in 65' cause of them mistakin' him for the assassin," relayed Perry. Both James and Jefferson were enthralled. Hathaway could tell a story. He went on. "There was a time when our Union agents viewed Hines as the man they most needed to apprehend! Apart from a short stay at the Ohio Penitentiary in late '63, they never did capture that slimy eel," joked Hathaway as he bellowed a laugh. Hathaway jawed and laughed as only an experienced vet could do. Having seen the horrors of war he still had the ability able to drain its tragic nature with an infusion of humor.

Daniel had walked to the house to get more cake and was returning to the family outside. Before entering the light of the fire, he paused. He could see the animated Hathaway emitting waves of emphasis that rocked his two brothers back in fits of laughter and amazement. He saw the young boys flipping the cup and ball in a heated contest while the girls played jacks with focused resolve. Margaret, Louisa and Mary Hathaway were rehashing the exciting day's events.

As he listened from a distance, the conversations blended to one. Celtic spirits were at work under the night canopy of the Illinois Prairie amid two Irish American families. What began as a quiet tinkling of a silver spoon at the bottom of a glass pudding bowl weeks before, was now resounding in full-voice on the O'Brien farm that night.

Chapter 8

Alva F. O'Brien

Leaving behind the calamites of their childhood, young men eventually become fathers and women bear their children. Families grow, older generations pass away and the young begin anew. The close proximity of extended families and the brevity of life itself heightened an appreciation of family lineage on the American Frontier.

For the next twenty-five years, in the prime of their lives, Daniel and Margaret O'Brien would raise nine children amid relatives from both sides and a rapidly increasing population in Momence, Illinois. Within two years of their wedding, their first baby, Lila, was born on April 14, 1874. A second girl arrived two years later in February of 1876. Margaret named her Clara.

In Momence there were children everywhere. Union School had been built at the cost of $20,000, replacing a scattering of country schools and the "Old Brick" school that could no longer handle new and expanding families. The O'Briens would add to the fabric of the young city and their children would carry the O'Brien name into the next century.

Momence was benefiting from its proximity to Chicago. By the 1870's the former Fort Dearborn reached 300,000 residents. Illinois was also becoming a very different place. Prospering farms and growing industries were taking hold. Thousands of new residents, having streamed in from Europe's oppression and poverty, were mixing with "established" frontier families. The new residents brought skills from their European guilds, a flair for design, and an intuitive vision of how communities should look in the new world. They built towns in the style of their homeland adjusting for the natural resources found here. The children of these European immigrants would return to Europe someday. But they would do so as liberators, freeing the millions who never left the old country.

The Kankakee Marsh east of Momence also experienced dramatic changes during this time. The summer months of 1871 were extremely dry and in October of that year Chicago burned.
Another fire destroyed Peshtigo, Wisconsin. Oddly enough, fires raged throughout the Marsh that fall as well. Island fires ignited leaving deep holes that resembled burnt out peat bogs. Much of the timber that did not burn was sent to Chicago to rebuild the city.

Finally, a continuous pattern of ditch digging in the Marsh began that would eventually drain it on the Indiana side for farm land. It would destroy one of the largest habitats for aquatic and terrestrial plant and animal life in America and eliminate a major portion of commerce for Momence. Illinois fought the drainage effort and the Marsh east of Momence was held in tact. In the early days barrels of frog legs, wagonloads of pelts, and railroad cars of game processed through Momence bound for Chicago. By the end of the 1870's that industry was gone.

Five months after daughter Clara was born, Momence and the nation celebrated the 100th anniversary of American Independence. Daniel and Margaret were once again at the Island Park on July 4th for the huge celebration. This time they were saddled with the responsibility of children, so Daniel had no time to join the young men playing baseball that day. As usual, Momence outdid itself by celebrating for an entire week. Few towns could throw a fest quite like Momence. Its flair for frivolity went back to the days of the raucous all night events first staged by the men of the marsh and their fur trading partners. The entire summer was fun-filled and both Daniel and Margaret experienced the vitality of life and the joys of young children. But in the waning days of that centennial year, the O'Brien family suffered a significant loss.

On September 12th, Maggie saw Daniel clearly carrying some burden as he tramped up the worn path to the house. "That's unusual," she thought. Margaret greeted him at the door, wiping her hands on her extensive white apron.

"It's Pop, Maggie," said Daniel as he clutched her forearms. "He's gone, Dan stated nearly under his breath.

"Gone? Gone how? Where did he go this time?" Margaret responded. She had mistaken Daniel's report as indication that Martin, a man of great wanderlust, had departed on another trip. It would not have surprised Maggie, had he gone back to Missouri for a spell. Martin had sold his farm in 1868, a mere two years after marrying Louisa, and moved to town.

"No, he's here. I mean he's not here," stuttered Daniel. "He's dead."

"Lord have mercy on all of us!" responded a shocked Maggie. "How did it happen?"

"I really don't know. Towne Denny said he saw him just collapse right before stepping up into Cromwell's Grocery Store step. He just keeled over!"

Dan was clearly distraught and Margaret opened her arms to him. His two arms hung drooping into her comforting embrace.

"Oh, Dan," she said affectionately before pausing.

"He was a wonderful man, your father," she whispered to Daniel as he had placed the side of his moist cheek against the lace collar. She held him as they stood in the doorway. Daniel could feel his tears taken into the fabric of the soft cotton lace that framed Maggie's homemade work dress. With that, a degree of pain left him. Maggie had a comforting way with her husband. She took life as it came, an ideal comforter in tough times. Her instincts were to help those around her when life's burdens appeared. It would serve her well in her life ahead.

Martin O'Brien, Irish immigrant, had sailed sixty days from his beloved Emerald Isle, walked, rode and traversed the great rivers of the new frontier with a spirit and zest that cast a wave of energy over all who knew him, particularly his family. He had found his home in the first frontier town of the Kankakee Valley and was buried in Nichole's Cemetery at Yellowhead. This is where he had first experienced the joy of independence, America's staggeringly abundant resources, and the open beauty of the great prairie. His life's journey had come to an end. But he had left his mark. Martin O'Brien had been the spiritual energy of the family. Daniel O'Brien was its soul. With Martin gone, the energy would have to come from somewhere else. It would not arrive for another decade but it would return ten-fold.

Daniel left farming and moved to town following Martin's death. It was his way of purging the routine of his father's presence from of his anguished soul. Two years after Martin's death, Elmer O'Brien was born to Maggie and Daniel in 1878. Lila was all of six years old and was mothering young Clara to help mommy along. Both girls were frail and leaned on each other as Maggie's family grew.

By 1880, Daniel was working around town as a general laborer. Momence was in great need of good and reliable workers. The loss of his father took Daniel off the farm permanently, something he had always loved as far back as his "tiny weeds" days when Amy was alive. Not since his war experience had Daniel been fundamentally shaken and redirected. He was an emotional man who felt the weight of life's pain. Margaret was his strength as she was for so many.

In Martin's time, Illinois was considered the West. Going west now meant going beyond the Mississippi River. The Indians that were escorted out of the Kankakee Valley by Parish and Vail soon discovered that the white man would not limit their claim to land east of the big river. Martin's long winding trek up the Oregon Trail during the Gold Rush Days did not compare to the post-war railroad migration that was now expanding across the continent. Four railroads alone would eventually pass through the City of Momence.

During the 80's, Momence continued to modernize. The Central House Hotel was erected by German immigrants Fred and Elizabeth Knighthart. It was a dominant four-story hotel located at the corner of Range and Front Streets. It anchored the intersection as the new center of town away from River Street. River Street led commerce in earlier times when the mill, tannery, blacksmith and tin shops were central to town life. Across the street from the new hotel was the W.I. Dixon Bakery where one could purchase a nine-inch blueberry pie for ten cents. There were other restaurants opening in town, along with grocers including Henry Reins' store which actually delivered items to the house, unheard of in earlier times.

Industry also came to Momence. The Tiffany Brick Company employed nearly 100 employees by 1884. The village board had voted unanimously to install an electric light plant with eight or ten lights strategically placed to light the city streets from early dusk to midnight in 1890. Superintendent L. W. Calkins was often called out at night to go throw a few more corn cobs into the furnace to generate power.

The Chicago and Eastern Illinois railroad purchased land south of the depot across from Columbia House where Daniel had first dined with Maggie. Two years later a round house, rip track and repair shops were located on the land south of the island hiring between forty to fifty men. The railroad was now an important part of Momence life.

The railroad eventually purchased the unused eastern half of the island park and turned it into a resort area. Boat houses were built, a dancing pavilion and bandstand was erected, rope swings and a merry-go-round were set up for the children. Picnic tables and refreshment stands completed the development. Opening day was a huge success as the beautiful new park, owned, controlled and recently improved by the C and E I road was opened to all citizens on Saturday, June 16, 1887.

The O'Brien children, like all others in town, relished the park and returned to it daily.

One year after the park opened, Maggie, as she was so commonly referred to in town by this time, added a new playmate to the O'Brien clan by giving birth to Clarence "Bud" O'Brien on July 29, 1888. The joy of a new baby was tempered a bit with the passing of Dan's oldest brother James that same year due to "the fever."

On October 12 that fall, Daniel purchased the home of William and Eliza Shrunk located at 53 Hill Street in Momence. It would ease the snug living conditions of his expanding family. Though many new beautiful homes were built in Momence at this time, the O'Brien abode was a moderate wooden house that provided only marginal relief from their previous quarters.

Alva F. O'Brien, the seventh child of Daniel and Margaret O'Brien, was born in their new modest home on Saturday, December 13, 1890. The new energy of the O'Brien family had finally arrived. No one knew it at the time, but "Pat," as they would call him from the very beginning, would have more energy than anyone ever seen in Momence. It was apparent from the start that God had sprinkled an extra dose of zest on this Irish child.

"My, my look at all the hair," said fourteen year old Clara O'Brien. Her mother was holding the newest addition to the O'Brien clan for all to see. The young child had plenty of dark black hair, seemed a bit longer than the previous babies and was actively twisting his arms and legs.

"He's so very active for a new born, hey mama?" Clara observed as she gently stroked the matted locks of her new baby brother.

"Yes, he's been active all through these last months inside, so I don't expect him to be any less persistent now," said Maggie. They both laughed.

Clara said to her mother, "You're a wonderful mother. I love you." Margaret, touched by her daughter's maturing ways smiled at Clara. "I love you too my dear."

Just then the baby squirmed and a mighty wail came forth. He was hungry and ready for milk. "My, what a persistent baby you are young Alva" Margaret said as she pulled open her loosely bound top. Clara looked on, intrigued as all girls are when they first start to understand motherhood. Persistence would be a remarkable trait of this new young O'Brien. "Pat" O'Brien would not only extend the O'Brien name into the 20th Century, it would make the name famous throughout the country and world.

At the time of Pat's birth, the final stages of removing Indian nations from the Great Plains was still in progress. The battle of Wounded Knee, generally considered a final act of the collective series of conflicts between U.S. forces and American Indians, occurred a month after Pat's birth. The government announced that the American frontier was closed to Indians. Based on populations in the West and the amount of land used for agriculture, the Indians were more or less officially a landless people, confined on reservations at the mercy of the latest immigrants.

The American frontier was running head long into the Machine Age. Industry was turning its mammoth iron ship toward western expansion and away from its European past. American history would tip on a fulcrum in 1890 and make a calamitous headfirst slide into the 20th Century. The United States would become an urban, industrial juggernaut that would spawn invention, form a new culture, and create unprecedented power for the United States. Alva "Pat" O'Brien had arrived at the opportune time. But while America turned its attention to building great cities and industrial centers, Europe was trying to shed the Victorian Age and there were early signs of the upheaval that would soon engulf the continent.

As Margaret O'Brien nursed her jittery baby boy, little did she know that like his father, young Pat would also go to war. It was clear that America would not experience another civil war. No one at the time, however, could imagine a war with other nations. But America would be forced to turn back toward Europe and help salvage some sanity in the old countries.

The strain in Europe at the end of the 19th century was driving immigration to America in unprecedented numbers. Ellis Island opened in April of 1892 and the flood of Europeans continued pushing the white man west of the Mississippi in droves.

The 1890 census recorded nearly sixty million Americans across the land, up twenty-five percent since 1880. That same year, Momence had 2500 citizens and was the largest city in Kankakee County. The City of Kankakee, itself was still young and developing.

Momence had developed into a railroad industrial center and people were moving in because there were jobs. French Canadian, German, Swedish, English, and Irish immigrants soon appeared. There were several African-American families who had lived in the community from its earliest days and in the years just prior to 1890, Danes and Poles formed close knit communities segregated much like Chicago to the north. A group of German immigrants formed the German Club of Momence in 1890, a community north of the Kankakee River east of town.

The influx of Europeans brought culture to Momence. The new Opera House became the cultural center of Momence the same year Carnegie Hall opened in 1891. The famed Momence Hay Palace, a major commercial venture, appeared in town four months before Pat O'Brien's birth and Chicago opened the World's Fair when he turned three years old. Both were landmark exhibitions designed to fuel commerce.

Momence was also becoming known as a city of beautiful homes. In the township were the gracious farm homes of Chatfield, Hess, and Schrontz, as well as the older Graham, Nichols and Metcalf homes. The city pointed with pride to the beautiful W. G. Nichols homes, the Chipman, Tiffany, Durham and Hardy houses and, above all, the Wikstrom home. "Villa Swea", a stately three story twenty room home that was not only a city mansion but a little bit of Sweden.

Daniel's home on Hill Street was no mansion. He was making a laborer's wage of approximately $1.25 per day, requiring the oldest three children Lila 16, Clara 14, and Elmer 12 to find ways to earn extra funds for the family. Margaret took in sewing and found odd jobs where she could. Packed into the small frame house were also Perry 9, Merwin 5, two-year old Clarence and newborn Alva. The house faced east and actually looked small in comparison to the open space around it on Hill Street. But it was home.

On a hot August day in 1893, Daniel and Maggie O'Brien sat back on wooden slat chairs in front of their modest dwelling. Young Pat was running around his father's chair — screeching with delight each time he missed Daniel's sudden jut of his right leg to trip Pat up.

The O'Brien's were discussing how lean the year had been financially. Thank goodness Clara had married in '92. She had married on Christmas Eve to a good man, Matt Clegg. He was an astute businessman and owned the only shoe store in town.

It eased Daniel to know that his older daughters were married to good men who made decent pay. Still, they were young. Clara was 16 when she wed and Lila only 19. But young girls married early then and, equally important, it provided more space for the growing O'Brien clan in their small house.
"I worry about the girls, Daniel," Margaret stated using a lace hanky across her brow to brush away the day's sweltering heat. "Clara and Lila are so young and with this terrible economic recession, I fear they will fail before they even begin," she lamented looking away.

"Why sure it's bad Maggie, but they will survive and as you said, they're young my dear," Daniel assured. "They'll do fine. They're good girls and they married good men.

The Panic of 1893, as it would be known, was a serious economic depression in the United States. It was caused by railroad overbuilding and shaky railroad financing which set off a series of bank failures. Compounding the railroad crisis was a run on the gold supply. It was the worst depression the United States had ever experienced to date.

Sensing Margaret's unresolved concern, Daniel went on. "It's bad, Maggie, I know it concerns you. Everyone is concerned and many have it worse than we!"

"I just hope we can hang on to the house. I've never seen times this rough," she said. "Hang on to it?" he said with surprise. "Why Maggie, I was actually gonna' discuss with you my idea on making it bigger!" Maggie turned to him with a smile that sneaked through her teasing smirk.

"The heat has gotten to you, you silly Irishman," she said with a good laugh.

"Now, now Maggie, just listen a minute, will yah," Daniel protested.

Her eyes rolled with all the charming smile of a sweet Irish lass.

Daniel made his case. "You see Maggie, with your father and mother in town and them Hansen boys, plus Perry and even Merwin, why with a little additional lumber, we consolidate our nails, tools, and saws – we could make the house bigger. I talked to your father and he agrees. We can disassemble the current house, add some foundation, then expand to the west," he explained. "I mean with this new baby coming and all and the way Pat seems so cooped up in the winter. We need the room, Maggie girl."

Margaret shrugged, "Well, if you feel you can do it, I'll go along."

Margaret was in her 5th month with their next child. The heat of the late summer was plenty to exhaust her but tonight young Pat was also scampering around his father's chair oblivious to the heat, adding to his mother's strain. Young Pat continued to have more energy than any of her previous six children. He was a firestorm but was a good natured boy. Even at the early age of three, he had charmed many a visiting mother and gave most men who witnessed his stern stance imitating the elders around him a good laugh. He often stared an adult down with his two fists planted firmly on both hips and say, "Watch it Mither," all done with a sinister but contagious grin.

"You know, I'm convinced that damn kid could jump right over my leg even if I was trying to trip him up," said the admiring father of his young son. "I've never seen a toddler anticipate and land so solidly on his feet. Heck, Elmer wasn't that agile at 4," Daniel boasted.

Margaret only smiled and wiped her brow. It would be nice to have a bigger house she thought. It struck her what a good father her husband Daniel had been and how positive he viewed life. Daniel found family time to be a great joy. Margaret felt blessed and the whole family gravitated around this good and decent man.

The 1890's would be difficult ones for the O'Briens. The admittedly inconsistent bounty of a family farm brings comfort and hope as each planting season begins. In town, resources and work becomes a continuous chase, often falling short. During tough times, families are often bound together. In the case of Daniel and Margaret O'Brien, help came from both sides of the family. The Hathaways, Hansens, and O'Briens all lived within a stone's throw of each other. It made for strong family ties.

Grandfather Perry Hathaway had moved to Momence in 1883 and that added to the support of the O'Brien's. It was a great comfort to Margaret that the O'Briens and Hathaways combined efforts whenever they could. Even her brother-in-laws, "the Hansen boys" as they were affectionately called, were willing participants.

In the months of September and October of '93, Perry Hathaway and Daniel O'Brien supervised the reconstruction of the O'Brien home. Brothers John and Theodore Hansen, married into the Hathaway clan, were good additions. Hattie and Arletta were never short of volunteering their efforts for any task. Matt Clegg was there to lend a hand and even the younger boys pitched in.

Margaret's baby, Forest O'Brien, was born in the new house on one of the coldest days of January 1894. He was a small baby and suffered through a harsh winter. Young Pat took a protective roll with his baby brother. Once the warm weather arrived he spent most of his time encouraging the youngster to smile by putting a dandelion under his chin. Forest could stand up by grabbing Pat's thumbs before being shook lose causing the baby to fall on his backside, much to Pat's delight. He laughed uncontrollably when he fell and Pat gave him a mock scolding.

It was the first time Pat found a focus outside his own needs as the mentor of his baby brother. Three and a half years later, young Forest would pass away from Chicken Pox. It would leave a deep void in the heart of young Pat. The memory and loss of his little brother would stay with Pat his whole life.

In 1896, Ivan O'Brien was born, completing the legacy of Daniel and Margaret O'Brien. Known affectionately as "Mulligan," he would become the focus of Pat's attention after the passing of Forest in 1898.

Chapter 9

Crawdadden'

Seventy-one year old Perry Hathaway sat on a big rock, right long side the churning waters of the Kankakee with two young and eager seven year olds. He was doing what so many men of his age like to do, repeat the joys of their youth. With him was his grandson Pat, who he enjoyed immensely, and Al Fontaine, Pat's closest chum.

"You know, my dad likes to go fishing too," young Al said as he studied the rough old hands of Hathaway tying off an expert knot on his line.

"He does? Why that's grand Al! I'll bet he knows how to catch the big small mouths," the old man said. Al gave one of those 'you betcha' nods, opening his eyes, pulling open his jaw under closed lips while nodding rapidly as he watched the old man.

"Now you see boys, you start with about 1 inch of line above the knot." They leaned in and studied his fingertips, their mouths now open and squinting intently.

"The knot?" Al asked.

"Yeah, shucker! Howdya' think the hook gets on the string?" young Pat stated as he took a light, glancing scrape across Al's double crown. Al's hair flipped up but there was no blow to the head He ducked just in time for he knew it was coming. The boys then tussled and laughed abruptly, always at the ready for friendly combative romp. Having his grandfather bring them fishing made Pat feel pretty special. As boys so often do, he demonstrated his superior stature by teasing his best friend.

"Shucker," taken from corn shucker, was one of a million contrived barbs made up by young boys intended for their buddies. The words can often be said in the presence of adults and in some cases are substituted for adult versions considered vulgar.

'Now Pat, don't act that way," said the old man. "Al's just trying to learn."

Oblivious to all that, Al gave Pat one last rabbit punch and the two boys yelped with glee before drawing in once again.

"Now look boys," encouraged Hathaway, "You leave about one inch, grab the hook eye and line with your thumb and finger of your left hand, then wrap that extra one inch around 3 times, but not too tightly. Then take the end and stick it through and pull."

The boys leaned in further and now both had their tongues sticking out of the corner of their mouth, biting down a bit as they peered in. When Hathaway tightened the knot with a few short tugs, both boys crinkled their faces as if they were slinging a sledge hammer on a chain gang. "Success!" barked young Pat as if all this wasn't new to him.

"Ok boys, now take your hooks and do it yourself," instructed Hathaway. "You can't be fishermen unless you know how to tie your own hook on the line, right boys?"

"Right, GeePa," said Pat. "Right Sir," sounded Al at the same time.

The two boys went to work bowing their necks deep into their inaugural knot-tying attempt. Their tongues appeared once again which Hathaway noticed with a smile then rose to his feet.

Perry Hathaway placed his hands on his hips and glanced downstream. The morning sun was sparkling off thousands of ripples and splashes as the water rushed further west. Perry had seen much in his life. Born in Shelby, Ohio 1826, he had witnessed most of the transition that had occurred on the American Frontier. His life reflected the migration of Americans to the west. The Hathaways had moved from Shelby County, Ohio to Indiana and since 1883 lived in Momence. He loved being around his children and grandchildren.

He had married off his daughters Arleta and Hattie Belle to the Hansen boys whom he loved like his own. Jeremiah, still single, lived in town and John was living with Arleta and Theodore since the parting of Ida, John's wife for a short time. How grateful was this good Baptist to live out his life with his wife Mary here in Momence. Both were outliving most of their peers.

All energy, focus and drive since the war, was directed west in those days. More space was west. New land was west. Indeed, all hope was west. It was a subconscious predisposition of Americans in the days following the Insurrection.

But Perry would not be following the Kankakee further downstream. He was as far west as he would ever be at his age. Like so many Americans of his time, when one perceived that life was in its final phase it usually meant there was no further moving to the west. It was something deep in the American psyche of the time.

The boys fished for about an hour and Perry Hathaway spent most of the time answering questions and refocusing their efforts. Young boys often lose interest in this slow hunt. Pat was particularly fidgety, always looking for action.

"All right boys, I think we've had enough," said Perry. "Wrap those poles and I'll take them back to the house. You boys go run off now and be careful around that river."

"Thanks, GeePa," stated Pat, using his pet name for his towering grandfather.

"Thanks, Mr. Hathaway," was Al's response.

The boys ran off. Perry held the poles and bait bucket for a spell as he watched the energetic boys sprint toward Range Street. The soles of their shoes were flashing back at him as they ran. It reminded him of the young colt he had observed years ago galloping away, having first found its legs. He turned toward home.

"I wanna go down to the island today, Al," stated young Pat. "Let's catch some crawdads," he said. "Where the heck can we get a can?"

"Here, go up behind the store. They probably got lots of cans there," said Al.

The two boys turned left behind the shops that ran along the west side of Range Street and began scrounging in the garbage behind the grocery store and restaurant. They found a discarded container and headed toward the bridge. They had their arms across the shoulders of each other – walking in stride towards their next adventure. Both bounced in time, watching their stomping feet the whole way as they crossed the bridge. It made a bit of a booming sound. Suddenly, they sensed someone in their way. It was a stately looking man with a mustache who dressed unlike most men in Momence.

Isaac Hardy came to Momence from England in 1893 with three sons, Ernest, Ralph and James Edward. The Tiffany Brick Company recruited him to come to Momence. With his special formula he started up a process in which the face of the brick was covered with a coating of porcelain in any shade or tint desired. The company became well known, winning prizes and recognition at expositions across the country and in Europe.

"Well young lads, where might you two gentlemen be off to this morning, might I ask?" he asked with a distinctive British accent.

"We're going crawdadden' sir," responded Al.

"Crawdadden'! Why, what in God's name is that?" asked the distinguished gentlemen.

Pat supplied an explanation. "Well you see sir, crawdads - that's what we call 'um here - are small crabs with double pinchers and a curled tail. They hide under the limestone rocks in the shallow rapids south of the Island. They're really easy to catch!" he said with enthusiasm.

"Ah, crayfish!" stated Hardy.

Pat continued. "See this can mister? Well, all you have to do is place this can behind the crawdad. He can't tell you're sneakin' up behind him so it don't matter. Then, once your can is in the right place, you … very slowly…. reach down and touch the crab on his nose and 'shoop!' he backs right into the can and you got 'um! It's easy" stated Pat as Al stood by nodding the affirmative.

Hardy could tell who the real stalker here was. The way Pat lowered his head and slowed his speech as he moved in for the kill was all the evidence needed.

"Why that's simply marvelous boys!" responded Hardy. "You two are quite the outdoor experts aren't you?"

"Oh, that's not all we do. There's a whole bunch o' stuff you can do around here," Pat said while casting his arm across the horizon to further demonstrate. You don't sound like other people in Momence mister. Why is that?" Pat asked.

Hardy explained. "Why no, boys. I do live here but I've only been here a short time. I'm from England!" His sharp British accent seemed quite apparent to the boys now
"England? Where's that?" Pat asked.

"Is it by Ohio?" asked Al. "Your grandpa's from Ohio, right Pat?" he pushed open Pat's shoulder to look him square in the eye.

"Hah! That's funny young man. Well, Ohio is a little closer to England than Illinois" said Hardy with a hearty laugh. "But England is across the ocean. It's close to Europe. Have you heard of Europe boys?" he said. Pat was nodding and Al was shaking his head. As with all Brits, he viewed England somewhat separated from Europe although, they obviously were not.

"Well, that's where many Americans came from you know," Hardy boasted. "Why, England is one of the greatest countries in the world!"

"My GeePa says that America is the greatest country in the world, mister. Is that what you think too?" Pat lowered his brow a bit.

"Why you're quite a bright young man aren't you lad. What's your name?" asked Hardy.

"I'm Pat O'Brien and he's Al Fontaine, my best friend," Pat said with great pride and a bit of bravado as he flipped his thumb toward Al on his right.

Now Hardy laughed even harder than before. The boy had charmed him. Pat was obviously good on his feet. "Why young O'Brien you're Irish and that's right near England. Did you know that lad?" Hardy smiled and was enjoying the exchange with such a bright young seven year old.

"Well," Pat began, "I don't know if it's the same England or not, but my GeePa..." suddenly he turned and said to Al, "GeePa's Irish too." "My Geepa told me that we're Irish, we're sure not English but we let them use the Irish Sea!"

Now Hardy was roaring! "You're quite a corker, aren't you O'Brien! Well boys, I must be off. You boys have a good time and be careful around that river.

Pat and Al stepped aside and the man crossed. Al placed his arm on Pat's shoulders so as to resume their rhythm walk to the Island.

"Let's Go!" Pat shouted suddenly.

Pat broke from Al and took off running as fast as he could. Al knew clearly that a race was on. Both boys were good friends and had nearly perfect instincts about what the other was thinking. They turned left on the Island and never broke stride the whole way. Once in the cleared area, they veered right and into the shallow limestone rapids. Al had the can. They spent another hour taking freedom away from about two dozen crawdads.

Unknown to Pat, he and Al had just run across the same spot where Margaret O'Brien had first shared her picnic basket with Daniel in the park, years ago. But it's only the elders that link the present to the past. Youth runs through the present uncaring and unaware of anything that has come before. The old pause and reflect. The young act. When the world requires action, it is the young that are called upon. And the old send them off knowing that the young will not be burdened with the past but will act. All progress depends on this.

Pat O'Brien and Al Fontaine were inseparable as young boys. They spent every free minute outdoors. The River was a natural draw but the Marsh is where they spent more and more time as they got older. Some days they'd have to fib their mothers about fishing on the Island when they had actually spent the day in the Marsh. Both boys carried sling shots and learned to hit squirrels, muskrats, coons and even an occasion birds from thirty feet away. They'd spend hours sneaking up on deer and, on occasion, avoided the coyote or cougar that regularly roamed the great marsh by escaping downwind. They learned to navigate and survive in the outdoors at a very young age.

One day while fishing along the north branch of the River they heard footsteps stomping down River Street. When they turned to see who it was the boys saw Pat's oldest sister, Lila, hurrying down the street to see Margaret. Seeing no relevance to their focus that morning they both turned back and returned to the task at hand.

Twenty-two year old Lila O'Brien, the oldest among Daniel and Margaret's children, was running from Range Street toward the house. She had tears running down her cheeks partly for joy but just as much for the pain in her joints. Lila had suffered from rheumatism since her teen years and found it difficult to move as gracefully as other ladies her age.

She had just met with Benjamin Franklin Worley of Lowell, Indiana. He had asked her to marry her. She was entirely consumed by an overflow of emotions. It was unusual for this kind and selfless woman to react this way. Many said she had all of the charitable traits of her mother.

"My God, I met him at the Styles hardware store!" she laughed to herself.

Worley had asked Lila to meet him there in a message delivered by her sister Clara. She remembered thinking how discouraged she felt when her younger sister passed her the note. Clara was carrying her young son Jack and was in a rush. She had just flipped Lila the note and said, "Here Lila, this is for you." Her younger sister was married at 16 and until her chance meeting of Ben a month ago, Lila had had little chance to get to know a nice man. Worley had recently lost his wife. They were both in need of a partner.

Nearly tripping up the porch stairs in exhaustion, she pulled open the screen and pushed her whole body against the heavy oak door of Margaret's house.

"Mother! Mother!" she yelled.

"What is it dear, what's happened?" Margaret pleaded.

"Ben Worley asked me to marry him," Lila gush with hardly a breath left in her body.

"Oh my, Lila! How wonderful!" Margaret responded as she shifted young Ivan to her other hip so the two women could hug.

Lila hugged her mother, resting her cheek against Margaret's and wrapping her arm around Maggie and the baby. "Oh Mother, I thought I would never marry – that no man would want to marry an old lady like me."

"That's crazy talk, Lila" Margaret retorted. "You're not old. And you are a wonderful girl, my dear. Ben is so lucky you are here for him. So sad he lost his wife."

About then her sister Clara arrived and all three celebrated their joy. Clara almost seemed relieved. She had grown concerned about her sister and felt bad every time she and Matt were together around her. She took Ivan from her mother. About then young Forest had waddled in to stand next to Maggie with a big smile holding on to her skirt. He would be three years old in a few weeks. He could tell everyone was happy and wanted to be part of the fun. Lila leaned over and picked him up.

"But when, Lila? When will you wed?" Margaret stated looking back at her daughter.

"Well, I know it's not a lot of time but we'd like to get married on February 14th – Valentine's Day!" Lila stated with much enthusiasm.

"Why, of course, how nice. It looks like all my daughters will be married on a holiday. Clara on Christmas Eve and you on Valentine's Day," Margaret said before realizing the short time to plan. "Lord, that's just three months away! We have so much to do."

Lila put Forest down but held him back as Margaret went into the kitchen to look for a pencil and paper. "It will be fine mother. I have good friends at church that will help me and the pastor will be quite pleased, I'm sure."

Looking down at Forest Lila spoke to him. "Lila's going to be married, isn't that nice Forest?" She had placed Forest so close that he stood on her feet and was looking her straight in the eye. Lila hardly noticed her physical discomfort having her little brother stand on her feet. Lila had always taken a motherly disposition toward Forest, not anticipating she would ever have children herself. Her mother needed as much help as she could acquire, as well. It was fall of 1897. Margaret had just turned forty-four.

About that time, Pat and Al came bounding into the house taking a bead on the kitchen. They had just walked home from the Marsh where they were setting traps and planning for the winter of adventure.

"You boys take your shoes off. I just cleaned this house and I don't want that marsh mud all over the floor!" Margaret shouted to the boys. Turning to Clara in a lower voice, "That Pat is always dashing in and out, to and fro. He never stops!" The boys appeared from the kitchen with a sandwich each. Two thick pieces of homemade bread with a big piece of cheese stuffed in between.

"Pat, take your brother with you. He wants to play," Margaret requested as the ladies sat down to devise a schedule for the newly announced wedding.

"Ok mom," was Pat's response. "Come on big boy! Let's go outside," Pat had also taken a special care of Forest. Pat was the type of kid that did such a thing instinctively. His buddies were drawn to him, as well as the younger kids. To Forest, Pat was the most important event of the toddler's day. Al and Pat let young Forest pummel them with acorns from 3 feet away, held races along the property allowing Forest to win and swung the boy back and forth like a hammock until everyone was exhausted. Everyone loved Forest.

As fall gave way to winter, play activity for Forest was limited to the indoors. Al and Pat ventured out to the frozen backwaters of the Kankakee to ice skate whenever they could and the marsh could be easily explored through January when the backwaters were frozen solid.

Wedding plans progressed as February approached and the whole family was anticipating another happy event in the O'Brien household. Two weeks before the wedding Margaret woke her husband before dawn.

"Daniel," she nudged him as he lay snoring in bed. "Daniel!" she said again shaking his arm.

"What is it dear? What do you need? Why are you up?" Daniel responded with his face still deeply buried in his pillow.

"It's Forest, he's convulsing. Come Daniel," Margaret said. The two went into the next room. Pat had been stirred and was standing over Forest as well. "It's ok buddy," he said. "It will go away soon."

Margaret had a bowl of cool water and had begun wiping down the back of Forest's neck and his hot forehead. Pat was hurriedly pulling up his trousers. Margaret had instructed him to get the doctor. Immediately, he was out the door. Pat ran eight blocks to the doctor and road back in his buggy. It was a long night but Forest was resting peacefully by midmorning.

One week later on Friday, February 11, 1898 little Forest succumbed to high fever. It was merely three days before the wedding and was a tragedy that rippled through the entire O'Brien, Hathaway, and Hansen families.

It had a strong impact on young Pat. It was the first time someone close to him would go away. It would not, however, be the last time he would experience such hardship. As all young kids do, he picked himself up in a matter of weeks and the adults mourned for months and years. But Pat often thought of Forest while at play. He would always think of him for as long as he lived.

They buried young Forest on Sunday the 13th and Lila was married on Valentine's Day the next day. It was hard on Daniel who cried for two days leading up to his oldest daughter's wedding. He was able to muster enough strength to pass Lila over to Benjamin and it would take the remainder of the year before the family would fully lift the shroud that dominated the O'Brien family. Everyone felt badly for poor Lila also but her only concern was her mother and father who had just lost their child.

But spring brought new life to the Kankakee River Valley and gradually there was laughter in the house once again. Pat and Al grew like weeds during the summer and extended their daring escapades deep into the Marsh and down every crevasse of Momence. In the fall they returned to Central School and on any given day one could see Pat holding court in the playground during recess surrounded by kids his own age with a ring of younger ones at a distance allured by his energy. Pat was an attentive student but was often distracted by more interesting topics and adventures.

In 1898, Momence still had a rural flavor to it including a bastion of roaming chickens that walked freely everywhere, mallard ducks constantly flying up and down the river, and stray dogs competing with raccoons for scraps tossed out at night. But as the millennium approached, the citizens of Momence could sense that the world was changing around them. Telephones arrived in 1899. Railroads streamed in and out of town like clockwork on four different lines.

Other things were changing in Momence and throughout the United States. The change was subtle but more powerful and far reaching than any rail line, gadget, or convenience. Certain fateful events were occurring that were fundamentally altering the character of the republic.

It seemed to start with the war with Spain in 1898, accelerated with the conquest of the Philippines in 1899, and would fully blossom with America's entry into the First World War in less than ten years. Until this time, American foreign policy followed the guidelines laid down by George Washington in his Farewell Address to the American people: "The great rule of conduct for us in regard to foreign nations is — in extending our commercial relations." It was Washington's subtle way of implying limits not engagement.

At the turn of a century, when people naturally reflect on the past century, Americans began to recognize a national identity and America's place in the world. It had taken two hundred years to span the continent and its unity was tested during Civil War. A civilization born out of America's expansion and conquest of its West had now shaped the psyche of Americans culture. That foundation would drive American actions in the world for the next one hundred years.

One idea of America was replaced by another as the century ended. If we were no longer individual pioneers content with simply claiming our acres, then who were we? If we shed blood in the Civil War to protect the right to be independent yet bound, then what value did we protect? If we had truly created the world's first "common man rule" than should we not stand for that? America would act very differently in the next century.

For the O'Brien's life in Momence changed little until late in 1901. Daniel O'Brien, patriarch of the family and veteran of the great insurrection that secured America's future, died in his home on Hill Street. He was only 55. Margaret O'Brien, surround by her children, brothers, sisters, father and mother would become the focal point of the O'Brien family on that fateful day December 7, 1901.

On the day before he passed, Margaret summoned the entire family together. From his deathbed, Daniel was able to sign over the deed to the house to Maggie with the sign of an "X" witness by those present including B F Gray, the notary and Perry Hathaway.

Six days later, Pat O'Brien would turn eleven years old. His father's death would be his second loss in three short years. It was a critical time in his life. But his unassailable zest for life would carry him forward as it did his grandfather, Martin. He would turn to Perry Hathaway for the guidance needed by a young boy entering his teens. Hathaway was a worthy step-father and his brothers would guide him as well.

Chapter 10

The Quarry

Perry O'Brien pressed his left hand over the right and pushed down on the heavy steel latch that locked the hatch of Maggie's coal furnace. He had just finished tossing in a full shovel of coal to stoke the fire.

"There's so many of us here, I don't know if we even need to heat the house tonight Clara," he said to his sister who was there to assist.

"I don't think we've ever tried to pack the whole clan in this old house," she responded. "We're busting at the seams!" They both laughed as Perry gave one last look to the pressure gauge, flicking it with his finger to nudge the dial.

It was Saturday, December 10, three days after the passing of Daniel O'Brien. Margaret had asked the entire family to gather at the house. With father now gone, Maggie seemed different to the family. Lila could clearly see it in her mother's cast. Margaret looked at her grandchildren differently. She looked at her sons and daughters differently. In three short hectic days, the entire O'Brien heritage seemed to be placed in her. She had become the Matriarch. The others drew strength from her. The children, as instinctively as young ones do, came to their grandmother in regular intervals that night just to give her a hug and a smile. They sensed that something was different in the house.

With Maggie on that cold winter night was Lila, and Ben Worley, Lila's husband. Clara had two-year old Jack on her lap. He was fidgeting with a ball of twine dangled by his father Matt Clegg, much like a kitten would play with yarn. Elmer was sitting to the right of his mother and Perry found his seat on his way back from the boiler check. Merwin, known as "Buck" and sometimes called by his middle name "John" or "Jack," was seated next to his brother Clarence who they called "Bud." They were discussing baseball. The American league had decided to move the Milwaukee Browns team to St Louis. The sport of baseball seemed to be an increasingly frequent topic of young men throughout the entire United States.

Both Hansen's were there along with Margaret's sister Arleta, called "Letti." Hattie who they referred to as "Heffie" or "Belle" was there with her husband. John, who they called "Jahnke," Margaret's somewhat relegated brother, was also present. At the time, he was living with Letti and her husband. Perry Hathaway and his wife Mary were sitting next to Margaret playing with the children who were seated on the small rug in the middle of the room playing with toys to occupy their time.

Pat was not there. He and his little brother were outside playing in the snow. Pat was showing young Ivan how to make a snowball and toss it. He enjoyed showing Ivan the way to do things.

"Come on in now boys," Clara called from the front porch. The two boys scampered to the door and entered the warmth of the house. Pat stomped his feet to knock snow off his boots and little Ivan mimicked him as he so often did, looking up at his brother with a big grin feeling like a big kid. "Pat, you should do that on the porch, not here," Clara instructed. "We'll have a puddle of water all over the floor!"

"See what you've done now, Ivan!" Pat said in a comical and artificial tone. "Better find the mop young man. We don't want Clare here slipping on her keester do we?" he joked. "Oh you," Clara said as she strong armed Pat around the neck and gave him an active but ineffectual "Irish rub" on the top of his head. Clara was partial to Pat and always found it hard to deal out any discipline to him.

It was Lila who settled everyone down. Standing and waving her hands she said, "Mother is very happy that you could all come and be together with her tonight. I know father's passing is a mere three days ago but...," she paused a moment holding back tears and Maggie reached out to clasp her hand, "but we felt that a number of things needed to be discussed with everyone. So before Ben and I head back to Lowell and others disperse, I think it's important that we have a family meeting." She turned to Maggie as she slowly sat back in her chair.

Maggie was direct and in full control. She spoke in an affectionate tone and everyone paid strict attention to her as she spoke of the love Daniel had for all of them and that he was looking down on everyone this night to take care of them as he had done all his life. She emitted strength to everyone in the room who, for the first time, recognized how significant she had been to the whole family over the years.

As is always the case, there needed to be discussions about the children and who could best help Maggie in the months ahead. The house was discussed and the men agreed that more room would be required as the young boys grew. Elmer, though divorced, was living as a border in Yellowhead Township at the time so he was independent. Perry, 20, was moving to Gary, Indiana where he had a job at the newly constructed Inland Steel operations along the shore of Lake Michigan. Remaining with Margaret was Merwin "Buck" 16, Clarence "Bud" 13, Pat, who would turn 11 the next day, and Ivan who was 5.

Perry Hathaway led a discussion regarding the house. The men of the family would plan to disable the small wooden-framed home and reconstruct a larger home on the same property at 164 West River Street. It was suggested this could be done next year and all the men and older boys could help. The men estimated the total cost would not exceed $900. The children would stay in Momence and continue at Central School until at least 8th grade and hopefully beyond. Perry pointed out to Margaret that since Daniel was a veteran of the Civil War, she would be entitled to a widow's pension from the military that could support the young boys until age 16. Margaret was relieved to hear this and Matt Clegg indicated he would assist with filing the papers.

The most critical topics were covered and the young children were particularly cooperative during the discussion as they recognized the unusual nature of such a large group discussion.

Just then, the front door opened. Pat and his little brother were leaning up against the door, there being barely any room in the cramped front room.

"It's Uncle Jeff!" Pat shouted as he jumped to his feet. He seemed generally jovial to see his uncle. Pat was the type of kid that, amid the seriousness and gravity of any situation, could bring a sparkle to events seen as only routine by some.

Daniel's brother, Uncle Jefferson O'Brien and his wife Lovisa had stopped by with two pies. Lovisa passed them over to Clara and the youngsters followed the transfer with unrelenting gawks. The O'Brien's were both in their mid-fifties and lived in Ganeer Township. Jefferson could still remember the passing of Martin O'Brien though he was only four at the time. He remembered a scene not unlike what he and his wife found upon entering the home this night. Lovisa moved to Margaret and placed a kiss on her cheek. After Jefferson placed a phantom punch toward Pat's exposed chin he greeted his nieces and nephews ending with a firm handshake for Perry Hathaway where he took a seat next to him.

Though he did not know it at the time, this night would be the last time young Pat would see all his family members in one place. As Clara brought in the first two pieces of pie in from the kitchen for the young kids, multiple conversations and laughter erupted in the room. The serious conversations were over. Young Pat stood back and watched for a moment. For despite his youth and jester-like nature, he grasped the meanings of things. Big events struck him and sharpened his perceptions. He was always capable of standing back and "taking it all in."

As he scanned the room, his eyes fell upon his mother who had paused lifting her fork to her mouth while balancing a small plate in her left hand. She was already locked on Pat's gaze. When their eyes met she gave him a warm smile. She recognized the reflective gaze of Pat when she saw it. It did not come often but it was easily observed. It was not unlike the look of Daniel's which she could still recall on the night the family sat gazing into the night sky follow their wedding.

That spring, Pat worked the summer carrying water for a local brick layer and made a few cents each week which he contributed to the family income. There was a little less time to frolic with Al in the marsh but everyone in the O'Brien household had to help out. It was 1902, a year to get back to normal. Pat got through seventh grade and lived a fairly independent life in Momence. He came and went as he liked. He was always up early, knew everyone in town and was trusted by Maggie. Pat O'Brien was a fatherless boy but rather than lament or retreat, his tough situation seemed to motivate him to take charge and without a thought he did just that.

In the spring of 1903, all of the O'Brien, Hathaway and Hansen men dismantled Maggie's house, expanded the foundation and rebuilt the home to provide more space for Maggie and the boys. About a month after the project was completed, Hattie and John announced that they would be moving to Cody, Wyoming near Big Horn National Park in Park County. New opportunities existed along the Chicago Northwestern Railway and pioneers engaged in cattle and sheep production and irrigated farming. The city of Cody had been founded in 1896 by members of the Cody Canal Co. and named for Colonel William F. "Buffalo Bill' Cody.

The movement to Wyoming by Hattie and her husband would start a migration of O'Brien's and Hansen's to the western states. Wyoming would provide job opportunities but would begin a disbursement of the O'Brien's, Hathaways and Hansens that would stretch the bonds that seemed inseparable on that cold December night in 1901.

In the spring of 1904, thirteen year old Pat O'Brien experienced his third warm season without his dad. Every day from dawn to dusk, he would scatter in any one of a hundred directions around Momence, along the river or out in the marsh. He would often be up before any of his buddies, checking on them in between a successful catch or entrapment of small unsuspecting raccoon.

It was an early Saturday morning in August and Charles Astle stood whisking the canopy crank of his general store in a rapid, circular, hurdy-gurdy motion. Astle usually opened well before the first citizen of Momence made their way to town for the week's rations. A few horses were still tied at the end of the street where late night revelers had obviously forgotten how they arrived and had walked home arm in arm singing some old trapping songs about life's foils.

The sun had just lifted over the tall trees at the east end of Front Street timing its arrival to the full extension of Astle's window cover. It was quiet and already warm. Suddenly, the early morning solace was cut through by a pulsating stomp of leather against concrete.

"Clamp, clamp, knuckle, clamp, ship, clomp, clamp, stomp, clamp" could be heard over his shoulder. He hurried the unveiling to see what was stomping down the sidewalk behind him. "Clamp, clamp, scuffle, clamp." "Sounds like a damn horse coming right down the street," he thought while turning to look.

It was thirteen-year old Pat O'Brien. Already up and running off to the day's events. Like every boy his age, summers and Saturdays were filled with exploration, adventure and newly discovered boondocks. Being full of energy, Pat never wasted a minute of the waking day. Most summer days he could be seen bolting out the front door on a mission to explore the wonders of the burgeoning little city of Momence.

"Well that figures," Astle said in an audible voice. "Only you could chew up a walkway like a bull." The hardware man had a big grin on his face as he put his scuffed fists along each side. "Where the heck you goin' so early young Pat?"

"Me and Al and the rest of us are goin fishin' today," said Pat. "We want to get there first so we get the best spot," he went on, still fluttering from his sudden stop.

"Gotta Run! If we don't get there first we'll lose the good spot on the south end!" he shouted as he looked back over his shoulder.

"Wait a minute! Where you boys fishin' today?" Astle asked. "The river?"
Pat froze. "Heck no - today we're going to the Quarry. Didn't yah hear?
The whole thing filled up with water from the river!" Pat said with a big
grin on his face. Then he waved and broke again with a joyful look only a
thirteen year old could deploy. The railroad had shut down the limestone
operation in early 1904. With pumps off, the deep hole quickly filled in with
water.

Adults that met young Pat recognized him as a stand out. He was always
moving about town, followed by a number of his young admirers. Any local
that encountered his regular band of four to six boys, was addressed by Pat.
He was the spokesman. He was the one that could explain away even the
most obvious suspicion on the mind of most adults. He usually won them
over with his demeanor, broad grin and convincing likeable nature.

"You be careful, now," shouted the caring "step-dad" Astle who himself
spent his youth exploring the adventures of the river and the marsh.
"Watch those holes in the shallow branch when you cross, hey?" Pat waved
high over his head without turning back as he ran up Range Street. Though
there were bridges connecting the island to both shores of the Kankakee,
Astle knew from his own youth how kids would usually walk across the
"frog pond," as it was called or more specifically the north branch of the
Kankakee which was shallow, marshy and led to the Island. The Kankakee
was also known for its holes which could swallow up a grown man,
depositing him in one of a hundred underground aquifers below the river's
bottom, never to be seen again.

Pat spent many a summer morning walking the rapids of the south branch
of the Kankakee River off the Island looking for crawdads under the flat
limestone rock that graced the bottom of the rapids like some fine imported
floor tile. Centuries of fast flowing water from Indiana made for
comfortable barefoot walking on rocks as smooth as the white surface of a
Tiffany brick. Local kids knew where the holes were in the river. Dads and
big brothers passed down warnings on where not to go. Many a newcomer
had waded out to a shallow point only to be drawn under by one of the
deep traps that claimed a life nearly every summer.

At River Street he met up with his buddy Al Fontaine and the rest. "Hi
Pat," they all said nearly in unison. "Well, where you boys off to? I don't
suppose you're thinking of taking a few smallmouths this morning, are
yah?" Pat asked. Though the day had clearly been planned in advance, they
all went along with the gag as if another spontaneous event was about to
drop in on their routine small town life. Even on a slow day, young oafs
with nothing to do had a better chance of finding a great adventure in the
company of "O'Brien's Herd" than on their own.

The boys crossed the north branch onto the island, then the wider south branch using the railroad trestle which extended from the Island and was nearly every boy's transit over the double tributaries of the Kankakee in 1904. Turning east on Lynd's Lane they walked along "the Lane" and found the quarry filled to the brim with water. The cart track and switch still held fast to the bottom and was submerged. They could see it through the clear glass surface of the water. They fished for about an hour when the conversation turned to a more daring adventure.

The water filled quarry had been formed when the C E & I railroad halted operations two weeks before. Fish populated it right away since the water came from the river. The quarry itself had been an important part of the growth of the city. The stone pit, 350 feet wide and twice that long, dug out in shelves varied in depth from 30 to 60 feet. Stone was loaded by hand into the carts and pulled by horse up the small rails to the crusher above. A system of pumps kept the pit from filling with water which constantly seeped in from underground springs and from the river at the north end of the quarry. When operations ceased the pumping stopped and the Quarry soon filled with water. It was a perfect swimming hole and source of fish for Momence boys.

"How much you boys wanna' bet that not one of us could swim the whole length of this quarry?" asked Carl Munyon, the dare master of the group. "You mean from here - north?" replied Al. The others looked away from their pole tips to see what wager might be in play. The dare is what prepares young men for survival. It's the glue of memories, the test of a young buck's manhood and the method by which pecking order is established among young boys.

"I'll bet one whole cent that no one here can swim the entire length non-stop to the other side," Carl said enticingly. But it was Al who knew what the next episode would be in this daring folly. While the boys considered wagers, Al new Pat was likely already considering the jump.

Though Pat and his buddies had swum farther distances along the banks of the river, crossing the quarry end to end provided no opportunity to cut to shore should a cramp or fatigue lock up a young boy's body. The Momence quarry was not a big body of water but it looked ominous to young Pat as he curled his toes over the rounded edge of its grassy bank. He was already standing at the edge while the others spent their time arguing any number of "what if's" - knowing none of them would take the plunge.

The quarry had a dark glassy surface and it was known to be deep. It was surrounded by trees that leaned over the bank's edge and provided few points of access. The bank itself was a roll of thick grass that tucked under at the water's edge like so many man-made watering holes. The unnatural banks were not as inviting as the natural beach at the crawdad spot on the river. Most kids froze at the edge of the quarry. It just didn't look inviting. They knew the river bottom "like the back of their hand" but the quarry had no bottom, to them.

The double-dares and bets were being tossed into a kitty like final antes of a trapper's poker game on Saturday night in Momence. The boys mimicked the sounds and bravado of so many of the bearded hooligans from the marsh but they used pebbles for currency. The sure bet to swim across the quarry for the first time was Pat O'Brien.

If anyone could swim its length it was Pat. Though he rarely boasted, he was always the one urged on by his clan of small town buddies when any of the numerous "dare you" events presented themselves to this group of eager, but hesitating, dare devils. Swimming the quarry required an instant decision. No procrastinating by wading in. You had to decide and then you had to go. Pat had never swum its length but even before the last wager had been placed, he had already decided he'd go. He had to. The betting didn't matter. He had to know that he could, he told himself. It had to be now. It was now or never. The adrenaline caused his stomach to flip, then he leaped.

The yelps of his buddies to "Go!" faded as Pat pushed off the grassy bank. The water was warmer than he had expected. Being still and having soaked up the summer sun it lacked the refreshing flow of Indiana spring water that characterized the Kankakee River. The water was heavy and he first felt the weight of his arms some twenty stokes from shore. Between breaths he looked up for the first time. The distant shore was not even close despite the fact that shouts from the urgent bank behind him were clearly some distance away. Had he taken on more than he could finish? Should he return or cut to right or left? No, it was back to the swim. Just pull and pump and swim. Stopping was no longer an option for he had reached the break point of his dare-devil swim. Surely, he had come half way by now but a second quick glance forward revealed the far bank to be no closer.

That's when everything slowed. Pat's physical prowess had not let him down, he was pumping and pulling at the same rate, but his mind slowed. He felt the urgency of sounds behind him and the small spec of dry land far in front. The middle was death. The quarry would swallow him up if he stopped. He would swim and not think. Just swim and not measure. The shore would get closer. The shore would come in time. Then he swallowed a rush of the warm muddy water. It felt like a whole apple being pushed down his throat. He was fading. "Cough," he thought. He did with a low guttural roar of a bear that rattled his chest. He then pulled himself up with a deep double breast stroke that raised his head above water for a second time and allowed a quick look ahead.

The shore was distant but it looked bigger and he had to make it. Just then his legs cramped. He could feel the pull of his abdomen on each stroke as if his arms and legs were mere paddles now, all being pulled by the center of his body in some flailing action that resulted in little forward progress. As a result each stroke lost its leverage. He could feel his body sink.

He called upon his reserve determined not to fail and finally reached shore. Exhausted, he pulled himself up and over the rising bank and sank into the lush tall grass then passed out. The shouts from the other shore could no longer be heard. Pat had crossed and someone else was dividing the spoils.

The boys were rushing along the east bank of the quarry toward Pat. One could see their legs pumping to run but gingerly hopping to miss holes and boulders that would surely catapult them into the quarry if they made one misstep. Their head would snap up to check on Pat. Was he alive? Was he ok? Then down again to navigate. Then up again to measure their target.

It was a clamorous collection of yelps and shouts of glee, arms flailing, shirts waving over head, young legs pumping like colts with an occasional glance up to check on Pat. After all, he was not moving.

Suddenly, they stood over him in a huddled form that blocked the sun from shining on their hero exemplar. Pat went into a humorous animated seizure routine ending with a classic frozen pose, exhale of air and a mock death - complete with tongue hanging out to the side of his mouth like a dead skunk.

Then suddenly he opened his eyes and said, "Where the hell you guys been?. A roar went up! "Pat O'Brien, you dirty dog!" Al barked. "If you ain't the biggest b'hoy livin' in this whole town," he shouted as the boys carried on, holding their gut for laughing so hard.

Just then Al noticed a shadow passing back and forth across Pat's face from the sky above. He looked up and saw a large eagle circulating over head as if checking on Pat itself. Smiling Pat had verified his exulted status with the gang once again. The whole day became part of the lore of "Smiling Pat," a name that would stick with him for years to come.

Chapter 11

The Beginnings of Flight

In the summer of 1904, the flooding of the quarry wasn't the only excitement in town. The first automobile appeared on the streets of Momence. It was a Jackson, owned by the Wennerholms. Gus Wennerholm had come to America in 1886 and settled in Momence with his brother. In 1893, they bought and operated Knighthart's livery stable and also owned a farm in Ganeer Township.

At Wennerholms Livery, men shoed horses one moment and changed tires the next. All over America livery stables, constructed for buggies and the horses that pulled them, were gradually being converted into auto repair shops available to change tires, fix engines, and replace fluids in the horseless carriage. Young Pat spent an increasing amount of time hanging out at Wennerholms. To him it was the most modern business in town. Most everything else was related to agriculture. Cars were different.

Older Americans were startled by the noise generated by these dramatic new contraptions. Compared to the natural intonation of the horse and buggy, the backfiring machines were intrusions with the potential to eliminate proven means of transportation.

But the youth of Pat O'Brien's generation had nothing to lament. Kids never experience the passing of old ways until they have memories to miss. The new century was theirs. This was their time. New was normal. Every young boy Pat's age was fascinated with the sound, power, and autonomy of the car. Boys roared with approval at the sound of a "backfire." The affection between the gasoline engine and most of America's boys was present from the beginning.

Along with the arrival of the Wennerholm Jackson that summer, residents could place a call to downtown Chicago as easily as they could call Grant Park, Illinois. Momence residents could take the train downtown to Chicago, shop at the Schlesinger & Meyer Department Store and return all in one day. The tractor was changing agricultural practices across the entire land, increasing yields and replacing unneeded farmhands.

But was not the automobile a revision of the buggy? Weren't the telephone wires hung on poles once used for telegraph messages? Trains were more modern, more convenient and reached more places but had existed for half a century and were natural extensions of the wagon trains that traveled west. Ten story department stores were city versions of small town confectionaries with more products, at higher altitudes and higher prices. And, finally, tractors simply removed the back breaking chore of the plow and produced more in less time.

But to the unimpressed, the young, and to those who embraced progress, there was one startling invention that did not extend ideas of a previous century. It was a man-made invention that catapulted human thinking, changed every man's perception of what was possible, and created hysteria like nothing in the history of the planet.

It was human flight.

"Look at this!" barked Pat to his buddies, all hovering underneath a tree on the Island.

Pat O'Brien had taken in stride all that he had seen in his short thirteen years to date, but what he held in his hand was a newspaper story that stopped the young paladin in his tracks. He had run all the way from Central House to the Island Park where his buddies were awaiting his arrival at the crawdad hole. Pat was busing tables in the hotel restaurant and had noticed the Momence Reporter left behind on his last table. He was galvanized!

"These guys have got a regular old engine, mounted on a kite for all I can tell!" Pat explained to his buddies as he unwound the local parchment.

He laid open the front fold of the paper before his devotees and pointed to the lead story. It was a reprint from the Dayton Herald dated December 18, 1903. Stories in larger newspapers were often reprinted in small-town rags for weeks until all of America finally got word. He read the headline deliberately:

'Dayton Boys Solve Problem," he carefully glided his finger tip to the sub-head. "Wilbur and Orville Wright successfully operate a flying machine in North Carolina.'

Pat looked up and gave his buddies a look of astoundment that they had never seen. "Listen to this, boys! A damn Flying Machine!" Pat exclaimed turning back to the print and pointing.

'Bishop Milton Wright of this city has received a telegram from his sons Wilbur and Orville who are at Kitty Hawk, North Carolina'

He was reading slowly but with quick breaths in an excited manner as Al and his buddies looked on with raised eyebrows following each word.

'Experimenting in gliding through the air in aeroplanes of their own make, and regulated by devices of their own invention, the Wright boys report that they have had gratifying success with their true flying machine built by them this year.'

"See, this proves it! It's in the paper and their father is a clergyman, mind you," Pat argued pulling back to look at their startled faces.

"These two guys flew in the air!" Pat emphasized again as the boys held stunned looks.

"It ain't possible, Pat," said Al. "I mean, you've seen the size of that engine in Wennerholms Olds. It's gotta' weigh 200 pounds and that's a two cylinder! There's no way a big kite with wire and cheap wood could even support an engine that heavy – let alone a man, too!"

The others agreed and Al gained confidence. For a split second Pat snapped his head back to the paper to double check his facts.

Al went on. "See, it says here that the Wrights used a four cylinder. Now you tell me 'Mr. Flying Expert O'Brien' how an engine nearly 350 pounds could be mounted on a two winged kite and then lift off the ground," Al insisted. "Why it ain't possible!"

He wasn't certain but Pat blurted out "Aluminum, you stupid Buffalo. Pat recalled being told by the old German that aluminum was much lighter than steel. Always able to think on his feet, Pat's answer seemed convincing and as it would turn out, he was right!

"They make it out of aluminum. It's lighter" Pat said.

Al shrugged. "Well, how the heck was I supposed to know?" he pleaded with the others.

And so went yet another energized and enthusiastic argument among young boys marveling at the latest invention of their age. Only they knew this one was different. Boys like Pat O'Brien, Al and their friends would now spend nearly every free moment talking about, reading about and otherwise arguing about the intricacies, limits and possibilities of human flight. All Americans were swept up by the success of the Wrights but the young were ecstatic. It was a confirmation to American youth that all things were now possible.

The summer of 1904 would turn out to be Pat's decisive boyhood summer. All young boys recall their last summer, free of encumbrance, full of memories and often accompanied by their earliest regard for female charm. It occurs prior to the realities of personal responsibility and the need to work for pay. Though young Pat carried water for Contractor Clark when he built the building on Front Street, ran errands for the "German baker" Oscar Conrad, bussed tables at the Central Hotel on occasion, he did so as an addendum to his final summer of play.

He was a handful to Margaret but a true joy to her at the same time. His 8th grade teacher wrote in Pat's yearend report that he was a "loveable trial to his grade school teachers." Pat didn't have much time for school books but performed rather well and had sights well beyond the limitations of Central School. His grandfather Hathaway, being a keen observer of Irish personality, said of him early on that he "had a way with 'Colleen' and a manner of respect for gentlemen."

Once news of the Wright Brothers landed in Momence, Pat O'Brien could focus on little else but flight. During his first year of high school that fall, Pat had an unusual number of "missed days." He liked school well enough but it seemed to Pat that there were so many more interesting and important things out in the real world. Margaret would surely see him bolt out the door for school in the morning but had little knowledge of his final destination. Sometimes he'd cut over to Pine Street, walk past the backside of Central School and find a friendly engineer at the north end depot who'd let him jump a train to Lowell. He'd visit the Worley's in Lowell or his Hathaway cousins making them promise that they wouldn't speak a word of his visit to Margaret. Nobody wanted to "rat" on Pat.

Pat completed his first and second year at Central School and then during the summer of 1906 worked more regularly to support the family. He still found time to explore his interests and help out the Wennerholms on occasion, learning as much as he could from mechanics who worked on engines. While a full understanding of the care and keep of horse was required by his Daniel, Pat believed that the more a young man understood about combustible engines, the better he would survive in the new, mechanized world.

He liked to pop in on the Wennerholms and watch the mechanics work on engines. His conversation with the Wennerholm Brothers often turned toward the feasibility of placing an engine on a winged glider but he got little affirmation from the men in the shop. They knew little of these "new-fangled contraptions" and thought it "unnatural" for a human being to be "trying to fly around with the damn birds!"

Pat would laugh in a respectful way saying with a frolic in his voice that seemed to disarm any disrespect, "They're doin' it already you old jawbone! Don't you read the papers?" Again, the men would look up at each other for a split second sharing a gut-induced honk and then snap their heads back to the task at hand adding one more jab just to charge up the sprite young man. Pat enjoyed giving them a hard time and they enjoyed it even more. They may have known little about engines but knew a great deal more about stirring up a fifteen year-old kid.

Pat and his friends talked about flying a lot. On a hot day, one could see the boys running along the trestle like a runway then leaping with arms extended out, bellies exposed to the shallow north branch simulating "man in flight." In the fall when school started one of Pat's teachers, knowing of his keen interest in the new idea of flying, gave Pat a small pamphlet highlighting Octave Chanute's 1894 publication called Progress in Flying Machines. The teacher had acquired it at the 1893 Chicago World's Fair.

The new mode of transportation went barely noticed amid the hundreds of special meetings held at the Chicago World's Fair. A French immigrant engineer, with roots in rail and bridge construction, held the world's first global conference at the Chicago World's Fair on the feasibility of controlled man flight. He discussed his planned testing of wings and gliders on the unblemished shores of Lake Michigan at Miller Beach. From the Fair's location on Lake Michigan's western rim, the white dunes of Indiana could be clearly seen if one looked southeast to southern shore which curved east into the neighboring state of Indiana.

"That's very near here, Al!" said Pat as the two boys read the paper together.

Octave Chanute was convinced it was only a matter of time before man would learn to fly. When he, his partner Augusta Herring and his three assistants climbed off the Michigan Central Railroad train at Miller Junction, Indiana on June 22, 1896, they attracted a good deal of attention. They walked the mile or so to the beach through downtown Miller from the train. They carried camping equipment, two gliders, and a kite. The first glider they tested was the Lilienthal glider that Augustus Herring had modified to his liking. Otto Lilienthal had attracted worldwide attention with his glider experiments in Germany in the previous years, and Herring had attracted a good deal of attention in New York flying variations of the Lilienthal glider.

"See Al, this is the guy that invented wings. The Wright Brothers figured out how to mount an engine and control the wings. But Chanute, he's the first one," said Pat.

Beyond their natural beauty, the sand dunes of Lake Michigan and the updraft winds they created played a key role in the establishment of human flight. For the most part, Chanute's two weeks on Miller beach went unnoticed by the world, with the exception of the local citizens of Miller, the Wright Brothers, enthusiasts that had met at the Fair and the 20th Century's first generation of Americans which included Pat O'Brien of Momence.

During the summer of 1906, young Pat O'Brien was fifteen years old. Having spent the previous summer visiting relatives by jumping on the train to Lowell, he migrated to the "big line," the C&EI, which ran north. An explosion of civilization the size of Chicago and surroundings did not go unnoticed by the highly curious Pat O'Brien. Bored with most of Central School's routine, he spent a lot of time reading but he read newspapers, books from the library and anything he could find about the Wright Brothers' successes at Kitty Hawk in 1903.

"Look Al!" Pat said showing him the paper. "You can see right here where Chanute flew the kites on the beach. It's not that far from here." There was a special feature in section two telling of the Wright Brothers' successful flight. For the first time, the reporter had added information on the important work of Chanute at Miller.

"I'm telling you Al," he said. "I know exactly where that railroad comes in. Look, I've drawn the whole thing out and I know Engineer Altorfer. He'll get me as far as Kensington." Pointing to his map, he went on, "The C&EI goes right to Kensington, then I pick up the old Michigan Central and it runs right through Miller!" Pat had figured his entire route. He had to see the beach. He had to see where Octave Chanute, now Pat's new hero, flew off the Lake Michigan Dunes.

"Heck I can't go all the way up there Pat," said Al. "What if something happens and we can't get home before supper? My mother would lynch me. Holy sikes!"

Pat would go alone. But he would go for certain. Just as he had jumped into the old quarry before Al and the boys had wagered all bets, Pat had already decided to act. He was going.

The next day, Pat O'Brien jumped up on the engine of Gus Altorfer at Momence and headed north to Kensington.

"Keep an eye on the pressure gauge for me Pat!" shouted Altorfer.

"I've got it Gus!" shouted back Pat. Pat had already affixed his gaze on five Bourbon tube gauges that measured the pressure now building rapidly inside the engine boiler as it pulled out of the Crete station. Pat knew enough to watch the gauges immediately after taking on water which Gus had done at the Crete stop. They were heading for Kensington where Pat would hopefully get handed off to the eastbound engineer from the Michigan Central Railroad and ride toward Miller Beach.

Trains fascinated Pat and he took every opportunity he could to ride with Gus and assimilate as much information as he could. Today, however, he had the winged glider on his mind. But until Gus gave a new command Pat only focused on the gauges.

Gus Altorfer was a thirty-year steam train operator. He had emigrated with his family from Germany in 1863 where they settled on the north side of Chicago. Pat O'Brien regularly rode the 8:03 a.m. train out of Momence and had gained the confidence of the old engineer. Each time Pat rode, he seemed to get closer to the engine car until finally Gus had him ride with him every time he appeared.

Pat would stand with his hands on his hips exactly where he knew the engine would halt. It was a spot well beyond the coal dump at Momence Station and the length differed every time depending on the number of cars on the day's run. Pat could instantly measure the required distance based on his glancing sweep of the train's length. His eye was keen and his sense of distance was impeccable. Gus always marveled at this intuitive ability.

Like all adults who met him, Gus enjoyed Pat. By fifteen Pat had expanded his wit, charm, and smile well beyond the boyish demeanor that caused ten year old Momence girls to giggle. But he had a gut enthusiasm for learning about new things and he loved trains. He could focus on specifics unlike most boys his age. When Gus gave young Pat a task, he could count on him to stay 100% on task until given the next command. Pat had the ability to celebrate the unpredictable calamity of life with all the Irish melancholy of his ancestors but the mind to lock on to a specific task with the instincts of a bloodhound when required. These traits made him stand out with most adults and forecasted his laser-like mind capable of improvising when conditions changed. He was already a good decision maker when the action became fast and furious.

The days of men shoveling coal into the coal bunker were nearly gone by the time Pat O'Brien was riding trains. Coal was moved from the tender just behind the engineers cab by means of a stoker which had a cork screw type design that moved coal from its permanent storage to the bunker to generate heat. Pat remembered seeing men shovel coal into the boiler directly but had never shuffled coal for Gus.

As the train pulled into Kensington, Gus had asked Pat to stand on the coupler between the engine and tender car to check the flow of coal while Gus backed down the train. Pat had often walked the running board of Gus' engine to tap on the sand box cap or steam dome on top with a metal rod about the length of an Irish Shillelagh. Had Margaret been able to see what Pat was doing on moving trains, she surely would have put a stop to it. But Pat never seemed fearful and had natural agility and the instincts of a cat.

The large, coal-laden steam train backed down as it approached the Kensington Station. Pat affixed his hat a bit more snuggly to avoid the windy day and panned the horizon. In the yard, Gus had a conversation with the engineer of the Michigan Central line and he agreed to take Pat to Miller if he'd assist on the way. It was arranged and Pat waved to Gus as he headed eastward toward Indiana on the Michigan Central line.

Pat could tell when they crossed the Indiana border. The extensive Calumet Lake area, the canal, and Lake Michigan itself were so much larger than any vista he had seen in Momence. It struck him that Lake Michigan had no opposite shore. It was the first body of water he had seen other than the Kankakee. The world was much bigger than Kankakee County. He was struck by the view and it excited him. About the time he'd stared nearly five minutes at the Lake's distant horizon, he turned his head forward to the east and the rush of six, eight, ten or maybe more trains steaming west to Chicago nearly took his breath away. He had never seen such power and mass before.

The train arrived at Miller Junction about fifteen minutes later. Pat shook hands with Engineer Henderson and followed that with a snappy salute. Henderson saluted back and grinned at the young lad. Pat jumped from the train. To the surprise of Henderson, Pat turned and saluted again then turned north. It was one of the many quirks he had picked up from his grandfather – the old soldier Perry Hathaway.

Pat O'Brien walked the same mile to the beach that Chanute had walked ten years before. Pat had a keen sense of history for his age and imagined Chanute carrying gliders along the same path. As he passed between two tremendously large dunes towering one hundred feet on either side of him, he took a quick glance but then opened his gaze to the north, to the lake and to the wind.

He felt the brisk north wind blow directly into his face in a way much different than the winds of the corn fields near Momence. The wind seemed to lift and had a force of unknown origin. His hat blew off. He knew at that moment that what he had read about Chanute and the Wrights was really true. It was not fiction. Flying was real.

He stood for nearly twenty minutes in the wind and let his body feel the power of the big lake's breadth. He studied the gulls hovering some one hundred yards off shore. Their wings were frozen in the breeze as they rode the uplifting drafts. They slid left and then right and then lifted skyward again in full suspension. It was an inspiring thing to witness. He noticed that with just a slight adjustment of their wings the gulls would be instantly lifted right or left and a reverse adjustment would just as quickly drive the birds in a headlong dive to the lake waters below.

He took a deep breath. He'd been holding it the entire time. He began breathing in short spurts. He turned to go and looked to see where the great winds had carried his hat. Some thirty yards up the beach lay his hat. He bent over to retrieve it, slapping the hat on his thigh shaking sand from its inner brim.

Just then he caught the image of a large winged bird over head casting a shadow of the white sands below him. Expecting to see a white gull like the hundreds so prominent along the beach, he looked up and was surprised to see it was an Eagle, bobbing in the winds of the Lake Michigan, holding position with still wings.

He experienced one of those flashing instinctive mental reactions that comes and goes in a second yet are never expressed in words - "What's he doing here?" he thought.

Pat flipped his hat on his head and gave the brim a firm tug to keep it affixed. His shoes sunk in to the white sand as he walked the incline up the beach to the road's edge through Miller. He paid no attention to his surroundings but looked squarely on the ground with focused concentration and a big smile on his face. He was having one of those conversations with himself, amazed that he was walking the very steps taking by Chanute before him.

In the distance he heard a whistle blow announcing the pending arrival of Thomas Henderson's steam train entering ear shot from the west. Pat broke into a sprint, suddenly realizing he needed to hurry to avoid missing his train back home.

"Let's Go, O'Brien!" shouted Engineer Henderson as Pat gutted out the last 50 yards to the train. "These trains run according to a schedule you know. Jump on it, son!" shouted the big Irish immigrant who looked almost oversized in his locomotive window. Pat leaped up on the wheel casing, stepped up to the engineer cab and reported on time as Henderson pulled the screeching whistle. The big wheels churned and the young and old Irish Americans headed west toward Illinois.

Pat nearly talked Henderson's ear off. He described how he could completely see why Chanute would select such a great spot for glider flights and how he'd love to take a kite there someday himself.

He went on. "I walked right between the two biggest dunes on the beach and wham the wind practically picked me up right there, I mean it felt like it was blasting out of the sand itself, then a bunch of sand blew in my face, I turned my head and my hat popped right off my head, it didn't take nothin', I wasn't even running," the exasperated young lad shouted.

"Slow down there, Pat," said Henderson. "You're talking so fast, I can't even follow yah. You sound like that wind blew down your belly like a balloon. Take a breath, boy"

"Well, you should have seen it Tom, what a spot!" Pat responded while flicking the gauges with his finger to make sure he was getting a good read. Talking the whole time, he was back on task earning his ticket back to Kensington.

At the Kensington stop he thanked the big engineer and waved as he had to Astle on the streets of Momence, turning back with a big grin in a full sprint to Gus's train waiting to head south. Like others, Tom Henderson was impressed with the young lad. He had enthusiasm for sure, but he had a focus as well and he was attentive to his duties during the entire trip. Tom pulled forward to switch lines and saw Gus Altorfer pointing out Pat's first task as the C&EI headed south toward Momence.

Pat talked gliders, flight, and the beach all the way home. Like the Wennerholms, Gus listened somewhat casually being a man of the railroad and not fully convinced that flight would amount to anything more than flying kites for fun. But like all middle aged men with a little wisdom of their age, he did little to discourage Pat.

Hardly a day would go by during the rest of Pat's young life when we would not think about flying. As the two reached the Kankakee Valley Pat saw the hills of Yellowhead appear on the left and the flat prairie fields on the right. He felt home again. He was excited to tell everyone about his trip. He could see himself bursting in the front door telling an amazing tale that would surely excite everyone. Little did he know that at that very moment, the mood in the O'Brien house was anything but excited.

The anchor of the entire Hathaway-O'Brien clan, Perry Hathaway, grandfather of Pat O'Brien had drawn his last breath not five minutes after Pat had jumped on Gus's train. It was March 30, 1906. Pat had lost another powerful influence in his young life.

PART THREE

DISPERSED

Chapter 12

Cody Wyoming

Pat O'Brien jumped from Gus' engine and gave his familiar wave while on the run. He ran south along the tracks toward the river where the street cut west and followed its banks through downtown. He and Gus had a regular wager. If Pat reached the river before the engine crossed the first trestle, Gus would flip him a nickel on their next run north. Pat used to joke, "Trains are fine for the long haul, but if you need a jack rabbit you need me."

As usual, Pat won the night's race but was clearly tired after his long day. He went into a slower gate as he headed west down Front Street toward his house. He was excited to tell Margaret and everyone about his thrilling day. But as he got closer to the house he could clearly see silhouettes in the front yard. He slowed to a more deliberate pace.

"Who are all those people at my house?" he wondered. It was rare to have visitors, even family, at supper time. All the lights were on in the house and as Pat reached Hill Street it was clear that something was wrong.

His sister Clara had seen him coming and stepped down from the porch to meet him before he arrived in the front yard. Clara wanted avoid Pat disrupting the solemn household with some loud and boisterous story upon entering. Pat had no way of knowing that his grandfather, Perry Hathaway had just passed away.

"Pat, it's Poppa," Clara said placing her hand on his shoulder reassuring him. "He passed earlier this afternoon. Come and see mother. She's been waiting for you." It was March 30, 1906. Pat was fifteen. His grandfather was eighty.

Perry Hathaway had died a mere three hours earlier, about the time Pat jumped back on the train at Miller. Family and friends were gathering at the house where Margaret was being consoled. Perry Hathaway and Mary Drake had been living with Hatte and John Hansen in recent days but the Hansen brothers moved Perry's body to Margaret's home at Mary Hathaways' request. She thought it would be better for everyone if he was there. It felt more like home to the family.

Pat walked in with his arm around Clara and saw his grandfather lying on the bed in the next room. Some family members were still sitting near the bed as though Perry were merely sleeping. Pat looked at his grandfather's face. It was ashen and his eyes were closed. He looked back at his mother and their eyes locked fixed on each other as Pat moved to console his mother.

Maggie's arms were already extended and she was thinking only about her boy. She was concerned for Pat. He had been fatherless for five years and had leaned heavily on his grandfather since Daniel's death. Perry was as much Pat's father as Daniel. In many ways Perry had a stronger influence on Pat during his formative years than had Daniel. Perry always took special care to pass along valuable lessons to his grandson. One was fortitude. Clearly, Pat had acquired much more from the old veteran than a snappy salute.

Perry Hathaway was one of the most respected citizens of Momence, a man of principle and considered a patriot by all who knew him. He was an early pioneer of Momence and a man of the 19th century. He was an original. Despite his advanced age, "Poppa," as everyone in the family called him, was solid as a rock. People would comment that few men like Perry Hathaway graced the earth. His passing struck the whole town and demonstrated that the "older generation" and the old ways were, in fact, passing away. Most of the early founders had died before Perry. He was one of the last to go. It did not go unnoticed by the people of Momence. Many would attend his funeral. They spoke of his life and the passing of frontier Momence in the same breath.

The day Perry Hathaway was laid to rest, Pat was surprised to see old men cry and women hold fast to each other in a tapestry of black garb. Sensing the mood of the adults, normally spry youngsters in attendance clung closely to their mother's side not wanting to make a sound.

Grandparents are anchors. Parents feel obligated to keep the family close to home so grandparents can be part of grandchildren's lives. But when grandparents die, permission seems given to consider moving away with no sense of guilt. And so parents often do. For the young, moving is a new adventure. The young look forward and seldom look back. Time moves on and those important today become history's lost men. Youthful generations wake up in the morning and see their world as having always been there, knowing little of the price paid by those who came before. The impact of events before children arrived goes unnoticed and unknown until they too are old themselves.

This was not the case for young Pat O'Brien. Hathaway's funeral day was a lasting memory for Pat and he sensed the loss of the family's legacy. This was, no doubt, due to the amount of time he spent hearing the old man's stories while fishing on the banks of the Kankakee over the past five years.

The summer following Perry's death, Pat O'Brien truly became a vagabond. Not only was his father gone but now his grandfather, who had anchored the family since Daniel's passing, was gone too. Pat was alone but found life all around him in the railroad, the river and in his daily pursuit of news about flight.

Within days the O'Briens and Hathaways were asking, "Now what?" Daniel's passing in 1901 was a blow but it also galvanized the O'Brien's and the Hathaways into one family with Perry as an anchor. Now, losing Perry pulled away the family's foundation. Margaret was now the glue and carried the weight of family decisions.

That Christmas, Pat was sixteen years old. Following dinner with the whole family, talk turned to more changes that needed to occur in the O'Brien clan. Unknown to Pat was the matter of his father's veteran's benefits. Since Daniel's death, Margaret received $8 per month in veteran's benefits for herself and $2 for each of her children under the age of 16. Since Pat's birthday on December 13th, Margaret had anguished over her personal finances and the ominous choice of sending Pat away. But in conversations over the past two weeks with Hatte, Clara and Arletta, it was decided that Pat would go to Wyoming and live with the Hansens.

"Pat? Come here sweetie," Margaret said to her young son. Pat knew something was up for Margaret reserved "sweetie" for Pat when bad news was about to be imposed.

"You know, Pat," pausing to swallow and then going on, "since you're 16 now, it's time for you to think about your future and," - she fought back serious tears – "starting in January, the army will no longer provide me the same amount of help now that you are 16. Arletta and Theodore could use your help and they'd like for you to move to Wyoming with them. It will be good for you son," she could hardly talk. Arletta stepped in.

"Pat, we'd really like you to come with us. Why there's a lot of great things to do there and you can't continue to do odd jobs here in Momence. You're almost a grown man now. It's time you find your way, and we will help you. You can finish school there, too."

It struck him heavily to hear the news but not out of fear. Mostly, it was the thought of leaving his home, his mother, and all that he had discovered and enjoyed his whole life. Thoughts spun around in his head but his response demonstrated how grown up he actually had become.

"Lette! I think it will be a fine idea," he said. "Naturally, I hate to leave home but I know it's been tough for mom. I need to earn my keep and we'll come back and visit and you'll visit us too, right mom?" His voice cracked a bit but his uplifting response lifted the tension in the room and the conversation continued about all the ways the O'Brien family would change in the year ahead.

Pat rattled on to his brothers, sisters and the youngsters about going west. The Irish humor echoed from the warm O'Brien home and a casual passerby, shuffling through the ten inches of snow that had blanketed the entire town of Momence that night could hear jovial laughter and love billowing from the wood framed house.

Yellow light glistened through frosted windows holding back the cold. A visible condensation of coal generated smoke rising from the house's chimney. It could be seen thinning ominously across the gleam of a winter's full moon. On this cold but happy Christmas night, Margaret Hathaway O'Brien and her family had no idea that forces in the world would soon press on their lives. For Pat O'Brien, it marked the true end of his youth. It would be his last Christmas living at home.

That spring, Margaret O'Brien stood on her front porch on Saturday morning observing the logistics of loading much of her family into two wagons parked in the front lawn. John Hansen was jockeying with a number of bags and items that he, his wife, children, and Pat would load on the train north to Chicago.

"Are you sure you can handle all that, John?" asked Margaret from the porch, her open hands planted along her waist line. "Perhaps we should ship a few bags after you? You certainly don't need your big coats until next winter, hey?"

"It's fine ma'am," said John. Hansen was a steady and quiet man. He always called Margaret 'ma'am' out of deep respect for his sister-in-law.

"My word, John," giggled his wife Hatte. "How many years have you known my sister and you've never called her by her first name, you daft man?"

"I think it's nice, Hatte," said Margaret, quickly jumping in. "I appreciate the respect you show us all, John. Besides, I am the oldest daughter now Hatte," said Margaret with a humorous Irish lilt to her voice.

"So you are, ma'am. I had not noticed," quipped John, playing along. He looked at Hatte who gave him one of those 'you cad" type looks so often issued by wives admiring the devilish ways of their husbands.

The wagon was loaded full and all those leaving seemed to keep their distance from it as if to avoid the inevitable. Theodore Hansen was tucking in a few soft bags and lifted the children up for the short trip through town to the train. It was decided to leave well ahead of the train's arrival and have breakfast at the Columbia Hotel across from the depot on Railroad Street. Pat had since exited the house with a small travel bag in his left hand and draped his arm over Margaret's shoulders.

"I'm glad we're having breakfast together, mom," he said to Margaret staring out at the wagon and not at her. "Yes Pat, I am too," Margaret responded looking straight ahead all the same.

Theodore and John had brought their wagons to the house to accommodate the family's ride. They were all loaded now and John was standing near the wagon waiting to help Margaret up. She had darted inside to grab her purse and remove her apron which she always wore from dawn to dusk.

Two wooden wagons rolled slowly up River Street loaded with O'Brien's and Hathaways. John's wagon was pulled by a workhorse and Theodore's beast was his old mule. Both animals, oblivious to the mood of this departing family, adjusted to their bits with a periodic snorts and brisk rise of their heads. At Range Street they took a left and the sound of horse hoofs could be heard bouncing off the buildings on each side. Instinctively the animals turned right at the Central House Hotel, for this was the way to the livery at the corner of Locust and Front.

Pat was uncharacteristically quiet and alternated looks left and right at the storefronts he knew like the back of his hand. There was Central House where he had bussed tables as a lad, then east past Astle's Hardware, Culver' Drugs, Brassard's Barber Shop, the bank. For a few blocks, he felt the tug of home and his normal enthusiasm for new things faded a bit until the wagons angled left at the end of Front Street onto Railroad Street, past the saloon and toward the depot.

John Hansen had reserved the dining room at the Columbia Hotel for the family and they filled the entire room. It was about 9:00 a.m. and the morning rush of railmen had just ended. The family climbed down from the wagon and the children rushed to the double doors with eager excitement. The doors were uniquely positioned across the corner of the rail stop inn and always seemed to attract the interest of the young children in town. John put his arm over Pat's shoulder as they stepped up on the porch. Margaret and Lette were continuing their last talk together which had lasted the whole ride there.

The thrill and excitement of "eatin' out of the house," as the kids called it, was evident through breakfast. Conversations were brisk and proprietor Drayer served much more food than normal in honor of the occasion. Halfway through the noisy breakfast Margaret had paused for just a moment and noticed Pat and his sister Clara sitting at the same table that she and Daniel had years earlier on the day he proposed. It was a melancholy moment, indeed, but it made her smile.

The men decided to move bags across the street while the women and children continued to talk over a final cup of coffee. Pat, John, Jahnke, Theodore, Ivan and Clarence loaded the bag cart at the station.

"Well, let's get the women," said Theodore.

"I'll wait here, Teddy," said Pat as he looked south to see any sign of the train.

"Me, too," John Hathaway said as he pushed bags toward the center of the cart.

The steam train slowed to meet the depot platform and with a loud squeal and steam blast it came to a halt. "Board!" shouted the porter as the Hathaway and O'Brien men passed up the bags. Like all train departures the passengers rushed to the windows to get in last chats and big waves to those craning below into the open windows to say their final goodbyes. Pat was the last one to board. He gave his mother a long and hug. It was nearly too much for her to bear. Suddenly, he pulled away, gave her a kiss on the check, turned and ran to the step-up giving his routine wave over his shoulder and flashing his broad smile.

The train pulled away and everyone went their way. Margaret started to think about life without Pat and smiled at one point remembering all the mischief he had created during his youth. For some reason, the image of young Pat as a toddler jumping over Daniels leg ran though her mind during the ride back to the house.

At Dolton, the travelers switched trains and continued their trip downtown. They arrived at LaSalle Street station in the heart of the city in about one and a half hours. The noise and calamity was a far cry from the small depot at Momence. Switching to the Burlington Northern occurred without incident and soon the family was heading west for the long ride to Wyoming. Two days and one night passed and they finally arrived.

Cody, Wyoming was a startling place to Pat O'Brien. Momence seemed like New York City compared to this western town. It was steeped in the traditions of the west unlike those of the "civilized" area of Chicago. Back home, rivers, lakes, and streams were the dominant feature of the land. At Cody, it was clearly the mountains.

Cody was located at the western edge of the Bighorn Basin, a depression surrounded by the Big Horn, Owl Creek, Bridger, and Absaroka ranges. Most of Cody had a spectacular view of Heart Mountain. Like all Midwesterners, Pat guessed these mountains were closer than they actually were. He could not imagine a "hill' so large as this. At the time of Pat's arrival, Cody had just over 1,000 citizens.

Buffalo Bill Cody, one of the best known showmen in the world at the time, helped found Cody, Wyoming in 1895, having toured the United States for over twenty-five years with his Wild West Show. He invested money in the town and established his TE Ranch nearby. There were more taverns than any other business in town and the dominant enterprise was clearly the Irma Hotel built by Buffalo Bill and named for his wife. Buffalo Bill maintained two suites and an office at the hotel for his personal use. Pat would meet him a number of times during his time in Cody.

"Cody has everything we need, Pat," said Lette as the family stepped onto the boardwalk at the new Cody Burlington Station stop. "We have electricity, running water and a sewer system!"

"Well God, I hope so," laughed Pat. The very fact that his aunt felt compelled to assure him of these fundamentals was added evidence to Pat that Cody, Wyoming was not going to be like Momence. He panned the horizon and could see the many hills and mountains in the distance. The town seemed plopped down in the middle of nowhere but he did notice a water tower on the far western edge of town quickly giving him some reassurance that the town at least had a plan. He'd soon find out that the plan was mostly Buffalo Bill's.

Cody was nearly void of cars but there was a cable car system surrounded by all variations of horse pulled carts, wagons and buggies associated with the West. What struck Pat were the number men just riding their horse in town. One seldom saw that in Momence anymore. He felt like he had stepped back in time – time he had not personally witnessed firsthand but had heard about from the old timers of his hometown, particularly his grandfather.

Buffalo Bill made the town of Cody his latest lucrative project and was still touring when Pat arrived. He drove one of the few cars in town and, in fact, Pat's first encounter with him was when he unexpectedly found Pat peering into his parked four-seater in front of the hotel. It was the fanciest car Pat had seen in Cody and the steering wheel was on the right which was not uncommon in those days prior to Ford's wholesale change of this practice years later
.

"You like that car, young feller?" asked the elder showman.

Pat responded without looking up as he studied the dash board. "It's quite interesting," he said. "I notice it has an rpm gauge right next to the…….."

He had lifted his eyes and saw the bearded Cody standing near the left front bumper with both hands on his waist. He was dressed in white including his hat. Bill Cody, having been a showman for over 40 years, had blended his private persona with his public one to the point that he was always Buffalo Bill – in dress, style, speech, and style. Pat recognized him right away.

"Why, hello Mr. Cody," Pat said. "I'm admiring your car. It's quite modern and put together well, isn't it?" Pat notice the big grin on Cody's face and returned the same.

"It's the best there is," said Coty. "And, if a better one shows up, I'll be dumping this old horse and getting' me the newest gem. Only the best for Buffalo Bill Cody, young man. Only the best!"

Pat related how he admired Cody's great shows though he had not seen one himself. Cody invited him to be his guest at the local show scheduled for the beginning of the next tour. Cody toured nearly to his 70th birthday but always returned home, developed a new production before the next season, and "tried it out" on the local residents before hitting the road.

Over the two years Pat worked and lived in Cody, he had a chance to talk to Cody a number of times. As a showman and promoter, Bill recognized the charisma of the young Irishman from Illinois. Though Pat never worked for Cody, he spoke with him often and was impressed with the influence of the man and Cody's ability to persuade and inspire audiences throughout the world. Cody was a quick read and recognized the magnetic personality of Pat right away.

Theodore Hansen had a unique, if not obscure, job in Cody. He ran the Stagecoach Station, still functioning but clearly in its final days in 1908. The family lived upstairs of the station and the addition of Pat would make accommodations a bit tight. But Lette made adjustments and provided a comfortable home for the family. She had a talent for cooking, even more so than Pat's mom.

Pat spent the bulk of 1908 and 1909 in Cody and the surrounding areas. He began work tending bar in one of the tavern's in town and came face to face with many a western ruffian. Cody, Wyoming was not unlike Momence of the mid-1800's, full of a variety characters ready to punch their way into or out of an argument, should someone look askance at them. Many were also good storytellers which fueled Pat's wit, enhanced his gift of gab, and sharpened his ability to spin a story.

Cards, dice and other forms of gambling were prevalent in Cody and local bar patrons taught Pat the fineries of these games of chance. Pat's favorite was the game of craps, an interest that would continue well after Cody. He also had many opportunities to "wise up," as the old cowboys would say to him, by downing an occasional double shot of harsh western whiskey at the command of local ring leaders.

In addition to bar tending, Pat worked various jobs in the fields, in town, and gravitated to what mechanical ventures he could find. He went to school at night to earn his high school equivalency, finding a new interest in books which became a refuge for him in the midst of the raw West. He was clearly far afield from the excitement of the city, steel, trains, and most of all, aeroplanes. After his first year, it struck him how long it had been since he had read anything about flight.

But Cody taught him about survival. It was the first time he felt a stranger in a strange place but he learned to adapt enough to survive. This would be a stop along his way, for as 1909 ended, Pat was clearly restless and wanted to move on.

Chapter 13

The Lure of Chicago

Pat O'Brien walked down the large granite steps of Union Station and onto the street of downtown Chicago on December 23, 1909. "What a town this is," he said to himself. "It's so good to be back in civilization." He was arriving one day early with plans to soak up all the conveniences of Chicago that were so lacking in Cody, Wyoming. It had been a long year and he was ready for a change.

There was a classic humdinger of a traffic jam in full stagnation as Pat approached the intersection of Dearborn and Randolph Streets. Pairs of cable cars were lined up end-to-end down the center of Dearborn. Pat could see power lines above each cable car sparking but it was only providing heat to the passengers inside. Nothing was moving.

Pat was in no hurry either. Enjoying the chaotic city landscape, he leaned back against a light pole near the Goodfield Shirt Shop to watch. Above was a sign that read "Smokes." All he could do was grin and watch the whole mess vibrate in front of him.

"Get the hell out of the way!" shouted a mustached man attempting to drive an ice wagon, pulled by a white horse. The horses all had blinders on and rapid shots of steamy breath pulsated from their snouts in the frigid air. Despite that, they were uncharacteristically calm amid the noise and confusion.

"Why, the horses in Cody would be rearing up for sure," said Pat audibly to those around him.

"What's that you say, son?" said a man with a derby hat and a long cigarette holder, puffing away while waiting to cross the street.

"Ah, nothin', just commentin' on the how calm these here horses are in all this traffic," said Pat. Just then it hit Pat, he sounded like a hick!

"Holy Jesus, I've been out west too long! The guy thinks I'm a cowboy!" Pat said to himself. It was just then that he realized that he was still sporting the floppy hat often worn by young men of Cody to keep the dust off their brow. It suddenly struck him how different he was dressed compared to nearly everyone around him.

The cigarette puffing man just nodded as if to say, "Oh, that's it then!" He took one last glance at Pat then stepped off the curb going about his business. Everyone just went about their business in Chicago. Locals hardly noticed the mess on the street.

"I've got to get some new clothes while I'm here," Pat thought to himself.

A policeman in a marked white hat, designating him as a captain, sat calmly on a white regal steed overseeing the calamity. Both horse and rider were motionless. Neither considered the chaos at Dearborn and Randolph to be out of the ordinary.

An open ended cart with fence-like frames at both ends and no sides or top was hauling empty white barrels stacked across the width of the flatbed wagon. Nearly twenty-five barrels were stacked five or six high and clanked noisily as the hard wooden wheels of the cart slapped over the irregular brick surfaces of Randolph Street. They were obviously empty, Pat thought.

People stood ten deep on the sidewalk waiting for a clear shot to cross. Pat noticed how many electrical signs hung out second floor levels. They were elevated to get the attention of the herds of people crammed on to the city's sidewalks. Women were dressed particularly crisply, revealing their tight waists, laced collars, fashionable flat hats, ornate white cuffs extending past the sleeves of their finely sewn coats, and shiny purses draped over their right wrists. In short, they had class. They were city girls. Few in Cody looked as these did. Pat removed his floppy hat and stuffed if in his bag.

Upon surveying the intersection he counted four cable cars, five horse-drawn delivery wagons, five autos, three officials on horseback, at least fifty men and women in the street trying to cross in every direction. There were two wood wagons, three men pushing hand carts in different directions and a man trying to change his rubber tire off the side of the street. Pat noticed a redheaded cop watching the whole scene considering it a matter of routine. Wires were strewn overhead head as thick as hedges bringing power to every office, lamppost, electrical sign and telephone occupying the eight, ten and fourteen story buildings in every direction.

Pat had a burst of energy. Suddenly, he wanted to get home. His train south would not leave for two hours so he decided to buy some clothes, including a new hat. He walked east on Randolph then took a right on State to Marshall Field's Store which was currently the world's largest department store. "Now, here is a store", he thought.

Pat replaced his floppy hat, bought a nice suit, shoes, tie and a few pair of wool socks. He also picked up a few gifts for the family, including a fine pair of gloves for Margaret. He felt like he had returned to civilization once again. He had forgotten how stimulating the city was and began to think about other options he might take in the coming year. He knew he did not want to return to Cody, Wyoming.

The ride home was slow. Full cars emptied someone at nearly every stop. The holiday season forced many travelers to stand until seats became available along the way. Pat slept most of the way but awoke just as the train pulled out of Grant Park, Illinois, six miles north of Momence. As the train began a low decline into the Kankakee River Valley, he could see the tree line escorting the Kankakee River through his home town. It warmed his heart to be home at last. Most everyone would be there except Theodore and Arletta. Lette was under the weather that Christmas and didn't think she could make the trip. Elmer was in California and also couldn't come home.

Pat stepped off the platform of the C&EI. It was three in the afternoon on the 23rd. He was suddenly surprised to see his old buddy Al Fontaine running from the Columbia Hotel where he had been waiting for Pat's arrival since noon.

"Why Al, how did you know I was coming?" said Pat with a large grin and bear hug for his best friend.

"Well, I talked to your ma and she said sometime on the 23rd so I figured based on the schedule to Momence it could be anytime in the afternoon. So, I just sat and drank coffee at the hotel until you finally showed," said Al. "It's good to see you, Pat. Will you stay a while this time?"

"Only a few weeks but longer than last year," Pat said. "We'll have plenty of time to catch up. I've done a lot this year. How's everyone?"

Al and Pat O'Brien talked all the way, catching up on happenings in Momence and strange things that had occurred back in Cody. As with all lifetime friends, Pat and Al had no problem picking the conversation where they had left off nearly one year ago.

The O'Briens and Hathaways, minus a few, spent another enjoyable Christmas together at home. On Christmas day, in the afternoon, Pat and Al exchanged visits at each other's house. Pat had everyone at Al's in stitches talking about the many oddities that had occurred in Cody over the previous year.

"It's good to see you again, Pat," said Al's mother. "Al has been so bored this past year without you." Pat just smiled and looked at Al in a teasing way.

Pat had a chance to see many old friends during his visit. He and Al also spent a day in Chicago and eventually looked up old Gus the engineer who still ran the C&EI cargo train daily. The young men found some time to venture into the Marsh and do some wintertime hunting. They even walked downriver to ice skate on a shallow section of the frozen Kankakee where nearly one hundred and fifty locals were negotiating a spot on the smooth space. It was very much like old times once again and Pat's time at home convinced him more than ever that his days in Wyoming were over.

On the Monday following Christmas, nineteen year old Pat sat down to talk with his mother one-on-one for the first time since arriving home. He asked her about her health and how the past year had been. "Are you making it ok, ma?" he asked. She confirmed that being alone more often was sometimes difficult but that the year had been rather uneventful and that she was feeling fine. After about a twenty minute conversation, Pat got to the topic that had been on his mind since the long train ride home.

"Mom, I've been in Wyoming for a while now and it's really beautiful and all but I need find somewhere else to go," Pat said to his attentive mother. "I mean, I love Hatte and Uncle Ted and all the kids for sure but there's such a limit of what a fellow can find in Cody. I miss the more modern life." Pat was respectful as always with his comments but he knew going back to Cody was not what he wanted to do.

"Well, I know Pat," said Margaret with her normal understanding voice. But you know Hatte and Ted have had such a tough time holding things together and they really appreciate you being around to help." She paused a second then went on. "But, I understand son, it's not your job to help them and you need to be happy with what you do," she continued, giving him support.

"It's just that after coming home and spending a day in Chicago and seeing all that's going on around me. Well, I'm just not on a path that suits me, mom." Again Pat felt badly about not wanting to return to Cody but could no more go back there than live on a deserted island.

"Well, Elmer's out in the Fresno area of California, Pat," said Margaret. "And as much as it hurts to see all my kids live so far, I'll tell you a little secret that only Hatte Belle your uncle John and I know about but you might as well know now, too. They're all moving to California. They'll be near Elmer. You could go with them Pat," she said with a little hesitation.

"What's it like there," asked Pat. "I mean is it a bunch of cattlemen, cowboys and saloons like Cody?"

"Why no, there are large farms where workers harvest more grain than anywhere in the country. There's a rush of farm folks from the Midwest going there now," she said. "People need work these days and Elmer suggested you're moving in with him in a letter he sent me back in October. I didn't want to suggest it at the time, particularly when your Uncle Ted and Lette were having such a hard time, but I think it would work better for everyone now. Besides, Elmer says there are other opportunities there including many more railroads. I know you like railroads."

Pat had a look of relief on his face, thrilled with the fact that his mother understood. He held back his excitement a bit so as not to show too much of negative feeling toward his aunt and uncle in Cody.

"You know your grandfather was in that area during Gold Rush days, Pat," informed Margaret. "Elmer is less than 200 miles from San Francisco. So you'd likely find opportunities in the city, as well." After divorcing his wife, Elmer had relocated to California to farm to find a new life.

"I think it would be a fine idea, mom. I'd like to go," said Pat.

And so it was decided. Margaret offered to write Lette and Ted but Pat insisted that he tell them. He had grown close to them over the last two years and he took responsibility for the decision. Though mischievous and adventuresome his entire life, Pat O'Brien never shirked a responsibility.

Upon returning to Cody a week later, he met with his aunt and uncle and told them of his plans. He began in earnest to prepare to move. He and Elmer exchanged a number of letters and in the early spring Pat said goodbye to the children who were all quite upset by his departure. This tugged at Pat's heart but he knew he had to move away. He waved to the entire family from the rear car as it pulled out of Cody and headed for San Joaquin. Lette cried and Ted fought back tears as they waved back. Pat's departure would take a lot of life out of the Hansen household.

Elmer lived in the Tulare area of the San Joaquin Valley and had sufficient room to provide Pat a comfortable place to live. The San Joaquin Valley was at the center of massive granary operations that produced nearly half of all the wheat and other arid grains in California. Large intensive farming practices were actively deployed by growers in the area who hired large groups of immigrant labor to work on large farms. This was in stark contrast to the family farms that dominated Illinois. Irrigation had changed the entire landscape of the historically dry California Valley.

Pat got to work right away. He saved his money and much preferred California over Wyoming. He was glad to see a number of railroads in the area and soon moved off the farm for good. He worked as a lineman for a small short line railroad that was bringing grain to the main lines. In his spare time, he read extensively about aviation

During his first summer in San Joaquin, he met Ed Hesser, one of the many amateur aeroplane enthusiasts building experimental aircraft in the Central Valley. Pat and Hesser built two crude aircraft during 1910 and early 1911 and it provided Pat his first "hands-on" experience with the practical application of aviation he had read so much about since his youth.

In July of 1911, during one of Pat's frequent trips to the local library in San Joaquin, he sat down to flip through the monthly newsletter of the Aero Club of America. This weekly publication was the only informational source for cutting-edge aviation experimentalists popping up all over the country.

He held his breath as soon as he saw the ad. The Chicago Chapter of the Aero Club was holding the 1st International Aviation Meet from August 12th-20th in Grant Park, downtown Chicago. In attendance would be Lincoln Beachey, Howard Gill, Cliff Turpin and members of the Wright, Moisant and Curtiss Flying Troops. The event was literally a "who's who" of flying mavericks. "Perhaps I could meet Octave Chanute himself," who, unknown to Pat, had died the previous November. Pat had to be there.

He quickly took out a pencil, scratched a note with the particulars of the show, and stuffed it in his pocket. He ran out the library and onto the interurban cable car to get home, as quickly as he could. Bursting into the door he startled his brother. "Elmer! I'm going to Chicago. I'm going home," said Pat.

After Pat read the long list of flyers from his sheet of paper, Elmer was successful in calming down Pat enough to tell his story. Elmer would miss his brother but there was no doubt that Pat was determined.

Two days later, Pat O'Brien made the long train ride home to Chicago. He arrived in Momence on August 10th, two days before the event. There was no time for a letter home and neither he nor Elmer thought to wire Margaret. It was just another surprise for Margaret O'Brien from her son Pat. There would be others.

There existed, at this time, an intense public interest in flying. From 1907 to 1915, over 5,000 aeroplane exhibitions would be held in the U.S. alone. Dozens of inventors put forth their latest dream machines and entrepreneurial investors, with widely different backgrounds, brought money to the industry.

Most initiatives were low-budget operations run by inventors who hired young, wide-eye kids between the ages of 17 and 23 years old as test pilots. The attraction of something as revolutionary as manned flight, as well as the opportunity make fast money, over shadowed any notion that their young lives were in danger every time they climbed into the latest "miracle machine." Sadly, accidents claimed young experimental pilots every week. During peak flying season accidents could occur on a daily basis. There were no parachutes.

Though the industry was in its infancy, it benefited greatly from the formation of the Aero Club of America in 1905. The Aero Club was a conglomeration of dozens of local and state chapters made up of inventors, enthusiasts, test pilots, investors, show promoters, engine manufacturers, and anyone eager to jump on the bandwagon. The club stimulated experimental flight activity by simply reporting on every significant and trivial flight event that occurred.

On his way through Chicago to Momence, Pat picked up a copy of the "Show Edition" of the latest Aero Club newsletter. He noted the number of experimental flying posts for young pilots. Pausing as a train pulled out of Crete, he looked up at the corn-covered fields. "I need to find a flight school," he thought.

Lowering his eyes once again, he read the first ad.

Demand for Flights will be Greater in 1912

"The outlook for the exhibition flier during the season of 1912 is extremely bright. The very successful season just closed in the northern half of the country will be certain to repeat itself, in the opinion of show-men, and professional fliers are likewise hopeful in their prophecies for the year to come.

In the west and middlewest it has been hard to find competent aviators during the past month and more than one of our better fliers found it necessary to refuse contracts because of lack of room on his schedule. Many were booked solid throughout the year."

He raced though one article after another in a gluttonous read, urgent to fill his mind with all he could. Pausing once again as the train pulled out of the Crete station, he looked up at the setting sun in the distant west. "This is what I want to do," he thought. "This is what I'm supposed to do," he said in a low voice. "I know it now. What a great time to be alive!"

Pat O'Brien had choices. He did not have to farm like his father. It was not unlike Martin's time when America reinvented itself at a rapid pace. By contrast, Daniel's time was one of repair after the war. War always spurs invention but it is the children of veterans that bring invention to form. Most veterans seek solace and the comfort of a life left behind in war. Pat sensed this for the first time during his quiet and reflective train ride home.

He continued to read the information filled publication all the way to Grant Park. There were detailed photos of engines by existing auto manufacturers seeking to find a new niche in flight, reports from the latest exhibitions, photos of new hangers erected at some obscure air field, stories of the significant achievements of mavericks like Curtiss, the Wrights, Moisant, Beachey and others. County Fairs posted interest in flyers for air exhibits to be added to their scheduled events. Already, promoters of local agricultural fairs had discovered that air shows could be their biggest draw. Demand for pilots far exceeded availability. And there were numerous obituaries to fallen young pilots everywhere. Pat noticed these stories but others drew his more conscious read:

Peter Christman, an 18 year old boy, of Green Bay, Wis., has built a monoplane which will be tried out in a few days. He will have it on exhibition at the Winnebago County Fair, Oshkosh, Wis.

An inventor in Racine, Wis., Martin Rasmussen, has a new machine ready for trial. It has an arrangement of planes and parachutes which it is said makes a sudden drop impossible.

C. W. Gulllck, of Muskogee, Okla., has built an aeroplane along original lines. He will have it on exhibition at the Muskogee fair.

Harold Brinker, who has been attempting aeroplane flights at Cheyenne, Wyo., for several months, has shipped his Curtiss-type biplane to Mitchell, Neb., where he thinks the heavier atmosphere will be better for practice flights.

Beckwith Havens, one of the latest to join the Curtiss squad, won $2,007 for the Curtiss Company flying at Chippewa Falls, Wis., the week of July 17.

George MacWilliams, of 696 Furley Street, Winnipeg, Canada, is organizing an aero club in that city. He is desirous of meeting with all others in his town who are of the same mind.

The Curtiss-type biplane, built in Danville, Ill., by Charles Baysdorfer and Claude J. Coddington, has been shipped to Mineóla, L. L, for trial flights. The machine, it is said, could have been assembled for work in Danville in very quick time, when the makers suddenly decided to take it east.

Pat looked up from his magazine and peered out the window of his passenger car as he left Grant Park. He noticed the hills of Yellowhead in the distance stood oddly stationary. They were a stark contrast to the rapidly passing foreground of trees, bushes and the consistent blur of a telegraph pole interrupting his view at regular intervals. It struck the young twenty-year old that everything old was like those distance hills. The new modern world was flying by him as rapidly as the obscure images nearest the train.

It was a moment that strikes a maturing young man when the fragments of youth crystallize when seen from a distance for the first time. It explains his past as a preparation for the present and provides a measure of his readiness to engage his future. In an instant, the familiar view of the horizon from a moving train synchronized all that had stirred Pat in his first two decades of life. He knew at that moment he would not be a man of the hills. His place was with the speed and transformation of modern times. His place was with the risk takers who had no sense of risk. He was, indeed, very much like his grandfather Martin. Only he was an extraordinary risk taker. He wanted to fly.

On opening day of the International Aviation Meet, Pat O'Brien stood at the eastern edge of a bridge near Grant Park in Chicago that connected the park to the beach over the IC tracks. Pat was looking to the east, shading his eyes to make out the huge number of machines positioned on the beach. It was early Saturday morning, August 12th and he had just walked from the Randolph Street to the center of the beach at about Monroe Street.

Air meets featured competition between teams of aviators for precision flying, take-offs and landings, altitude records, and other events including speed, aerobatics, and minor stunts. Spectators who watched experienced a wide range of emotions from sheer exuberance when their heroes won, to the utter horror when their favorites crashed. And they did crash. Aerial competitions became the leading form of entertainment during this time.

"Watch it fella," a voice from behind Pat barked. Pat turned and saw a young man about his age, walking toward the beach. He was adjusting the straps on his leather helmet.

"Sorry," Pat said. "Where you heading? Are you flying today?"

The young man paused by Pat making a final adjustment to his straps on his helmet the whole time.

"You bet I am," said the young man. "I'm Jimmie Ward," said the young pilot, extending his hand. Now Pat looked as though he too might be a pilot himself. The proximity of their age convinced Jimmie that Pat was likely a test pilot himself. Perhaps Pat was flying in the show's afternoon group, he thought.

"I'm Pat O'Brien," Pat stated, reaching out to give the young pilot his firmest handshake.

"Glad to meet yah," returned Jimmie Ward as he stepped off the bridge deck and proceeded towards his plane.

A hundred feet above Pat's head, a Herring-Curtiss biplane flew toward the water, bucking a 25 mph wind. Sitting in front of the boxy-looking Aeroplane's laboring motor sat the pilot, 19-year-old native Chicagoan Jimmie Ward. He represented youth, adventure, and daring to the thousands who cheered him. A tremendous urgency came over Pat.

Ten cannon shots opened what would become known as the greatest aviation meet held in the U.S. during the Exhibition Era of flying. The concussion of the great guns reverberated off the skyscrapers that faced Lake Michigan. It startled the pigeons that rose frantically, beating their wings in the air above a cloud of gun smoke. In typical Chicago style the explosive volley opened the show with fanfare. For Pat O'Brien, it would put him in direct contact with the nation's leading flyers and amidst more aeronautics than he had ever experienced to date.

The event was held on the beaches just east of Michigan Avenue. Across the street from the wall of skyscrapers on the eastside of the street was Grant Park. East of the park was the extensive array of Illinois Central tracks running into the South Water Station. The tracks were below grade in a canyon-like sublevel with bridges connecting the park to the beach. This week, only aircraft were allowed on the beach which extended a mile wide. It was full of aircraft. Pat had never seen more aeroplanes in one place.

Some 34 aviators vied for over $70,000 in prizes. One of the highlights of the event was Lincoln Beachey's altitude flight. He flew until he ran out of fuel, slightly over two miles above Grant Park. He then began a long glide back to earth and won a world's record. Lincoln Beachey also won the Auditorium Hotel Trophy for the fastest 20-mile flight, which he made in 23 minutes and 12 seconds.

It wasn't long before the crowds' demands had pilots stunting all over the sky. Planes banked sharply around pylons at ground level, dipped up and down along the race track, zoomed, stalled and "volplaned" or glided down to dead stick landings. During the week, two men died. William Badger, flying a Baldwin biplane, attempted to pull out of a dive too close to the ground and the wings collapsed. His body was smashed under the plane's engine. St. Croix Johnstone, a local Chicago boy, whizzed out over the lake in his Moisant monoplane, the engine blew, and when he hit the water the wreckage pinned him into the cockpit where he drowned in forty feet of water.

The large number of meets and exhibitions, during what would be called the Exhibition Era of flying, created a tremendous demand for pilots. Flying was a young man's game. Point in fact, Chanute never flew a motorize aircraft after testing his gliders at Miller Beach. Accidents were frequent occurrences – often ending fatally with a total loss of the equipment, as well as life. Few exhibitions or tests of new equipment occurred without failure. The equipment was hit or miss. Even experienced aviators crashed. In 1908, Orville Wright went down during Army acceptance trials, killing his passenger, a US Army lieutenant, who thus became the first military person killed in a powered fixed-wing aircraft.

Pat spent the entire week at the show. He met pilots, mechanics, and promoters associated with the young industry. By the end of the week his enthusiasm for flying was at its highest level. Flying was once an isolated hobby to Pat but at the Chicago show he had seen the entire industry. What seemed like a quirky interest shared by a few was, in fact, a rapidly expanding field

Chapter 14

West Pullman

"It's nice to have you in this house once again, Pat. We all missed you so much, dear," said Margaret as she poured a second cup of coffee. In mid-sentence she moved to the kitchen table to sit with her son. "Tell me about the air show, Pat. Was it fun?" Margaret asked as any mother would inquire about her child's fancy. Pressing her palms down on the top of the table, she eased herself in to the kitchen chair.

"Fun? Why, mother, it was surely fun but much more than that, mother," Pat responded. He was still all aglow from his experience the week before. He went on.

"You see mother, flying is brand new but it's also the future. There's people with money who think flying will change the whole world." Margaret smiled in an approving way while she sipped her coffee. "No, really mother. It's not just young fellas like me anymore. There's some real important people involved now. Even manufacturers who know that this is big business and paying good money to test their machines!" he explained.

Pulling her cup from her lips, "I heard there were two young boys killed at the show last week," Margaret stated with concern. "Why, I heard one machine blew up over the lake and the boy drowned a mile off shore!" Pausing, she went on, "I don't know Pat, it seems that railroading is a much less risky business and it's more established. Your brother tells me that there are more and more rail opportunities in California every year and he'd help you get on with the Central Pacific. Don't you think the railroad makes more sense Pat? I mean really, flying's so dangerous," she said.

"It's not more risky than railroading. It's just a different type of risk," said Pat. "And flying's only going to get bigger and bigger. It won't be long when everyone will use planes as much as we use trains today. Maybe more!"

He could see the concern on his mother's face and she took another sip of her hot coffee. Pat did the same to fill the long pause in their conversation.

"I'll make a deal with you, mom," Pat said, breaking the silence and feeling a little guilty for stating his case so strongly to his mother. "I'll spend the fall and Christmas working here and then start flight school in January at West Pullman. I can help you out, take the train each day and if things don't work out by the end of the year, I'll move back to California to work on the railroad."

Margaret considered the silver lining of having Pat home against the idea of his flying Aeroplanes for a year. She could use the help now that both Hansens, Elmer and the others were out west. Margaret considered the circumstances and then mustered enough of a positive look and said,

"Alright son, let's see how it goes. But you must be careful with those machines. I can't afford to have you laid up for a year," she said. "I'll be back to doing all the work myself, again." She spoke those words in a light-hearted way but was terribly frightened at the prospect of Pat getting involved in flying. In a lower tone she finished, "My, what your father would think about these Aeroplanes, Pat."

Pat was relieved. He rose, gave his mother a big hug and kissed her on the cheek explaining, "You'll see mom. Everything will work out grand. Besides, it will be nice to be home once again.

The proximity of Momence to Chicago presented a great opportunity for Pat O'Brien and his interest in flying. Though 50 miles south of the downtown, Momence, like most towns in the Midwest, was directly connected to the city by rail.

At the beginning of 1912, there were two aviation fields in Chicago - Cicero and West Pullman. The Aero Club of Illinois opened Cicero Field near 22nd Avenue & Cicero Avenue in the fall of 1911. In 1914, it would relocate to 83rd Avenue & Cicero Avenue, at that time, just outside the city limits.

At Cicero a new aeroplane design was tested nearly every day. Among the dozens of models tested there was the "umbrellaplane." Andre Ruel was busy making "short jumps" daily with many odd machines. His tests demonstrated that there was usually little difficulty getting weird looking machines off the ground. The problem was controlling the machine in the air. Accidents continued to be too frequent.

Flight school was located at a convenient location for Pat. He jumped on the C&EI line to Dolton then switched lines to Kensington, a familiar route. This time, however, instead of heading east on the Central Michigan Line toward Miller Beach, he went west to West Pullman where the Illinois Central crossed. On certain days, Pat would take the IC home to Kankakee and then catch a ride to Momence from a farmer or merchant returning to Momence.

At the West Pullman Field, work had just been finished on a hangar for the American Aeroplane Manufacturing Company. Two of the company's training machines were housed there when flight school commenced on Monday, January 8, 1912. Pat O'Brien and fourteen other pupils were in the first flying class at the school.

The school's director was Andrew Drew. Drew was a real pilot and won the respect of his students on day one. He was fresh from the St. Louis meet held in October where he had won the quick-starting contest by taking off with a run of only 179 feet. He also won the accurate-landing event by stopping 47 feet away from his target. Drew made the closing flight of the day performing circles, "figure Eights", and "ocean waves," at a height of 200 feet.

Like so many amateurs of the day, Pat's experience constructing and flying planes was self-taught and rather happenstance. The new flight school at West Pullman would be his opportunity to learn the principles of flying from some of the most experienced pilots of the day. The involvement of established manufacturers at the Cicero and West Pullman School assured that students were trained and tested on the latest equipment. Most early schools were opened by manufacturers and investors who attracted spirited youth to become the first test pilots. Flying was new and a natural aphrodisiac to the young who are always drawn to novelty with no concern for risk. Coincidentally, these were the same "indestructible" youth that so often march off to war. No war existed for this generation in 1912. Not yet.

The West Pullman School utilized many of the principles found in the "Curtiss Aviation Book" which included training methods used by the Curtiss Team. Curtiss was an aviation pioneer who built many of the first functional aircraft in North America. He was a serious competitor of the Wright Brothers for both military and commercial contracts in the early days of aviation.

Pat's course at West Pullman covered wind currents, engine adjustment, balancing and turning aircraft, gliding without power to "feel" the controls, taxing, landing, take-offs, short hops, long hops and inspection - all done in sequence. Risk was kept to a minimum and then scaled up in subsequent tries. Throttles were limited to half power in the beginning to prevent aeroplanes from getting enough lifting power so desired by beginner students. This "grass cutting", as the student pilots dubbed it, taught them to steer a straight course.

In the fall of 1912, Chicago had a second aviation meet on September 12th-21st. Pat O'Brien and his class viewed the show with an entirely fresh set of eyes having experienced Drew's training for nearly a year. For the first five days, contests were on the Cicero field and the remainder of the program was carried out on the lake front of Grant Park. The graduates were much closer to the action this time and were allowed to meet nearly every pilot, study each aircraft. It was the capstone of their training at West Pullman. Compared to the 1911 meet, the 1912 Grant Park Meet was a smaller affair but over 100,000 people attended.

As in 1911, the meet was marred by fatal accidents. Paul Peck, a noted flyer, was practicing in his Columbia biplane on September 11th at Cicero. He had reached a height of 100 feet when he tried to make a spiral descent. As the West Pullman graduates looked on, the machine reached 30 feet off the ground when Peck lost control and it fell straight to the ground. It made a lasting impression on Pat and everyone in attendance. There would be others deaths like these in the years ahead but this accident was close to all the students. After all, each student spoke with Peck prior to his take off and shook his hand.

A third meet, The Bennett Cup Race, was held at Clearing, Illinois during September, and was an embarrassment for U.S. aviators. Not a single U.S. machine was able to fly. As the year ended, it was clear that the peak of the Exhibition Age in America was waning. Investors still in the game directed their resources at fewer, yet proven, successes. The forefront of aeronautical development was shifting to Europe.

For Pat O'Brien and the students of West Pullman, the prospects of beginning their careers as professional pilots in the United States seemed, at best, to pause. With so many design failures, most of the idealists who had poured good amounts of time and money into their dream machines exited the activity as 1913 approached. In the 1912 alone, 100 different models in Chicago would be tested. Less than 10 would fly.

The few aviation companies that managed to stay in business after 1912 in the Midwest would cater almost exclusively to the needs of exhibition flyers and wealthy sportsmen. At the start of 1913, a number of manufacturers would still be creating machines in the hangers and shops at Cicero. Nearby Ashburn Fields and the West Pullman Field were closed. The Aero Club fields in Chicago served as Midwest headquarters for exhibition flyers from April to October each year. This drove exhibition pilots south to warm climates leaving behind skeleton crews who were hibernating, testing equipment and otherwise waiting for the next exhibition season in the spring.

The 1913 exhibition season was anticipated with some dread. It was widely assumed that the peak of such activities had passed, and great concern was expressed over the enormous number deaths of aviators which were occurring with sad frequency. These were young kids losing their lives. Even so, some 1,200 real aerial exhibitions were given that year.

Another trend exacerbated the downward spiral of exhibition flying. A significant number of intentional frauds, using phony aviators, took gate receipts to shows and "flew" in an earth-bound sense, on the next train out of town. Promoters of fake exhibitions stalked the unsuspecting countryside, arranging fraudulent meets. All in all, 1913 would be a difficult year for exhibition aviators.

The burst of activity tied to the Exhibition Age had clearly reached its peak. The remaining few aviation developers were among a group of innovators that would form the bedrock of aviation in its next stage of development. For Pat O'Brien, it meant putting his ambitions on hold for a while. By Christmas Eve 1912, Pat was 21 years old. He would spend the holidays at home, reassessing his prospects. He was old enough to be pragmatic but young enough to still have dreams.

Regardless, by the end of 1912, Pat O'Brien had all the fundamentals needed to become an expert pilot. Every pilot knew that the basics of flight, while critical, would require adjustments from one plane to the next. Understanding the idiosyncrasies of different plane designs and how planes reacted in different conditions was always on the mind of an astute pilot. Flying savvy could only be learned with experience. For those who would someday use their flying skills in war something new would be added. An entirely new set of skills would be required to meet that ultimate test of aircraft maneuvering. Neither Pat nor his classmates knew of such things in 1912.

Aviation would require a new impetus to energize once again. In hindsight, the Exhibition Era was merely a warm-up. A new demand would not come from eager entrepreneurs with a passion to experiment. It would come from Europe where other passions were stirring. It would come as a result of the gargantuan requirements of war.

Pat completed his training in the last fall and spent the rest of his time in Momence helping his mother and calculating his next career move. As the year drew to a close, he only had a faint idea about what next steps to take to further his aviation career, such as it was.

"So now what, Pat?" asked Al Fontaine to his long time buddy as he and Pat shared a sandwich and beer. They were spending the afternoon at their favorite bar in Momence after buying Christmas gifts all morning for family. It was Christmas Eve and downtown Momence was all abuzz with last minute shoppers. Most were the men of the town who could no longer delay the inevitable.

"Well, looks like I'll be going west again to work the railroad or some such thing. It just doesn't look like there'll be much call for daredevils like me to get hired on flying Aeroplanes, right now" said Pat taking a swig of the local Radkhe brew.

"Flying is not dead, Al. There's a lot of smart people out there dedicated to making it work. There's no doubt that man can fly, now. Don't pay attention to all the new-fangled machines made by a bunch of newcomers. Watch the big boys, like Curtiss, The Wrights and others. They know what works,' said Pat with a convincing resolve.

"But Pat, you're about the only guy I know that really knows how to fly planes professionally and all that. There can't be many out there that know what you know about machines, can there?" retorted Al.

"Are you kidding? Why there were a whole bunch of fellas fighting for a spot on the exhibition circuit last year. They're still around and everyone's looking to work for the big boys now that shows have fallen off. Flying will boom again soon but I just can't wait around. I've gotta eat, Al, you can't live on air, yah know!" Pat raised his glass of beer in a toasting fashion and they both belted a hearty laugh.

Al tipped his bottle back and finished raising his brow stating, "I supposed you're right." Deep down, Al hoped Pat would stay around Momence but he knew that would not happen. Not Pat. Al knew Pat O'Brien better than anyone. He also knew that Pat and he were different. Al liked stability more than anything. He and Pat were good friends because they were opposites and balanced each other.

"Well either way Al, I promised mom, that if I didn't find work at the end of the year, I'd go west and hook on with a rail line. My brother Elmer has got contacts with the Central Pacific but that puts me right back in the grain fields of San Joaquin, which is about one hour short of the long nap I took in Cody Wyoming!" They laughed again.

Ordering one more beer they went on to repeat a few previously shared stories about "Pat, the cowboy" which Al found hilarious. "Well, you're definitely not a cowboy O'Brien," snorted Al. "The only thing that interests you is saddling one of those loopy motorized kites 8,000 feet up! You're nuts, you know that?" Pat gave him one of those, "who me?" looks.

They both enjoyed the visit and matched cool bottles of beer well into the afternoon before walking back to Margaret's house on Hill Street. Christmas Eve dinner was planned at the O'Brien house. Pat had invited Al to join him as his guest. The seven block walk back to the house was an animated slow stroll. Both young men knew that there was a good chance it could be their last time together in Momence.

Christmas dinner was heartwarming for everyone and Margaret had outdone herself once again. As the night went on, a few neighbors stopped by for a quick nutmeg, leaving a plate of Christmas treats in return. On holidays, the O'Brien house was often bursting at the seams with family and friends. Since the time of Daniel's death, few forgot to visit Margaret during the holidays. This year, fewer Hathaways were in attendance.

Two weeks after Christmas, Pat O'Brien was on the train back to California. He stopped to see his brother in the Valley, gathered what few belongings he had and headed for the San Francisco Bay area. He had scheduled a meeting with James McCracken who had responded to an inquiry Pat made about working for the Santa Fe. His destination was a unique small town on the eastern shore of the San Francisco Bay called Point Richmond.

Point Richmond had recently become the designated Western Terminus for the Santa Fe Railroad and was hiring on to complete the line into the Bay Shore community. It was as far as the railroad could reach. From there, cargo and passengers would fairy across the Bay to San Francisco.

[153]

Augustine S. MacDonald, a real estate promoter in the bay area visited Point Richmond for the first time in 1895. He conceived the idea of the transcontinental railroad terminating at "the point," as it was called, with ferry service continuing across the bay to San Francisco. What really attracted MacDonald to the point area was the opportunity to expand Point Richmond eastward. He would need to convince the Santa Fe Railroad to abandon its plan to run rail to Oakland.

Point Richmond was a peninsular shaped bulge on the eastern shore of the San Francisco Bay sixteen miles directly across from San Francisco. MacDonald convinced the rail road to bore large tunnels through the eastern hills providing entrance to his new found opportunity. The bay along Point Richmond contained a deep water section of shoreline that could clearly serve as a ferry port and a large marshy area to the south.

MacDonald presented his idea to the Santa Fe Railroad and in 1899 the railroad established its western terminus at Point Richmond. The first overland passenger train arrived in Richmond from Chicago in 1900. In 1901, Santa Fe moved its shops to Richmond and the Standard Oil Company built its major western refinery along a portion of shore previously composed of wet marshy soil.

Pat's train steamed into Richmond and he filed out with dozens of others arriving on a rare sunny day in March of 1913. The hills to the east were not as big as the familiar Rockies near Cody but they were stunning nonetheless. As the train headed for the round house, Pat turned and saw the bay. Point Richmond was set in Shangri-La geography but with the human activity of an ant farm. There were few people at Richmond before the Santa Fe but once it arrived, Point Richmond became an instant tent city. By 1913 it was still a boom town. Pat saw rows of cabins for railroad workers in an area called "Smokey Row." This is where cheap labor lived when trains first arrived. The railroad created another city as it had so many times over the last half century.

There was no shortage of entrepreneurs greeting new arrivals at the terminal. Men with buggies were on hand to direct Pat and the others to their local destinations. Nearly every man arriving in Richmond was looking for a job with Santa Fe or the Standard Oil Company.

"Where you headin' mister?" said a young man with a small horse and wagon. "Can I take you somewhere?"

Pat had a hand bag and a sack of books on flying from West Pullman that he had slung over his shoulder. "I need a room," said Pat. "Where's the nearest rooming house?"

[154]

"Go to Stiefvater's next to the post office," the young man pointed down Washington Avenue.

Pat began to walk east toward the center of down. It looked familiar. Richmond was much more like Momence than either Cody or the small towns that dotted the grain fields of the Central Valley. Pat sensed it was like a "big Momence." It had that same local feel, but larger. Point Richmond was a bustling community of just over 15,000 people but its quaint setting and natural isolating boarders of hills and water made it feel cozy. It had a small town feel but with big city options. It also had a hybrid of citizenry not unlike his hometown. Pat felt comfortable right away. Like Momence being within reach of Chicago, Richmond was close to San Francisco. Though accessible by Ferry Boat rather than rail, it took about the same amount of time to get to the big city.

Pat located Stiefvater's Department Store quickly. They had a small sign in the window that read "rooms." He decided to look further, as it was obvious that rooming was a secondary business for the sizable department store. The young fellow at the station was working on commission to fill the empty second story rooms at Stiefvater's.

Pat found the town interesting. He reached an area referred to by locals as The Triangle at the intersection of three main streets – Washington, Park Place, and Richmond Avenue. It was the center of town. The Richmond Library was on one corner and just in front of the library stood a statue of an Indian. It was just over six feet tall, made of 100% copper and mounted on a five foot high bronze base. It formed the center of an elaborate water fountain. There were three fountains at its base. Two were for people and the third was designated for horses and dogs.

On the same intersection stood the police station. Pat passed by Spiersch Brothers Plumbing, the Enterprise Steam Company, numerous bars, and a good number of hotels. When he reached the St. James Hotel and he went in. The St. James was obviously the primary hotel in town and the Ivy Inn, housed inside, is where an outsider could learn quickly about the particulars of the bubbling metropolis of Richmond, California. A few locals called the hotel home but it was largely populated by a variety of new arrivals.

Pat walked into a large lunch room area of the Ivy Inn and notice it had a confectionary off to the left. It sold small items, ointments, toiletries newspapers and other necessities sought by travelers. He found the local newspaper and flipped it up on the counter, reaching for a handful of coins in his pocket.

"How much?" he asked.

The friendly clerked smiled and looked Pat squarely in the eye and said, "one jitney"

"One what?" responded Pat.

"Oh, sorry. You must be new. A jitney. Five cents!"

Pat place the coin in the clerks open palm and thanked him for his help. Pat had actually paid with a brand new Indian head buffalo nickel first produced that year in San Francisco. The jitney was a common slag term for the 5 cent nickel at the time. Pat had not heard that term back in the Midwest.

Pat turned and looked for an open table in the lunch room. He was hungry. He found a small table near the window. "Perfect!" he thought. He could read the paper and watch the busy street outside. Already, Pat could tell that Richmond would be active. It was a welcomed relief from the fields of San Joaquin or dusty roads of Cody, Wyoming. After ordering he began reading through the Richmond Record Herald looking for a room and scanning local news to get sense of his new town.

The paper told him a lot about Richmond. The town had a brick company, a point of nostalgia not lost on Pat as he thought of the Tiffany Brick company back in Momence. The brick company made over 9 million bricks the year before and Standard Oil had bought ninety-five percent of them. The digging of a new quarry had begun in February which also reminded Pat of home.

The town had recently celebrated the opening of the Point Theatre just up the street from the hotel and Pat noticed at least three movie houses in Richmond alone. He was surprised to learn of a third big business just north of Richmond called Winehaven. In 1914 Winehaven, near Point Molate on the bay, was the largest winery in the world. It brought a smile to his face. "This town has everything!" he thought.

Like Momence it had its share of characters too. It looked like the local police had their hands full in Richmond. Pat nearly laughed out loud as he reviewed the tidbit column about local happenings:

"Three-hundred people watched 2 dogs fight for 30 minutes last New Year's Eve near the Triangle."

"Chief Arnold and 2 police battled a boat load of Italians off shore of the Chinese Shrimp Camp on the north shore of Richmond. They were trying to smuggle fish from the camp."

[156]

"The fourth Chinese Laundry of the year went up in smoke last week."

Pat found it interesting to read that it was 'a common occurrence in Richmond' and wondered why."

"Police arrested bandits who had held up a train for $1,400 brandishing pistols. The money was recovered"

"Three men were arrested at the Central Brick Yard attempting to steal cement. They were rumored to be recent escapees from San Quintin prison. Two were murdered by police when they returned fire and the third was still at large"

"What a town," he thought. "Looks like I'll at least have a good time on the weekends."

Just then a man approached him. "Mind if I sit with you young man?"

"Not at all. I just ordered," replied Pat extending his hand. "Pat O'Brien. Yours?"

"Jerry Solich, glad to meet you O'Brien," Said the young Yugoslav sporting a thick Slavic accent. "Vhat you doin' here in Richmond? Looking ver verk?"

Pat was about to respond when the waiter came to their table. Jerry placed an order then reached for the bread that had been placed in a basket at their table to share.

Solich had arrived in Richmond in 1911 from Belgrade. He knew the lay of the land in Richmond pretty well and spoke good English despite his thick accent.

"Virst, I come from Belgrade to Richmond and get job here with Oil Company. Ve work long hours but pay was good and they give us bunk housing near the refinery. I am velder by trade and veld many plates together to form large tanks you see up on the hill at Point," said Solich. Pat listened with interest and was enjoying getting the "straight story" from someone who, like him, came to Richmond to find work.

The Yugoslav went on. "I vant to get job with Santa Fe and vant to get interview with man from railroad," he said. "Railroad work hard but better pay and new tracks come to Richmond now. Lot's of vork. Good pay!" said the friendly man about the same age as Pat.

"I'm going to meet a man from the Santa Fe this Thursday named McCracken. Maybe you can come with me Solich and speak to him about working, also," said Pat.

The Yugoslav was excited to hear that Pat too was planning to work for Santa Fe. It struck Pat that Solich was probably more excited about the prospects than Pat himself. He felt a little guilty seeing rail work as his second choice and Jerry so excited about moving into a better job. He decided it was time to be enthused himself, enjoy Richmond, a town that just felt right to Pat on day one. He knew that it was time to put some money in the bank. Flying could wait for now.

The two talked through lunch and Pat was filled in quite a bit of information from his new friend.

"I tell you O'Brien. The best room for you now is at Anderson's," said Solich.

"Andersons?" was Pat's response.

"Yah, you go down Washington way to west end. It is nice hotel with single rooms and they are clean rooms. Good for your start. Walk seven blocks to intersection of Richmond and Washington and you vill see big building. On the front reads 'E.B. Anderson.' They'll take care of you," he said.

Pat thanked Solich and shook his hand. The two made plans to meet the next day at the Santa Fe office. Pat felt like he had had a good first day. Solich departed and O'Brien had some ice cream while he watched the street out front of the St. James hotel. Milk wagons passed like clockwork delivering dairy to homes and restaurants. A rough looking man slowly pulled a cart full of unidentifiable fare. He was shouting over and over "rags, bottles, sacks! – "rags, bottles, sacks!"

The trolley car passed a number of times as did horses pulling carts. The young ladies were dressed in typical garb but all seemed to wear hats. A large vegetable wagon passed and as the waiter cleared Pat's table she said to him, "There goes Veggie!" Veggie was the name everyone in Richmond gave the local street vendor of farm goods.

Before Pat turned to leave, after laying his second "jitney" on the table, he saw a sight never seen in Momence. It was a Chinese man with a large bamboo poll across his shoulders with two wicker baskets of fresh seafood for sale.

Just then the waiter came up to collect Pat's tab and noticed him looking at the Chinese vender. He took a quick glance out the window then shouted to the bar tender, "Hey Jake, it's Shlimpy! Do you want me to get some fresh shrimp? He's got a new batch." The bartender waved him off indicating that the kitchen had an adequate supply. The waiter turned to Pat, "That's Shlimpy. We all call him that. He supplies the whole downtown with seafood. You ain't had shrimp till you've had one from the shrimp camp.

This was northern California and the Chinese who played a big part in building American's railroads were prevalent in every area of the bay. Pat O'Brien had completed the first day of yet another new adventure in his life. He felt exhilarated.

Chapter 15

Santa Fe

The next morning Pat was surprised to learn that the hotel had no baths per se but had an agreement with Gus Gily's barbershop next door to provide guests with a towel, soap and bath. Gily made baths available to hotel patrons and sold the service to anyone off the street for 5 cents.

Pat O'Brien and Jerry Solich met for coffee at the Ivy Inn in the St. James Hotel where Pat had spent his first night in Richmond. They walked some distance down Ohio Avenue for over a mile until they reached the rail yard at about 9:00 a.m. Pat checked his letter from McCracken which contained a map to the administrative building where his interview would take place.

Walking through the yard they saw a flurry of activity. Richmond was an impressive operation. After all, it was the western terminus of the Santa Fe and facilitated both freight and coach switching. It was a "flat yard" requiring a large number of switch engines to build trains and reposition cars. It was also a receiving yard, departure yard and repair yard all in one, plus it featured an engine roundhouse providing complete locomotive repair. Pat hadn't seen this much steel since his days hitching rides with Gus Altorfer.

The two men walked toward the far end of the yard. They passed the control tower and walked between catacombs of freight cars, carefully dodging train building activity. "Heads up fellas!" shouted a yardman who had just thrown a switch diverting a switcher locomotive down the track that Pat and Jerry were walking on to get to the roundhouse. Everywhere the two rookies looked there was activity. They had stumbled into the middle of the morning train building activity. When they reached the roundhouse, they decided to walk through it. The strength of any railroad is where the locomotives live.

"Have you ever seen so many engines in one place?" asked Jerry.

"Not since Chicago but you can sure tell this is the end of the line," said Pat. "I think we'll find some work here. There's plenty to do, that's for sure."

They walked down a ten foot wide brick-laden work area in front of massive engines being checked for their long run back east. It reminded Pat of the old dairy barns back home with the nose of fifteen locomotives all shoved forward getting checked by expert railroad mechanics. A number of iron workers had hot buckets stoked to the max and Pat felt the heat and power of the huge iron machines as the two men passed. They got through to the far side of the big repair house and saw a brick building clearly identified as the administration building and went inside. Their meeting was on the second floor.

"Hello, I have an appointment with Mr. McCracken at 9:00," said Pat to the attractive but orderly receptionist. Without looking up she asked his name and then made a mark off a long list of names. Pat was surprised by the number of names on the list.

"Take a seat over there Mr. O'Brien," she said, still not looking up. "I'll call your name when they are ready for you." It was obvious to Pat that she had been checking in dozens of job seekers for some time as a matter of routine. Without hesitation, Pat decided to break the ice a bit.

"Thank you ma'am. Say, ma'am, I wonder if you might have an opening for one more interview for my friend here Mr. Solich. Perhaps you've had a cancellation or your day's not full? I'd like to see if he could meet Mr. McCracken, also."

The studious women looked up ready to deliver her negative response. As she was about to speak she saw what she considered to be about the most handsome young man with the biggest smile she had ever seen.

"I don't......," she focused on Pat. "I don't think that would be a problem whatsoever Mr. O'Brien. What's your friend's name?"

"Gerald Solich. He has a lot skills and he's as honest as the day is long, Miss....?" He said pausing to perhaps elicit her name.

Pat had successfully executed the old "treatment" as he called it during his days in Momence when young gals giggled at the simple tip of his hat.

"Johansson. Sharon Johansson," said the awestruck woman.

"Well that's just fine, Miss Johansson. Fine indeed. What time might you have for Mr. Solich?" Pat was holding his hat at his waste with both hands in an accommodating pose. Miss Johansson never looked down.

"I can fit him in right after you Mr. O'Brien," she said in a light airy tone catching her breath.

Pat was called promptly at 9:00 and met McCracken for 25 minutes. That was 10 minutes longer than scheduled. He worried that Solich might miss his chance but the receptionists squeezed him in nonetheless. Pat's interview went well and McCracken was impressed with Pat's experiences to date for a young man of twenty-two.

As it turned out McCracken also had a general interest in aviation and asked Pat as many questions about Cicero Field and the Chicago Show as he did about Pat's qualifications. Regardless, he recognized the leadership qualities in Pat and made a note next to his name. He'd see how Pat worked and keep an eye on him to see if he might be management material.

"You ever heard of our local guy named Bott, Obrien?" said McCracken leaning over his paperwork.

"Can't say that I have. Who is he," responded Pat.

"Was. He was, O'Brien. He's our local claim to fame in aviation but he wasn't too successful. Frankly, I think the guy was a failure more than anything else but you know how flying is. Every town has its story about their local Orville Wright, yah know."

Pat smiled but not in a condescending way as McCracken told the Bott story.

"Before coming to Richmond, about 1894, this Professor Robert H. Bott writes a thesis called Botts' Air-Ship - The Problem of Aerial Navigation, under the name of Barnet H Bott. He arrived in Point Richmond in 1900 with the intention of building two steam-powered flying machines which would make aerial expeditions to the North Pole. Can you imagine?"

McCracken went on, "He built a toy model, showed pictures of it all over town, and then convinced a bunch of local businessmen to buy shares to pay for the real thing.

In January 1903, Botts took his machine to the top of Nicholl Nob for its maiden voyage scheduled for the next day but a storm blew in overnight and the machine was tossed off the hill where it landed - wrecked beyond repair. Or so he said!" stated McCracken, leaning back in a matter of fact way while smirking in disbelief. "As is usually the case with these "promising" aviators, Botts had much to gain, and a lot of other peoples' money to lose - so he quickly left town."

Pat dared not speak of his dreams to fly and didn't want to mention his ultimate ambition to do it for a living. But rather than say anything, he just held his breath. Seeing the look on Pat's face, McCracken encouraged him. "There are some fellows around Richmond that have an interest in flying. And, of course, if you get to San Francisco you'll find more. As long as it doesn't interfere with your work on the railroad, feel free to pursue your interest young man."

"Thanks, Mr. McCracken. I appreciate your support," said Pat, finally exhaling with ease. With that, McCracken reviewed the various positions open at Santa Fe. He offered Pat a job as a laborer laying track for the new second line being run to the Richmond Yard. He'd work five full days and Saturday mornings at $1.25 per hour.

"Buck and a quarter, huh?" responded Pat. "Is there an opportunity to move up?" He asked.

McCracken tried to encourage Pat that other positions would open up to him soon if he proved his worth. A crew boss made $1.50 per hour. From there Pat could advance to Fireman and get paid $3.85 per 100 miles. Firemen essentially were responsible for maintaining fuel to the steam engines on long trips. Fireman was one of the first jobs "off the rails" and on the train itself. If he proved himself, he could advance to other positions of responsibility and make more money.

"That's fine. I appreciate the opportunity," responded Pat. The details of the whole arrangement caused Pat to glaze over a bit, but he agreed to start and shook McCracken's hand. He was still pondering Botts.

"See the girl in the lobby outside my office there and she'll give you the proper papers to sign, O'Brien." said McCracken.

As the summer of 1913 progressed, Pat made a number of friends both on the job and in Richmond. On Jerry's recommendation, he moved to a more permanent room in the Anderson Rooming House. Thankfully it had a private bath and a larger bedroom with a window. There was enough room in the kitchen for a table and two chairs. Pat finally felt settled in his own place once he moved into Anderson's.

Pat focused hard on his new job and by the late fall was promoted to crew boss, overseeing men who were laying the final twenty miles of track from Stockton to Richmond. Many of the crewmen were older than Pat and a good number were immigrants who spoke little English. They all looked up to Pat just as the old gang had during the Momence quarry days. Pat worked hard, was fair, and made work fun. He drove his crew hard and reprimanded them with a disarmingly broad smile. The men liked Pat and worked hard for him.

As the year came to a close, Pat started to earn more money. Just before Christmas he opened a savings account at the Bank of Richmond. Standing in line, he began to remember events in his father's life including the time he and Daniel stood in line in the Momence Bank when Pat was eight years old. He hadn't thought of his dad in a long time. It brought a smile to his face.

"Odd," he thought, how being in a Bank would bring thoughts of home. The last bank he was in was Parish Bank & Trust in Momence. "Banks all smell the same," he thought. The scent of mahogany wood, paper and ink had subconsciously thrown him back in time. He would be alone for Christmas in 1913. It would be the first time. He thought of his day with Al and Christmas Eve one long year ago. He also pictured the family together in Margaret's home and how he would be missing.

On his way back from the bank, Pat thought about being grown up and independent for the first time. He felt good. Working and living on his own was a satisfying feeling. But he knew that railroading was only temporary. The passion to fly was still there. He decided that he would explore aviation in his spare time again in the year ahead but in a more logical manner than when he rushed off to West Pullman in 1912.

He had an extra sense of confidence, greeting nearly everyone he passed on the street. They all seemed to notice his levity – or at least it seemed that way to Pat – and it fueled his excitement about the prospect for the coming year. A new job, time to explore aeroplanes again and the unexplored town of Richmond all buoyed his spirits. Pat's enthusiasm for life had returned. He realized now that the two years in Cody after the death of Perry were down years.

A few blocks from Anderson's he stopped in at the post office to pick up mail. There was one letter. It was from his brother Elmer. He was coming to visit for Christmas.

"How fantastic!" shouted Pat. "I won't be alone for Christmas after all."

Elmer would ride up from San Joaquin and spend four days with Pat during Christmas. It was very common in winter for Californians to take the Southern California Railroad to Richmond and the Bay area. The San Francisco area was generally ten degrees warmer in winter than San Joaquin.

Pat decided to treat himself to a fine beef dinner at the Ivy Inn to celebrate his new sense of permanence in Richmond. He sat at the same table he had gotten into the habit of selecting that overlooked the streets of Richmond. As he took long hard draw from his draft beer he relished in the moment. This was the best day of his life since his first solo flight at West Pullman. Though Pat was alone, he felt connected to home and his family as never before. He pictured Elmer stepping off the train in a few days and played out their likely first day together when Pat would show him Richmond for the first time.

"Elmer!" shouted Pat as he saw his brother step off the train two days hence.

Elmer O'Brien was twelve years older than Pat but as close to him as brothers Bud, Buck or Pency after their two years together in Tulare. Elmer had grown close to Pat, having taken him under his wing. But the Pat O'Brien he saw at the Richmond Station was a more mature fellow than the "young kid" Elmer had sent home a few years before. Pat had spent 1912 flying planes and his eleven months on the railroad filling out his physique significantly.

"If I didn't see that mug of yours, I'd never guess it was you!" exclaimed Elmer grabbing his younger brother's shoulders beaming with delight. "What the hell you been doing carrying these trains around Richmond?"

"Hey, try slinging a sledge hammer nine or ten hours a day and you'd look like me too," said Pat. Pat was always good looking and tall but he now had obvious upper body strength from working on the railroad. Many a young lady in Richmond held their breath at even the slightest glimpse of handsome Pat O'Brien. He was known as a "real looker" among the eligible young women in town.

Elmer had come to California following his difficult divorce from LuLu DuCharm O'Brien. His wife chose to take only one child, the boy, Elmer Jr. Little Marie was taken in by the Worley family in Lowell. Like so many before and after, Elmer came to California for a new start.

When Pat decided to give up farming and return to Illinois in 1911, Elmer felt a bit abandoned. To a degree, Pat replaced Elmer's boy who he never got to steer into manhood. Just as Perry Hathaway took over for Daniel during Pat's early teens, Elmer provided guidance as Pat entered his 20's. Elmer was glad that Pat was now within a five hour train ride. He hoped he had had a positive influence on Pat.

Elmer O'Brien was also a good looking man but lacked the stature of his younger brother. As is often the case with divorced men who finally reconciled the dissolution of their marriage, he enjoyed his night out with his younger good looking brother and the chance to visit women again. He was reassured that his chances of meeting a young pretty gal increased as a result of their dual efforts. Pat always drew a crowd, particularly the ladies.

"Come on, Elmer. You must be starving," said Pat placing his arm over his brother's shoulder while picking up his bag. "You need a good meal and a cold beer and I've got just the place for you. We're meeting a few of my buddy's at the Ivy. You'll like it."

The two O'Brien's walked some length to the center of Richmond where Pat checked his brother in the St. James and dropped his bags off before they headed for the Ivy.

"Jerry, meet my brother Elmer. Elmer – Jerry Solich. My partner in crime," said Pat. "Don't worry about his English, I've been trying to teach him the Irish dialect for nearly a year, but it keeps coming out sounding Polish or some other dialect!"

"Yugoslav, Pat. I'm from Belgrade, Yugoslavia! Damn it!" said the indignant young Slav.

"Don't pay attention to him, Elmer," said Pat. "The boy don't know his geography either! Pat and Jerry had acted out this same routine many times over, often to break the ice with a group of eligible young ladies. Jerry was funny. Pat was both funny and handsome. They made a dynamic pair.

The three men worked their way to a gathering of rail workers sharing a large table near the bar. Pat had arranged to have most of his crew mates present. He wanted to show Elmer a good time. Elmer was exhilarated by the rowdy bunch of railroaders. Pat was clearly the ring leader. He introduced Elmer to everyone in a heartfelt and jovial manner. Elmer was touched by this.

"So have you taken your brother to the Avenue yet, Pat?" asked Peter McLaughlin, a member of the assemblage.

[166]

"Who? Elmer? Why I'd never do that. He's my older brother. I'm not supposed to know about all those things anyway," said Pat while the others roared in laughter. Elmer had enough confidence in Pat to laugh, as well. He liked the feeling of Pat being more grown up – more like his pier now. It was like finding a new friend.

In fact, Pat hadn't spent a minute on Railroad Avenue. Richmond was a wide open town and the Point had its fair share of bordellos. Good citizens considered Railroad Avenue out-of-bounds and no decent woman ever walked that street. By 1913, complaints coincided with the passing of a State Red Light Abatement Act, and the Railroad Avenue bordellos were made illegal. Enforcement was convenient, since the jail behind the firehouse was close at hand.

Pat and his brother spent four great days together. They took the San Pablo Ferry from Ferry Point in Richmond to San Francisco. It was Elmer's first time in the "City by the Bay." Pat, Jerry, and Chuck Pearl, Pat's closest friend in Richmond spent a day touring the city. Pearly was the conductor on Pat's train. They had dinner each night at the Ivy. Pat showed Elmer around town and they explored the shores near Richmond.

On the day before Elmer was to return home, they took a ride north on the Central Pacific Railroad along the coast to Port Costa on the Straits of Carquinez to see the largest wheat barge in the world. Being an employee of Santa Fe, Pat was able to acquire complimentary passes for them both from the CPR.

The Solana was owned and operated by the Central Pacific and was of great interest to Elmer who worked in the wheat fields of San Joaquin. He wanted to witness firsthand how wheat got to the market. The Solana was, at the time, the largest ferry boat in the world, six rail tracks wide. It would take entire train cars across the Straits loaded with wheat where it would link up with Union Pacific bringing grain from California to the East.

The next day, Pat gave his brother a big hug as he saw him off to San Joaquin. It was Friday, December 27th. They had rekindled their bond. Elmer was proud of his younger brother and Pat enjoyed sharing his new life and close friends with Elmer. As the Southern Pacific train rolled south, Elmer had a sense that his brother had found a home. Normally rather stoic, Elmer felt his eyes well up and a strong knot in his throat as the train departed south in the direction of San Joaquin. His eyes stayed focused on Pat's face as Pat waved energetically until no longer in sight.

"My God, he's got a zest for life," thought Elmer. It moved him deeply, particularly knowing the tough life Pat had growing up thus far. Yet, it seemed to be Pat's strength and Elmer vowed right then to stop feeling sorry for himself as he had ever since leaving Momence.

As the spring and summer of 1914 passed, Pat O'Brien continued to acquire more responsibility at the railroad and was promoted to Fireman for Santa Fe's Stockton line in June. While he was no longer working with his crew buddies during the day, he continued to mix things up with them at night. Pat, Chuck, and Jerry were always seen together on the weekends along with Frank Hanson, another conductor Pat worked with and a mixture of their entourage at the Ivy Inn. Pat was clearly the kingpin. Jerry continued his role as straight man and Chuck became a real confidant of Pat's.

In August, Pat took some time off and visited Elmer in the Valley for two weeks. It was a vacation long in coming. While there he also visited Edwin Hesser. Hesser had some new aeroplane designs and the two refine and tested them. They were smaller but were better aircraft than they had built in 1911. The two spent a few days working on the latest prototype.

In the first run the plane struggled to sustain flight. Pat told Hesser, he'd return as often as he could when visiting his brother. Hesser valued Pat's flying abilities and instincts with an aeroplane not unlike older men understood their horse. Pat had that natural feel for flying and for relating to every part of an aircraft at all times. It was a natural talent that would he would call upon many times more in the future.

On a September day in 1914, Chuck Pearl came to Pat before their last run back to Richmond. Knowing Pat was currently training an understudy, he invited Pat to ride the last leg home in the passenger car which was always added to the freight train at the beginning and end of each day to accommodate business travelers.

"Pat, there's a fellow on the train, I think you should meet," said Pearl. "Why don't you have that new student fireman do your last run and ride in the passenger car with me? I'd like you to meet this gentleman. He's into flying."

Pat glanced at Engineer Frank Hansen who gave him the ok to take off his final run home. Chip Walter was an eager and bright understudy to Pat and was ready to do an unsupervised run. Pat joined Pearl and the mysterious passenger up front. Conductor Pearl directed Pat to the dining car where Mr. and Mrs. Joseph Cato were having coffee.

[168]

"Mr. Cato, Pat O'Brien," said Pearl while extending his hand. "Pat, this is Joe and Madge Cato of Stockton. Joe is an inventor. He flies Aeroplanes."

Pat's ears perked up and he shook hands with both Cato and his wife Madge. They were both pleasant looking folks and seemed pleased to meet Pat.

"I understand you have some flying experience in Chicago, Mr. O'Brien?" said Cato, getting to the conversation right away as men with a spirited interest often do.

"Yes, I have had some experience. I completed flight school at West Pullman in 1912 and constructed a crude plane in San Joaquin in 1910 with a local race car buff and a few of his friends. I've got a general idea on the mechanics of aeroplanes. I hope to fly for a living someday!"

Pat's enthusiasm was noticed by Joe Cato right away. Pat went on. "I attended the Chicago meet in 1911 and the Bennett Races at Clearing, though they weren't too successful as you may have read. Since coming to Richmond I've not had a lot of opportunities to pursue it but hope to have more time this year. I've even been to the beaches of Indiana where Octave Chanute first tested his glider."

This interested Cato greatly since he too had created a glider wing in 1903 and had reviewed notes and reports of the Chanute tests. "Did you ever meet Chanute?" Cato asked.

"No, but I came close. By the time of the first Chicago meet in September of '11, Chanute was dead. He died in November of 1910, you know." Madge Cato was sipping her coffee but became interested in Pat's story, hearing of his experiences in Chicago.

Joe Cato set his cup down and explained. "Well, I'm looking for an experienced flyer, Pat. And Chuck tells me you're quite knowledgeable about machines. I need someone to test my planes and enter them in events. But I'm looking for a young man like you that has real training and knows how to handle a glider."

Cato proceeded to tell Pat of his experience with planes. Cato had worked in a machine shop after school in Stockton as a young man. He later moved to San Francisco and attended night school in engineering where he read all he could about gliders and the experiments of the Wright brothers. While Joe Cato was not the first man to build a glider, Pat learned that he was an early pioneer as far back as 1903. Cato had a glider with a wing span of twenty-eight feet back in Stockton. It was covered with muslin and had both horizontal and vertical rudders which were controlled by ropes. The ropes were attached to a rudder bar operated by the hands.

"I've seen models similar to that," said Pat. "In most of the planes I've flown I operated rudders with my feet. Seems like hand controls would keep a pilot busy." Pat's comment confirmed that Pat was, indeed a pilot with hands on experience.

"You're right O'Brien," Cato confirmed. "That is more common today but back then, I was guessing! My first two attempts included gliding my machine in winds of about 10-15 mph by jumping off a barn out over a straw pile." They both laughed. "The first attempt resulted in failure but early in the summer of 1904 I was more successful gliding about 200 feet. Unfortunately, due to air turbulence the machine crashed and was wrecked. That's when I gave up whole project for about ten months."

In no time, their train was at Richmond and Cato asked if Pat might join him and his wife for dinner in Richmond to talk further. Pat was keenly interested, having met his first flight enthusiast since arriving at Richmond. Cato was two years older than Pat.

The two mavericks hit it off from the start. Madge Cato, having sat through many of her husband's passionate discussions on flying before, encouraged the men to continue their conversation over dinner while she did some window shopping nearby. Secretly, she wished the topic might be of a more social nature, finding Pat an engaging and handsome young man herself.

Over coffee the two men were locked in an intense conversation. What became evident to Pat was that Cato knew engines as well as gliders. Most men had an expertise in one or another but Cato had both. Cato related how he once answered a nationwide request for bids on a powered aircraft for the military. The War Department awarded the contract for the first Army Aeroplane to Augustus Herring. Pat was thrilled to hear this.

"Herring was one of two the two men who spent two weeks as Chanute's assistant at Miller Beach in 1896!" said Pat with a raised voice.

"How interesting, I did not know that. The only reply I received was a form letter from the Signal Corps stating that they would procure aircraft through regular channels," said Cato. They both laughed and Pat exclaimed, "What the hell did that mean?" Cato shook his head in reflective disbelief. Pat noted Cato's reference to the Signal Corps.

"So the Signal Corps will use planes?" asked Pat.

"Well, it makes sense, O'Brien. They're doing all the balloon work for the Army so I guess the military sees the Corps as the most logical bunch to experiment with machines. As you can see, though, the Army doesn't seem to be in a rush," Cato said, lifting his coffee cup half way and looking Pat square in the eye he punctuated his point, "Normal channel! Ha!" Pausing shortly then adding, "Typical Army."

Cato built a Curtiss-type single surface biplane which he had solo hopped using a 35 horsepower engine. The plane was owned by Ames Tricycle Company of San Francisco who operated the flying school at the Alameda marshes referred to by locals as Sunset Field.

"I'd like you to help me test my newest plane, Pat," said Cato. "It's a double surface biplane with Vernon-type landing gear and ailerons. The engine was taken from a Pope-Toledo car owned by a farmer. It's quite innovative!"

Ailerons were hinged control surfaces attached to the trailing edge of the wing of a fixed-wing aircraft. They were used to control the aircraft in a roll. The two ailerons were typically interconnected so that one goes down when the other goes up. The Vernon landing gear was a tricycle system that reduced damage to the skids of an aircraft upon landing. This was all very familiar to Pat and he asked enough questions to confirm to Cato he had found the right man.

Cato's biplane was at Gustine, California, a town east of San Jose. But he told Pat that he preferred to have him head efforts in Stockton at the end of his rail run. The two men agreed to work together. Pat was back in the flying business once again. He was thrilled.

Chapter 16

The Unrelated Perturbation

In the summer of 1914, Pat O'Brien was still testing aircraft for Joe Cato. Cato had six planes at Gustine and more at his location in Stockton. He and a handful of other young flyers kept Cato's stable of aircraft in shows and tested many new designs. Pat regularly traveled to the Joaquin Valley. He worked on Edwin Hesser's planes that were finally getting off the ground more consistently but still had parts of the Aeroplane flying off in midair. Both men had more than one tough landing but the planes did fly and Pat got used to bringing down damaged planes. He had more than his share of bumps and bruises but that was nothing new to the world of experimental flight.

In Cato's stable there was Ed Neville a young 18 year old loner that seemed to have no roots and seldom talked about family. Curley McNeil, Claude Craig and Tim Reardon, all twenty years-old, were from Southern California where aviation was the most active in the state. They were particularly fond of pushing the limits of speed and altitude. Testing the functionality of maneuvering mechanisms was more the fancy of Buster Wolfe and Mike Fisi who were San Francisco kids, both twenty-one. Being the most experienced of the lot, Pat spent time exploring the ability of Cato's planes to stunt, handle quick loops, dives and other aerobatic moves. Pat had become as good a test pilot as could be found in Northern California in 1914. Cato knew this. Though it was the stunt flyer in flying shows that most people knew, men like Cato's crew were at the cutting edge of aeronautical invention at this time in the United States.

Along with this part-time hobby, Pat was steeped in a whole lot of work on the Santa Fe. Like all twenty-three year-olds, he had great resiliency and still found time to meet regularly with the entourage at the Ivy Inn. By now, his fellow test pilots were regular members of "Smilin' Pat's Pack," as was known there.

He flew planes between runs while his train was being assembled in the Stockton yard each day. On Fridays he would send a student fireman back to Richmond and work in Cato's shop at night, and then fly all day Saturday and Sunday testing planes. Once a month he flew at Gustine where he also worked on engines. Pat met other inventors of aircraft in the Bay area and spent nearly every free moment flying. He was considered one of the best test pilots in the area.

Needless to say, Pat's group of railroad and flying buddies focused nearly all their attention on the immediate needs of the moment. During the summer of 1914, the Richmond boys and many other young Americans were filling twelve hours days with hard work and ambition. They took little notice of events that had no impact on their daily routine. Anything that got in the way of these aggressive young men of ambition was viewed as an unrelated perturbation. As Pat's flying chum Mike Fisi put it, "Don't bother me with that babble. I've got planes to fly."

"Neville!" shouted Pat walking into the shop to find his flight partner for the next run. "You in here?"

"Pat, where the hell is Sarahjevo, O'Brien?" said Neville as he continued to read the front page. Test pilot Ed Neville sat at the roll top desk in Joe Cato's work area just inside hanger #2 at Stockton Field. He had the San Francisco Chronicle elevated to eye level as the rising sun cast a bright light through a window behind him on to the front page.

"Where?" asked Pat.

"Sarahjevo. Some Archduke was killed there today. Those crazy Europeans are always fighting," said Neville, repositioning the paper down to read the top of column two.

"It's in Bosnia, right below Hungary," said Pat as he hung his bag on a wall hook near the window. "What happened?"

"Here, you read it. I just finished," said Neville rising from his chair to get his gear. "I've already read it. Some Archduke. The newspaper says it's gonna' be a tinderbox!"

Pat picked up the paper and glanced at the front page news.

Special Cable to the San Francisco Chronicle

Sarahjevo, Bosnia, June 28 - Archduke Francis Ferdinand, successor to the throne of Austria-Hungary, and his wife, the Duchess of Hohenberg, were shot and killed by a Bosnian student here today. The fatal shooting was the second attempt upon the lives of the couple during the day, and is believed to have been the result of a political conspiracy.

General opinion here connects the assassins with the Serbian faction, and it is feared it will lead to serious complications with that unruly kingdom, and may have far-reaching results. The future of the empire is the center of general discussion. It is felt that the Serbians have been treated too leniently, and some hard words are being said about present foreign policy.

Pat mumbled under his breath as he read slowly "serious complications....huh!"

Pat flipped the paper on to the desk, grabbed his goggles and walked out to meet Neville on the grass runway.

"Sounds like the boys in Europe are still finding it hard to get along, huh Ed?" said Pat as he pulled his chin strap firmly against his jaw.

"Yeah, their problem is that they all live too damn close to each other over there. Ain't like here. If you don't like your neighbors you can just move far away without crossing somebody's border. Whatever they're doing, I don't want any part of it."

"Get in. I'll start her up," Pat said, proceeding with the process. Neville climbed into Cato's latest version of a two-seater, fashioned after a Burgess Company model that Cato saw fly in southern California ten months earlier.

"Contact!" Pat shouted and Ed Neville barked back. Pat gave a hard pull on the large prop and the Curtiss engine immediately roared to full rotation. He ran around the left wing and climbed in behind Ed and they were off. The test run was strictly to check the functionality of the aircraft.

In Europe, young test pilots were beyond testing functionality. They were fully engaged in exploring the acrobatic rubrics of air war.

By July 29th, Austria-Hungary invaded Serbia. Three days later, Germany declared war on Russia then declared war on France the next day. On August 4th, one and one half million German troops launched an invasion of Belgium. By the end of that day Britain declared war on Germany as required by one of a dozen agreements between European nations at the time. Thus began the 980th war on earth since the dawn of civilization. Pre-war treaties had aligned ultimate foes well before Serbian terrorist Gavrilo Princip aimed his pistol at the Archduke Ferdinand in Sarajevo.

 The day of the shooting, President Woodrow Wilson declared the United States neutral, not knowing that the 20th century would refuse to tolerate Americans turning their eyes away from Europe's chaos. Wilson also didn't understand that by the end of the summer all of Europe would be fully engaged. So would the Japanese.

On August 14th a few local British subjects from a small ferryboat town in southeast England watched thirty-seven primitive aeroplanes take off from Dover, England bound for war. It was the first mass flight in history. By November, merely three months into the war, the Allies had suffered one million casualties, a figure never to be eclipsed in any three-month period for the rest of the war. The Aeroplane had been responsible for virtually none of these dead and wounded. At the beginning of the war the aeroplane was a side show. By the end it would be fully engaged as the new weapon of human conflict and critical to ultimate allied victory.

On the afternoon of December 21, 1914, the German newspaper Kolnshche Zeitung carried a story on one of its back pages. The one-line header read, "A German Naval Airman Over Dover." First Lieutenant von Prodzynsk threw several bombs, one of which reportedly hit the harbor railway station.

That same day, eight time zones away in San Francisco, Pat O'Brien walked into the local office of Aero Magazine to get some news "just off the press." He was not seeking war news. His focus was on information regarding an air show scheduled to open in February in San Francisco. The show was to be held in conjunction with the upcoming Panama Pacific International Exposition. The big draw at the air show was the famous stunt pilot Lincoln Beachey. Americans were still flying aeroplanes for sport. The Europeans were imagining their use for war.

Aero, along with a few other magazines and newsletters in the U.S., reported on aviation activities around the world. The December issue, Pat was told, had a feature on the upcoming Panama show. Though not as extensive as the two air shows of 1912 in Chicago, Pat wanted a chance to see Beachey once again. He had met him at the Grant Park, Cicero and Clearing events when Pat and the West Pullman boys were allowed on the field.

Pat took the elevator to the third floor of the Sheridan Building. He exited the elevator and took a right down the long hallway. The fourth glass door on the right read, "Aero & Hydro Publishers." He walked in.

"Hello ma'am," said Pat, tipping his hat in familiar fashion. He then removed it.

A red-headed young lady looked up to see the same smiling face so often responded to with a smile in return. "Yes?" she managed to mutter.

"I wonder ma'am, if I could purchase a copy of the new *Aero* magazine just out?" Pat always seemed to take a polite tone with the ladies. He had found out at an early age that more was achieved with sweetness than bragging when it came to the female sex.

"Well, I'm sorry Mr..?

"O'Brien, ma'am. Pat O'Brien"

"Indeed," she responded. "Well, I'm afraid Mr. O'Brien that the December issue will not be released until this Friday morning. We're holding the shipment here to be placed in the mail Wednesday."

"Oh, that's a shame. Say, how about if I order a subscription while I'm here?" Pat said reaching for his wallet and continuing to speak as he took out a few bills. "You see, I made the trip all the way over from Richmond on the ferry and hoped I could read about the upcoming show in July. I hope to be there and see an old friend from Chicago"

"Oh, are you a flyer?" she said while considering the risk of sneaking Pat an early edition.

"Why yes ma'am. I am. Do you like flying?" he asked handing her three dollars.

"It seems very dangerous but it does look exciting," she said then went on. "Mr. O'Brien, if you can keep a secret, I'll take your subscription and include an advance copy of the December issue. I'd hate to see you have to take that slow Ferry all the way back Friday just for the sake of a deadline."

Then catching herself for being overly sweet in tone, she said "As long as you don't reveal it to anyone!"

"Now Miss…?"

"MacMillan. Agnes MacMillan," she said with a blush but a penetrating Irish smile.

"Well, Miss MacMillan, that's very nice of you. I won't tell a soul," said Pat with sincerity in his voice. Pat really wanted to learn about the show. It would be the first meet he'd witness since graduating from Pullman two years before. Agnes MacMillan was pretty and he admired her caution in breaking rules while empathizing with his situation.

"Thank you, miss," Pat said.

Agnes went to a back room coming out with a copy of the "secret" magazine.

Pat thanked her. "Perhaps when the show opens, I could escort you to the air show Agnes? I know it's not until February but I could stop by to see you a few weeks prior to make arrangements. That is, if you agree?"

"That would be very nice, Mr. O'Brien. I work here Mondays, Wednesdays and Fridays, 9 to 4:30 p.m." Again she tried to calm herself down from her elevated enthusiasm.

"I'll keep that in mind, Agnes," he said pausing on her first name giving it emphasis. Agnes felt a chill run down her back. Both were moved by their first encounter.

Pat turned and left the office, turning back for one last smile to Agnes MacMillan while he closed the door. Agnes stared out her office window for about a minute. She wasn't thinking of anything in particular - just staring. Pat headed down the elevator, out the door and onto to the sidewalk. The entire time he was flipping through the *Aero* monthly. He turned to the section on Lincoln Beachey and headed in the direction of the San Francisco Ferry Station.

Beachey was born in San Francisco and was only three years older than Pat. The two enthusiasts had had a friendly conversation during one of Beachey long breaks at the Chicago meet. Lincoln was engaged in his aerial career, working with balloons the year that the Wright Brothers first succeeded at Kitty Hawk. By January of 1911, he was considered a professional aviator. By mid-1911 he was famous throughout the U.S., flying over Niagara Falls and then, less than a month later, he broke the world's record for altitude at the great Chicago International Aviation Meet.

Many of Beachey's aviator friends had perished and some in the press blamed Beachey for their deaths, accusing him of setting a bad example by flying in a "dangerous" manner. In truth, Beachey was pursuing the outer edges of what was then still a very new art. Flyers were considered either "safe and sane" aviators, those who made large sweeping turns and valued the perceived safety of low, straight and level flight. The others were called "flying fools." They made steeply banked turns and sought the excitement of higher flight. Beachey was clearly in the second group.

The exhibition season of 1914 had belonged to Beachey. He was one of the first aviators in the U.S. to loop an aeroplane, and he did so over 1,000 times between November 1913 and November 1914. His races with legendary race car driver Barney Oldfield drew tremendous crowds, thunderous applause and over $250,000 in receipts. His most notable exhibition would occur in San Francisco in the spring of 1915. Pat's visit to *Aero* Magazine that day would assure that he would be on hand to witness the newest stunts of Lincoln Beachey at the Panama Pacific Exposition.

The Panama Pacific Exposition was held within boundaries the 3,000 acre military establishment in San Francisco called Presidio. The Presidio of San Francisco was located on the northern shore of the San Francisco Peninsula. As a U.S. Army post, it protected commerce and trade and played a logistical role in every major U.S. military conflict since 1848. World events and events occurring on the home front from military campaigns to the rise of aviation, from World Fairs to natural disasters, left their mark on Presidio.

On March 14, 1915, eleven days after his 28th birthday, Lincoln Beachey crashed into the Ocean at the Panama Pacific Exposition while performing one of his stunts. Over 50,000 fans including Pat O'Brien witnessed the crash. Beachey had overstressed the wings on his aircraft. Navy divers from the battleship USS Oregon recovered the wrecked plane and his body from the Bay. It marked the effective end of exhibition flying in the United States. Lincoln Beachey's death was so visible and shocking that it marked the end of the first exhibition flying period. A small number of aeroplane exhibitions, usually by individual aviators, would continue into 1916 and a second craze would occur ten years later when returning ace pilots launched the golden age of barnstorming. But the freewheeling experimental period of the Beachey era was over.

Pat was shaken by the crash. Beachey had agreed to meet him after the show that day. They never had the chance. Pat had neglected calling Agnes MacMillan to attend the show. His busy schedule got away from him and the day of Beachey's failed stunt was one of Agnes' workdays. In hindsight, he was glad he had not called on her for it was a sad day for Pat. But like all aviators, he had seen many die testing and stunting in Aeroplanes. It was part of the business. Two years before his instructor from Pullman, Andrew Drew had died in a crash in Ohio.

Pat figured he would look up Agnes another time.

Two weeks after Lincoln Beachey crashed his stunt plane into the San Francisco Bay, Pat O'Brien was walking down Market Street heading for the Sheridan Building. As he often did, Pat was reading at the same time – this time it was the morning's editorial page.

Oakland Tribune – April 1, 1915

"The direct cause of the mishap which resulted in the death of Lincoln Beachey was the same spirit that ruled at Rome in the time of Nero. A public, thirsting for novelty and the desire for "thrills," has not been sufficiently entertained by exhibitions of flight through the air; it has demanded that the performance be accompanied by hazardous variations.

Before the public consents to be interested there must be "loop the loops," "death dips" and other incidents of a hair-raising kind. Beachey is only one of many victims of this craze to see somebody do a hazardous thing. It may be that civilization may some day reach a point where normal and wholesome things will satisfy the human appetite. But that day is not yet."

Beachey's memorial service and funeral was one of the biggest the city of San Francisco had seen to that time.

The Mayor of San Francisco, James Rolph, presided over the matter, and Beachey was buried at the Cypress Lawn Memorial Park. The reaction to the death of Beachey was a far cry from how the boys at Cicero Field were remembered. When test pilots died, recognition went no farther than the crew below who witnessed the horror.

As it was, Pat O'Brien never had an interest in the show aspects of flying. It was the art, science, and personal thrill that possessed him. Surely, the inspiration of Chanute himself molded Pat's relationship with the aeroplane. During his time in Richmond, Pat developed as a technical flyer. He was a pilot that understood his machine and an aviator in the spirit of aviation's earliest pioneers who flew for the love of flying.

Though Agnes had missed Beachey's final tragic decent, the Exhibition was still on through the summer of 1915 and Pat had promised to escort her to the flying field to watch the daredevils fly. As he folded up his paper tucking it under his arm, he skipped up onto the steps of the Sheridan Building accelerating with youthful double-time before entering the big brass doors of the building.

"Pat!" It was Agnes standing in the lobby. She and Pat had agreed to meet in her building even though Thursday was her day off. Agnes lived in the Noe area southwest of downtown.

"Hello Agnes," said Pat. "You look very nice." She did, he thought. Agnes smiled and Pat extended his left arm which she took as they exited the downtown office building. They walked northeast to California Street where they jumped on a cable car heading west toward Presidio.

"So, how do you get to your office each day, Agnes? And where do you live?" said Pat trying to start the conversation.

"Well, San Francisco is a very modern city and the cable car runs right by my apartment in Noe Valley. I only have to make one switch and it doesn't take too long," She said.

"I find the city to be so stimulating" said Pat. Then after a pause, "Agnes, if you saw the little town I came from you'd see why. Even though it's small, it has an urban flavor to it and of course it's close to Chicago. It's called Momence. Another pause. "My mother is there." Then in a more upbeat tone exclaimed, "Now Chicago! There's one turned-out town!"

"I've never been out of California. But I like San Francisco. It feels like home," she said.

Their idle chatter continued all the way to Divisadero Street where they switched trolleys, headed north to the Bay Shore, and arrived at Mason Street entering the fair through the eastern most entrance.

The Exhibition was more than a person could view in one day. The grounds were along the San Francisco Bay about 8 city blocks wide and twenty-four blocks long. Just inside the park was Fort Mason. The piers and sheds of Lower Fort Mason were built in 1912 and warehoused army supplies and provided docking space for army transport ships. Fort Mason was the primary point of embarkation for the Army on the west coast.

It was early morning so Pat and Agnes decided to spend time walking through the grounds to the airfield, stopping at a number of interesting exhibits along the way. Just past Fort Mason, was the automobile exhibit, the Panama Canal exhibit and behind that, the huge Southern Pacific Railroad exhibition. Pat was drawn to all three then realized he had dominated choices, thus far.

"What would you like to see Agnes?" he said, a little embarrassed.

"I've enjoyed these very much, Pat," perceiving his sudden concern. "I'd like to see the gardens, though" she said pointing to the map in her hand. Pat agreed and they proceeded to view exhibits more to the liking of a female. They walked through the horticultural, fine arts and food palaces. They then passed through country exhibits from around the world before finally arriving at the grandstands about noon where flying exhibitions were about to begin. The grandstands were along a one mile race track. The drill ground and aviation field were at the west end of the infield, an athletic area was in the center with a polo field on the eastern end.

"Would you like a sandwich and some lemonade, Agnes?" he asked. "I'm famished!"

"Yes, that sounds nice," Agnes answered, continuing her agreeable and pleasant ways. As Pat turned to the wagon vendor behind him, Agnes looked at him and smiled. "He's a sweet guy," she thought.

The two had their lunch in the grandstands and watched numerous pilots spin, loop, and race through the skies of San Francisco Bay. Agnes marveled at Pat's knowledge of flying and particularly his passion for it. He seemed to know each plane, each pilot, and each move they would make before they made it. They both had a wonderful afternoon and their cordial first date quickly evolved into a relaxed time complete with laughter and light ribbing of each other over such trivial matters that only two young courters find funny.

Pat was likely the only person in the grandstands that day studying the skills of each pilot. Everyone else winced, gaped, and shrieked in reaction to the near death experience of stunt flying. Agnes recognized this as she sat next to Pat watching the show at Presidio.

Pat would look up pointing and explaining all that was occurring in the skies above them, thinking Agnes was looking up the whole time, as well. But Agnes was looking at Pat. She watched his eyes. She watched his hands. She heard his voice. She studied his strong manly profile and for the most part, she did not breathe. She saw the passion and deep connection between Pat and those noisy machines overhead.

It is often in those instances when women see the worldly passions of their men that they fall in love. Some women love them for it. Others compete against it. Agnes immediately wanted to embrace it because it was Pat. Agnes fell in love with Pat on that day for what was inside him and for all those other jumbled emotions that sweep away young lovers when cupid calls.

Once the flying was finished they walked a bit west into the great military reservation of Presidio where competitive drills and army maneuvers were taking place. Pat was taken by the scale and precision of what he saw. Though he certainly knew of his father's, uncle's and grandfather's record in the military, it was the first time he had really been around troops in his life. He found it exhilarating. Agnes enjoyed the marching and military music.

The sun soon set on the young couple's day. After enjoying a dinner of beef and spicy Mexican tortillas on the Fairgrounds, they settled at one of the most popular and beautiful features of the Exposition. It was the electrical illumination, an entirely new system of flood lighting. It created a soft, restful, yet perfect light near the courts each night, revealing the facades and walls of the palaces. The natural colors of the shrubbery and flowers illuminated gave an effect as bright and soft as daylight. As Pat O'Brien and Agnes MacMillan sat and talked as young twenty-four-year-olds do, Pat reached out and held the hand of Agnes as the band played "Hello Frisco" which was the great musical chart-topper of the day.

The day ended with a long leisurely walk down the same route they had needed a trolley to traverse that morning. In no time, or so it seemed to these two enthralled conversationalists, they were back at Agnes' building and walked one additional block to the trolley stop connecting to Noe Valley. As they stood face to face holding hands, Pat stopped talking, lowered his head to the side of Agnes's left cheek, and kissed her with some length. Though it was just on her cheek, it was given with affection and care. It had a heartfelt quality but possessed a subtle and respectful reserve, thought Agnes. Agnes' hands involuntarily squeezed his as a lightning bolt of excitement rushed through her.

As the summer advanced, Pat and Agnes returned to the fair once more. They met Pat's friends at the Ivy frequently and attended the Dreamland Rink near Fillmore Street. There were seven movie theaters lining eight blocks on Fillmore and early vaudevillian acts were starting to appear. Fillmore was an area uniquely spared during the 1906 earthquake and was a hotbed for entertainment in 1915.

Pat and Agnes were considered a couple and were regularly seen together in the Bay area where young people met to enjoy the excitement of a bubbling metropolis. Agnes had moved from publishing to a retail cosmetic shop in the central city where she grew in sophistication and beauty. They were an attractive couple and seemed to fit like a glove. The Fair and the young optimism of young people like Pat and Agnes were lifting the pall that had hung over the Bay since the great quake of 1906.

[182]

By August, most of the local San Franciscans had seen the fair. Crowds now were mostly travelers who continued to swell the city's population for the rest of 1915. But in August of 1915, local San Francisco residents were stunned by the tragedy involving General John J. Pershing, once head of military operations at Presidio.

Since late 1914, Pershing had led several small expeditions into Mexico to quell border skirmishes along the Mexican-United States border. Now stationed at Fort Bliss, Texas, Pershing decided to move his family there to be near them more often. The arrangements were almost complete, when on the morning of August 27, 1915 he received a telegram telling him of a tragic fire at Presidio. The lacquered floor of their Queen Anne home had caught fire and rapidly spread, resulting in the smoke inhalation deaths of his wife, Helen, and three young daughters. Only his six-year-old son Warren was saved.

Many who knew Pershing said he never recovered from their deaths. After the funerals at Lakeview Cemetery in Cheyenne, Wyoming, Pershing returned to Fort Bliss with his son, Warren, and his sister Mae. Filled with grief, he turned all of his attention to his work.

Pat O'Brien, like many local San Francisco residents, was particularly saddened by the tragic events. It made him think of his young brother Forest for the first time in years. Pat had spent increasing time near the military base at Presidio. He spoke to soldiers, watched them drill. He talked flying with them, as well, and learned that the British, French, and Germans were seriously engaged in flying for war at a sophisticated level.

Clearly, the latest innovations in aviation were now occurring in Europe. He was startled at the advancements of aircraft there that he learned from a few officers at Presidio who followed the war. He knew the future of flying would now be in the military.

On Sunday morning, January 9, 1916, Pat and Agnes were having a breakfast at the Noe Valley Bakery, in Agnes' neighborhood. Pat had asked Agnes to meet him there and Agnes suspected the worse. Pat hardly ever came to Noe and why, she thought, would he have such an interest in breakfast early on Sunday. Perhaps he plans to propose, she thought. What if he has found another woman, she fretted.

"Joe Cato tells me he's moving," Pat said looking down, rearranging his eggs and potatoes with the tip of his fork.

"Yes?" she said, blending the brown sugar into her oatmeal.

Pat handed her a letter he had received from Cato over Christmas. Joe Cato had joined the Sloane Aeroplane Company, Bound Brook, N. J. This company was owned by John Eyre Sloane, who was Thomas Edison's son-in-law. The Sloane Company was financed by Edison himself. Flying was becoming big business now and Joe Cato had dozens of underlings doing his old job. He needed more experienced flyers like Pat O'Brien. The letter invited Pat to join him.

Agnes read the letter from Joe Cato in silence while Pat dove into his steaming breakfast. As Agnes read Cato's letter and felt tears swelling up in her eyes, Pat spoke without looking up.

"Seems with hardly any air shows around and the big push to build planes for the army and Europeans, everyone is chasing the new money. I mean, Agnes, I've moved up as far as I can at the railroad and of course you know how much I want to fly."

"You're going to New York?" Agnes uttered raising her eyes to meet his.

"No!" Pat seemed surprised. "I'm going to San Diego," was Pat's response.

"San Diego! Whatever for, Pat! " she said a bit louder now and startled by this.

"To join the Signal Corps," Pat responded. He thought it to be terribly obvious from the letter, thinking Agnes would take it better knowing he was still on the west coast.

"Look Agnes, flying is about to wear an Army uniform! The military is where aviation is going, Agnes. It's just starting here in the States but the Europeans are way ahead of us and the U.S. has to catch up. After all, we invented flying and now our military needs experienced men like me and others to show them what planes can really do! The old officers today have no idea how aviation is the future of war."

Agnes saw the passion in Pat's face once again and was struck by how little he mentioned what she felt was the more important implication of all this, namely, their relationship. But then, what claim did she have, she thought? Had he given her his word to marry? They had hardly spoken of an engagement. Was she being a fool, here? No, they both had discussed how fond they were of each other. Her head was spinning. She struggled to speak and Pat clearly could see she was upset.

"I'm sorry, Agnes. I didn't mean to upset you," he said, suddenly dislodged from his mood of excitement. "It's just that this is my chance to finally be more than a test pilot." He was gaining confidence in his rationale.

"I know Pat," said Agnes, "It's just such a worry thinking of you going away to the Army, not knowing when you might return or what dangers you will encounter. I understand you have to see this through. It's what you've dreamed of for so many years."

Agnes was sincere about her wanting to support Pat. No woman is ever happy hearing such news. No man speaks it knowing why the passions for adventure sweep over him in the face of affection. But the rumbling in Europe created a stream of passion that, like all young men, Pat could not resist.

The two finished breakfast and exchanged feelings in soft, gentle, and loving tones. There were long pauses and expressions that emanated from the very bottom of their souls. Pat knew that his opportunity was now. Agnes knew desires would need to be put aside.

It was not the first time a young lady was told good bye by a young man going off to war. But Agnes MacMillan felt like the first.

PART FOUR

FLIGHT

Chapter 17

Signal Corps

From his many chats with the Presidio boys, Pat knew that the only place to fly Aeroplanes in the American military was with the Army Signal Corps. When the Wright Brothers, Glenn Curtiss and others began selling their planes to the military, the Army chose the Signal Corps to develop these new weapons of war. Before planes, the Corps was flying balloons in reconnaissance missions to aid ground Troops. But within the Signal Corps itself, only few officers saw the need to use planes for combat. Still, the Signal Corps was Pat's best opportunity to continue flying.

As an enlistee with flying experience, he was assigned to basic training at Fort Sill, Oklahoma for six weeks. From there he would move on to North Island in San Diego. North Island was home to the Curtiss School of Flying. Beachey had trained there and Glenn Curtiss was under contract with the Army to train the small number of Army Signal Corps volunteers interested in the new machines of war. Using Curtiss provided the U.S. military with a training program already in existence and the time they needed to develop an aviation division.

On the day Pat traveled south to Fort Sill to be introduced to war, it had already been introduced to nearly 30 million soldiers on the European continent. After only eighteen months of bloodshed, Europe was deadlocked along a series of back-and-forth trenches that moved ten yards at a time in alternating directions.

Little did Pat know that while the U.S. Army Signal Corps was struggling to get six air craft to fly consistently, the Imperial War Office of England had just allocated $250,000,000 to build Aeroplanes for the Royal Air Force. The loss of planes and British-born personnel in the first two years of the war had the RAF looking to Canada to fill the need for new fresh pilots. Pat was unaware of what was developing in Canada. As far as he knew, the U.S. Army Signal Corps was his only opportunity to fly in the military.

The British and French were getting chewed up by German Ace Max Immelmann and other Hun pilots who had recently stolen the technology from England to shoot machines guns through propellers. Britain was reeling from what was being called the Fokker Scourge named for the famous Dutch aircraft designer who worked for the Germans after being rejected by the Brits.

It was the British who made it a practice of referring to the German enemy as "Hun." The original Hun went back centuries and was part of the long passed formation of the German race. But during the Great War, the Allies found it an appropriate derogatory term that inspired the troops and caught the fancy of the general population.

At the start of 1916, the need for fresh pilots and ground troops was so chronic that Canada's Prime Minister promised the King of England a half million men, despite Canada's population being only 8 million people. At the time, Canada was fully under British rule and Britain was running out of Fly Boys.

On February 1, 1916, twenty-five year old Pat O'Brien stepped on to the station platform at Richmond, California holding the hand of his girl. He was heading for basic training at Fort Sill, Oklahoma to begin learning about war. To the strangers milling about, his long embrace of Agnes MacMillan looked like any other young man simply kissing his gal goodbye on his way to work. No one would have suspected he was off to war. Americans had not yet marshaled it's young for the battlefields of Europe. But that day was coming.

"Good bye, Agnes," said Pat as he looked down into Agnes' teary eyes. "Basic training will be over quickly - then flight school - and I'll be home on leave right after that." How many times in history had a young man spoken those words to his sweetheart? It mattered little to Agnes. It was the first for her. She let her arms go free in a surrendering way as Pat gave her one last passionate kiss. She was exasperated over his departure.

Pat picked up his bag, flashed his patented smile, turned and walked up the platform to board the awaiting train. Agnes watched his confident gate as he walked from her, hoping he'd look back one more time. He did not. Then, after showing the conductor his ticket, he turned and gave Agnes a huge sweeping wave of his right arm crossing left to right over his strong physique. Pat's smile beamed and drove a painful lance through her heart. He stepped up and was gone. A loud burst of steam wafted over the platform and Agnes closed her eyes in sad disbelief.

Finding his seat in the second car, Pat extended his long frame upward, placing a bag in the luggage rack above his seat. The car was about half full so he tossed two books and a copy of Stars and Stripes into the window seat. The train suddenly jolted forward causing the heads of passengers to jar back and then forward again. Pat was still standing and quickly grasped the overhead luggage rack to keep from falling.

Once the train was stable he took his seat on the aisle and opened the military "rag" to read the latest reports on the war in Europe. He had purchased the magazine at Presidio the day before. It contained plenty of news about the war in Europe and this particular edition also featured an article on the latest efforts of the Signal Corps to adapt aviation. His concentration was locked and did not stop reading for fifty miles.

"America is the one country capable of relieving Europe of such crap," he thought. His reaction to Europe's folly was common among Americans at the time. Domestic and foreign challenges provoked American's "Yankee can do" spirit. This attitude had begun to assert itself at the end of the 19th Century as Americans shed the divisions of the Civil War. Determination would eventually carry American troops into the European conflict. But it would evaporate in the hearts of many individual soldiers waiting for a November armistice on the muddy moonscape of Europe's "no-man's-land" in 1918.

Pat's train rolled south to an Army hardly embracing aviation as a weapon. But Pat O'Brien was a ball of energy. Europe was way ahead of the United States in 1916. War was stimulating demand in Europe and therefore, innovation. Germany, France and Britain were in a battle to develop superior advantage in the air. The Europeans were no longer adapting Aeroplanes for war. Their planes were built for war. It was the cutthroat competition among German designers, engineers and manufacturers that was producing superior machines in 1916 and wreaking havoc on the Allied forces. Pat knew that American aviation was not ready. He also knew that aviation would be required to turn the tide. Most of the current U.S. Army brass viewed planes as toys.

Pat lifted his eyes for the first time since pulling out of the Richmond Station. He stared off at the hills in the distance and thought about Agnes and Richmond and his buddies back at the Ivy Inn. A broad grin flashed across his face before he was interrupted.

"Mr. O'Brien?" said a man in a blue uniform. "Yes?" Pat replied.

"Are you Pat O'Brien?"

"Why yes," said Pat setting down his newspaper.

"Well Sir, I'm Charles Lundquist. I'm the conductor on today's run," stated the portly man extending his hand. Pat extended his hand with a big smile.

"Glad to meet you Mr. Lundquist," said Pat.

"We received a note from your old supervisor at the Santa Fe...a Mister... uh...Pearl?'

"Chuck Pearl!" Pat exclaimed. "Well, I'll be damned. Chuck Pearl sent me a note?"

"No sir. Not exactly, sir," said the formal rotund man. "He sent a note to our Engineer. Told us to make sure you had a comfortable trip. So Mr. Goggins, our Engineer, asked that I extend an invitation to you to have meals in the diner car at no charge." He handed a note to Pat. It was handwritten by Goggins on railroad stationary inviting Pat to partake of the diner car as a guest of the California Southern.

"Well thank you very much, Mr. Lundquist," said Pat. "That's very nice of you."

"Not me, Sir. You can thank the California Southern," he said with pride.

Pat grabbed his magazine and two books and headed for the diner car. Passengers were generally preoccupied with either the view out the window or a variety of reading materials. There were businessmen, a group of laborers playing cards, a few ladies in large hats and one or two families. Pat nodded with a smile to those that looked up as he passed.

He arrived at the diner car and took a seat at an empty table in the middle of the car. Setting his books and newspaper to the right he ordered coffee and a Danish from the waiter, then reached into his pocket for change, forgetting for just a moment that his food was on the house. He felt 5 die in his pocket, pulled them out, looked at them then smiled.

Pat first learned craps for his grandfather Perry Hathaway, picked it up again in Cody, Wyoming and on daily runs between Richmond and Stockton, he and Charles Pearl played craps during mundane runs. Placing the five die back in his pocket, he reached into his inner coat pocket and pulled out a packet of information received from the Army.

His paperwork listed activities at Fort Sill and North Island where he would attend flight school. There was a small amount of information about aviation including an official letter from the head of the flight initiative in the Signal Corps, Captain Benjamin D. Foulois. Foulois was the one officer in the United States Army who was convinced that the aeroplane would change the outcome of the war.

During the summer of 1915, before anyone in the Army ever thought that someday Aeroplanes might need runways, Captain Foulois' First Aero Squadron moved onto what was then just a relatively open sand-gravel desert. They unloaded their trucks and set up what they called an aerodrome at Fort Sill, Oklahoma. Foulois and his squadron pitched canvas hangars next to canvas living quarters then moved canvas Aeroplanes inside. They dodged coon-tail rattlers, ate sand in their beans, cursed their wood-and-wire flying machines and coaxed them into the air from time to time only to have the Curtiss JN-3 "Jenny" aircraft balk at the dryness, the heat and the wind. The First Aero Squadron had an ominous beginning. But Foulois was determined to bring aviation to the U.S. Military.

Captain Foulois, who would eventually become a brigadier general, was the first Army officer to fly a dirigible and the first officer to fly an aeroplane. He taught himself. The Army had ordered him to Fort Sam Houston, Texas with the Signal Corps aeroplane No. 1 to teach himself to fly. He was told to bring "plenty of spare parts." In that first machine he experienced his first takeoff, first solo flight, first landing and first crackup. His instructions consisted of letters sent from the Wright brothers whenever he wrote them for advice.

Most high ranking Army officers viewed planes as a curiosity or at most "something we should study." Upon seeing his first aeroplane arrive at Fort Sam Houston, the head commander told his officers, "Turn off those fans. They're scaring the horses!" Indeed, Calvary men that volunteered to fly Aeroplanes were still required to wear their spurs in flight in the beginning.

The rather academic endorsement of military aviation, along with the fact the all aircraft development was still left to private citizens like Joe Cato and small companies like the Curtiss Company, stunted military aviation development in the U.S. military. Foulois was a genuine enthusiast, however. He was one of the few officers that knew how to fly and he expected his officers to do the same. Pat saw this as hopeful.

"Hell, with my experience at Cicero Field and California, I've probably got more hands-on flying time than most of the U.S. Military officers," Pat thought. He couldn't decide at first if this would be a positive or negative for him. He'd wait and see how things looked once he got to flight school but he felt confident that he could bring something to the effort.

Pat knew from information he had read before enlisting that The United States military was easily five years behind. As he pored over the aviation article in his copy of Stars and Stripes, he learned that the Signal Corps was still struggling to establish a consistent force.

The U.S. Army didn't test its first Aeroplane until 1908. Ironically, the Wright brothers built the plane and it crashed during the test for the Army, killing Lt. Thomas Selfridge and injuring Orville Wright. The Wrights spent the next ten months making improvements. On July 30, 1909, a modified plane was ready for approval. Orville Wright and Captain Benjamin D. Foulois tested the aircraft. Wright piloted and Foulois flew as observer. The plane was approved. In July of 1914, the Aviation Section of the U.S. Army Signal Corps was created and Foulois was put in charge.

Beginning in August 1915, a mere six months before Pat enlisted, the 1st Aero Squadron was at Fort Sill, Oklahoma, training at the Field Artillery School with eight newly-delivered Curtiss JN-2s. After a fatal crash on August 12, the pilots of the squadron met with squadron commander Foulois and declared the JN-2 unsafe because of low power, shoddy construction, lack of stability, and overly sensitive rudders. Foulois and Capt. Thomas D. Milling disagreed, and the JN-2 remained operational until a second crashed on September 5. The aircraft were grounded until October 14, when conversions of the JN-2s to the newer JN-3 began. Two copies of the conversions were received by the squadron in early September.

Pat finished reading, took one final sip of coffee and then returned to his seat. He decided to sleep a while but just before he closed his eyes he heard the conductor call out, "Bakersfield!" He knew the train would now turn east and head across Arizona, New Mexico, The Texas panhandle, and on to Oklahoma City, his final rail stop.

The entire trip was about sixteen-hundred miles. During the day he was able to enjoy views of the desert, play cards with the group of laborers on board and in turn teach them craps. At night the accommodations for sleeping were quite comfortable in the all-steel sleeper made by the famous Pullman Company of Chicago. Pat had noticed a brass tag on the side of his seat that read "Pullman." He recalled his days jumping cars with Gus on his way to explore the Dunes or connect to the city. The route from Momence to downtown always took him past Pullman at 103rd street. And of course, the name Pullman always reminded him of his first days learning to fly planes at West Pullman. Though no railcars were made there, it was founded by Pullman workers who had grown tired of George Pullman's factory commune requirements.

On his final day traveling, Pat had dozed off in his seat after a hearty breakfast. Half asleep, he felt the engineer begin to back down the train as they approached Oklahoma City and he opened his eyes staring up at the luggage rack. Pat's leg had fallen asleep so he reached up and grabbed the luggage rack and pulled himself up out of the seat shaking his right leg.

"Pretty solid," he thought. Indeed the luggage rack was weighted down with chests and suitcases yet gave little when Pat pulled himself out of his seat. He gave his right leg a quick massage to get the blood flowing again, began organizing his belongings then felt the last squeal of brakes gave way. On his way out he thanked Lundquist for the accommodations and asked if he might pass along his gratitude to Engineer Goggins.

As Pat made his way down the platform, an orderly was calling his name.

"I'm Pat O'Brien," he said to the tidy looking young sergeant holding a clip board.

"Come with me," he said.

"Welcome to the Army!" Pat thought to himself.

When Pat entered boot camp at Fort Sill, the entire U.S. Aviation Section of the Army had 46 officers, of which only 23 were pilots, and 243 enlisted men with only eight pilots among them. Pat O'Brien would become the ninth. He was likely one of the most experienced pilots in the force before his training even began. For the next six weeks, however, he would experience an element of war making that the Army understood quite well – basic training.

As the bus pulled into Fort Sill Pat could hear the frantic activity of a training camp preparing for war. "Yer-lep......Yer-lep.....Yer-lep, right....Lep," shouted the distant drill sergeant into the left ear of a willing but frightened would-be doughboy. The recruit's feet were at odds with the majority of his squad parading away in the distance.

Once they exited the transport all fourteen new candidates, including Pat O'Brien, destined for flight school at North Island, San Diego, stood against the late afternoon sun each tightly grasping a gig bag that rested aside their leg. Their right arm was at their side and none of the men wore hats. Pat heard the driver put his bus in gear and pull away behind him heading back to Oklahoma City for tomorrow's run of recruits from the train station. He knew that civilian life was behind him now.

"You scraps are meat to me and it doesn't matter if you're off to fly Aeroplanes after your time here or metamorphosing into General John J Pershing himself! To me you're not worth much more than the remains of an overly pastured cow! At this point you're about as worthless as a stupid cow eating hay. But I'm going to change all that," stated Captain Daniel McGintney, facing the men, his back to the sun.

[195]

"Well this goofy ass sure has a way with words, don't he?" thought Pat as he stared at the sun's glare on the horizon.

McGintney would regularly serve up some meaningless gibberish to his new recruits. But it was the way he said it that somehow felt insulting to all those that heard him. He was a skilled manipulator. Pat, being older than the others, took it in stride and understood the motivation of Captain Dan. He could not really see McGintney's face because the Captain's silhouette was placed squarely in line with the sun.

"Well, it's all the better I can't see the man's face," Pat thought. "I wonder if he has a face!" Pat fought the temptation to smile at his own humor. Like all others entering boot camp, the only humor possible amid the heat of the day in the face of Sergeant McGintney was whatever lived in one's mind. Pat was never short on humor even if confined to his imagination. It was an Irish and O'Brien trait that made life easier to absorb. It was obvious to even the youngest recruit that whatever was viewed as hilarious should never be displayed on one's mug. A successful camp in the eyes of the Army would mean that humor too would leave the consciousness of all fourteen new recruits within the week. Very few maintained it. Pat was the exception.

Pat O'Brien's new "friend" continued his oration.

"You've got three minutes to ditch those lacy bags of yours in your barracks at the foot of your bunk, fully opened, so that my orderly can dig through each bag and remove the female dress clothes from your possession and outfit you with proper Army issue. Upon depositing your bags, you will strip down to your skivvies and assemble outside your barracks for our little run to the cattle barn." The "cattle barn" as it was called was where the camp executed mandatory physical exams. "You, my fine young ladies, are the cattle. You've got three minutes."

And so went typical Army indoctrination.

There was a five second pause, silence and then McGintney shouted, "What are you waiting for ladies!" upon which the fourteen bolted for their barracks, having lost a valuable five seconds in the pursuit of their next deadline. Seconds would instantly become the time of measure for six more weeks and each man would learn to time his day in small succinct, action-filled seconds. It was critical to all war-time decision making. In war, seconds count and are a matter of life and death. It was a concept drilled into trainees from the moment they set foot in camp.

Pat would spend every day in training like any other Army recruit. The only consolation to his group of fourteen was that all but two were destined for flight school at San Diego. Two were scheduled for radar school but they would all experience military boot camp together as a means of forming squadron unity literally from the ground up.

As the weeks passed, basic combat training and individual training became the focus of each day. There was plenty of marching, rifle range, tactics, and weaponry and army regulations to learn. There was a lot of conditioning including wall climbing, rope swing, close combat, pull ups, pushups, and more pushups. And there was running, miles and miles of running.

Pat's days on the railroad served him well. He was clearly one of the stronger and best conditioned of the group and this added to his aura as a leader and a risk taker. The men looked up to Pat just like the quarry gang back at Momence had and the chums at the Ivy Inn. He was well respected and a natural leader.

In the final week of boot camp, Pat and his fellow recruits were still doing the one routine that had not changed since day one. They were taking their morning run. Pat, while strong and in good shape, added a good degree of stamina to his condition since his arrival. The recruits were running up to ten miles each day and Pat felt as strong as ever. He hadn't run this much since his youthful days in Momence. On their last day, Pat and the other fourteen were running again - this time for fifteen miles.

"Did you hear about 1st Aero, Pat?" said Phil Dodd as the two men ran side-by-side just before sunrise. Phil had heard about The 1st Aero Squadron making the first sortie in the history of U.S. Army aviation supporting Pershing's Mexico campaign.

"No, what?" said Pat.

"They were a total bust! Foulois had them flying into Mexico at night for Christ's sake! He's really crazy. Only one plane got close. They're spotting for Pershing."

'Yah, Yah, I know!" said Pat as the two went into their first turn.

"You know Pershing. He wanted them there at a certain time and that meant night." said the experienced flyer. "Man! Obrien, what have we gotten ourselves into?"

Dodd, who was from the east coast, had previous flying experience before entering the Signal Corps, like Pat. The two met on the bus ride into camp six weeks earlier and were bunk mates during camp. Their common experience flying outside the military created a natural bond between the two men.

"What were they flying?" Pat asked, setting the pace for the pack of runners.

"Hell, it wouldn't matter would it?" retorted Dodd. "I mean they hardly have maps of the damn country and understand it was cloudy so the stars didn't even help them.

"Oh, Christ!" Pat said with a laugh. "You can't find your way in a country like that at night with no stars as a guide."

"But that wasn't really their biggest problem!" he stated catching his breath in between words as the two men picked up the pace.

"Like I said, what were they flying?" Pat asked.

"Well, you know. I heard they had two JN2's and some "threes" and a few N8's but as you know the N8 ain't worth a shit either," laughing then coughing a bit as the men hit the three mile mark.

"Yeah, Foulois has his hands tied. He's good leader and has the right vision. He just needs planes and Curtiss isn't making them good enough," said Pat. "I mean the Europeans are so far ahead of us it's alarming. We're not ready to join that war yet Dodd!" he said. "What good is it if they recruit experienced pilots like you and me and then give us crap to fly?"

Dodd went into detail how the first reconnaissance mission of the United States Army Signal Corps one week earlier had been an operational failure.

The 1st Aero Squadron flew mostly Curtiss planes on the mission from Columbus, New Mexico into Mexico. They were supporting General Pershing's Punitive Expedition to retaliate against Poncho Villa by reporting the location of the enemy. Villa had attacked the 13th Calvary at Columbus on March 9 and Foulois, under orders from General Pershing, had planes, trucks, and crew shipped by rail from Fort Sam Houston where the 1st Aero Squadron was based at the time. The squadron performed all pre-flight preparations and assembled the planes, launching their mission seven days later on March 16. Of the eight planes, only one got significantly into Mexico. Poor maps, seven different compasses, and darkness caused six planes to turn back. One plane crashed on take-off.

Since the "raid" of March 9th, the efforts of the 1st Aero Squadron continued to have problems, most notably the poor quality of their first air machines. The Curtiss "Jennys," as they were called could not climb over the 10,000 to 12,000 foot Sierra Madre Mountains surrounding enemy Troops as requested by Pershing. High winds and dust storms frequently grounded the "Jennys" during the Mexican Expedition which would continue through August. While the campaign appeared to be a disaster in one sense, it marked a turning point in U.S. military aviation. It was the first time ever that an American tactical air unit would be tested in the field under combat conditions.

Twice Foulois' pilots would bring objections to him about the safety of the planes and request they be grounded. Following the first fatal crash, Foulois refused to ground the planes. When a second fatality occurred six weeks later, he was forced to do so.

What was ominous to Pat O'Brien and his running mate Phil Dodd was that these inadequate planes were shipped off to the Army Signal Corp Aviation Training School on North Island, San Diego. That was Pat's next assignment and he wasn't feeling confident. Dodd was somewhat panicked. Both men knew machines and knew the limitations of every model.

There was no break between basic training and flight school so Pat did not have the opportunity to visit Agnes between assignments. Camp ended on Friday and the new pilots were to report to North Island on Monday morning. Before boarding at the Oklahoma station, Pat dropped a letter in the mail to Agnes explaining his unexpected timeline.

On the train from Fort Sill to San Diego, Pat felt part of something he had not experienced his entire life. As he flipped through a magazine on the Troops train somewhere in western Texas, he glanced down at the stitching and buttons of his military issued uniform. For the first time, Pat O'Brien felt part of something. He felt part of something bigger than himself. It was not the same as the old gang at Momence. It was more than the collection of test pilots at Stockton. It meant more to him than even the old gang at the Ivy. He felt pride for the first time with basic training at Fort Sill now behind him. He felt American for the first time. In a sense, the boy who lost his father at age eleven and left home to earn his keep at 15 had found a family once again.

Suddenly the laughter of his fellow flight school chums broke his isolated thoughts about life in the service. He glanced at Rogers, Smith, and Luther Streck, jostling four seats ahead of him as the train chugged west toward California. Dodd was sleeping in the seat across the aisle from Pat. The rowdy bunch was playing a game of quickness where one man would see if he could remove the hat of the other before the other could remove it himself. He took a second to watch their sophomoric antics, smiled then returned to his magazine. After a few minutes, he went over a sat among them.

"All right, all right gentleman, who wants to participate in a real game of chance?" said Pat pulling the five dice from his coat pocket.

The assemblage of would-be aces all removed their hats in sync with a cacophony of approval and enthusiasm. Luther grabbed the serving tray from the porter's drop table which served as a more than adequate dice table. And the game was on.

Pat held up the dice in his right hand and spoke in a humorous, pompous tone.

"This randomizing device, my fellow pilots is the only true contrivances of the purest form designed exclusively to legally allow me to take your money!" Pat emphasized the end of his speech as he threw down his first venture. Dodd heard the commotion and joined the aggregation.

The young men swirled in a joyful cluster of fun, friendship and their favorite game of chance. A middle-aged woman was dutifully knitting from her window a number of seats back of the brood. The revelry attracted her attention. Lifting her eyes, not missing a stitch, she smiled at the youthful future pilots admiring their zeal and freshness before returning to her busy hands.

Miles of desert landscape passed but went unnoticed by Pat and his band of gambling enthusiasts. As darkness fell, the men shifted to a slightly quieter activity and dealt poker hands until 1:00 a.m. by flashlight. When their youthful energy finally faded, each man stretched across an empty seat rather than retire to the sleeping car on this night.

Pat was still awake peering out the window. Illuminated by a sky full of stars and the month's full moon, cacti with human-like form drifted into Pat's view in the shale-grey night. The desert plant seemed to be waving goodbye in an uncanny way, he thought. Pat felt Momence, Cody, Richmond, and everything in his past pulling away behind him. Closing his eyes, he thought to himself, "Trains - seems like I've been on a train my whole life." He then thought of Agnes, the Ivy, then Elmer, then Al, his father lying in bed on his dying day, then Margaret at Christmas, then baby Forest. He then drifted off to sleep.

He passed through Amarillo and Albuquerque, and could now feel the new southward trajectory at Flagstaff as the Santa Fe line pushed toward San Diego. The rising sun lanced his eyes and woke him fully as he turned on his right side away from the bright sun. It was 6:00 a.m.

Being a railroad man, he could feel the strain and release of an engine passing over varying terrain. He could also tell how fast or slow the train was traveling as any veteran of the railroad would know. Around seven a.m., the irregular rhythm of the Santa Fe stirred Pat's conscious thoughts and he sensed they were approaching their final stop.

"Today," he thought, "I'll see my first aircraft in nearly two months."

Chapter 18

Pack up Your Troubles

"Are you O'Brien?" said Bill Rickey holding a clip board as Pat bent down to pick up his bags.

"Yes, I'm O'Brien, what can I do for you?"

"Private Rickey," said the somewhat fidgety German-American, extending his hand.

"Glad to meet you," said Pat shaking the man's hand.

"I'm looking for a Private Dodd also. Private Phil Dodd? Do you know him?"

"Phil? Yeah, he's with me." Pat saw Dodd one car down looking for his bag amid a pile on the concrete walk.

"Phil!" yelled Pat to his army chum. Waving him his way, Pat continued, "This way!" he said waving a second time.

Dodd nodded, then turned back looking again for his bag. He found it and headed up the walkway. Rickey was talking to Pat about the trip from Sill as they waited.

"What's up?" Phil Dodd asked as he approached a little out of breath.

"We're going with Bill here," said Pat. "Bill Rickey, meet Phil Dodd. Looks like we've got a personal escort Phil," Pat said with a broad smile while flinging his book sack over his right shoulder.

The three men turned and walked toward the rear end of the train where Rickey had a truck waiting to take the men to North Island. There was flurry of activity at the new station. As they walked alongside the new Santa Fe Depot the talkative Rickey provided a bit of a local history. The depot had been completed in 1915 by the Atchison, Topeka, and Santa Fe Railway to accommodate visitors for the Panama-California Exposition held in conjunction with the San Francisco Fair at Presidio.

This was the same fair attended by Pat and Agnes. Pat thought of Beachey's crash and then Agnes flashed in his mind once again. As they walked up the platform, he looked at the clean structure admiringly. San Diego, he thought seemed pleasant and sunny.

They tossed their bags in the back of the roofless military truck. Pat climbed into the passenger seat in front and Phil Dodd jumped in back. As they pulled away, Bill Rickey explained his mission.

"As I said, O'Brien, I work for Captain F.J. Morrow at Signal H.Q. Well, it's not actually H.Q. but we call it that even though it ain't much more than a camp site, in fact."

Rickey was a rapid talker and the two new recruits leaned forward to better hear his report. As their truck sped up the road Rickey was shouting his story.

"So anyway, I'm to pick you two men up to report directly to the Lt. T.S. Bowen. That's Bowen from the 1st Aero," he said with an elevated voice. "You know Bowen, right?"

"Can't say we do Bill," said Pat, also shouting. "How are the other men getting to base?"

"The bus is taking them but I've got orders to meet you two fellas and get you to Bowen as soon you arrive," Rickey answered.

"Why's that?" asked Dodd.

"Heck if I know, you'll have to ask Bowen that question. I just follow orders. I've got you in my truck and we're ahead of the bus so I'm getting my job done," he said laughing. "Glad I found you so quickly."

"So who's this Morrow and Bowen?" asked Pat.

"Well Captain Morrow's my boss but Bowen's the guy you need to see. He's been assigned here from 1st Aero Squadron. Broke his nose and got banged up flying for Foulois out of New Mexico. Never made it to the border. He was trying to land his plane – Jenny's you know – piece of crap" Pat looked at Dodd with a regretful stare. Both men new that the plane Bowen ditched was an upgrade from the J2's that awaited Pat and Phil Dodd.

"Anyway, he was caught in a whirlwind and crashed from one hundred feet. The plane was completely wrecked, but Bowen escaped with a broken nose and a few scrapes. He's got a hell of a bandage across his face so when you meet him try not to focus on his nose!" advised the nervous driver.

"Crashed on his first sortie for Pershing! Boy, what a way to start your career," Dodd shouted from the back seat. "At Fort Sill the talk was that Foulois' mission was a bust!" said Dodd as Pat looked back at him and then back to Rickey.

"A Bust? Well, yeah I guess you could say that," said Rickey. "But you gotta understand. Just getting the chance to take such an order from Pershing and being asked to support a real campaign, hell that's big for us!" retorted Rickey, a man accustomed to saluting several times a day.

They turned onto the main road to North Island at Imperial Beach. North Island was not an island at all but a peninsula connected by the isthmus called the Silver Strand or "Strand" as locals called it. Pat could still see the damage left by heavy rains that had cause the Otay Dams to breach in January, sweeping away everything in the Otay Valley.

North Island lay in San Diego Bay. It was a flat, sandy island about four miles long and two miles wide with a number of good fields for land flights used in new pilot training. The beaches on both ocean and bay sides were good level stretches for starting or landing an Aeroplane. An old farm house served as headquarters and the hay barn had been converted to a hanger. The San Diego Aero Club had added two more canvas hangers for Curtiss back when he ran his school there and the Signal Corps was using them since the Curtiss stopped operating there in 1913. At the north end of the island opposite the old Curtiss school structures stood the official military structures.

Ricky went on to describe their base. "The hangers are only made with canvas and tarpaper. The wind blows them apart almost weekly," Rickey said while speeding down the dirt road onto the island base. Pat looked back at Dodd with a smile and raised brow only to see terror on Phil's face which made Pat laugh.

The truck arrived at headquarters and Rickey dropped the two men off. "Second floor, gentlemen. I'll watch your bags" he said. Pat and Phil double-timed it up the steps, then proceeded to the second floor were they saw a sign reading, "Aeronautical Training." They knocked and a firm voice invited them in.

"Private Pat O'Brien reporting as requested, sir," stated Pat as he came to attention before Lt. T. S Bowen. Phil Dodd repeated the official greeting and the two men stood at attention awaiting recognition, trying the whole time to avoid looking directly at Bowen's sizable bandage across his nose.

"At ease men," stated Lt. Bowen, flipping through a file on the two men before him. He was sitting informally on his desk with his left foot touching the floor and the opposite leg swung over the corner of his desk. "Sorry for my appearance men. You may have heard I got a little banged up chasing Pershing in Mexico a few weeks back.

"Yes sir!" the two men said in unison.

"I appreciate you coming directly to me upon your arrival. I've read your backgrounds and understand you both have extensive flying experience in civilian life," stated Bowen. The two men acknowledged the officer.

"Well, with your backgrounds, I plan to use you in the hands-on training. Most of the boys coming here have only flown two or three times, just enough to qualify for Signal Aviation," he said. He went on to inform them that his orders were to place both Pat and Phil Dodd in positions of leadership but with no higher pay. "Frankly men, there are so few experienced flyers in this new initiative, we've got to make do with anything we have," he said looking up at them both.

"Yes sir," said the two in unison.

He dismissed them and asked that they attend an instructor's breakfast the following morning at 06:00 where they would get an overview of the planned training curriculum for the latest new pilot candidates.

"Thank you, sir," stated both men who then saluted, turned and exited Bowens' office.

Once out of the building, Pat turned to Phil and said, "Finally, a chance to fly and show these boys what we can do, hey Phil?"

"Yeah, finally," Phil responded.

They were greeted again by Rickey who was standing by to help them get processed in before attending the first meeting of new recruits. Pat was interested in finding the men from Sill who were already moving into their barracks at the north end of the island.

"You fellas ready?" their cordial escort asked. "I'm going to get you settled in. Lots to do before school opens in the morning. How'd it go with Bowen?"

"Went fine, Bill," said Pat as they all three climbed aboard the same army issue truck.

Rickey drove them to the supply depot where the two men were issued all the required ordinance, medical and relevant quartermaster supplies. They proceeded to their assigned barracks where the other Fort Sill graduates were already moving in. The structures of the aviation school on North Island were temporary, the buildings consisting of a scattering array of huge sheds-like barracks. Floors were wood and elevated about a foot off the ground. There were windows on the sides and bare light bulbs hung down the center of the building just enough to cast average light at night. Bunks were aligned with just enough space for one man to pass and each man had a trunk at the base of his bed. A twenty foot walkway cut down the center of the barrack.

"Where the hell you been, O'Brien?" came a call from the back wall as Pat and Phil entered what would be their home for the next few months. "Ah, go to hell, Lynch!" retorted Pat. The whole group roared as Pat and Phil flopped their bags on bunks.

Naturally, they all wondered where Pat and Phil Dodd had been all this time and a good degree of skepticism resonated inside the barracks upon hearing their official explanation. With no required meetings that night, it didn't take long before the dice were being tossed. Flight school began first thing the next day.

At the instructor meeting the next morning, Pat and Phil were given a review of the training program. Both men saw gaps in the training but kept their opinions to themselves. It was obvious that the flying initiative the Army Signal Corps and the training initiatives at North Island were suffering growing pains. Those attending the meeting also learned that the Army was still negotiating to stay on the island. The Army had not formally established either a lease or acquisition agreement with the owner of North Island property where military aviation training was already taking place.

To be successful an aviator needed to possess caution, judgment, and technical skill. Technical skill was the focus of any good training program. Deficiencies in caution and judgment, being temperamental in nature, were rarely remedied through training. Hopefully, the Army knew enough to screen its flying recruits in these two areas. Pat felt confident that the fourteen men he had arrived with from Sill were solid. Less than ninety days were allowed to qualify as a junior aviator, and if in that period the officer's skills were found to be lacking, he was assigned to a non-aviation company.

The fundamentals of repair were part of the training course, as was the use of the gasoline engines in motor trucks and aircraft. A thorough knowledge of meteorology was repeatedly emphasized in the lectures and then applied in real air conditions met during daily flights. San Diego weather provided the ideal lab for weather related training.

Theory and practice were closely linked. Two lectures on theory were delivered each day, while the early morning hours were devoted to flying. Pilot-observer machines equipped with double controls were used in instruction. Pat O'Brien and Phil Dodd spent all their non-classroom time in the air teaching and observing the skill development of the new young pilots. One afternoon, a number of instructors invited Pat and Phil join them for a drink and to discuss some of the more subtle elements of flying. The two "students" had many more flying hours than most of the military instructors at North Island at the time.

During morning flight training Pat ascended with the student pilot and allowed him to manipulate the controls. Pat only assumed the control of the Aeroplane in an emergency. Needless to say, it was potentially hazardous duty and full of thrills. His job was to be on the alert to correct errors in the manipulation of the machine. After every trip Pat reviewed, point by point, the features of the flight, showing the pupil his deficiencies and explaining how he could avoid them in the future.

It didn't take Pat long to realize that the challenges with the rejected J2's were not the only issues holding back aviation in the U.S. military. As the weeks when by, it was evident that some sort of split existed within the officers of the Signal Corps as to who had authority within the Aviation sector. Army brass in D.C. were still discouraging the training of enlisted men for flight, and had it not been for officers such as Billy Mitchell and Hap Arnold, there probably would have been even fewer enlisted aviators than the law called for. The Signal Corps authority to train more enlisted men was largely through the efforts of Mitchell and the passing of the National Defense Act of 3 June 1916.

By this time, the Aviation Section consisted of the Aeronautical Division, the Signal Corps Aviation School at San Diego, the 1st Aero Squadron - then on duty with the expeditionary force in Mexico, and the 1st Company, 2nd Aero Squadron, on duty in the Philippines. In October 1916, Aviation Section plans called for two dozen squadrons--seven for the Regular Army, twelve for the National Guard divisions, and five for coastal defense plus balloon units for the field and coast artillery. By the end of 1916 the seven Regular Army squadrons would be organized. Twenty-four squadrons were scheduled to be formed by early 1917, but after Pat's four months in camp 1st Aero Squadron remained the only one fully organized and equipped unit.

Something occurred late in the summer of 1916 that created a potential opportunity for Pat O'Brien that he had not considered. The first foreign officers to become flying students in a U.S. Army school reported to the U.S. Signal Corps Aviation School at North Island. The first were four army officers from Portugal. Pat was called on to give them their first flight lessons. There were officers from other countries in camp as well.

One day in the mess, Pat noticed some young aviators speaking English but wearing a different uniform color and pointed caps that he thought he recognized as Canadian.

"What brings you fellows here?" asked Pat as he sat his tray down to join them at lunch.

"We're training to fly," answered the youngest looking lad with a serious sun burn across his face.

"Where you from?"

Kip Wells, the most senior of the group introduced the men. "Well, he's from Calgary, I'm from Toronto, Murphy here - he's Vancouver, Dupuis from Quebec, Williams is an Edmonton boy and poor Sharp there - he's from Saskatoon. The Canadians all laughed and Pat smiled. He sat down to enjoy his lunch and meet the new Canadian students.

"I'm Pat O'Brien. I'm a recruit also but I help teach the new pilots," he said.

The group of six Canadians along with Pat and Phil Dodd proceeded to share stories common to all Troops regardless of country. What interested Pat was the size and scope of the Canadian Pilot training program compared to what he had experienced thus far at North Island.

[208]

"So why are you here?" ask Dodd getting a sense of the serious approach being taken by the Canadians.

Both Dodd and Pat O'Brien learned of the Canadian urgency to train pilots ready for war. The Canadian government had recently committed huge numbers to England and boys from all across Canada were being recruited to fly in Europe. As they talked through lunch, Pat realized that training in Canada was not limited to flying and observing ground troops. The Canadians, under the British training program, planned to teach pilots to fight and attack by air. These young pilots were getting trained to fly in San Diego but their second phase of training at Toronto and later in England would be in the art of aeronautical warfare.

England had committed money for planes to be built in Toronto by Curtiss. He formed the Curtiss Aeroplanes & Motors, Ltd. and partnered with longtime friend, J.A.D. McGurty. McGurty was operating a commercial flight school in Canada at the time. An engineering graduate of the University of Toronto, McGurty was made famous for successfully flying the Silver Dart off Baddeck Bay in Nova Scotia, Great Britain's first control and powered flight in a heavier-than-air machine. San Diego would allow the Canadians to train recruitestts in the middle of winter, something that was impossible in the north.

Not since Pat first learned of the sinking of the Lusitania was he as stirred to fight as he was that afternoon when he first learned of the Canadian effort. The Canadians had confirmed that a small number of Americans were joining the force. What peaked Pat's interest was that a separate Canadian citizenship would not be required to join the force but applicants were required to be of pure European ancestry. Being Irish-American qualified Pat in that regard but he was concerned to learn that while age requirements were 18 to 30 years old, priority would be given to men twenty-five and under. Pat would be 26 in December.

The only question in Pat's mind was whether or not he had served long enough to resign his county's services and enlist with his North American cousins. He figured he'd lie about his age. "I just have to get into this fight," he thought as he walked towards Bowen's office the next morning. Pat was already scheduled to meet with Bowen regarding an upgraded assignment with the Aviation School. He didn't want to be a teacher much longer. He wanted to fly. He wanted to fight.

"At ease, O'Brien," said Bowen. " Take a seat, son. I'd like to talk about promoting you in our instructor status."

"Well sir, I was actually considering resigning my position to join the Canadians," stated Pat with serious look on his face. He then gave his eyebrows a hopeful rise and flashed his patented smile.

"You're what?" said Bowen looking up from his clip board not certain of what he had heard.

"Yes sir, my one year is coming up in a few months but I'd like to exit early," said Pat.

"Early, why there's no possible way…"

Interrupting Bowen Pat continued, "But I'm not trying to shirk my responsibilities sir, far from it! I want join the forces in Canada and get to Europe. Why, if I stay here on North Island full term, I'll be waiting forever and may miss the whole war, sir." Pat spoke with a raised voice. He stopped suddenly, realizing his enthusiasm may have gotten the better of him in front of his superior. In a lowered tone he continued. Bowen was not offended for he respected Pat and his efforts.

"I was hoping, sir, that you might be able to affect such a release with the condition that I join the Canadian effort. Perhaps you've heard they are establishing a huge training operation at Toronto. I've just got to get into this fight, Lieutenant"

"Well, O'Brien, you have served honorably and you're a fine pilot and a good leader," said Bowen sitting on the edge of his desk as usual. "Let me see what I can do and I'll get back to you in a few days."

"Thank you, sir!" Pat was thrilled. This might be his real chance to get into the fight. He stood at attention, held his salute until dismissed by Bowen. He ran back to the barracks and shared the news with his buddy Dodd.

Naturally, Dodd was a little disappointed that he and Pat might not be together going forward but hid it well and congratulated Pat on the prospect. Dodd assured Pat that he'd keep it to himself until such time as it did actually occur.

"Thanks, Phil," said Pat. "Of course it's not final but Bowen understands my dilemma. I can tell. I think he'd like to go himself!" The two men laughed. "I'm ready Phil. You are too! You should consider it. Who the hell knows if Wilson will ever get into this war? Why, the Brits are getting chewed up over there. Why do you think they are looking to the Canadians?

They're running out of pilots! Don't you see, Phil? They've been losing pilots by the hour since July. You heard what the Canadians told us. We've got to jump on this opportunity. We just have to," he finished with resolve.

Dodd sensed the intensity and determination in Pat's voice. The tall Irishman seemed ready to pounce. His physique was taut, yet the whole time a broad grin of confidence was on his face. Phil Dodd, like others before him, was experiencing the "Pat O'Brien Presence." Pat had an inner confidence and a determined will. His intense resolve, coupled with the ease of his exterior, caused those around him to believe Pat O'Brien could get things done.

Two days later, a call came to the barracks around 7:00 a.m. "O'Brien! It's for you!" shouted Chuck Sprague, one of the fourteen. Pat put the final touches on his bunk brushing out wrinkles with his left hand as he ran the narrow space between beds and then down the center walkway to the phone mounted on a post.

Pat looked at Chuck who was handing him the phone covering the mouthpiece, "What the hell?" said Sprague with an inquisitive look on his face. Privates never got calls on the phone unless they were in trouble and the fourteen had an unblemished record in that regard.

"O'Brien here," Pat said looking up and listening. "Yes. Yes ma'am this is Pat O'Brien." He smiled at Chuck who stood nervously to the side. "That's swell, ma'am, swell. Sure, give me a second."

Covering the phone, "Sprague! Get me a pencil. Paper, too," Chuck Sprague grabbed the tablet and pencil that was sitting on the edge of his bed and handed it to Pat. Pat tucked the phone under his chin.

"Ok, I'm ready." Writing on the tablet he then continued, "Yes. Captain S.W. Cooper. Yes, I have it, ma'am. Oh, and ma'am, please pass on my appreciation to Lt. Bowen, ma'am. Will you? Yes, thank you, ma'am."

Captain Cooper was none other than the man in charge of the Gunnery section of the Imperial Royal Flying Corps being formed in Canada. He and Bowen were old friends and Pat was to call Cooper in three days.

Pat hung up the phone. "Well, that's it Sprague. I'm off to Canada."

"Canada! What the hell?" responded Sprague. "Say, O'Brien what gives?"

By this time, Phil Dodd, Henry Wayman, Lee Ruffe and Earl White had gathered around Pat, as well. Pat turned to Dodd and said in a lowered voice, "It's on!" Pat then told the group of his meeting with Bowen two days before. Frank Maloney joined them just as congratulations and some hearty back slapping was being bestowed on Pat. Suddenly, Frank broke out in song singing the first two lines of the Felix Powell song "Smile, Smile, Smile" a tune hugely popular since 1915. It was a common strain among the fourteen and was the unofficial song of the group whose informal leader among them was "Smiling Pat."

> "Private Perks went a-marching into Flanders
> With his smile his funny smile."

Soon all but Joe Longhorn had gathered round, joining in as they arrived, arms slung over each other's shoulders crushing the middle where stood the six foot, two inch young Irishman from Momence, Illinois. Singing somewhat under their breath they went on.

> "He was lov'd by the privates and commanders
> For his smile his funny smile.
> When a throng of Bosches came along
> With a mighty swing,
> Perks yell'd out, "This little bunch is mine!
> Keep your heads down, boys and sing, Hi!"

Unsuspecting, Joe Longhorn returned from the latrine, swung open the door to a roar. The boys were in full voice now, belting out the famous tune as Joe quickly ran to the horde, setting down his toiletries on his bunk first. He barnacled on to his swaying pack of buddies. They were now all marking time in a rhythmic stomp that echoed loudly off the wood floor. He joined in. They were singing as only a boisterous brood of young men can do. As they hit the famous chorus their head fell back erupting in hilarious tones to the ceiling as they marched, looking like young birds feeding from their mother's nest.

> "Pack up your troubles in your old kit-bag,
> And smile, smile, smile,
> While you've a Lucifer to light your fag,
> Smile, boys, that's the style.
> What's the use of worrying?
> It never was worthwhile, so
> Pack up your troubles in your old kit-bag,
> And smile, smile, smile."

Three weeks later, Pat O'Brien was on a train heading north to Richmond. He had his honorable discharge in his pocket and would spend two weeks on leave. Technically, however, he was not on leave at all. He was not associated with any military in any country at this time.

Bowen's contact in Canada, S.W. Cooper, was pleased to hear of Pat's experience and felt he would be an asset to the training program at Toronto. Pat wasn't particularly pleased to hear those words since he had had his fill of training but he was confident that his enlistment in the Imperial Royal Flying Corps would get him to Europe sooner than President Wilson's strategy. The only technicality required of Pat would be the requirement that he swear allegiance to the British Crown. He would not have to give up his American citizenship. This swung the deal for Pat. American he'd stay.

During 1916 the great struggle of the war was occurring. The battle of the Somme Valley was essentially a flank motion from the north to relieve the French at Verdun east of Paris. By the end of the battle, the British Army had suffered 420,000 casualties including nearly 60,000 on the first day alone. The French lost 200,000 men and the Germans nearly 500,000. All this occurred between July 1 and November 16 in 1916. In October, President Wilson won reelection promising to "keep us out of war." Many, including Pat O'Brien, knew that that was impossible.

The Aeroplane had become an offensive weapon. The British lost 782 planes and 576 pilots during the Battle of the Somme. War's arm of death would now reach across the Atlantic Ocean as Britain called on Canada to generate flyers as quickly as possible. Few Americans were aware of this development. Pat followed the war nearly daily since its beginnings. It was his belief that Canada was about to experience an overwhelming demand for pilots. He would be proven right.

On the day that Pat was traveling home to Richmond, Canadian aviation was no more developed than it was in the United States. Canada had launched a small effort in 1914 but disbanded the Canadian Aviation Corps seven months later. Though the British were pressuring Canada to form an aviation component within their military throughout most of 1916, Ottawa had refused to budge. The British War Office and the British Admiralty viewed Canada's aviation potential strictly as a source of recruits for the British air services. By 1917, the situation was grave. Britain was running out of pilots.

Pat had arranged for the Ivy Inn gang to meet him in Richmond once he arrived. He could not reach Agnes. She had moved and changed jobs. Pat wrote a letter to John Keeton, his good friend and fellow fireman on the Santa Fe, asking him to inform her of his pending arrival. Keeton also informed Charles Pearl that Pat would be arriving soon. John Keeton had outdone himself after received Pat's letter. Not only did he alert Agnes of Pat's arrival in Richmond, he had the entire entourage standing on the platform when Pat's train pulled into Richmond.

"Hi all!" shouted Pat as he stepped off the California Southern at Richmond Station. He was clearly surprised to see such a large group there to welcome him. He spotted Agnes right away who was being escorted to the front of the group by wives of a few of the Ivy Inn chums. Pearl, Keeton, and even Jerry Solich were all there. Hearty handshakes were executed with equal fervor as Pat greeted each friend. Suddenly, Pat was face to face with Agnes. They embraced deeply and Pat's friends cheered.

Keeton had dinner ordered and the entire entourage proceeded to the center of Richmond where many times before they had reveled late into the night. It was like old times once again. Pat had nearly forgotten how much he missed everyone but the night brought back great fondness for his old gang. Agnes had never left his mind. Still as the revelry sustained through the evening, Pat would occasionally pause and think of the "fourteen" at San Diego. He wondered what they might be doing this late October night. His Army experience had made him a more serious man. Agnes could sense it too. Watching him as she did that afternoon at the air show months ago she asked Pat a number of times, "You alright?"

Pat just smiled and assured her. But Agnes could see that Pat was a more resolved man. He had not shed his zeal for fun and a good time. But she could tell that more weighed on his mind than before.

Chapter 19

Canadian Crossing

Early the next day, Pat and Agnes headed for the Redwood country, their favorite outdoor recluse. Pat had convinced Agnes that the best way to be alone would be to get up at dawn while the others slept off their Ivy Inn "fog." On the train ride north, Pat's conversation had made a steady free-fall from the nervous energy of the Army to a relaxing exchange with Agnes about trivial news around Richmond and local oddities that had occurred while Pat was away.

The Russian River Valley was their favorite spot to relax. They had spent many weekends enjoying the beauty of the river and the breathtaking views of the Redwood Forest. It was truly one of the most heavenly spots on earth to them both where they shared their most closely held thoughts, rarely expressed to anyone else.

"The sandwiches were good, Agnes," said Pat, resting his head against a massive Redwood in Sonoma forest. Pat stretched out his long legs and reclined taking in the fresh autumn air.

"Sandwiches," laughed Agnes. "My word, Pat O'Brien, only you would pay homage to a chicken sandwich amidst the most beautiful spot on earth."

Agnes was touched by his appreciative comment regarding their picnic lunch. Brushing off a few twigs from their blanket, she laid along Pat's left side resting her head on his chest.

"Well, you might think I'm nuts, Agnes but if you ever lived off Army chow for months on end, you'd find those chicken sandwiches plenty to talk about!" said Pat.

"Oh Pat, you nut," she said waving him off.

"Besides, Miss MacMillan, I know what the most beautiful thing on earth is," said Pat as he pulled Agnes toward him on their blanket.

The two embraced and Agnes lowered her head once again. They both fell silent. Birds and other small animals of the forest accompanied the slow rise and fall of the couple's relaxed exchange of outdoor air. This was absolute peace to them both. Agnes adjusted her left arm around Pat's neck and nestled closer under his chin. She fell asleep.

Pat looked up at the towering Redwood overhead. As relaxing as the morning had been, it seemed hard for Pat to turn away from the intensity of his rapidly changing life. It was late October. Pat would turn twenty-six in December. A lot had occurred since Margaret shipped him off to Wyoming eleven years ago. His thoughts flashed between Momence and all that had occurred since. He panicked for a second when it struck him how long it had been since he had written his mother. He vowed to send her a letter the next day.

Pat began mentally mapping his days ahead. He'd spend time in Richmond before reporting to the Imperial Royal Flying Corp recruiting office at Vancouver. Being too old for entry, he decided he'd have to lie about his age. "I'll tell them I'm twenty-four," he said to himself. "They need trained pilots so bad they won't have time to check. I don't think they'll refuse me just because I'm a few weeks over their age limit anyway."

Pat would be proven right. The rush to sign willing and trained pilots overshadowed everything else except bad eye site. Pat never had that issue. Recruiting offices at Vancouver and other remote locations were being manned by civilian and medical personnel whose primary responsibility was to administer a health exam and "recommend" recruits based on casual observation, shipping them off Toronto as quickly as possible. The goal was 600 cadet recruits by the end of 1917 with 1,800 planned for 1918. Britain was bleeding pilots over the Somme.

From Vancouver he'd go to Toronto and hopefully a trip back to Momence before Europe. "Europe!" he thought. "Those bastardly Huns! I can't wait to give them some of our business," he thought. Pat began a wayward daydream. He could see himself taking off, soaring over smoky battlefields applying his skills and demonstrating how wedded he and the aeroplane truly were. Others would sense it. They would easily see the years of experience Pat had by the way he flew. He'd strike fear into the heart of any flying Hun that witnessed his mastery of the aeroplane. "My God," he thought. "Who else but me! Why, I've walked on the beaches of Chanute himself!" Pat performed the type of commencement all young untested men issue themselves when they envision their dreams.

The panic of a son forgetting to write his mother was suddenly overtaken by the significance of what flying in France could mean to everything that Pat loved. It also struck Pat how his decision to cross the Canadian border escalated the uncertainty of his future. But like all young men who go off to war, the zeal to defeat an evil enemy and the excitement of the unknown took prominence over the potential abolishment of all things past and present in Pat's life. He had an intense urge to act. No longer, the willing apprentice, Pat could feel life's tipping point discharging him toward his destiny.

Agnes stirred and Pat was suddenly brought back down to earth. He brushed Agnes' hair from her face and kissed her on the forehead. She awoke, smiled and reached up placing a warm kiss on his lips. It was a long embrace. For Pat, the kiss touched more than this his lips. It sealed the moment. It felt like goodbye. It was goodbye. Goodbye for now, he hoped.

Through November and December, Pat was able to visit his friends and even ride the Stockton run a few times with Charles Pearl and his Santa Fe firemen buddy John Keeton. Joe Cato's place was closed up but young Ed Neville was flying mail and repairing Aeroplanes. Curley McNeil had returned to Southern California when Cato went east but Pat had a beer with his fellow Cato pilots Claude Craig and Tim Reardon about one week before his departure. Jerry Solich was doing well with the railroad and Pat particularly enjoyed seeing his first friend in Richmond happy and recently married.

It was a satisfying visit. Pat got to spend time with a lot of people that were his good friends. Elmer even came up from the Valley for Pat's 26th birthday on December 13th. They were able to duplicate the same fun-filled weekend with the boisterous Ivy Inn gang. Of course, Pat spent time with Agnes and it seemed like old times until the morning he was to take the Oregon & California Railroad north to Seattle. It would be a two-day trip from Oakland's 16th Street Station.

"Good luck, Pat," said Charles Pearl as he shook his hand. John Keeton, Jerry Solich and his wife were on hand. Pat was holding Agnes' hand, standing in a long coat, grasping his bags tightly in his other hand.

"Thanks Chuck, John," Pat returned, letting go of Agnes hand to shake hands with his railroad chums. He turned to Jerry. "Solich, I'm sure happy to see how well you've done. Why if it hadn't been for you, I might be still looking for the Santa Fe yard!" Pat slapped him on the shoulder and the two men embraced, slapping each other on the back.

"Well, it's time" Agnes said.

"Why of course, Agnes," encouraged Jerry's wife. "Let's get along Jerry, gentlemen. Give these two a chance to say goodbye alone for Lord's sake!" Alma Solich was a stout jovial Slavic women and she singlehandedly corralled the three men off the platform.

"Good Luck Pat!" John said waving as they walked into the terminal building.

Pat and Agnes said their last goodbyes. Pat was flipping back and forth in his mind again between the serenity of Agnes and the compulsion to get to the flurry of war. After a final embrace, Pat turned and walked up the platform as he had on the day he left for San Diego. Agnes saw no reduction in his determined gate as he walked toward the conductor who was taking tickets.

As he had done before, he turned prior to stepping up on to the train and gave that same broad wave of his right arm across his physique, left to the right. Agnes had tears in her eyes as Pat stepped up and vanished. She stood frozen until the blaring whistle of the engine on her right announced the departure making her stomach flip. She turned and walked slowly into the terminal as the train pulled out of Oakland Station, still clutching her handkerchief against her chest. She did not want to watch the train leave.

Pat's route went through Sacramento, then the snow covered Cascades, through the Willamette River Valley to Portland and Tacoma and finally Seattle. At Seattle Pat transported to the Western Seattle Ferry and completed his trip across Puget Sound arriving at North Vancouver in a few hours. He disembarked and walked to a second ferry landing where he boarded The Senator Ferry and crossed the Burrard Inlet finally entering the City of Vancouver after nearly three days of travel.

Pat walked up the ramp from the Vancouver landing and spoke to a carriage driver who was feeding his horse out of a canvas bucket. Pat asked if the driver might take him to the Hotel Vancouver. The short man, wearing a top hat, acknowledged he could and soon Pat arrived at the new hotel ready to rest after his journey. It had been a long trip and Pat's lack of sleep since Richmond had clearly caught up with him. He would report to the Imperial Royal Flying Corp enlistment center the next morning.

Enlistment at Vancouver was not what Pat expected. Missing was the extensive processing he experienced arriving at Fort Sill. This was due to the extreme urgency of the moment. Britain needed pilots so quickly it set up recruiting committees before the main training school was completed in Toronto. Each local committee was composed of three influential public men and a few medical doctors for health screening. Recruits were not signing up for the Canadian Air Force. Canada would not form its own air force until well after the war. They were joining the Royal Air Force of Britain. Canadians were Royal subjects and duty bound.

The Department of Militia & Defense in England told the Canadians to recruit and recruit aggressively. Screening amounted to an interview, a simple medical exam and filling out an application for transport to Toronto. Other similar recruiting centers had been established in Montreal, Charlottetown on Prince Al Island, Winnipeg, Regina, Calgary and Toronto itself.

"Well, you're surely a unique recruit, young man," said John Stallworth.

"Why you're American, I see. Quite good you know. You've got extensive experience, I see," said the man twisting his long handlebar mustache.

"Yes sir, I've just left the Signal Corps where I trained and taught flying in San Diego," said Pat.

"San Diego, indeed," Stallworth said as he made notes on Pat's enlistment form. "You know Mr. O'Brien, I'm going to make mention of your background on your enlistment form. Make certain when you arrive in Toronto that you point this out to processing people at the University."

"University, sir?" asked Pat not certain of his reference.

"Yes, processing is at the University of Toronto and much of cadet school occurs there," handing Pat his paper work. "Now take this form Mr. O'Brien and present it to the clerk in the next room."

"Where do we fly in Toronto?" Pat asked turning back as he stepped away.

"They'll tell you that when you get Toronto. We just sign you up, boy. That's all we do here," he responded. Good luck to you son. Next!" barked the busy official as lines of young recruits were schedule for processing by noon.

Pat presented his paper work to a grandmotherly like lady who was a volunteer on the committee.

"Thank you, Mr. O'Brien. Here is your train ticket, your coupon for meals and sleeping car access ticket," said the woman with a warm smile. Pat smiled back and took the paperwork from her hands.

"When do I go?" said Pat, somewhat surprised at the informal process.

"Your train departs at 3:45 this afternoon," she said. "You're to report thirty minutes ahead of time to a man with a list on a clip board with your name affixed. Alright, Mr. O'Brien?"

"Thank you ma'am," said Pat flashing his famous smile. The woman was already taking paperwork from the next recruit.

Pat looked at his watch. It was 10:15 a.m. He had time to return to the hotel, get his things, check out and have lunch near the station. Completing this, he walked through Vancouver then grabbed a bite to eat at The Patricia Café on Hastings Street. Pat had a nose for a good restaurant and it was obvious that this was a favorite spot of the locals. He ordered what he thought could likely be his last opportunity for fresh seafood. About one o'clock he polished off his second beer and headed for Waterfront Station. Waterfront was the Pacific terminus for the Canadian Pacific Railway that ran to Montreal and Toronto.

After checking in with the official on the platform, Pat stepped up and found his seat against a window. The car was only partially full so he turned, leaned back against the window and dosed off just as the train pulled out of the station. Toronto was 2,500 miles away. He'd spend another five days on a train. Just before he dosed off, he said to himself once again, "Trains. It seems I've spent my whole life on trains."

The steep grade of the Canadian Rockies put a weight against Pat and caused him to awake toward the end of the first leg of his journey east. He awoke to witness the incredible view of Kicking Horse Pass cut through the Cathedral Mountains. The grey shale of Mount Stephen hovered over the climbing train as Pat held still against the window for some time after opening his eyes.

Midwestern boys are always struck by the mountainous terrain and Pat was no exception. Suddenly, the bottom fell out of the train bed as they crossed the 5,300 foot Lethbridge Viaduct over the Oldman River. Pat sat up quickly to look down. It was a 300-foot high steel structure that, like the tunnels, helped the Canadian Pacific Railroad traverse the Canadian Rockies. Pat was struck by the scale and beauty of this region of Canada

The pace of his journey provided him a fairly consistent day and night views of each Province, though once over the Rockies the mundane mass prairies of Alberta, Saskatchewan and Manitoba redirected Pat's attention to the train's interior. As they passed through miles and miles of sameness, Pat struck up conversations with nearly everyone in each car. Newspapers, books, cards, and Pat's pocket full of dice occupied much of his time. There were a few others on the train destine for Toronto and Imperial Royal Flying Corp training.

On the second day of his journey, Pat struck up a card game with three men headed for Camp Borden Cadet School. Though he had no way of knowing it at the time, one chap, Frank C. Conroy, would be part of Pat's eighteen-man Squadron that would depart for England in June. Clearly the experienced and eldest of the group, Pat shared his stories of flight with the amazed and eager boys who ranged in age from 18 to 22. He told them of his early days traveling to Miller Beach as a young lad and the schooling at West Pullman. All three had heard about the great Beachey and were stunned that Pat had met him briefly in Chicago and witnessed his crash in San Francisco. When Pat completed his narrative on the exploits of Joe Cato and the Signal Corps at San Diego, his three fellow gamblers were convinced he was a "man of the world." Again, the presence of Pat O'Brien had made itself known with these boys and by the time they reached Ontario Province three days later he was known throughout the train.

On the morning of the fifth day, Pat's train was completing its large swing to the southeast around the protruding Great Lakes. By noon, the openness of the countryside gave way to Toronto's congestion as the Canadian Pacific slowly drifted into the new Summerhill Station. Pat was eager to exit his five-day home and stood at the top of the steps as the train pulled to a stop. Once removed, he stood on the platform and stretched his arms and legs for some time. He straddled his bag so as not to lose it in the clamor of exiting passengers. When he entered the station he gazed up at the bright forty-foot high ceiling and the huge bronze suspended light fixtures that projected a sense of the urban aura similar to San Francisco. Pat was pleased to be in a city again. "That's enough wheat fields!" said Pat humorously to himself.

The group of fifteen recruits, including Pat O'Brien, took a military bus from the depot to cadet training school at the University of Toronto. Sitting next to Pat was Frank Conroy. Everyone else on board was Canadian except for Ed Gannet, and Hank Boysen who, like Pat, were Americans who hadn't the patience to wait for Woodrow Wilson.

The bus arrived at Charles Street and pulled alongside Burwash Hall. The British had established their central operations, primary quarters for officers and housing for cadets within the various campus buildings. School officials and professors gave up space willingly as the military moved in. Pat would be housed at Burwash.

Burwash was a collection of buildings linked together. It was comprised of a large dining hall and attached student resident units called "houses" which would be home to the new recruits while they were on campus. Actual flight training and other outdoor activities would take place at the various barrack camps in the open areas outside Toronto. Housing at the barrack camp was in white "Bell Tent" and men were shuttled back and forth depending on their stage of training.

"Hello, gentlemen," said a smart looking Lieutenant standing on the curb. "I am Lieutenant James G Howling and I will be processing you today." Howling had a distinct British accent which seemed to project an increased aura of respect for the men that was missing from Pat's official greeter at Fort Sill.

"First, gentlemen I have a number of procedural announcements," said Howling.

"You are the final group of recruits, housed here at Burwash, to arrive today. Indeed the Burwash complex is now completely full and now, therefore, we will assemble the entire barrack in the food service area in approximately one hour. You will enter through this door," pointing to his right, "where you will be greeted by corps personnel who will direct you to your rooms. On your way in, you will be given three blankets and a mat which you will install on your assigned bunks. Alright gentlemen, let's proceed."

"Let's proceed!" laughed Pat to himself. "These Brits are a far shot from the boys in Oklahoma," he thought. Pat rather took to the whole thing. Being self-motivated, the entire hullabaloo used within the Signal Corps did little but distract him from his mission. This, he thought, would be a much saner approach.

"Flying takes focus," Pat said to himself, "Those barking methods work with the infantry but not in the air corps." Pat knew this instinctively from his experience in the air. The English understood, as well. They had already made the transition.

The U.S. Army still had Calvary and infantry officers managing their aviation initiatives. "I mean hell, I still can't believe they required those boys to wear spurs in the cockpit!" This time Pat chuckled about out loud but still to himself. He liked the difference of Canada already.

Pat and his fellow Cadets moved in an orderly manner into Burwash. He grabbed his three blankets and mat from a young staffer who also handed him a small card with a room number. Pat looked down, and it read "325." He entered the stairwell after glancing quickly down the hall. He could see the large dining room where they would meet shortly. He climbed to the third floor, where he found his room and opened the door to find another Cadet already settling in.

"Well, hello man," said the Cadet in a quick, snappy way brandishing a grand smile. "I'm Paul Raney."

"Pat O'Brien," said Pat as he extended his hand. "Looks like we'll be in the same room, hey?"

"Looks that way," said Paul standing with both hands on his waist after shaking hands. He watched Pat place his bag on the bunks. "Some bunks huh? Let's see a piece o' wood, this mat here, which doesn't look like much more than comforter and three blankets. First, the mat, a blanket to lie on, blanket to fold for a pillow, and blanket to cover yourself. What accommodations!" he stated with a humorous tone.

"Welcome to the Flying Corps!" said Pat turning his back to Paul.

"Welcome, ha! Where you from O'Brien?" asked the young Canadian.

"California," said Pat.

"California! A west coast boy, huh?" was Paul's response.

"Well actually, I'm from Illinois where I grew up but I've been in the San Francisco area for a while now so I guess I'm from there too," Pat responded.

"Ah, you Americans, you're always from all over now, aren't you?" quipped Paul.

The two exchanged a good deal about their background, families, and adventures to date. Paul Raney was from Toronto and had just graduated from the University of Toronto the past May. He decided to join the Imperial Royal Flying Corp right out of school. His father William was a prominent lawyer though Paul didn't describe him that way. William Raney was Minster of Justice in the province of Ontario. He had recently taken a position on the Supreme Court of Ontario.

Paul, for all his pedigree was not pretentious. In fact, he downplayed his background and was extremely interested in all Pat had done in his life thus far.

"We better get down there, O'Brien," said Paul looking at his watch.

"You're right, let's go!"

"Gum?" said Paul, extending a small pack of Beech-Nut.

"Oh, I love this stuff!" said Pat pulling a stick from the yellow wrapper.

The two Cadets entered the long dining hall. Large cathedral windows started four feet above the doors and extended to the vaulted ceiling. The whole environment was so uncharacteristic of the typical military base. Pat was shocked at the contrast between his new quarters and the canvas tar covered tents of North Island.

At the one end of the hall was the head table where Howling and his aids sat waiting for the start of the meeting. Over the Lieutenant's head hung the burial flag of Queen Victoria given to the college when they took on her name. Victoria College was secularized from its original Methodist roots and incorporated into the University of Toronto 1892.

There were 16 long tables grouped in four rows extending from the head table through the length of the great hall. Each table sat 16 cadets on bench seats. Paul Raney quickly surveyed the room and directed Pat to two open seats. As they sat down Pat did a quick survey of the room. Every seat was taken. There were 256 cadets entering training. "This is more like it," thought Pat.

Howling rose to the lectern and the young man that issued Pat his bedding barked, "Attention!" in a booming baritone voice that reverberated throughout the large hall. Instinctively, each man stood to greet their commander.

"As you were, gentlemen," said Howling. They all sat.

"On behalf of the King of England and the Royal Flying Corps, let me first welcome you to Toronto and the Royal Flying Corps of Britain."

Howling paused and looked out at his recruits. Each man's face was affixed to his. A serious tone came over the entire hall.

"As you men know, the evil of the Hun has overrun Europe and is locked in a bitter struggle with free-loving British patriots and the proud French. The last six months have been devastating for the Royal Flying Corps and the Allied Expeditionary Force in general. The British Crown turns to you now to add your efforts to our cause to drive the bastard Hun not just back to his land but to a position that will never let him destroy the sovereign countries we fight for ever again." Howling spoke with resolve and each man could sense his commitment and the serious role they would play in the days ahead.

"Finally, gentlemen, you will find my officers and their aids to be quite capable in their work. Listen to them and follow their direction. Those of you with low experience will find yourself here until you are ready for deployment. Some of you will complete the training quickly. There is not a predesigned length to your training. You will pass through the organization depending upon your capacity to learn, and the requirements of your flying units. But you will learn. And you will be a force to be reckoned with. And gentlemen, you will be victorious.

With that, almost on cue, Howling's aid barked 'attention' again and the entire hall rose in unison.

"As you were," said Howling in a lowered voice. The men took their seats once again, this time with a corresponding murmur in obvious response to Howling's words.

Howling's aids took over and made logistical announcements to the cadets. Lieutenant Brandish spoke to the men next. "Following dinner, each man will receive a thorough physical exam and be issued their uniform and other equipment needed to begin training at zero six hundred tomorrow morning," he stated. "Dinner will be in this hall this evening at half past five, where you will also receive additional information regarding the Corps and our current status in Europe. Until then gentlemen, dismissed!" he said raising his voice on the final command.

It was three in the afternoon and each cadet would be fully processed and ready for the next day's events by ten that evening. Pat O'Brien was excited to see the level of organization and intense commitment of his new commander. At 9:45 the entire group had been processed, examined, and issued a uniform.

They were instructed to retire to their quarters and get in full dress, including cadet hats and report to the dinner hall for the final activity of the day. Aids would instruct them in the proper placement of the Royal Flying Corps Cadet Hat. None of the men knew what the final activity of the day would entail but they all reported on time. At five minutes to ten, the men were called to attention and told to raise there right hand. Each man in full voice repeated his oath:

"I, (each man's name was spoken), Swear by Almighty God that I will be Faithful and bear True Allegiance to His Majesty King George, his Heirs and Successors, and that I will, as in Duty bound, Honestly and Faithfully Defend His Majesty, his Heirs and Successors, in Person, Crown and Dignity against all Enemies and will Observe and Obey all Orders of His Majesty, his Heirs and Successors, and of the Air Officers and other Officers set over me."

Chapter 20

Mallards in Formation

As the men were dismissed from Burwash Hall on that first night, one of the officers with Howling stepped off the front of the officer's platform and walked toward Paul Raney and Pat.

"Are you O'Brien?"

"Yes Sir," said Pat.

"O'Brien, I'm Major Allen. I handle all personnel matters for Lieutenant Howling"

"Yes, sir," Pat confirmed not knowing this but offering an appropriate response to his senior officer.

"We understand you flew with the Signal Corps in the States and have experience in the air prior to service, is that right O'Brien?" asked Allen.

"Yes, sir, I flew and instructed at North Island, commercially in San Francisco, and was originally trained in Chicago," indicated Pat.

"That's grand, O'Brien. You see we reviewed a note from the gentleman that registered you in Vancouver."

"Right, I recall him asking me, sir," Pat responded with no tone of braggard.

"Good. You may know, O'Brien, Lieutenant-Colonel Howling and I arrived in Canada January 19th under Major Hoare. Unfortunately…" he paused a moment thinking of the best way to put it.

"You see O'Brien, it's been such a quick start for us. Well frankly, we don't have all the instructors we need for our effort – at least at this time," The Major was being delicate so as to not alarm either Pat nor Paul of the situation and yet to give some justification or his request. He was a classic polite Englishman, indeed.

He went on. "We know you're here to receive training but we'd also like to take advantage of your experience and ask that you spend your time training in the field rather than repeating a lot of what you already know. Does that sit well with you, Mr. O'Brien?" he asked.

"Yes Sir, I can assist you as you see fit," responded Pat, though the conversation sounded hauntingly similar to the one he had on North Island.

"Don't misinterpret me, O'Brien. We need you in Europe as quickly as possible but we'd like to take advantage of some our more experienced pilots at the same time so we can move this thing along," pausing again, "all within the establish timeline mind you. It would not delay your departure date. All right, O'Brien?"

"Yes sir. I will be glad to contribute," said Pat, feeling a little more assured that his training role would not delay his arrival in Europe.

"Very good," responded Allen. He shook Pat's hand after which Pat saluted Allen. The officer returned the salute, turned, and exited the hall, tucking a roll of paper under his left arm in a smart British way, Pat observed.

"So, what do you think of that?" asked Paul. "Sounds like you're going to be my teacher, O'Brien."

"Well, you being a college man and all that, you can help me with the classroom work. How 'bout it?" Pat snapped with a smile.

"Sounds like a fair trade," Paul responded.

They headed outside where new recruits had gathered to meet their fellow cadets for the first time. The boisterous conversations were waffling into the cool spring night and the men were animated, smoking cigarettes and introducing themselves to those they didn't know but who would soon count among their closest mates. Pat and Paul knew little of how close they would become in the days and weeks ahead.

The entire Canadian training program was under the direction of Major Cuthbert Gurney Hoare and his six senior officers, who were all British except for one Lieutenant John K. Aird, a highly educated Canadian.

When the British War Department called Hoare in on January 1, 1917, they told him not expect any direct help from Britain. Britain was tapped and needed all their resources to maintain the western front. In the last six months of 1916, the allies lost 782 aircraft and 576 pilots to the superior German equipment and expert pilots. The allies were on the ropes. Little of these conditions were present in the psyche of the American public. That would change soon.

The key to the entire Canadian recruitment initiative was to harvest young men from across Canada and bring them to England within three months. Britain's high command chose the very capable Hoare to ramp up, recruit and deliver capable pilots to England as soon as possible. It was a herculean task, but Hoare was an incredibly driven and detailed man who required little sleep. He would often initiate orders and planning for the next day at 10:00 p.m. when his senior officers were ready to end their day.

London had gained assurance from the Canadian government that Canada would secure all needed facilities. They gave Hoare a budget of $96 million to set up the whole operation. He secured a commitment from the University of Toronto to turn over much of their campus. When Hoare asked about planes, the British indicated they could spare none. With that, he struck a contract with Glen Curtiss to establish a manufacturing plant in Toronto and upgrade the JN3 to meet English standards.

Britain would need 600 brand new pilots in 1917 and 1,800 the following year. Within four weeks, aerodromes were being established by Hoare's team, despite record snows covering southern Ontario. The largest camp was Camp Borden about 45 miles north of Toronto proper. Hoare visited the area designated for Borden for the first time on January 25. He issued orders to complete construction in 60 days. In addition to the landing areas, crews built barracks, officer quarters, stores, indoor and outdoor training areas and offices for administrative staff. A "bell tent" camp was erected for cadets in the field who would quickly learn to apply their classroom instruction. Additional aerodromes and training camps were built at Long Branch, Leaside, and three other locations. Pat would eventually train pilots at both Borden and Long Branch.

Though airfields and other outdoor facilities were still being built when Pat arrived, classroom training was beginning immediately. Even for Pat, there was plenty to learn. Signal Corps training had consisted of flying and observation. "Flight training" in the Royal Flying Corps meant "military flight training." Here, pilots would be taught how to use their machines as weapons, a major upgrade from San Diego.

The British were much further along than the Signal Corps. After all, each cadet entering the Royal Flying Corps already held a commercial pilot's license. Most averaged 500 hours in the air. Pat had many more hours than most.

The lab and classroom instruction was extensive. Even though a full supply of machine guns would not arrive for three weeks, Paul Raney and Pat went through gunnery school and qualified on a single Gatling shared by twelve Cadets. The gun was mounted on a tripod and cadets formed a half circle behind it, alternating attempts to hit moving targets one-hundred and fifty feet away.

They completed wireless training, reconnaissance, bombing techniques, engine repair, air craft construction, and navigation. By mid-March Borden was open and ready to train cadets on actual aircraft. The weather had warmed so the "bell tents" were more accommodating. Pat spent his outdoor time training other less experienced Cadets at both Borden and Long Branch. He was one of the first cadets to graduate receiving his pending designation of 2nd Lieutenant around April 15th. Final designation would be issued once he completed training in England and earned his wings.

One Friday afternoon, Pat was demonstrating for a group of thirty Cadets who were observing him from the ground. The day's topic was on avoiding offensive enemy actions in an aircraft. Pat had learned some unique moves in the air during the exhibition days and had seen Beachey and others perform moves in the air that were rarely used in the military.

On his final pass over the group of Cadets he demonstrated what became known in camp as the "O'Brien Loop." It involved three essential turns of the aircraft that would rapidly place a pilot on the tail of his enemy escaping the reverse position. It quickly turned the enemy into the pursued rather than the pursuer. Pat was the first Royal Flying Corps Cadet to perform a loop at the Canadian school.

His reputation as a daring pilot would follow him into France. The "unapproved" move was ignored by Pat's officers. The British officers knew that such moves, while not in the "official book" could be life savers in the heat of battle. Besides, they had more urgent things to be concerned with than monitoring the initiatives of an innovative instructor.

By the end of May, Pat and Paul Raney had spent hours together in the classroom, in the field and in the air. The two roommates became close friends. Both bright and full of life but different in background, they instantly bonded and always enjoyed each other's company. During the last week of training, they sat outside the row of "bell tents" at Borden and talked about their pending trip to England.

"I think we're going in by mid-June based on what I hear around camp, Pat," Paul said, gnawing on a long dried piece of grass which he did regularly as a habit.

"Now, what the hell are you going to do when we're sailing the Atlantic and you can't find a piece of old Canadian weed to chew on the whole way there," said Pat giving his buddy a humorous, hard time.

"It's not weed, Pat. It's fine Canadian wheat!" Paul said. "Do you know how many things can be made from wheat as fine as this?"

"Well sure, but you dumb Canuck, you're not supposed to chew it raw!"

The two friends pretty much ribbed each other all the time. It broke the monotony and tension of the moment and both enjoyed the mental gymnastics of the other's quick wit.

"Pat, if we are going to Europe, why don't you come with me to visit the folks?" Paul said. "I'd like you to meet them. And besides, I'd like someone going with me to know them." He paused a bit establishing a more serious tone. "Have you even thought about that, Pat?" asked Paul.

"About what?" Pat was reviewing paperwork to determine if he could sign-off on any recent Cadet qualifying flights.

"About the war itself?" responded Paul. "You know about...well, not coming back."

"You mean finding some French girl, getting married and staying there? No, hell, I'm going to marry an American girl!" Pat clearly knew what Paul was bringing up but poked fun at him, nonetheless.

"No, you stupid Yank! Getting shot. Getting shot down! Getting killed!" With the increased level of their fighter training it had begun to cross Paul's mind.

"Well, sure. Everybody knows that's part of the game, don't they? I mean you're a smart guy Paul. You know what it means. But hell, we take our life in our hands every time we take those rickety Curtiss machines into the sky anyway!"

They both laughed it off. The two friends provided a sounding board for the other. In the service, soldiers often pair up with a confidant. Pat and Paul were no exception.

Over the weekend, Paul Raney brought Pat home to meet his folks. William and Jessie Raney took an instant liking to Pat and felt good that Paul had found a buddy who would travel to England with him.

"Will you be in the same group, Paul?" asked Paul's father hoping they would.

"Yes, Mr. Raney," interjected Pat. "They just announced the formation of our squadron yesterday. We've got 18 fly boys in our group and we'll all go to England at the same time to earn our wings."

"That's grand, Pat," said Mrs. Raney clearly, nervous over the entire prospect.

In the days before departing for France, Pat would become a frequent visitor at the Raney's. As time went on, Paul's family viewed Pat more and more as family. Most who met Pat O'Brien had a similar desire to draw him in, thusly. Beyond his magnetic personality he had that subtle but recognizable persona of a young man on his own at an early age. He had, in fact, been on his own for a long time and people could sense it. Men, recognizing his uncanny resolve and maturity, wanted to help him and women intuitively sensed a need to provide comfort and affection.

Following one of their last dinners together, Mrs. Raney announced they would all have one grand meal on the Sunday before the boys departed for Europe. She choked up attempting to make her grand announcement. There would be a two-week leave before France. Paul would spend the time at home and Pat would travel to Momence.

The next day, Pat was once more looking over the hills of Yellowhead Township as his train from Chicago approached the Kankakee Valley and his hometown. Such an emotional, and yet, distant feeling came over him as he returned to his boyhood home, perhaps for the last time. Somehow on this trip, he was moved to study everything in detail. Home looked the same but he had forgotten how green Momence was in the spring. Those who leave their hometown for the last time, have equally heart-tugging good byes with green hills, the odor of a gin mill, the sound of birds and, in this case, ducks and geese, barking dogs, familiar homes, kids at play and, of course for Pat, the river. Suddenly, his train slowed as it approached the Momence depot and he felt his stomach flip and his day dreaming ceased. He was one of only three passengers to exit the train that day. He did not recognize the other two.

Clara O'Brien Clegg stepped down from her carriage and tied her horse securely to an iron hitch post that still stood aside Railroad Street. Momence was still a blend of automobiles and carriages though cars had certainly increased in visibility around town. Clara had both. She stepped toward the platform. When she took her first steps up on the far south end a short man in a suite and derby hat exited the train, then a woman with a big hat. Finally, a tall broad shouldered soldier stepped out carrying a small bag. They were walking toward her and she toward them with her eyes fixed on the train car door. Perhaps Pat was gathering his things, she thought.

Suddenly, her eyes drifted five feet to the left and she saw an unmistakable face with a smile stretching ear to ear. She had not seen that smile for such a long time. It was Pat. Pat was the soldier walking toward her. She did not recognize her little brother. He was such a strikingly handsome and bold looking man. Her arms dropped and her body collapsed against her frame. She burst into tears and was flooded with emotion.

"Oh, my word, my dearest Pat, we've missed you so much!" she whispered through a flood of tears as Pat took her in his arms and held her firmly, kissing her on the cheek and caressing her hair.

Pat, too, had tears in his eyes as he held her. Clara's face was buried in his chest and his six foot-two frame allowed him to easily look over her shoulder to the south. Suddenly, The Island and the flow of the river in the distance came to his visual consciousness. The river. This meant home to Pat. They both embraced for some time. Clara was still recovering from the loss of her husband Matt Clegg who had died on February 18th. He was a prominent businessman in Momence when he died. The town was shaken by his sudden departure.

"Pat, I hardly recognized you," said Clara as they turned toward the carriage. She had her two arms woven around his left forearm. "You've filled out so much. Is this your uniform?

"Yes, it's my Royal Flying Corps uniform. Canadian version, though. It's a little different than the British," Pat told her.

Clara's carriage took a right down Front Street and headed west to the center of town. It was a familiar vista to Pat but a vista none the less. There were a few new stores here and there but things looked pretty much the same. When they got to Range, they turned left then right at River Street arriving at the O'Brien home.

Margaret was stepping off the porch as they approached, wiping her hands on her apron with a large Irish smile on her face. Pat jumped from the carriage and embraced his mother. All three entered the house and soon the house was filled with friends and other family arriving for a picnic lunch. Margaret had been cooking most of the day and tables and chairs were arranged in the yard.

"Al Fontaine!" said Pat as he rose to greet his boyhood friend. "How are you Al?"

"Pat, you look a little broader in the shoulders there chum," said Al. "Have you been working in the coal mines somewhere??

"Railroading," said Pat. "I shuffled coal but into a large train boiler"

The two close friends found time to catch up. Al had completed trade school and learned masonry. He was currently working on some new buildings in town. He was married and happy. It is common for two childhood friends to not only be quite different but to take different paths in life. No one could be more opposite than Pat and Al but they loved each other as brothers. Pat had forgotten how much he missed his old friend but the two weeks at home reconfirmed his feelings for Al.

On June 5th, Pat and Al walked up to Ganeer Township Hall and registered for the draft. The United States had entered the war in April and President Wilson had called for conscription of all young men. Most who saw Pat thought it odd to see a man wearing a uniform registering for the draft. Al and Pat got a few laughs from that.

During his time at home, Pat visited family and friends and his brothers were able to take a few photos of him in his smart new Canadian uniform, complete with pointed cap. More than one gal from Momence swooned seeing him in uniform. American soldiers were not yet common place at this time. The United States had yet to view the war as theirs. No American boys were in training. While it was Pat's love of flying that put him in uniform, it was the Royal Flying Corps that placed in him the sense of urgency that possesses a young man heading off to war. All soldiers have it, all mothers sense it and all armies require it.

The two weeks in Momence were a welcomed rest from the grueling pace of camp. Pat reconnected to his family, his hometown, and many of the friends from his formative years. A letter had arrived on the tenth day of his visit. It was from Paul Raney. In it he informed Pat that they would sail June 21st. It was time for Pat to depart. This time he would take a step so significant that it had the potential to remove him from Momence forever. He didn't think about that much but his mother certainly did. He would leave for Toronto on the train in the morning.

There are a lot of beautiful days in the Kankakee Valley but few would exceed the early morning of June 16, 1917 when Pat awoke before most of Momence had opened its eyes. The red sun could be seen beginning a slow ascendance through the tall trees along the river. Summer's full heat had yet to make an appearance and Pat could feel the soft spring air against his skin. June weather in the upper Midwest is some of the most complimentary to be found. It reminded Pat of San Diego where moisture and warmth find an ideal balance.

Pat sat on the porch sipping a cup of hot coffee. He felt in perfect harmony with the world around him. His spirit blended into the air and the sounds of his hometown. He could hear the ripple of the river to the south as it picked up steam heading west. Mallards were calling out their approval as they surveyed the awakening town and Pat could hear a faint squeaking sound drifting all the way from downtown. Chuck Astle was lowering his canopy over the window of his store as he had done daily for years. The shopkeeper paused and looked up at the "V" shaped formation cutting across the southern sky. Like so many others in this sweet river valley, the flight of the mallard lifted his spirits amid yet another mundane routine. The same flight of ducks now approached Pat and he followed their flight directly over Maggie's house and west down the Kankakee.

Two stray dogs were working their way up and down the north-south alleys that cut through town. Pat watched as the scavengers made quick decisions regarding the remains of the previous night's human feast. A few pulled open a paper sack pouncing on their found prize. One turned and looked toward Pat. It had a large pork chop bone lodged in its jaw and seemed to be watching the parameter should a third party catch the scent of their prize. The second dog now sensed Pat's presence. "Shoo!" whispered Pat loud enough to stir them but not enough to awaken the neighborhood. They were unmoved and turned back to the bag. The entire scene brought him back to the details of small town life. He soaked it all in somewhat not focused on his scheduled departure for Toronto in a few hours and then England in a week.

Pat watched intently, imagining the instincts of such dogs as different from men. All that was whirling around in Pat's mind, including the calamity that was about to greet him in Europe, was so far removed from these two dogs scavenging for breakfast. Yet scavengers they were and certainly the world seemed similar in 1917.

The scene dissolved instantly as the sound of the screen door springing shut broke Pat's daydream. Maggie stepped out to join him for a quiet visit. Rather than sit in the two wicker chairs squarely positioned on the porch, they sat on the steps with their feet nestled in green grass that was a few days too long. The conversation was deliberate, softly spoken, and close. Margaret often spoke at length to family, neighbors and friends in the wicker chairs but when she and Pat talked they sat together on the steps.

"You know Pat, when I sent you away to Wyoming years ago, I was so overwhelmed with everything. I don't think I paid much attention to what you went through. But you know, you've done quite well for yourself," she said regretting his leave.

"Well, mom, it was the best thing and did me a lot of good," Pat responded. "Besides, I was still with family. Even in California Elmer was close."

"I know. But it seems I sent you away so many years ago, you've come back and now you're off to Europe," she said with a slight tightness in her throat. "I don't know where the last ten years have gone Pat, but it's really sad I'm sending my boy away. Suddenly, I wonder why I ever sent you at all." She broke down a bit.

"Mom, you know there's not much we can do when things happen. With pop gone, you had little choice. It was the right thing to do. I know you didn't want to send me away but I just had to start a little earlier than most, that's all. I would have been gone in two to three years anyway," said Pat trying to console his mother.

"I have an idea mom, why don't we walk to the depot this morning? It will be nice, just you and me. If any others come to say good bye, we can meet them there."

"Oh Pat, I don't think I could make that walk anymore. I can't walk as far as I used to son," she said. "Why don't you and Al walk together? It will give you both a chance to talk. I know he's going to miss you. I'll ride with Clara. We'll follow you there, ok?"

"Sure, ma. I guess it is kinda' far from here," said Pat. It struck him that despite how mature he felt about himself, he had forgotten that his mother was ten years older, as well. Like all young adult children he had failed to notice the aging of his mother. Life's cycles are always new to the young and often missed when they leave home.

Margaret went in and came out with the coffee pot, pouring Pat one final cup. They spent another hour talking about the past and about Pat's pending trip. He told her about his train ride across Canada, his good friend Paul Raney, and about Agnes. As only a woman could and certainly as any mother would, Margaret could see Pat's feelings for Agnes on his face as Pat spoke. It made her particularly curious. "Is she a nice girl, Pat?" asked Margaret.

"Why no ma, she's a real trouble maker," said Pat with in a humorous tone. They both laughed. "She's a real sweet gal, ma." We had a lot of fun together and had a fine group of friends in Richmond. Those were fun times. It was hard to leave but I'm glad I'm going now. I would be going either way now that the U.S. is in the war. This way I can do what I love – fly planes."

"You've always liked the aeroplane Pat, I'll say that much. Margaret was happy to hear how settled Pat had become in Richmond. "You've done so much in your short life," she paused. "Your father would have loved to hear your stories. He'd be very proud of you, Patrick," said Margaret. Margaret's use of Pat's full name matched the serious tone in her voice. Both she and Pat were keenly aware that this talk on the porch could be their last. Pat was awash with everything that made him right, that gave him strength, and that held him back.

He spent his last hour at home on the porch telling Margaret where he would go in England. He described the many steps he would take before earning his wings, his likely flights over France, and his excitement about getting into the fight. Like all mothers, it all seemed too overwhelming and the prospect of Pat flying into combat distressed her to no end. Still she offered encouraging words and forced a smile in response to Pat's excitement.

About eight o'clock Al showed up, as did Clara. After double checking his bags and taking one last look around the house, Pat and Al began their walk to the station. Margaret was wrapping some applesauce cake for Pat's trip. She carefully folded four corners of a napkin over the warm treat then headed out to Clara's awaiting car, a 1914 Monroe Coupe. Clara's husband Matt, being a successful merchant in town, possessed one of the few automobiles in town.

"Pat, I wonder if I get drafted and end up in France if I'll see you there?" asked Al.

"Well, if you do, you'll be seeing me overhead. My job will be to keep the Hun flyers out of the sky and away from the boys in the trenches. It's a big theater over there. I'd be surprised if we met in Europe. I'm afraid we'll just have to wait 'till we both come home," he assured his closest friend. Pat felt different leaving Momence this time. It felt more profound. He would sail for England in a matter of days.

The two life-long buddies ascended up River Street toward Range talking all the way as they had hundreds of times as kids. Margaret and Clara followed behind. At Range Street they turned to the north. Then east onto Front Street where Chuck Astle was standing in front of his hardware store wearing a long white apron with his hands on his hips. He waved good bye. Pat ran over and shook his hand. "See yah, Mr. Astle," he said, looking up at the ornamentation of the brick building that marked the town, then back to Chuck. "We'll be back as soon as we push the Hun back behind his own border.

"Good luck, Pat. You'll do fine," returned Astle. Pat turned and ran towards Al, much as he had done years before on his way to the Quarry to swim. Astle knew more of what Pat would face than the young, enthusiastic O'Brien. Astle turned and entered the hardware store, choking up at bit before placing the "open" sign in the window.

Pat and Al arrived at the depot a few minutes later. Margaret and Clara were exiting the car. None other than Gus Altorfer was still running trains north from Momence. Pat gave Al a solid handshake. Al stepped back as Margaret took Pat's arm and the group walked up onto the platform. Pat was the only passenger boarding the train this morning. He stood with his arms around Margaret and Clara as Al lifted Pat's bags up onto the train.

"Good-bye Clare," Pat said softly giving her a kiss on the cheek. Clara held tightly to her kerchief dabbing the corners of her eyes.

"Ok ma, I'm off," Pat said to Margaret. He kissed her on the cheek and gave her a big hug. As they pulled apart Pat flashed her famous smile and Margaret smiled through her tears. Pat lifted his right hand and placed it aside her warm cheek.

"I'll be back mom," he said.

As the train pulled away Pat stood at the bottom of the steps hanging outside to look back at his mom, Clara and Al. Suddenly, he gave that familiar wave of his right arm as he had to Agnes many times before. Margaret said a short prayer for her son's safety and Clara could do little more than watch him leave with tears streaming down her face.

On the way home, Margaret's face was frozen with terror. She and Clara did not speak a word. They both cried all the way home. Stepping up onto the porch when they got home, Margaret took Clara's hand. "Let's have some applesauce cake, huh, Clare?" Clara smiled, "Yes, let's do!" she said.

The contrast between the O'Brien household and that of Paul Raney's could not be more dramatic. On the day Pat sat on the O'Brien front porch, the Raney's were serving a big meal on a large mahogany table for family and friends in honor of Paul's departure. The Raney's were well known and Paul's father was beginning what would become a notable political and legal career. Paul and Pat had little sense of their differences and had instantly become close chums.

One similarity between the two men was their unlikely protestant faith. Pat, possessing an iconic Irish name was assumed to be Catholic by many, yet he was Protestant. Raney, being of Huguenot ancestry was a descendent of a minority line of French known as the Protestant French. What really counted between them was that Pat and Paul both loved flying and had a great sense of adventure. They provided each other the type of instant therapy present exclusively reserved for two best friends.

Once in Toronto, Pat paid one last visit to the Raney home before sailing for England. Mrs. Raney felt as though she was sending two boys to war. During Pat's short time in Toronto she, like so many before her, took a strong liking to Pat and considered him a "second son." It was obvious to her and Paul's father how close the two boys had become. Pat had charmed the entire Raney family.

"You two be careful, mind you," said Mr. Raney to Pat and Paul standing on the platform at Toronto's Union Station. Sensing that the Paul's parents may want to say good bye to Paul alone, Pat turned to talk to Ed Garnett, one of the eighteen heading for England. Paul shook the hand of his father in somewhat aristocratic manner but said good-bye to his mother Jessie in much the same manner as had Pat.

The eighteen pilots that made up two flights "A" and "B" were bound for St. John, New Brunswick. Nine of the flyers were British subjects and the other nine were Americans. This first batch of Borden trained pilots all had previous experience flying which accounted for the large contingent of Americans. Like Pat, they had joined the Royal Flying Corps impatient to join the action. All but one Canadian pilot, H.K. Boysen, was saying good-bye to relatives on the platform. Boysen was from western Canada and had said his goodbyes at home in much the same way as had Pat. Only one American, had relatives on the platform that morning. His name was Frank McClurg from Buffalo, New York.

The trip to St. John took most of the day. The eighteen spent the first hour somewhat pensive about their departing. But in no time, Pat had them all working the dice game while others played cards. Travel with Pat was never boring and the men extended their fun until arriving at St. John Union Station where they exited the train.

"Borden Flights 'A' and 'B' load this vehicle immediately!" shouted a stout Duty Officer picking them out as the eighteen exited the train. The group took a short ride to the port area where they laid eyes on the R.M.S. Megantic for the first time. The steamship Megantic was launched in April, 1908, just in time to see duty as a troopship during World War I. The steamer was large for its day, at just over 550 feet. She offered accommodations for 260 first-class, 430 second-class, and 1,000 third class passengers. Troops were housed in third class with officers in first-class. While designed to carry both passengers and freight, the Megantic was pressed almost immediately into service as a troop carrier between Canada and England.

The entire port area was teeming with military shipments both inbound and outbound. Hundreds of infantry were streaming up planks onto the Megantic which was clearly one of the largest ships in the harbor, if not the largest. Pat could see what seemed like acres of stevedores loading munitions, food, machinery, and horses. It was a scene that startled every man in his flight.

"Jesus Christ," said Paul, somewhat surprising Pat by the use of the Lord's name. "Look at them!" Paul exclaimed. "Pat, have you ever seen so many men and so much equipment in your life!"

It was truly a startling sight and the eighteen got a sense for the first time of the scale and mass of the war effort coming out of Canada. "I can't imagine what England looks like," said Pat as the two picked up their bags and followed the Duty Officer to the point of embarkation.

Prior to taking the ramp to board, Paul turned to Pat startled, "Pat, look at that! Germans!" shouted Paul. Indeed the Megantic also served as a prison ship bringing captured German infantry from France to prison camps in North America.

Once settled in their cabins, the eighteen came on deck to see the New Brunswick coast slip away. They would spend two weeks at sea and there was plenty of chatter among the troops about German U-boats hell-bent on intercepting their arrival at Liverpool along the way.

Chapter 21

An Urgent Flurry

Pat, Paul Raney and the sixteen others from Borden arrived in Liverpool on June 28, 1917. Liverpool made the port at St. John look like a small fishing village. They were stunned by the intensity at the port where thousands of men were boarding North American ships and pulling off much needed supplies that were all destined for the fields of France and camps throughout England.

"This way, gentlemen," barked yet another duty officer showing them the way. "O'Brien, Raney, Robinson!"

"I'm O'Brien," said Pat.

"Raney here," stated Paul as he shuffled up to the two walking briskly in front.

"You two are to take the train to Lincoln along with Robinson. Where's Robinson?" asked the duty officer.

"Chuck!" yelled Paul. Charles Claude, or "C.C." as the men called him, was double timing up to the three men.

"I'm Robinson," said Chuck.

All four together now, the Duty Officer spoke to them as they walked briskly toward the trains.

"I've got to get you three on the next train out, post haste. You are going to start advanced fighter training tomorrow. You'll post with the 23rd Training Wing and fly to the aerodromes at Scampton, South Carlton, Waddington and Doncaster for specialized training. Perhaps time at Thetford, as well. The others will join you later but they will start at Thetford first. From there, you'll go to Oxford and Reading University for specialize training. That will be in about three weeks.

"And after that?" asked Chuck. The officer looked up from his clip board at Chuck with a rather uneasy glance. Then, just as suddenly, he dropped his eyes back down.

"More trains, huh, Paul?" said Pat, trying to break the ice. They both had a laugh but the officer was strictly business and never flinched. They walked one hundred yards to eleven awaiting trains that were all heading in different directions and loaded with troops. The rest of the Borden group followed about forty yards behind. When they all got to the platform Pat, Paul and Chuck said goodbye to their mates assuring each man they'd meet again in France. Handshakes and backslaps were quick as the duty officer had no time for goodbyes and the train whistle was signaling departure.

Pat and his two mates stepped briskly behind their duty officer to an awaiting train. "I might not see any of those guys again," Pat thought to himself. The week together on board the Megantic had galvanized many friendships. He was glad they took many photos on the trip over. His favorite one was of him and Paul on the deck of the Megantic, basking in the sun half-way across the Atlantic. In the photo, the two were sitting on pallets of cargo, grinning like school kids and enjoying their last days before war.

War is full of sudden and unexplained separations. They distressed Pat a bit. The sudden breakup of the gang from Borden at the train depot would be the first of many such evaporations. More would occur in the days ahead. Based on the RFC track record in the Great War to date, no more than twenty percent of these men would be alive in two months. That fact impressed most who heard it. Men who focused on their own survival didn't give it much thought. Pat gave it due respect and had the ability to draw strength from his past friendships. It made him more determined to defeat the enemy but the partings were always tough.

Suddenly, Pat found himself standing in a long line, cued up to board in sequence as each man flashed his orders to the officer at the bottom of the steps.

"Now, how's a fellow to get rid of these sea legs if all they do is put us in a boat, then a train, then the spacious cockpit of an aeroplane?" Pat asked, soliciting more laughs from his two buddies. Still, the officer delivering them to the train held his serious tone. Pat had a quick flash of his days running down Front Street or off to the Quarry for a swim. He hadn't had that much exercise in weeks and he missed it.

"Well, that's that, I guess. We won't see those Borden fellows again" said Chuck as they shuffled into line.

"You don't know that, Chuck," Paul interjected. "We may see them at Thetford or even France," he added with a hopeful tone.

"Come on you dog faces, we're here to kick the Hun, remember!" said Pat. They boarded but had to sit separately as the car had only a few open seats.

Pat tossed his bag overhead above his seat. Knowing he was in for another long trip, he grabbed the overhead rack with his two hands and let his body weight drop so as to take some of the tension out of his back. He then took his seat and Paul sat just behind him. Chuck was two seats up and across the aisle. After some artful negotiations, Pat talked an officer across the aisle to switch with Chuck so the three could talk on the trip. They were scheduled to ride straight across England to Lincoln in just under two hours. Their destination was the Central Flying School and aerodrome at South Carlton near Lincoln.

Advanced training at the Central Flying School was designed not so much to produce aviators as such, but professional war pilots. This was to be achieved by accepting only men who already held a Royal Aero Club Certificate for advanced training. Many graduates of the school had extensive and honorable records from Somme and other battles over France. The great Billy Mitchell and even the First Lord of the Admiralty, Winston Churchill, who influenced the use of aircraft in naval operations, studied flight at Central Flying School. Having recently obtained their Pilots Certificates, Pat, Paul and C.C. would be taught to fight in all types of aircraft. This explained why the three Borden graduates were scheduled to fly out of multiple aerodromes.

The school's head was Captain Alan John Lance Scott who never became a great pilot himself but was a pugnacious dogfighter whose solo missions sometimes got him into trouble. After crashing and breaking both legs, he continued training on canes and had to be assisted into the cockpit. Scott's appetite for the daring set a tone at the school. It would embellish the likes of Pat O'Brien and other young men like him who tossed caution to the wind. There was order to Scott's process but it was his feeling that the school was training pilots for frontline duties and instructors should not teach by the book. Scott drew his instructors from men who had faced the Hun and used every instinct they had to kill first and survive second.

All talk on the train was about what the three men might experience at South Carlton. A few men familiar with Britain's fighter pilot school shared what they knew. It struck Pat that no one used the term "pilot" in Britain. They'd refer to them as "fighter pilots," "scouts," "bombers," "spotters" and other titles specific to their finely tuned skills. The train arrived at Lincoln in no time, fueled by the non-stop, two hour conversation in Pat's car. The busy shuttle train unloaded yet another payload of young men like ants from an ant hill, backing out of the Lincoln Station almost immediately to retrieve another full load at Liverpool.

South Carlton consisted of 7 large canvas and brick hangars on a grass area with 2000 yard sides. Living quarters, stores, meeting area and offices were all wooden huts. When the men arrived they were immediately directed to what would become a ten minute orientation with about forty other new pilots.

There was a decisively different tone to training in England compared to Canada and certainly San Diego. Every minute of the day had an intense urgency about it. It was assumed you knew how to fly. Scott's men were being trained to be aggressive fighters, to kill and lead others into battle to kill. This difference was immediately noticeable to Pat and his buddies.

Following a morning lecture each day, the men went through a series of training devices after lunch that they would repeat daily until a passing score was reached. On the first day, Pat was placed in a pivoting chair and spun violently for one full minute, then did his best to walk sixteen feet down a narrow plank. In the first week, he fell off nearly every step. As the days went by he was able to walk the entire plank without falling off. Holding balance and focus after performing an erratic maneuver to avoid the enemy was critical to survival.

Peripheral vision was expanded through the use of small model planes on sticks which were moved gradually into their visual range from behind the head. A standard was set for recognizing the approach of these models at a certain points from the left and right side. There were extensive shooting ranges with one-hundred feet of track running parallel to targets. Pat and his fellow pilots were placed in a gyrating fuselage without wings on a small rail car and slid rapidly back and forth on the track by four running men. The goal was to meet accuracy standards while shooting the Gatling gun on the move. Every attempt was made to duplicate battle conditions in the air.

And the men also flew constantly. A good portion of their training involved actual distress situations in the air created purposely to teach pilots how to come out of a dive, land after loss of fuel or damage to their landing gear or to climb out of their seat to free up a jammed machine gun. It was not unusual for casualties to occur in training.

The most famous story that every new pilot heard in short order was of Captain Scott's adventure when his plane climbed to 6,000 feet, rolled over only to have Scott's safety belt snap tossing him from the plane. The plane was such that Scott was "caught" by the tail wing, allowing him to hang on and crawl back into his cockpit. Such tales about men skirting death became part of every man's daily diversion throughout the war. The story about Scott was true and parachutes were not used.

All three men were thrilled at the level of training they received in their three weeks at South Carlton and the other three aerodromes. Twice they flew to Thetford, south of Lincoln, and were able to visit with a few of the original eighteen. The school gave Pat and his mate's exposure to some of the top pilots in the world at the time. They intensified their abilities as fighters and survived to transfer to the next stage of training.

On July 20, their final day at South Carlton, Pat and the other forty assembled for a final send-off with none other than Scott himself who tried to personally commence as many of his graduate classes as he could. Wasting little time, Scott addressed the men.

"Alright, Gentlemen, we will proceed with our final regiment this morning to review some critical elements of aerial combat. First of all, let's review some basic assumptions." He pointed to a large blackboard with his wooden prompt. Pat, Paul and C.C. focused intently as Scott read the list, tapping aggressively on each line as he read.

"One. Never fly in a straight path. Constantly vary your pathway to be less vulnerable. Second, keep your head turning at all times in all directions." Holding up the standard white pilot's scarf he added, "This silk scarf, my fine gentleman, is not to embellish your looks. Always wear your neck scarf so as not to cause irritation from constantly turning your head in every direction. It's a tool of war as much as your gun."

"As scouts, you will always approach your target from above with the sun behind you so as to make yourself invisible to their spotters. When you close, close fast - firing the entire time and approach your target from behind where he is most vulnerable. And make every bullet count," had stated.

He then reached for the pistol lying on the table in front of him. "By the way, you'll always carry this!" He held the pistol in his right hand somewhat in the direction of his temple. "It has six shots but only one is needed. And believe me fellas, it's a better way to die than burning alive," he stated coldly. The room sobered up. Pilots carried pistols to kill themselves rather than burn in a fiery crash during a spinning nose dive.

The meeting ended around 10:00 a.m. The ever present duty officer appeared with his clip board and yet another gathering began to evaporate. There were no festive congratulations, just a few quick handshakes as the men hurried to get their bags, board their train and exit camp.

It was the twenty-second day in England for Pat, Paul and C.C. After grabbing their bags, they jumped in the back of a truck with six other men and were driven quickly to Lincoln. After the regimental cueing and clipboard check-in, they boarded the train and headed south to Reading, England.

Their destination was the No. 1 School of Military Aeronautics just south of London and the No. 2 School of Military Aeronautics at Oxford, a mere twenty-three miles from Reading. They would receive some additional officer training, fly different model planes, including their first two-seaters, and prepare for France. It would be their final week in England.

As the train clicked south carrying a full load of both military and civilian passengers, Pat sat reading the morning paper from London. He constantly read and never entered a train without a newspaper tucked under his arm, a habit he had acquired back in the Stockton Run days.

"My God, Paul. The Russians have quit!" said Pat looking over the London Times where reports were coming in regarding the turmoil in Russia.

"What do you mean, quit?" Paul asked.

"It's a revolt. Chaos!" exclaimed Pat. "Listen to this," Pat began reading the latest London Times report from Petrograd.

About 500,000 workers and soldiers in Petrograd demonstrated, again demanding "all power to the soviets", "down with the war", and "down with the ten capitalist ministers". The Provisional Government opened an offensive against the Germans on 1 July but it soon collapsed. The news of the offensive and its collapse intensified the struggle of the workers and the soldiers. A new crisis in the Provisional Government began on 15 July.

"So where does that leave the eastern front?" asked Chuck.

"I'd say if the Germans weren't so tied up with us in the west, they could waltz into Russia," said Paul.

"I'm not so sure. Which army would you defeat?" Pat asked. ""No one knows who's in charge! It doesn't appear to be the Czar, that's for sure!"

After Pat finished the story, he passed the paper to Paul and eventually Chuck read it as well. It was just one more report of calamity that was grabbing the world by the throat. Pat and his two Borden chums were one week away from landing amidst the chaos in France but the Russian withdrawal wore on the minds of men fighting all across Europe.

Arriving at Reading around noon, they immediately proceeded to the airfield which was located at Coley Park. Camp for Pat's group, which was scheduled to spend most of their final week in the air, was established near the airfield.

They would spend time taking "dual instruction" as it was called, flying double-seaters. This was a much more difficult type of aircraft to operate. The Avro 504 was in use for this purpose. It also allowed Pat to experience heights of over 10,000 feet for the first time.

It was the Sopwith Pup, however, that was finally chosen for Pat and his buddies. Each pilot was matched to a plane. Much of the selection process had to do not only with the needs of the Corps but the skills and personality of the pilot. What Pat did not know at the time was that being assigned the Sopwith Pup also destined him for a particular squadron in France. It also meant that he, Paul and C.C. would be fighting scouts, the most daring and dangerous duty in the sky. Only the most aggressive men were chosen as fighting scouts. The three Borden pilots were at a heightened state of readiness.

On July 24, Pat took his final exam to "officially" earn his Wings. Only Paul Raney passed the written exam but Pat and C.C.'s extensive flying background prior to the war allowed them to receive their wings as well, due to their obvious flying abilities despite not passing the written exam. Paul's engineering training and university schooling prepared him well for such tests. But it was common that pilots with the skill and daring of Pat and C.C. were routinely issued "Wings." The need was great and time was short.

The next day, orders came for Paul Raney to report to Boulogne, France immediately. Pat and C.C. were stunned. They had not considered that their tidy trio would fall victim to war's evaporation process. Pat was particularly hit hard by this for he knew it could be the end for their tight friendship. There was a mere fifteen minutes for good luck and good bye wishes and Paul was off. Pat spent much of his day in the air with his new best buddy, The Sopwith Pup. His readiness for the unpredictability of war was evident in the fact that he was able to put Paul out of his mind and get down to work.

The next morning at breakfast, Paul and C.C. were stunned to see Paul Raney walk in to the mess hall.

"Paul! What the hell are you doing here?" Pat asked. "Yeah, what gives?" Chuck said.

"I have no idea. All I know is we crossed the channel. I got off the boat and there was a duty officer with a megaphone shouting my name," said Paul. "Raney, Lt Paul Raney. Looking for Lt Paul Raney, 66th Squadron. Paul Raney." I could hear the guy as soon as I stepped off the ship."

"What the hell!" said Chuck.

"So I went up to the fellow and said to him, 'I'm Paul Raney.' Then he proceeds to tell me there's been some mistake and I'm to re-board and head right pack to England," Paul said nearly out of breath. "And so here I am back with you jockeys!"

"Well, I'll be damned," said Pat.

"That does it, gents," inserted Chuck. "Look, no more of this splitting up for us. From now on we look for assignments in threes and if one of us gets called up we do everything we can to press that the other two come along as well, deal?"

"Right! We've got to stick together. We know how we work and if we're going to go into that mess let's at least try to do it together," said Paul.

"Then that's it," said Pat. "We'll all press to go as one."

Later that night, when they were having dinner alone, Paul turned to Pat. "If we can't get all three of us. Pat, let's at least do everything we can to make sure you and me are together as far as we can go."

"Sure, Paul," responded Pat. "Let's try to find three but if it doesn't work out, we'll go as two. None of us know what will come in the next day, or the next hour or the next minute for that matter," Pat stated as he cut his piece of ham in a rapid hurried manner as if he had somewhere to be. Paul ate slowly, pondering his fate.

Before anyone else was awake the next day, Pat was up and ready to go. He had already gotten up and walked to the mess where he grabbed his first cup of coffee. He checked the morning board. They were scheduled to go this morning, in the first round. He was full of energy and anticipation for his flight across the channel. Setting his coffee down, he ran back to the tents.

"Let's go!" shouted Pat, waking up his buddies before reveille. "We go to France today!" Pat stood with his hands on his hips smiling broadly at his two mates. He turned and flipped open the tent flap, then turning back he said, "I'll be back."

Paul slowly folded back his cover, not saying a word. His body was moving but his brain was not fully functioning yet. C.C. was awake with his eyes open already but was facing away toward the interior wall of their tent. He'd been lying awake for an hour waiting for the official signal to start his day.

It was July 28, 1917. The men had just spent their last night in England in a tent at Coley Park and were scheduled to depart for France in sequence beginning at 07:15. The infantry took boats across the channel from England but in the case of the Flying Corps, a casualty usually meant a plane was lost, too. So when new pilots crossed over, they brought a new plane with them. Manufacturers would deliver planes to the aerodromes and replacement pilots got them to France.

Pat walked briskly across the field toward the mess for one more cup of coffee. There were dozens of men in full uniform scurrying about, others brushing their teeth in undershirts with white towels slung over their shoulders walking back to their tents. Some were gathering their belongings while officers stood observing and sipping coffee. "First runs," as they were called, walked briskly toward the air field. There were a few handshakes and lots of chatter. Out in the distance Pat could hear the roar of gnomes coughing to full start and still others soaring to their maximum power to lift "Pups" into the air. Pat noticed the dew only slightly lifted from the airfield. He thought about the weight of the air for takeoff. Most significantly, he could see himself in every man moving across this snap-shot landscape of the moment. Pat felt so enormously alive amidst it all.

There was no better marriage of man and machine than these aggressive recruits in the company of Pat O'Brien and their Sopwith Pup aircraft. Perhaps it was the single-seater with all its speed, quickness, and maneuverability. Perhaps it was due to that fact that these pilots were a literal stew of unique and aggressive men from Britain, Canada Australia, New Zealand, U.S.A., South Africa, Ireland, and Argentina, led by Officers that, in the main, were quite young. But clearly more than anything else, it was the internal make-up of every man who, much like Pat, had a special character that only a few men possess. It is inbred in their souls, nurtured in their youth and present at the right time, under the right circumstances, through some fortunate divine timing that elevates the state of mankind.

Clearly the Sopwith Pup was new. It had been introduced to the Royal Flying Corps in January of 1917. Few planes inspired more affection from its pilots than did the "Pup." Agile, responsive, docile, and forgiving, it was originally designed for Harry Hawker himself, then a test pilot for the Sopwith Company. Like many great airmen, the Australian Hawker had roots in engines, automobiles, aeroplanes and had flying in his veins at an early age, like Pat. At the Sopwith Company, in 1915, Hawker had the personal use of a small aircraft he helped refine. That plane developed into the Sopwith Pup.

The "Pup" was superior to the German Fokker scouts and more than a match for any of the new Halberstadt and Albatros scouts. Armed with a single synchronous machine gun, it was lighter and less dangerous than its successor, the Sopwith Camel. Although underpowered, pilots liked the Pup because it was fast and maneuverable. It could climb and hold its altitude better than any other fighter at the time. For Pat O'Brien and the others it meant they would be picking fights with Germany's best, not defending. They were thrilled.

In the last three days at Oxford, Pat lived with his "Pup." He became fully absorbed in its inner workings, maneuverings, and idiosyncrasies. All good fighter pilots "marry" their plane. It is critical to success, as short lived as air combat could be.

Eighteen brand new Sopwith Pups sat at the end of the grassy runway at Coley Park at 07:00 on the morning of July 28. Coley, built on a low-lying ground near the River Kennet, served as the airfield and small aerodrome for the Aeronautical School at Reading. It was also a "jumping off point" for aircraft made in England and destined for France. Newly commissioned 2nd Lieutenant "Patrick Alva O'Brien," as the British documented him when he officially acquired the rank at dawn, was preparing his "Pup" for flight to northern France. His squadron would deliver the planes to the "Pilot Pool's Mess" just behind enemy lines and near a number of Squadron bases engaging the enemy at Ypres.

"How's she look, Pat?" asked Paul Raney who was inspecting his "Pup" to Pat's right.

"She looks clean, Paul," Pat responded. "I'd say they're ready. I know I am!" he said with a broad smile.

Squadrons were comprised of eighteen planes. Each squadron contained three flights of six. Pat and Paul were schedule in the first flight over the Chanel. C.C. was staged just behind them in the second flight, with a third behind that. All eighteen planes would be in the air by 07:30 and on their way to the most northern of the twenty-seven regions in France.

With inspections completed, Pat climbed into the cockpit. The steering wheel of the "Pup" was flat on the bottom, allowing him to see the dials on the dash just below. The entire skeleton of the plane was easily viewed from the interior cockpit. A Vickers 303 engine was mounted squarely in the in the center of the fuselage ahead of the steering wheel just over the crossing wires that formed an "X" in the pilots view. They held the struts and wings secure in the center.

Three prominent instruments on the dash showed altitude, fuel, and pressure. An eight inch curved glass gauge filled with oil and a steel ball showed the attitude of the plane and there was a small crank at the bottom of the dashboard to tighten the drum for the machine gun. Spent shells were shot out the side of the plane from a metal tube that ran behind the dash to the right side of the fuselage. The throttle was on the left, mounted on the inside wall. The rim of the cockpit was lined with leather edging for pilot comfort and the stick was just slightly to the right of center with a handle somewhat in the shape of a lacrosse stick without the webbing. After Pat did all his pre-flight checks on his Sopwith Pup, the grounds crew manned the wheel chucks and a third grabbed the prop of the plane and gave it a few turns to prime the oil pump.

"Contact," shouted Pat as he turned on the magnetos.

"Contact" was repeated and his aid pulled down hard on the propeller. The "Pup" immediately roared to a start. A puff of blue smoke blasted from the rotary gnome engine. Paul and the other five in Pat's flight were in sequence and all six planes were freed of the wheel chucks. First Paul, then Pat, then numbers three through six were in the air heading north. Each man executed a wide turn and reformed heading due south, toward France and the real thing. Second and third flights got off the ground with ease and soon all eighteen were over the channel.

The eighteen were heading for a pre-staging area called the Pilot Pool's Mess near the Pas-de-Calais Region of France. Planes at the Mess replaced casualties from various squadrons who were engaging the enemy for the control Ypres, Flanders, and the Western Front.

As they drew near the airfield, Pat looked toward Paul and pointed below. Around 09:15, the group began their descent one mile from the air field. Officers on the ground, peering up with clip boards in hand, were awaiting the latest "fresh meat," as they were fond of calling incoming pilots from England. Pat could see dozens of wings, some stationary, others taking off, and many taxing across the green field of the Pilot Pool's Mess. He saw the airfield, a few small buildings, rows of white tents, farms and a white stone church in the center of a town near the Pilot Pool's Mess that he would later find out was Estree'-Blanche.

"Hell, that town is smaller than Grant Park," he thought.

There were so many planes landing and departing simultaneously that Pat thought they looked like hawks sweeping down over the Kankakee Marsh to grasp an unsuspecting smallmouth bass for breakfast. As he and the others approached the runway, they could see a flurry of activity in every direction. Suddenly, the green field pushed toward him and he landed his "Pup" on the north end in the direction of the hangers. There were not a lot of structures at the aerodrome. Most planes came and went so frequently that few, if any, were ever stored in hangers.

Pat was finally in France and his war was about to begin. Paul was right behind him and all eighteen had landed with ease. Once they were checked in and squared away their planes they walked through rows of white tents to find number 27. Pat and Paul had arranged for C.C. to be their tent-mate when they arrived. Being in the third flight, Chuck got word at check in and caught up with the two who were squaring off their bunks.

"Meeting in fifteen minutes, gentleman!" shouted an aide walking the tent rows as new pilots arrived. The entire squadron would receive a fairly extensive orientation prior to lunch. The aerodrome was teeming with pilots, planes, trucks, and other military including mechanics, weatherman, radar, signal men, and all the needed personnel to execute and support an attack behind enemy lines. They were all replacements in waiting and they were all new to war. But the Mess was still behind enemy lines and not nearly as chaotic as what was churning in the battlefields five miles south.

For a country hell-bent on expansion, and despite its cunning for war, Germany had a distinct disadvantage. It had enemies on the left and right. To the immediate east was Poland and Czechoslovakia, not exactly a natural buffer between The Deutschland and its feared enemy, Russia. To the west lay France, a formidable foe, but vulnerable nonetheless. South were the great Alps in neutral Switzerland. Most of Germany's northern border abutted the Baltic Seas and North Seas, with the exception of the northwestern corner that touched Luxemburg and Belgium.

If Germany invaded France head-on it would expose its backside to the Russians, ending any notion of a successful conquest. German high command knew that a victory in France would have to be quick so troops could race back east before the Russians could marshal an invasion from the rear.

German Field Marshal Alfred von Schlieffen devised a plan to capture France quickly by attacking through the northwest corner via Luxemburg and Belgium. His plan would then take out British support on the coast before wrapping a noose around Paris and coiling the French Army into their grasp in a sweeping hook motion. From there the Germans would "run to the east" to confront the Russians, who they contrived would not have time to attack before the defeat of France was complete.

Unfortunately, two things in the air were bogging down the large hooking motion along the coast of northern France, rain and the Royal Flying Corps. The "sweeping hook" had been bogged down since 1914 in places like Liege, Marne and Mons. Britain focused on securing the English Channel ports and the British Army's supply lines. The French dug in to prevent German forces from outflanking their troops in the north and charging toward Paris.

As a result, the Germans stalled, ending of the first battle of Ypres. But the toll on both sides was significant. Horses and waves of men had spent months marching head-on into certain slaughter with little effect. Desperate for a breakthrough, tear gas had been introduced throughout Flanders during the second battle of Ypres in 1915 with still no significant advantage to either side.

Pat and Paul had often discussed of the advantages of flying well above the insidious weapons of war on the ground. They viewed such ground tactics as an extension of old, tired warfare now trumped by an air war that they would bring to the fight. The young new warriors in the air understood this before anyone else and it added to their sense of confidence. By war's end, no army would believe a war could be won without the aeroplane.

In 1915, the longest battle of the war ensued at Verdun where the Germans made their first attempt to extradite the British from France. But Britain was still there in force at the start of the great Battle of the Somme in July 1916. Unfortunately, the Germans had deployed one million men to do in the British once and for all.

On the first day of Somme, the British lost 58,000 troops. By the time both sides relinquished the deadlock in November, the Royal Flying Corps was devastated, a significant portion of it from Captain Baron von Richthofen and his 'Flying Circus'. It was Somme that created the unprecedented urgency to bring pilots from North America so quickly.

But the largest and most costly third Battle of Ypres flared up on July 21, seven days before Pat and his mates left Coley Park in their brand new planes. The battle would not end until November. Also, known as the Battle of Passchendaele, in which the British, Canadians, French and other forces recaptured the Passchendaele Ridge east of the Ypres, it would cost nearly half a million casualties to all sides.

When Pat, Paul, C.C., and the rest of the squadron had left England, the gore of war was simply an abstract idea. As Pat learned more about the ground war from various men at the base, he was glad his war would be fought in the sky. With all their hours in the air, all the bullets expelled from their Gatling guns and numerous near-fatal accidents in the field, there was one experience that none of them had yet experienced. No one had seen the pointed end of a bullet coming in their direction. After all, the Pilot Pool's Mess was eighteen miles from enemy lines.

PART FIVE

WAR

Chapter 22

The Scout

The eighteen planes brought in by Pat's squadron found their place in a congested parking area that seemed to cover a space the size of six football fields.

"Alright, each one of you men, turn in your paper work to me and you will be released from your aircraft," shouted yet one more duty officer working his clip board. Thus, were eighteen more planes checked into inventory.

"Go stand in that line in front of the middle tent over there," stated the officer pointing the eraser end of his pencil in the direction of a large sign that read "Pilot Check-In."

Pat and the others walked across a large grassy field toward the tents, peering in every direction at a hornet's nest of activity both on the ground and in the air. Pat felt his guts churn with excitement over the sheer scale of the force and the energy that emulated from it. The Pilot Pool's Mess was congested with planes, pilots and support personnel from all over the British Empire. Typical of new recruits, Pat and his squadron were extremely eager to get assigned to a squadron and eager to fight.

Arriving ahead of the others, Pat stood in front a rough looking wooden table with a sign hanging off the edge that read "check in." The table looked rather make-shift and sat in front of a large white tent which was the closest thing anyone might identify as an administrative office. "O'Brien," barked Pat to the clerk checking names.

The officer looked at his list. "O'Brien, O'Brien, O'Brien," he mumbled. "Ah, yes. O'Brien. Are you Mike O'Brien?"

"No, Pat."

"Pat, Mike, you Mick's are all the same," said the smart-alecky Brit.

"Hey, Limey! I'm American, ok?" said Pat, a little perturbed at the duty officer's attitude. "I'm only here because you Brits haven't been able to put the Hun in his place yet, you see? So, get on with it." Pat tolerated a lot of things but seldom allowed anyone to take a shot at the U.S. or his Irish heritage without retort, even if in jest. After the words came out of his mouth, it struck him how intense he had become. He'd always been aggressive in his life but for the first time, he realized how successful Britain had been in preparing him for war.

The British clerk tried to ignore Pat's comment. "Ok, yes, here you are. Right then! Currently, there is no assignment for you Lieutenant. You will check in at the provisions tent, pick up your bedding and essentials and proceed to tent number 73 which is located in the northwest corner of the field barrack in that direction."

Pat didn't react but was frozen on the clerk's words, "no assignment for you." Seeing little reaction from Pat, the clerk added "You do see the area don't you, O'Brien?" looking up at Pat and pointing north.

Pat looked a little befuddled. "Yes, beyond the hedge, right?" he said in a hesitant tone.

"Correct." Then in a dismissing fashion, the clerk shouted, "Next!"
Paul Raney stepped up.

"Name please," said the clerk looking down at his list.

"Raney. Paul Raney," Paul responded

Pat stood about fifteen yards from the check-in table awaiting Paul and casted his eyes on the undaunted actions around him. He felt like he might explode if he had to wait much longer before seeing action.

In similar short order Paul was checked-in and walked up to Pat, breaking his thoughts. "Somewhat disheartening, signing over our aircraft, hey Pat?" said Paul as they stood waiting for C.C.

Still looking out over the scene before him, Pat responded, "Well, that's to be expected. We were delivery boys on this mission, Paul. I'm sure we'll get our chance plenty soon. We damned well better. I'm tired of waiting. I've been trying to get into this fight since San Diego," he said, somewhat to himself.

He gazed over the anthill that was the Pilot's Pool Mess, squinting to focus closer on the detailed preparations of pilots, officers, drivers and grounds crew. Paul noticed the intensity of Pat's stare and the gnawing of his tense jaw muscle, finally adding, "What about San Diego?"

"Uh, nothin', let's go," Pat responded.

One hour later, Pat, Paul, and C.C. were sitting amid rows of benches positioned under large Corsica trees that fully shadowed the day's sun from the pilots below. Standing before them, in front of a large blackboard, was a Captain Reynolds. Reynolds had a reputation for being honest and direct, but fair. The men were told they would get the straight dope from Reynolds. They were about to discover this reputation was authentic.

It was not lost on Reynolds that the sole reason men sat before him each day was to replace a continuous stream of death and carnage that was falling from the skies over France, relentlessly for months. The dominance of the Hun kept the Pilot Pool's Mess in a constant state of high alert. For Reynolds there were no days of distinction, just a continuous stream of red faced eager pilots in the morning who went away and never came back.

There was an authentic tone to his voice. He was not attempting to impress the new recruits with bravado but spoke with a resolve that only a man of his experience could muster. Reynolds had been shot down three times and had a "replacement leg of wood," as he called it, from his last and final flight.

"Alright, let's get started then," stated Reynolds, holding his own version of the now familiar clip board.

"This will be rather brief. You men are all experienced in the Royal Flying Corps routine and have a good number of hours in the air. Let me explain how things will work here." Pat and his mate listened eagerly for the one bit of information they all had on their mind - "when do we fly?"

"You are now residents of the Pilot Pool's Mess and everything you see around here is designed to be minimal and temporary, including your accommodations. Our very location, in fact, is a secret. We could move tomorrow, depending on how the front is developing. The Mess is nothing more than a transfer point, a "throughput" you might say, for newly trained pilots such as you chaps who are all waiting to be assigned to a particular squadron. The selection criterion has little to do with you or any of us here at the Mess. It has a lot to do with the men you will replace," said Reynolds. "They go down. We call you up."

Pat welcomed Reynolds's urgent tone.

"You see those six men there, walking fully geared toward the air field?" Reynolds asked, pointing as the men all turned their heads. "That will be you as soon as we get word from Squadron control of losses that need filling." The word "losses" did not quite register with each man as they were all hell-bent to simply get in the air.

"Some of you could go this afternoon, tomorrow or next week," stated Reynolds. "There's just no way of knowing when, but I guarantee you that we've got plenty of fresh coal to fill the fiery furnace," he said, pointing to the huge number of tents beyond the trees. Lowering his voice, he went on.

"We do have a Chaplin here at the Mess if you are so inclined. There will be little time to think of such things once you get your Squadron assignment. If you are the religious type, I suggest you deal with your souls now rather than in the air."

"Alright, with that said, here is how our system works," Reynolds began elevating his tone once again. "When we get a call from Squadron, you'll hear a large bell – right there," he said pointing to a large cast iron bell atop a thirty-foot poll near the administration tent. "That indicates we are initiating a 'call-up.' A call-up means that we are posting assignments for pilots – generally in flights of six. You'll see these postings within the barrack section of the camp, at the air field, in the food tent and near the bell tower. Orders can change by the minute so stay alert. You can expect to see postings almost simultaneously to the sounding of the bell."

"One final word," Reynolds continued, placing his pencil behind his ear. "You've been assigned six men to a tent. I can tell you that those men may or may not be called up with you and may not even be in your same squadron. Each call-up is based on the needs in the battle area, not of the Mess."

To Pat, Reynolds' comments alluded to the now familiar "evaporation process." But Pat barely paid it any mind. He wanted to go. The "call-up" bell rang eleven times the first day and rang so frequently each day after that, it put all men at the Mess in a constant state of anxiety, wanting to be called so badly, being stirred to their feet each time the bell rang and then walking back disappointed at not seeing their name on the list.

They bitched to each other about the whole thing in order relieve some of the adrenalin flow from their body. The pilots at the Mess were in the right state of mind as far as the RFC was concerned. Good RFC pilots were to have one focus – to get to the front!

To fill time, the men waited, played cards, wrote home, and did their regiment of exercises. Pat O'Brien conducted "games of chance" during the downtimes with the infamous dice he still had from Richmond. He also ran daily, more than any other pilot. He wanted to be strong going into battle. He wrote letters to Margaret, Elmer, Clara, and of course, Agnes. He also sent a note to his buddy Charles Pearl informing him that he had arrived in France.

On Sunday morning, August 12, at 7:37 the first bell of the day sounded. Not every man exited his tent but spotters were sent to check the board. Pat always went. He and Paul glanced up at the posting which read, "The following men report to airfield for immediate departure. Aircraft: Sopwith Pup. Squadron: 66th. Location: Estree'-Blanche." Then the list of names. The first four were not recognized by Pat or Paul, then "Lt. Paul Raney," and one more man named Keeler. Paul was thrilled. Pat could not believe it but he congratulated his buddy.

Paul and Pat turned and headed for their tent. Paul's gate was significantly quicker and for once, Pat was working to keep up with his shorter mate. Paul grabbed his things and headed for the airfield. Pat walked with him as far as the airfield, watching him depart until he could no longer see the plane. He choked up a bit, not for his lacking a flight but for his close buddy whom he loved like a brother.

Pat paused before heading back to his tent. "No bells," Pat thought. "There's usually two or three by now each morning." Frustration began to settle in again. "When will I go?" he said under his breath.

Nearly three hours went by and nothing, no bells, no messages, no word. Pat was fighting his feelings of frustration, always one to view negative situations in a positive light.

Meanwhile, Paul and the other five pilots were checking in with the last personnel officer they would see holding a clipboard. As they were doing so, a messenger ran up. "We've got another one, sir," stated the young orderly out of breath.

"Well, call the mess right away and we'll set him up with these boys," said the personnel chief. True to his promise, Paul pressed the officer that he'd "be nuts" not to call up Pat.

"Alright, ask for O'Brien," said the busy officer. He had little preference. His main focus was to make sure he delivered six pilots and six planes as ordered.

[263]

Back at the Mess a steady rain was softening up the entire terrain. An orderly rode a motorcycle through the muddy paths between barrack tents counting backwards as he passed, "77, 76, 75, 74…..73" He jumped off the bike leaving it running and popped his head inside Pat's tent.

"You O'Brien?" he said with a nervous voice.

"Yeah!" responded Pat.

"Let's go! You're up!"

Pat was in his breeches but didn't want to wait. He tossed on a rain coat and bolted from the tent. He swung his leg over the motorbike sitting behind the orderly as the bike slammed into gear. They shot down the tent row, spitting water and mud out the back of the cycle and good amount on Pat. The orderly shouted information over the roar of the two-cylinder bike. He snapped his head back to the right so Pat could hear him, then quickly forward again so as not to lose his direction. Pat only stared forward as if he were steering the bike himself.

"You're going to be driven in the supply truck to the aerodrome at Estree'-Blanche. It's not far and they've got an aircraft for you."

The motor cycle slid to a stop, grinding its wheels into the stone lot where the truck was waiting. Pat jumped off. A driver was waving him over to the truck. Pat bolted toward the truck then suddenly noticed "brass" on his right. Halting abruptly, he turned, went to attention and gave a hearty salute. "What a dumb-ass salute these British have!" he thought.

"Welcome to the corps, young man," said one of the officers.

"Thank you, sir," Pat returned while releasing his salute before bolting for the truck. The two officers had a good chuckle over the enthusiastic American.

"Must be a Yankee!" said one British officer to the other as they stood watching the hurried scene. "No one but a Yank would have the cheek to show up that way, you know!"

"Where's the man's flying breeches?" said the other. Pat's coat had blown open while running, revealing his incomplete uniform.

The lorry backed out and rushed off to the 66th squadron aerodrome. When it pulled up at Estree'-Blanche, Paul was chatting with a few "experienced" pilots. He stopped that conversation as soon as he saw Pat exit his transport.

"What the hell!" said Pat reaching Paul who turned and grabbed Pat at the elbow, steering him in the direction of the airfield.

"Just as I was meeting our officer, this orderly came up and said they needed another. So, naturally, I pressed them to call you up," said Paul as the two men walk briskly across the field.

"Well, I'm glad you did. I was about to go nuts back at the Mess," stated a relieved Pat.

"Where the hell did you get all the mud?" asked Paul.

"Oh, that goofy ass that runs the motorcycle through field barracks picked me up. It's raining like cats and dogs back at the mess," said Pat. "Anyway, I got here as soon as I could."

Pat and Paul walked to the edge of the airfield where 2nd Lt. Ralph Arundel Stedman was looking over a flight plan posted on a board which had been nailed to a tree. A pile of discarded paperwork was held down by a fist-sized rock on a table next to the tree. Pilots would sign their sheet, place it under the rock and run off to their aircraft. Stedman had just executed his and Pat could see Ralph's signature in the lower right corner on the top sheet as it flipped in the wind.

"Ok, Ralph, we're here," said Paul Raney to Stedman as they ran up. "This is Pat O'Brien."

"Hello, O'Brien," The two men shook hands.

"Ok, I've been assigned my plane and have done preliminary inspections. Paul, you've already signed, right?"

"Yes," said Paul.

"O'Brien, sign here," said Stedman pointing to Pat's plane order. "This gives you an aeroplane.

Pat looked up at three Sopwith Pups about thirty yards from the men.

"It's the one on the right, Pat," said Stedman. "They're all new machines."

[265]

Pat read the plane number, "B1710. Hum, my first plane." He signed his name. Stedman took the paper and placed it in the pile, plopping the rock on top with a soft thud.

"We'll depart just before dusk, tonight" said Stedman. "It will be just you two and me. I've been up a few times. My job is to take you men over the line, get a look at things, map out our location in case you're ever lost, locate the forests, lakes, and other landmarks, and get the general lay of the land, ok?" Pat nodded aggressively.

"We'll only be out about twenty minutes or so and right back here," said Stedman.

"It's that close?" asked Pat.

"Sure, very close," answered Paul who had picked-up that bit of information during his first ten minutes at the aerodrome.

"Now, it's not likely we'll see any Huns tonight, but you should approach the flight as if anything could happen. But if we do see them, we'll avoid engaging them at this point, alright?" said Stedman. Both men nodded this time.

Prior to the flight, Ralph Stedman and two other pilots talked to Pat and Paul about flying over enemy lines. Stedman related his experiences thus far and the others, who had flown the front for one month, talked about their experiences. These men, still alive after a month, were considered veterans in the dangerous world of air battle. Average life expectancy in the RFC on the Western Front was two weeks. Pat and Paul considered the information helpful but they knew so little about actual combat that they really had no way of fully understanding.

They departed at 19:50 reaching the line in about two minutes. Stedman lead them to some key landmarks, pointing down and flashing fingers which he planned to reference when they returned. The men saw no enemy and soon turned back toward the aerodrome.

"When do we go out next?" asked Pat.

"Tomorrow morning. Two hours. Also, somewhat of a practice flight but there's a greater chance you'll see Hun," said Stedman. "You depart at 07:45. I'm not going with you. You'll fly with Bill Keast."

Pat and Paul didn't know Keast but they sought him out and the three men talked late into the evening about their flight in the morning. Keast had been over the line about 12 times.

On Monday the 13th, Pat was up at five and quickly grabbed coffee and a bit of toast. Keast, Paul, and Pat lifted off the ground exactly at 07:45, Pat's second flight. In three minutes they were over the line flying at about 6,000 feet. They were laying high up in the sky, keeping the sun behind them so as not to be spotted by enemy below. Pat panned the space above and below his plane though the likelihood was that if they saw the Hun it would be below them.

Just five minutes in, Keast was pointing. Three German two-seaters were at about 3,000 feet. They were bomb droppers, edging toward the allied side of the front to destroy artillery. It would be a challenge. The pilot had a front machine gun and the observer-bomber also had a gun on rotation that could shoot in any direction. Keast rotated his right hand horizontally indicating that the planes had a rotating gun. He flashed fingers to Pat and Paul indicating who would attack which plane below and the three planes rolled into a dive.

The speed was exhilarating. Pat kept his eyes one hundred percent on his target. The earth seemed to push quickly toward him. He was focused on the plane farthest east in the group. Suddenly, at two hundred yards from his target, Pat squeezed the gun and an explosion of bullets leaped into the guts of plane three. The observer was pumping lead right at Pat but to no effect. Pat could hear the shots wiz by but didn't think about it. Suddenly, he was on top of his target and flew past. Performing an acute loop Pat approached the Hun from the bottom.

A burst of his bullets emptied into the two-seater which was now exposed and possessed little ability to shoot in a downward direction. Instantly, there was a burst of smoke and the plane rolled, going into the spinning nose dive. Pat looped again and looked down to see the wings of his victims plane peel away from the fuselage, flopping in the wind. He held his direction and watched the Hun crash. It was Pat's first kill.

There was a second burst of smoke on the ground to the right. Paul had gotten one, too. The third was getting away. Pat arched his plane hard to the right chasing Keast who was trailing his stubborn Hun target. Paul had also turned and all three men chased full throttle for two miles. Suddenly, Keast waved them off and the third Hun got away.

It was time to get back before more "heat" arrived. Pat's appetite was forever moistened. He was thrilled. The two rookies had outdone Keast. All three planes landed back at the aerodrome at 09:25 hours. Paul leaped from his plane and ran towards Pat who was standing aside his plane looking for holes.

"Boy, some practice run, huh, Pat?" said Paul, also looking at Pat's plane before both men turned to head back to check-in.

"What a run," said Pat. "We had those Huns running scared, didn't we? After checking in, the two friends went to grab lunch.

"That certainly didn't feel like practice, huh Pat?" stated Paul as he took his seat.

"Yeah, what the hell constitutes a practice verses what we did this morning? Seemed pretty real to me!" laughed Pat. Pat was finishing off a second helping of potatoes. He and Paul talked about their flights posted for the afternoon. They were scheduled for separate flights. Paul's run was a routine patrol near Roulers and Pat's included strafing trenches at ground level near Passchendaele.

"Those two fellas we talked to this morning?" asked Paul.

"Yeah?" responded Pat.

"They said our first or second patrol would give us a taste at low altitude attack, so we might as well get used to it."

"Use to it? Ha! That's a joke." Pat looked down smiling. "What a difference from Borden," he said.

"That's for sure," responded Paul. They were joined subsequently by Eve Lascelles, Edgar Garland the New Zealander, and Frank Wilkins. They all had tales to tell about their first experiences over Belgium and each man spoke of being eager to "get at it again."

The five involved in Pat's patrol met at the airfield at 18:00 hours. Joining him was Lt Evelyn H Lascelles and Lt. Frank S Wilkins along with Keast and Stedman. Stedman was the Patrol Leader and reminded the men to double check their engines.

"Remember men, war bread in Germany is bad," said Stedman, referring to the potential to be shot down, captured and held in a German camp. He also reminded the men to remember where the hospitals were. On their first run in search of landmarks, hospitals were a significant identification, something all pilots were told was important. This Patrol would likely exceed two hours. All five planes were in the air by 18:30.

The planes went deeper into enemy territory than on previous flights. After downing a single bomber that was uncharacteristically flying solo, the group lowered to 1,000 feet, then 500. They had entered a long ridge area northeast of Ypres in the Passchendaele area. Pat could see the extensive network of trenches cut through the devastated landscape.

Allied attacks on the German frontline were intense despite very heavy rain that turned the Ypres area into a swamp. The situation was made worse by the fact that the British heavy bombardment had destroyed all drainage systems in the area. Floods had blanketed the whole of the Flanders plain. The newest shellholes, already half-filled with water, were flooded to the brim. Rain has fouled this low, stoneless ground and every man was soaked through, standing or sleeping in a marsh. Pat and his fellow scouts were about to make infantry life even more miserable for the Germans.

Stedman signaled Pat, Wilkins, and Keast to strafe below. He and Lascelles would stay at 500 feet in case interference came from above. Pat and the other two rolled and dove toward a dark, grey, and misty landscape. As they neared the ground they pulled out of their dive and could be seen by German infantry, scaling across the ground at a mere fifty feet! It was a horrifying site to the Huns as the three planes looked like devils coming at them at 75 miles per hour just over their heads with the full force of the Vickers gun spraying metal across the horizon.

"Tucka, tucka, tucka, tucka….exploded over head as the three planes unloaded at close range. The Germans could hear bullets slug into the mud, hit metal, and wood in the trenches like a hailstorm. Men hit by the avalanche of unfair advantage screamed in pain adding to the horror. But the horror was not all one sided.

It took steel nerves and blind action for Pat and the others to dive head-on into a barrage of bullets whisking by their heads from the trenches below. While the three aeroplanes had machine guns, the trenches also had them and a lot more. The advantage for the planes was their speed. One, two, and finally three long runs extended from one end of the trench to the other for nearly a mile.

It lasted for twenty minutes but felt like two hours. Pat made all three runs until the attack was called off. It was a gruesome battle with no one lost from Pat's squadron but plenty of carnage below. Strafing was the only type of warfare that put the modern fighter pilot in close range with enemy infantry. It was a meeting of old and new warfare and another tactic that changed war in the 20th century. Pat's squadron delivered the new technology.

Nearly three hours later, Pat drifted gingerly back to the safe terra firma at Estree'-Blanche. His plane had bullet holes throughout the entire fuselage and wings. He was exhausted and felt cramps in both hands, no doubt brought on by the sustained squeeze of his equipment and the Vickers machine gun. It was the most intense experience of his life.

"Holy Jesus!" said Paul looking over Pat's plane as he helped Pat down of the Pup. "What the hell did you guys do?"

"I don't even know how I came out of it!" said Pat, still reeling from the experience. "How many shots do you think I took, Paul?"

"I can't tell. I started counting your left wing but I can't tell!" said Paul. "We didn't do our strafe but took out a number of bombers and were back in two hours. I had a successful run. Took out an Albatros and a German two-seater identical to the one I encountered on my first flight out."

"Hell, we didn't attack planes. We were no higher than fifty feet off the ground" said Pat. "I couldn't tell you how many men I killed. I guess the only thing I can count is holes in my aeroplane." Both men laughed. "Thank God the engine didn't get hit. You know Paul, it's muddy down there and I didn't pack my boots from Wyoming!" A good, hearty laugh came from both men.

The two buddies spent much of the night detailing each minute of their respective flights. Late into the night men passing by their tent could see shadows of Pat and Paul arching their arms in sweeping motions to describe one dive after another. Despite the obvious life-threatening experience they had just experienced, both were in their glory having finally met the enemy head-on and with success.

The next two days were free of flying. Pat met a number of fellow pilots who had experienced the strafing of the trenches and Paul talked to other pilots about the vulnerability of the German two-seater verses the Albatros. It was a chance for the men to catch their breath and blend into the ranks of the 66th.

It was the practice within the 66th to send flights of six men out twice a day, once in the early morning and close to the dinner hour. On Wednesday night August 15, flights for the next day were posted. The two friends were thrilled to see they'd be flying together on the day's runs.

Chapter 23

Downed

The boys met Captain Angus Bell-Irving at the airfield at 07:00 the next morning. Pat's fourth flight over Belgium would include Paul Raney, Ralph Stedman, William Keast, Eve Lascelles and Bell-Irving. The presence of the Captain indicated to the squadron that some intense fighting was anticipated.

Rain through the night assured pilots that mechanical errors would continue to plague their aircraft. The airfield was fully saturated but the rain had finally stopped around 06:00. All of Flanders to the south however was a muddy mess. Rainy conditions had stifled all attempts to clear the Huns of the Ypres salient for over two weeks. But a break in the weather had Allied ground forces stirring once again and the Royal Flying Corps was rising to support their efforts. Pat and his flight was one of many scheduled to depart today.

Ypres, and all territory west to the French border, was under Allied control. Germany occupied the land north, south and east of the city surrounding it on three sides from positions of greater elevation. It was a bad situation for the Allies. Ypres was the only major city in Belgium not in enemy hands. Losing it would put all British supply ports in jeopardy and open the door to northern France. Today's flight was in support of Allied efforts to drive the Imperial German Army from Langemarck, to the south of Ypres.

All six planes were off by 07:30 and over the line in five minutes. Lascelles experienced gun trouble and pulled off, landing at the 1st Squadron aerodrome where his gun was replaced. Not five minutes after Lascelles troubles, Pat's "Pup" was spitting at 6,000 feet. It was having problems getting fuel and he decided to slow the engine a bit so it might recover on its own. That didn't work. He then shut it off and restarted it but it coughed and a puff of smoke billowed out, washing over Pat in the cockpit. The plane characteristically dipped. Pat revved the engine but the machine would not go to full power and was in no condition to do battle. He waved off to Captain Bell-Irving and turned back toward the line. His morning run would be a "wash."

Not wanting to chance not making it back, he remembered an aerodrome just over the line and closer than Estree'-Blanche. Pat headed in the direction of the aerodrome as best as he could remember. As he drew close to the line flying at about 10,000 feet, he saw a lone two-seater nosing around the boarder scouting Allied movement toward the front. Having a crippled aircraft he avoided any contact, hoping the Hun would not see him.

Pat landed at the unknown airfield and discovered it belonged to 100th Squadron RFC at Treizennes. They were a bomber squadron. Fortunately, they had a solid team of mechanics and Pat was in the air again at 11:30 arriving back at Estree'-Blanche just before 14:00. His flight-mates had already returned and had met with success. Recording Officer, 2nd Lt William Topham, known as Bottom Topham, recorded Pat's return from Treizennes as his 5th flight over Belgium.

Pat's 6th flight was later that day just before 6:00 pm. It included everyone from the morning with the exception of Stedman and was led by Captain Bell-Irving, once again. The Patrol Flight engaged a number of German bombers and Pat was successful in shooting a two-seater Albatros from the sky. The entire Flight returned ending a successful run.

That night, Pat, Paul and the others were talking about the day's flights during their late-night dinner. Everyone agreed that the morning flight went well. It seemed more "textbook" than previous flights. Not having completed the run, Pat listened to his fellow pilots and could tell that they were hitting their stride. They spoke in different tones, used more defined verbiage and all seemed to agree that each man had made the right moves in the air. Young scouts became professionals quickly. They had to. For those who returned, tactical discussions such as these kept their minds off losses and sharpened their skills for the next run.

"So, if you fly past and you're heading straight down, which way do you pull up to approach the belly?" asked Keast. The entire group provided its answer in unison and Keast nodded, while chewing a tough piece of beef.

"I'm not always certain when to pull off when I'm diving pumping lead," said Paul. "A few times I felt if I could have held a few seconds longer I would have finished the job, but I was afraid I'd fly right into him, myself."

"Don't forget, Paul," responded Keast, "you only need to clear your bottom and he's not likely to pull up if you're diving onto him from above."

As Pat listened to the men and reflected on his own experience thus far, he felt he was beginning to understand the routine required of a Fighter Scout. Not that each flight presented the same challenges. It just seemed that options in the air were becoming more intuitive with each run. He realized he was learning how to pace his day, how to mentally prepare for each flight, how to remember even the most minute detail that could add to his capabilities and allow him to better make instantaneous decisions in the air. Pat was hitting his stride, a tribute to the training program of the Royal Flying Corps where pilots learned quickly.

In this war, man and machine were blending just as the Calvary soldier and his horse had done in all wars previous. Every day, on nearly every flight, new methods of air warfare were being developed out of necessity. The inventory being taken at the supper table that evening by Pat's group was duplicated by hundreds of others every day. They were incubators of aerial fighting methodology that would impact the entire century of wars.

Pat O'Brien felt highly engaged and at the cutting edge of life itself. All his years had come into focus in the Flanders theater of war over Belgium - when intensity would never be greater, risks never more perilous and challenges no more demanding of his skills, intellect and guts.

Since arriving five days earlier, Pat and Paul had six kills between them. True to the war's evaporating process, 2nd Lt SJ Oliver was killed on the 8th, three other men at Estree'-Blanche were wounded in action in the last week.

So focused was Pat on his daily tasks that he stayed oblivious to the conditions around him. He already viewed MIA and KIA reports as a matter of routine. He executed his job, enjoyed the work both on the ground and in the air and was at the peak of his skill level as a pilot.

On morning of August 17th, Pat and Paul Raney were scheduled for different flights. Pat rose at 04:30 and grabbed his ritual cup of coffee, ate a piece of toast and tossed a few slices of cold meat into his mouth as he walked out of the mess hall tent toward the airfield. He had not eaten much the previous day. By 05:30, Pat, Charles Morley along with Lieutenants Huxley, Hunter, Harper and Bill Pritt were all doing final inspections of their machines at the north end of the field.

Today's target was an area of the Polygon Wood which lay along the angular front between Ypres and Roeselare. It was at the apex of an intense German offensive that was making a final attempt to hook around Ypres, push into France and cut off all Allied ports along the French and Belgian coast. Allied forces planned a preemptive attack but the Huns were blocking the entrance. It was into this salient border region in Belgium's northwest corner that Pat and his mates were scheduled to run.

This Third Battle of Ypres found the Germans desperate to punch through as increased instability of Russian forces on the eastern front made Russia's withdrawal from the war more certain each day. If the Russians were to leave the war, it would enable Germany to pull its entire eastern army west, dramatically increasing Germany's reserve strength for the push into France.

Essentially, Pat's squadron was about to dive into the very center of the Schlieffen hook in support of the renewed Allied offensive which had begun the day before. After destroying the entire Polygon Wood, the Allies had been bogged down in monsoon-like rains since July 31.

Ground conditions were horrid. Continuous shelling had destroyed drainage canals in the area, and the heavy rain turned areas into a sea of mud and water-filled shell-craters. The troops walked up to the front over paths made of duckboards laid across the mud, often carrying up to one hundred pounds of equipment. It was not uncommon for them to slip off the path into bomb craters and drown before being rescued. Trees were reduced to blunted trunks and the bodies of men buried following previous action were uncovered by the rain and shelling.

With rains subsiding, the Allies began taking back the nearby city of Langemarck. Pat learned in his morning briefing that Allied infantry and RFC bombers were now clearing the remaining Germans from Polygon Wood so the Australians could dig in using their "bite and hold" technique to keep Germans back once and for all.

Pat's patrol was in the air by 06:30 and drifted over the line heading toward the muddy front. Pritt had engine trouble and turned back but rejoined the Patrol by 7:30. In the first hour over Belgium, they observed no enemy. About the time Pritt found his squadron again they came across an Albatros above them canvassing the landscape.

The entire patrol led by Morley who was Patrol Leader at this point pulled back on their sticks firmly soaring upward in pursuit of the two-seater over Langemarck. Morley was unable to climb up and handed over lead to deputy leader Harper who led the "Pups" skyward. The German rear gunner was blasting lead out the tail of the Hun plane and all five "Pups" could be seen weaving and dodging to avoid being hit while in hot pursuit.

"Damn it!" shouted Pat as Morley signaled the group to peel off in a southward direction toward Ypres. The expert rear gunner had held off the pursuing "Pups".

About 20 minutes later, Pat spotted a two-seater to his right over the town of Warneton. He pulled right and dove at the Hun plane at maximum speed. Before he was close enough to fire the Albatross spotted him and dove. Pat was unable to overtake it and pulled out to rejoin his group. Having scored no kills, the patrol headed back to Estree'-Blanche intact but frustrated that they had not won a prize that morning. Not every run was successful but each run added to the experience of every man.

Now, while it was not an accepted practice within the 66th following a scheduled run, Pat often desired to take an additional hook back into enemy territory on his own once the squadron crossed back into friendly territory. He had a fever for "getting one more," or in this case, getting one at all. He would often think of taking an extra run in the vicinity of the line with the hopes of nabbing a Hun plane nosing around on the allied side. He hoped the Corps would not frown on such entrepreneurial escapades, as long as he returned within a time close to the squadron's return.

On the way in that morning, Pat had noticed two German balloons at about 500 feet. He decided that as soon as his morning patrol was over he would go off on his own and see what a German balloon looked like close up.

On his way back from Warneton, Pat was at 15,000 feet, too high to see the balloons. He shut off his motor and dropped down through the clouds hoping to see the two balloons which were about five miles behind enemy lines.

When he emerged from the clouds at about 1,000 feet and four miles closer to the line, he could not see the balloons but saw a large contingent of artillery firing below. Just below him was a German two-seater doing artillery observations, directing the German guns on the ground who were blasting Allied troops.

When the artillery spotted Pat they put out ground signals to the German airship warning them of Pat's presence. The German plane immediately took a nose dive to escape. He was in a vulnerable position. Pat rolled and was soon chasing him straight down at nearly 200 miles per hour, shooting the entire time at the diving Hun.

In this situation the dangers for Pat were simple. His wings could break away at such speeds. He could also run out of sky. If Pat pulled out of his dive at the wrong moment he would become an easy target. As he dove, blasting away at the diving German plane, he yelled at that top of his lungs.

"Hold…. Hold…. hold together…. hold together! Hold you son-of-a-bitch!" he barked, releasing adrenaline as only Fighting Scouts routinely do.

He could feel the stress on the aeroplane as the speed increased. He measured his gains on the Hun against the speed with which the earth was rushing toward him. He was fully connected to every vibration, every sound, to the onslaught of pressure against his body, the wind, the stick, new sounds, louder sounds and the instinctive calibration made by all experienced pilots which determines the point at which he must pull out or face certain death. Should his speed exceed the amount of sky available to arc horizontally once again he would meet certain death.

His mind raced. Such tension between the limits of the machine and initiatives of a pilot has always been part of battle flight. He chose the moment and pulled out of his dive. The Germans never did. Pat had driven the Albatros to the point where no skilled pilot could pull out and the two-seater Hun plane lanced deeply into the muddy terrain instantly killing both pilot and observer.

Unfortunately, the depth of Pat's dive put him within reach of machine guns on the ground and every pilot's biggest fear, "flaming onions." Flaming onions instantly set fire to the canvas planes and meant certain death to the pilot. "Archie," or anti-aircraft fire, was spitting past his plane as well. He could hear the rip of canvas as he flew the "Pup" as fast as it would run toward the Allied side.

Fortunately, none of the shots landed until about one mile from the line when "bang," his engine was hit and put out of commission. Pat had enough altitude to glide to the Allied side as ground forces fired continuously at him during his decent. A slight wind carried Pat nearly two miles behind Allied lines. He was safe but now needed a place to land.

Pat viewed the terrain below for a place to land. He saw an empty field filled with shell holes but a few pathways that look straight and might allow him to land. He glided to a clear spot along the eastern tree line and rolled to a bumpy stop.

He immediately jumped out of the plane to inspect the damage but looked up in every direction to assure no one had followed him in. Pilots were often killed standing next to their plane after an emergency landing failing to anticipate they'd be "followed in" after escaping their pursuer. There was no one.

Despite "Archie" having reduced his plane to a glider by damaging the engine, the aircraft itself was not badly damaged. Pat felt if he could repair his engine he might be able to get his plane off the ground again and return to base. He was bent over checking the tail assembly when a shell came whizzing through the air and knocked Pat to the ground, landing only a few feet away. Pat ran to the nearest shell hole as the artillery blazed away.

Suddenly, two huge explosions occurred and his plane received a direct hit blowing chunks of Aeroplane into the air. Pat hunkered down in the water and mud that filled the shell hole. He was reminded once again why war in the air was still preferable to the life of the infantry soldier that seldom experienced a dry day in Flanders.

"Damn, I must be close to the line," said Pat out loud. "I forgot about mortars." He purposely closed his eyes. "What's wrong with me?" he said. "Where in the hell do I think all these other holes came from?" He had learned another lesson.

After what seemed forever, the shelling ceased. Pat lay in the shell-hole another fifteen minutes fearing that the Germans might send over one more "lucky shot." Not experiencing further bombardment, he crawled out of his hole, shook as much mud off him as he could and went to look over the spot where his machine had once been.

"Talk about evaporation!" he said in a humorous tone. He actually laughed to himself in a rather nervous manner, so common when men suddenly survive a near-death experience. He looked around for even a small souvenir of his "Pup" but couldn't find a piece worth pocketing anywhere.

Pat walked northwest until he arrived at a local road and turned left in the general direction of Estree'-Blanche. After about fifteen minutes, he heard a convoy of English lorries approaching him from the east. Waving them down, he asked for a ride to the nearest base. They were delivering fresh supplies to Infantry Headquarters where Pat could contact Estree'-Blanche. Once there, he phoned Estree'-Blanche and gave them a report. About one hour later, a car appeared and too Pat back to the aerodrome.

Back at Estree'-Blanche the men were discussing Pat's fate.

"He's gone!" said Wilkins to the group of pilots that had gathered for the mid-afternoon review.

"Don't count on it, Ed," Paul responded. "That Irishman will be back if he has to walk! He wasn't exactly hatched from an egg under the blazin' sun in the middle of a wheat field, yah no?" Paul said this half in jest and half in fear, showing obvious intensity on his face.

"What!" they all exclaimed. Paul's buddies really laughed at that one. Every once in a while an odd Canadian colloquialism would come out of Paul's mouth and bust everyone up. It was particularly amusing when Paul got a little worked up.

Few believed Paul until the car pulled up and out stepped the scruffiest, mud-covered pilot anyone had seen. The boys roared with delight. Pat leaned against a tree exhausted for a spell and told the story. He had a crowd of fifteen pilots around him by the time he finished. Pat O'Brien was a natural story teller and even more potent when the story was true and happened to be about him. The boys delighted in his tale but their laughter was not at his expense. Everyone under the tree that day saw the same energy and determination others had experienced many times before. There was a subtle moment when each pilot sensed they were in the presence of a leader.

"I need a shower, fellas," said Pat, pushing off the tree and receiving handshakes and backslaps from his friends. He told Paul he'd meet him at dinner. "Think I'll lie down a bit," he told Paul.

A few hours later Pat and Paul were having dinner.

"Looks like another long run tonight, Pat," said Raney, gnawing on a piece of tough beef.

"Oh, yeah?" said Pat. "Are we together?"

[279]

"I'm sure you're not going!" said Paul.

"Why the hell not? I'm here, ain't I?" said Pat.

"Yes, but we go at 05:30," responded Paul.

Paul wasn't really surprised by Pat's response. Still, at about 04:30 the two checked the posting for the evening run. Pat's name wasn't on the list. Pat went to Captain Bell-Irving and insisted he go. After some back and forth, the Captain relinquished as long as they could get another plane.

"There's tons of aircraft out there!" said Pat, pleading his case. "Pick one! I'll fly it," he said. The Captain, Paul and the three other pilots in the squadron who had come along for morale support all laughed. "Pick one! I'll fly it!" they all repeated. It was one of those standard one-liners that sticks with the troops and is used over and over again when things get rather crazy and the boys need a little cynicism to ease the tension.

"They found a plane," Paul said to Pat as he took a seat next to Pat at dinner. "Good," said Pat, sipping a spoonful of potato soup. Pat was uninterested in the particulars of the next run. This was unusual for Pat, always focused on the details of his next flight. But he just wanted a plane and he was hungry.

Normally, Pat would check the board as soon as he returned from the previous run. But he was rapidly acquiring the routine of a professional pilot. The experienced pro assumes he'll be on every flight. He cares little of his next target or what type or number of enemy planes he will encounter next. He is ready for whatever gets thrown at him. He spends downtime engaged in activities that contrast the furious intensity of the dogfight. He speaks of the previous run for only a short time upon his return and mostly about the skill of his fellow pilots, his enemy or the calamity they faced going down. He never lives in the past and does not count on the future. He just acts and stays ready.

Pat, being one of the more experienced pilots in the squadron before military service, was at this advanced stage before most in his squadron. He had become a professional soldier quickly. It happens to all instinctive warriors if they live long enough. In a platoon, squad or squadron of the air, these men stand out from other men, particularly the overly zealous new recruit.

The "old pro" has the profound look of a man who has seen battle but has learned to operate as efficiently as his weapon. They are the informal leaders within every division of military life. They can also be recluse since they are often a minority in any unit. Pat was not the reclusive type but he had acquired a quiet confidence that each man of the squadron recognized early.

Captain Angus Bell-Irving and his flight were inspecting their Pups at about 17:00 as the sun began to create small shadows behind each plane. Paul, Bill Keast, "Eve" Lascelles and Lt. Edward Sivewright Bacon were on the run. Pat's name had been penciled in. Bell-Irving told the boys they should expect a three hour patrol. Each man knew what that meant - fiery patrols with a lot of danger.

All planes were in the air at 17:45. Before they saw any enemy, Bacon pulled out with engine trouble. Pat turned his head and watched Bacon's wide arcing roll to the rear. For some reason, he watched until he could no longer turn his head away from forward trajectory. Pat was ready for battle but tonight his mind was quiet and reflective without a lot of scattered busy thoughts. Perhaps he was getting used to the routine. "Not possible," he thought. "I think I'm just a little tired. Well hell, who wouldn't be?" he went on to himself. "Look what I've been through in a week!"

Just to take his mind off of things for a second, Pat tried to picture Momence at dawn. It suddenly struck him that it was Friday midday at home. He could only think of home a second or two then was back to the task at hand. "I'll do that later," he thought. "Let's see. How do my dials look?" He took a look. All seemed fine. Pat turned right and left to check on the others in his flight. "Ok, they look fine," he said to himself. He then looked forward at the horizon, then up at his wings and finally forward again at his gun mounted atop the fuselage. He was fully in tune with his surroundings and ready for battle.

The squadron was far enough north that Pat could still see the coast. He looked again in that direction and noticed some movement. He looked harder. A large group of Hun Albatross planes was combing the coastline. They were far and low enough not to be an immediate threat. But he was a bit alarmed to see so many enemy planes in such plain view. The patrol had a different target and the Hun planes were not in a position to be aware of the Pat's group. Still, he felt concerned.

Captain Bell-Irving was leading them to an area near Roeselare on the Mandel River. Roeselare was located in the Flemish province of West Flanders. Its name was derived from two German words meaning "reed" and "open space." The land contained large marshy areas in a forest glade not unlike the Kankakee Marsh. He could see the nearby towns of Beveren, Oekene, Rubeke, and to the southwest, Passendale, no more than ten miles away. The landscape was barren as was most of Flanders by now, having been blasted hourly by explosives from both sides.

Just as Pat was completing his check of instruments, Bell-Irving signaled and the Squadron began to descend. For some reason, Pat glanced at the time. It was 8:15 in the evening. The Captain had observed three outnumbered Bristol Fighters below at 3,000 feet engaging the enemy. The "Bristol Fighter" or "Biff" as it was called was an attack and reconnaissance plane. Despite being a two-seat bi-plane it was an agile aircraft and could hold its own against an opposing single-seat fighter. The trio of Bristols was descending on nine German Albatros fighters. Pat was exhilarated at the thought of jumping down on this scrap but knowing a group of additional Hun machines were just to their north near the coast didn't sit with him well.

Obviously, the RFC pilots below had not seen the additional German strike-force along the coast and as soon as Pat's squadron joined the battle, they could be drawn into the melee, he thought. Pat did some quick math. "Let's see, five of us, three of them, that's 8-9. Let's hope by some miracle those Huns to the north don't notice us." That was not likely and Pat knew it. There were 17 aircraft along the coast.

"But for the Grace of God," he said out loud. "Were the shoe on the other foot." Pat thought, "we'd be glad to get the help no matter what the odds."

Pat's plane went into a dive with the others. He shouted "Here comes supper!" as his Pup lanced downward at over 150 miles per hour. It was an intense dog-fight and fairly even for the first fifteen minutes, when they were still eight British against nine German planes.

The Captain dove in on an Albatros firing about 30 rounds in to him at close range. The Hun headed down spinning and then went out of control. Bell-Irving continued further toward the Bristols to assist.

Suddenly, as Pat had feared, the other Hun machines had arrived from the coast and were diving in on the pack. Looking up, Pat saw four Hun machines diving down on his plane.

"Holy shit!" he said out loud as he rolled his plane, banked left and right and generally did all he could to avoid being an easy target. The Huns were firing their guns all the way in and using tracer-bullets which Pat sensed were getting closer and closer every second.

"God damn it! Give me a fighting chance will you!" Pat implored the almighty sensing the desperate condition he was in.

"Clink!" A bullet hit his instrument panel and destroyed his pressure gauge. Then another blew apart the attitude indicator. Pat barely paid attention. He was trying to escape disaster at this point.

"Immelmann! Immelmann!" Pat shouted, getting his senses back. The Immelmann turn was attributed by the French to the famous German pilot who had died some time ago. Pat new it well. After making a high speed diving attack on an enemy, the attacker would then climb back up past the enemy aircraft and just short of the stall, apply full rudder to yaw his aircraft around. This put the plane facing down in the direction of the enemy, making another high speed dive possible. It was a difficult maneuver to perform properly, as it involved precise control of the aircraft at low speed. Pat, however, was more than capable.

He zoomed up to a near-dead stall, applied full rudder to the Pup and was now facing down on the Hun machines. Though he was outnumbered, at least he was in the advantageous position. It was an aggressive and risky move but Pat's only option.

He suddenly found himself no more than ten yards from one of the four. The German looked at Pat with a face that expressed his now hopeless situation. Pat had instantly reversed the advantage just enjoyed by the German machines and fired a tracer-bullet. He saw it sail past the German pilot's head by less than three feet. His second volley hit his shoulder, the third lodged in his neck, then Pat unleashed a volley of metal that sliced the pilot severely and the Hun aircraft headed down in a spinning nose dive.

The entire time, three other Hun machines were firing at Pat. He ignored them. He was focused on what he could control. Kill one and worry about the others later. Pat called upon every bit of his intuitive skills, years of experience, and expert training from the RFC. He possessed an uncanny ability to focus his mind in high stress situations. This was a critical skill required of all good fighter scouts.

When a dog-fight ensues, aircraft in battle lose altitude. Pat knew this and glanced at his instruments. He was 8,000 feet above the ground. Then, suddenly, a barrage of bullets blew up his entire instrument panel. Pat watched what was left of his control indicators evaporate before him.

Then it hit. No sound, no warning, just an intense heat in his mouth and in his throat. The same gun that obliterated Pat's dash board had found Pat. The bullet entered from above, passing through his upper lip, out the roof of his mouth and lodging in his throat. Adrenaline rushed throughout Pat's body. It stung more than hurt in the first few seconds. The bullet sliced close to the carotid artery but did not sever it. It lodged against the trachea avoiding any penetration of the spinal area. No doubt the bullet's path from above, passing through the upper lip, teeth and gum curtailed its ability to pass deeper and deliver a deadly blow.

He suddenly went dark. Then alert for a few seconds. The plane's roar stirred his consciousness. "Pull up…" he thought. "Wait, no…what is that?" Then out again, falling rapidly and spinning. Then wind. Wind in his face. His mind went back to the plane "Pull up!" "Pull!" More speed, descending with force. Sensing his hands, then… "Pull!" Then black. Then awake. "Oh, it hurts there…there…my face…no, it's my mouth." And Back to plane, "How fast am I…..It's quiet." Then Out.

His plane went into a spinning nose dive from 8,000 feet. He had actually altered its course little, though more than once he possessed some level of consciousness that told him to pull up. But to no avail. Pat's strength was drained but the wings of his plane were still affixed. This gave him a chance to survive. His engine finally cut off and reduced his rate of decent.

The canvas and wooden structure sliced across the upper branches of a grove of trees. The thin upper branches slowed his speed. The Pup's wings acted like big open arms that snapped but also broke branches releasing some energy as Pat skimmed the treetops. Both wheels were clipped leaving them dangling but still attached.

The grove gave way to an open meadow and Pat's plane clipped off the treetop edge, dropping hard but at an angle to the ground. It lessened the impact. His plane crimped up like a piece of paper, full of holes from the dogfight with most of the canvas fuselage ripped from the trees. The wooden frame that once shaped the skeleton of the plane was horribly twisted and snapped. A good amount of blood was present on Pat's face, in his mouth and on his flyer's jacket but he was alive.

Eighteen miles away, 2nd Lt. Edwin Bacon, who had experienced engine trouble in Pat's ill-fated flight that night was back at Estree'-Blanche standing alone in open field looking skyward for the first sign of his patrol. "Have they all been killed?" he thought. "Were they forced to land elsewhere? Did the Huns get them all?"

Just then Bacon could see a single Sopwith Pup dotting the southern sky and wondered if it might be the first of his patrol returning. It was not quite 8:20 in the evening and remnants of daylight still lingered. He ran north along the airfield looking sideways toward the landing plane as the Pup sat down on the grass runway and continued a bouncy arrival toward the north end. The Pup came to rest and Bacon recognized Captain Bell-Irving climbing out of his machine.

Running up to the plane out of breath Bacon shouted "Have you seen any others?" The Pup was still winding down spitting an occasional back fire.

"Hard to say," returned the Captain. "We got caught in a hell of a mess. I barely escaped without getting downed myself."

Bill Keast arrived five minutes later, then Lascelles and Paul Raney.

"Who's in?" asked Paul.

"So far, everyone but O'Brien," reported Ed Bacon.

Bell-Irving was talking to Lascelles and getting a full report. Keast, Lascelles and the Captain turned toward the mess to grab some coffee.

"You coming, Raney?" asked Bill Keast.

"No, I'm going to wait a bit longer for Pat," Paul replied. This time something in Paul's gut told him that "the crazy Irishman" might not return from this run.

As darkness completed its cover of the aerodrome at Estree'-Blanche and the cool air arrived to occupy the spring night, Paul Raney stood with his leather helmet in his left hand and both hands on his hips looking one more time into the now darkened sky for his friend Pat O'Brien. He delayed turning away four or five times in the hope his buddy might appear. He never did.

[285]

"Well, that's it then," he said to no one as he turned and started his walk back to the officer's mess. He was the sole figure on the airfield. It was quarter past nine in the evening. Paul did not blink once all the way back but walked diligently staring wide-eyed at the ground swinging his helmet in his left hand, his neck scarf blowing in a stiff breeze, rain hitting his face.

Pat O'Brien sat slumped and bleeding in what could hardly be described as the cockpit of a Sopwith Pup as it was twisted and crushed around him. Less than a mile away, three German soldiers were climbing into a truck headed to the spot where it appeared Pat O'Brien had crashed. Whether dead or alive, Pat would soon have company and they were not on his side.

Chapter 24

Prison

In a semi-blacked-out state, Pat O'Brien kept migrating between two translucent scenes. First, he imagined himself lying against the grassy embankment of the Momence Quarry. Al Fontaine and Carl Munyon were holding down his arms and oddly enough Al kept insisting on calling Pat a "lucky ass" the whole time.

Then suddenly, his mind would shift and a man hovered over him, uttering the word "lachgas" over and over again. Al and Carl still held him down but as Pat's mind moved back and forth between the two perceptions, his friends faded from the picture and suddenly were no longer there. Pat was being held down by two leather straps pulled firmly against a makeshift gurney. A sneering Prussian Surgeon was leaning over him calling for more nitrous oxide to keep his patient sedated. It was pre-dawn on the morning of August 18th. As the doctor finished and the gas eased, Pat felt a tremendous pain in his throat. He could not move and finally sensed where he was.

The make-shift hospital was a private low level brick house that had been confiscated by the Huns the day before. It was dirty and had four rooms filled with approximately eight beds each. There was also a stable attached to the building and it, too was holding a number of injured men lying rather hopelessly on beds of straw. Doctors and their orderlies saved those that had a chance to survive and left men with little chance of living to die in the stable. A facility such as this was common in the field. Should the front move, it could be abandoned at a moment's notice.

"Hier ist es," said the surgeon in a low almost inaudible tone, placing a blood covered bullet on a tray held by his aide. His orderly reached in with a cloth swab dabbing at the wound, then handed the German doctor a thread.

"Schau mal, er ist ein Amerikaner," said the doctor to his aid. He had noticed the identification disk chained to Pat's right wrist which read, "Lieut. Pat O'Brien RFC. U.S.A." It was rare to see an American in the war at this point as the U.S. had only joined the effort three months before Pat's ill-fated flight and few were pilots.

The somewhat perturbed surgeon completed his work, sewing Pat's upper lip and closing the wound in the roof of Pat's mouth where the bullet had passed. As the doctor was finishing, Pat became conscious and opened his eyes for the first time. He was in terrible pain. The doctor paused a second, lifting his hands away to view Pat's gaze.

"You're an American, aren't you?" Pat nodded ever so slightly, causing a jolt of pain to his throat. The Prussian responded with a sneer. "You Americans who came into this before America is at war with us are no better than murderers! If I had my way about it, I 'd take you out, back you up against the wall and have you shot!" The doctor spoke clear English and continued to comment.

Pat gave no reaction and could not speak but closed his eyes again, trying to block his thoughts from the tremendous pain he felt in his neck and mouth. In addition to the bullet wound in his mouth, he had a four inch-wide swelling that ran from his forehead over the top to the back of his head.

The German went on. "You may be alright as a sportsman, but you are a damned murderer just the same for being here," he said in an angry tone. "You Americans are no better than common murderers and you ought to be treated the same way!"

The doctor stepped away and Pat was lifted on a cot by two orderlies and carried to another room. Once there he fell asleep. Awakening again in the mid-afternoon, he was given some broth. He had a few sips, closed his eyes and wondered what could have happened to his squadron. It suddenly struck him how short the war had been for him. He stopped thinking and fell asleep once again. Around 7:00 PM he awoke and lay in extreme pain for three hours. Only a thin blanket covered him and he shivered for nearly two hours before falling off to sleep once again. Through the night he awoke numerous times in pain then finally fell into a deep sleep for two hours before being awoken by three German flying officers around five in the morning. The two Huns spoke to him.

"The pilot you shot down was from Bavaria and a good pilot," said one of the officers in clear English. Pat listened but didn't move. His pain was very intense. The second officer showed Pat the hat of the Bavarian and offered it to him. Pat tried to express his thanks with eye contact and the young German seemed to understand his response, setting the German cap at the foot of Pat's bed.

The third pilot was examining Pat's leather helmet and showed it to him. It had been split front to back by the bullet which explained the soreness and swelling atop Pat's head. Pat noticed how curiously they examined it and wondered why. They made a few comments about Germany's defense of the homeland and stated it was curious that Pat would fight with the British for the sport of it. Pat had little sympathy for their biased views but was too sore to think about such debates and had no way to speak anyway. Their comments still angered him, however. The officers left and Pat fell asleep once again.

A few hours later, Pat was awakened by two orderlies who carried a wounded German pilot to the table next to Pat. The pilot was laid on his side facing Pat. Pat closed his eyes but would, on occasion, glance at the pilot, finally causing the pilot to stare back. The next day, Pat felt stronger but had not spoken a word. Finally, in the afternoon the German had had enough of Pat's occasional stare and spoke.

"What the hell are you looking at?" said the German in clear and unaccented English. Pat was shocked. Seeing this, the German then smiled.

Pat whispered with great pain, "I can't speak yet."

"I'm told you are an American," said the German. "Which part?" he said.

Again Pat whispered, "California."

The German pilot was not a German at all but a German-American who had answered the call of his fatherland and was serving in the German Luftwaffe. Ironically, he was from San Francisco and the two men had much in common and knew many of the same places. Over the next two days, as Pat's ability to speak slowly returned, he and his newly-found "mate" discussed many topics but surprisingly agreed on little regarding the war. Though an American, the German officer clearly either had strong pro-German opinions or dared not say different in the presence of many German medical personnel, many of whom understood English.

On his fourth day in the makeshift hospital, Pat was well enough to write a brief message intended for his squadron. He knew that if they received the report, it would be highly likely that word would be sent home to his mother in Momence. Not wanting to worry her, he wrote "feeling fine" at the bottom though he was obviously not feeling very well, at all.

Pat slipped his note inside the sock of his right leg, hoping there would be an opportunity to request it be dropped over Allied lines. As he folded his sock over the wrinkled note, the orderly entered calling for Pat.

Pat raised his arm to indicate who he was and the orderly presented Pat with a postcard which could be sent home to his family. He addressed the card to "Mrs. Clara Clegg, Box 18, Momence, Ill." The back of the card was a standard format designed by the Germans. It read:

"I am a Prisoner of War in Germany"

He was, in fact, in Belgium. The card was dated August 21, 1917. Pat was able to fill it out himself. Name: "O'Brien," Christian Name "Pat Alva," Rank: "Lieu't," Regiment: "Royal Flying Corps." About forty-five minutes later, the orderly returned to collect the card. Pat had addressed it to his sister feeling that the formality of the message may be too harsh for his mother to read at first. Clara would break it to her gently.

"Lieutenant, there is quite a battle in the air above us," said the young orderly. "Perhaps I could wheel you outside for some sun and you could also watch the dog fight overhead." Pat nodded and the orderly brought Pat outside where a number of German patients and officers were pointing to the sky and watching the engaging battle.

It was a battle royale. There were six British machines, all Pups. Pat concluded it was highly likely that the planes were from the 66th. Unfortunately, sixteen Hun machines had the six under intense fire, highly outnumbered. The Pups were piloted by men so highly skilled that they held their own for what seemed like an excessively long time, considering the odds.

The Germans were not shy about cheering on their colleagues and Pat, never to be outdone, raised his fist a number of times in salute of the marvelous efforts demonstrated by the exceptional English pilots. Suddenly, two British planes, which had been targeted by six Hun Albatros aircraft, were driven from the sky and crashed below the visible horizon. A large cheer when up around Pat. Then two German planes succumbed and the group fell silent. Pat elevated his two hands overhead, tearing up in a mix of joy and sadness. Feeling a strong pain in his throat he realized his over-exuberance was more than his injury could handle and settled back in his chair. With two Pups downed and taking advantage of the Huns' distraction watching two of theirs crash, the other four Brits quickly scampered off toward the Allied line.

Pat handed a scribbled a note to the orderly. It read, "Could I see the personal belongings of the downed British flyers? They could be from my squadron."

The orderly was willing and ran off in the direction of the black smoke which was still lifting skyward from the western horizon. Twenty-five minutes later he returned and handed Pat a photo of one of the downed pilots. It was Paul.

The picture was of Pat and Paul taken on the deck of the Megantic. Paul stared at them both smiling broadly looking like kids without a care in the world. A chill ran through Pat's body. "Poor Raney," he thought.

"Was he killed?" asked Pat.

"Yes. This one, dead, other pilot, I do not know," said the orderly unmoved.

Pat did not lift his gaze. His vision was blurred with tears, his body froze and he was without thought. He felt as though the blood in his veins had stopped flowing and his breathing paused. He blinked and a droplet fell on the photo. Pat felt the tear vibrate the photo between his fingertips.

There was only one. Pat had given it to his good friend. There was no doubt it was Paul who died so gallantly in the dogfight. Later that afternoon, the same orderly returned and handed Pat a detailed map indicating Paul's specific burial place in Flanders. Pat vowed to deliver it to Paul's parents should he survive his time in prison and the war itself.

"Any news regarding the other pilot?" asked Pat.

"He is not dead, but they have taken him to interior hospital," said the German. "I do not know his name." Pat wondered who it could be. Was it Wilkins? Keast, Captain Bell-Irving? He was not certain.

Pat spent the next two days in quiet recovery. He slept as much as he could which not only helped him recover but allowed his mind to be free of the terrible events of the last seven days. Injured pilots continued to arrive at the small makeshift field hospital but for the most part Pat slept through the continuous activity. His wounds were checked at least twice a day and bandages were reduced as his wounds healed.

His voice began to return slowly but it still hurt to speak. He had continuous headaches likely caused, he thought, by the jarring of his teeth which were jumbled when the bullet entered his mouth. He had asked his surgeon if a dentist might be available at some point to adjust his bite but, lacking much sympathy, the Hun doctor had told him he'd not get much to eat going forward anyway. The near scalping Pat received when the machine gun bullet grazed the top of his head was a continuous cause of his headaches, as well.

Looking in the mirror while shaving on Friday, the morning of the 24th, Pat thought it might be a good idea to grow a mustache which could conceal the scar that would likely develop on his upper lip. The wound was much too sensitive to shave anyway. He hoped he might move to more accommodating quarters soon with better facilities and a chance to bathe. Despite his condition, Pat had moved beyond the hopeless state and was now thinking of ways to improve his lot and ways he could possibly escape.

On the morning of August 25th, an officer entered Pat's "ward" and woke him from a deep sleep.

"Lieutenant! Lieutenant, stated the young German officers. "You are to come with me."

Pat pulled himself up and sat a moment at the edge of the bed, clearing his head. It had been a night of interruptions with both men and bombs making regular appearances in and around the field hospital.

"We are going to German Flying Department office," said the Hun. "They wish to speak with you."

Now it was not unusual for official department personnel from either side to interrogate downed pilots in the hopes of gaining additional information about enemy tactics and locations. Pat knew that this was likely but also knew he would reveal little.

"Take your things," said the driver. "You'll not be coming back here."

Pat was relieved to hear that! He wondered what might be in store for him after his interviews with the Huns. During officer training, the likelihood of interrogation, both casual and intense, was reviewed for all pilots. Noticeably older than the average RFC pilot, Pat wondered if the enemy would believe that he had but a short time fighting at the front.

He was driven to the Department of Intelligence about one hour from the field hospital. The car pulled up to a large two-story residence that had been modified to serve German Intelligence for the northern front. Pat stepped from the car.

"This way, Lieutenant," said the young driver who was strictly business and had not spoken to Pat the entire trip. Once inside, he led Pat down a long hallway and opened the last door announcing the arrival.

"Lieutenant Pat O'Brien, Royal Flying Corps, 66th Squadron," stated the driver to a three-man panel awaiting Pat's arrival.

"Have a seat, Lieutenant, said the lead officer. He was smoking a pipe. Another held an eyepiece firmly in his right eye. The third, a bit younger than the other two, was incessantly tapping his pencil on a clothbound manual, as if impatient for the inquest to begin.

Pat sat at a table across from German officers, folding his long coat over his lap. He felt chilled and perceived that a fever had likely developed on his hour-long trip. The pipe-smoking officer began to ask him a series of questions. Where had he trained? How many aeroplanes were with him when he was shot down? Where was his aerodrome? How was it that he, an American, was flying for the Royal Flying Corps?

Pat was not informative and when the tapping young officer probed hard regarding British strategy, Pat simply informed them how little he knew of such things. As Pat expected, they perceived his age as older than most young pilots and expressed doubt that he had such limited experience in the air. Pat eventually convinced them, without revealing significant information, that he knew little of RFC strategy.

There were few breaks in the morning, a very brief lunch consisting of two pear slices then four more hours of interrogation in the afternoon. For dinner he was given onion soup and a piece of bread. He skipped the bread. It was hard and dark brown just as he had been warned in England. His injury would not allow him to chew or swallow dry bread. He tried soaking the bread but is fell apart in the broth. At the end of the day, he was taken to a small room with a basic cot and wooden chair. Pat lay back fully clothed, chilled and fell asleep on his back.

The next day, he was taken from his room and handed two small crackers for breakfast which he promptly put in his pocket. His guide took him directly to the interrogation room where the same three officers sat waiting.

In addition to the information Pat was trained never to reveal, there were many answers that a man such as Pat, having seen action for such a short time, could not answer. Though he was certainly weakened from the experience, Pat still possessed the same convincing manner he had his whole life. Even the German's were intrigued, if not charmed, by this young American from the Midwest, though they did not show it. As for Pat, their broken English presented little challenge having heard a good amount of that in Momence as a kid.

At the end of the second full day of questioning, possessing very few answers from Pat, the Germans decided they would get little more from him and announced that Pat would be transferred to the Officer's Prison at Courtrai. A young clerk made note of this declaration in a large leather-book and then asked Pat to stand and face the panel.

"We are sending you to Courtrai," stated the German hearing officer in charge.

Pat did not respond. He was not certain where Courtrai was located but knew it was deeper inside enemy territory than his current location. Slowly reaching into his pocket, he made a request of the officers.

"I have a note here for my squadron. I wonder if you might drop it over the line next time you execute a Notice of Killed and Wounded to our command," asked Pat. It was a common practice for both sides to notify the enemy of those pilots that were either shot down or taken prisoners.

"Where would you like the note dropped, Lieutenant?" asked the pipe-smoking German officer, trying not to be revealing.

Pat smiled and shook his head for he knew their only purpose was to identify, and subsequently bomb, the aerodrome of the 66th. "No doubt you Huns would be dropping more than notes on our airfield," said Pat. They were disarmed by his cavalier approach.

The second German officer tried a different tactic. "Perhaps we will simply drop it over Estree'-Blanche, hum, Lieutenant?" probed the officer, attempting to get a response that would confirm the squadron's location. The others leaned forward staring at Pat. From this Pat realized that German intelligence was at least on par with the British expertise on the Allied side. "The Huns are not stupid," he thought. "Idiots, but not stupid."

Having a better a "poker face" than anyone in the room, Pat didn't flinch. The German officers stared Pat down for what seemed a full minute but Pat did not change facial expression. It was no use. They'd get nothing from this experienced gambler.

The second officer put his pencil down and the third removed his eyeglass, nodding to the clerk who was taking notes. Following two days of questioning, Pat understood more than ever that the Hun was a devious and cunning enemy. In addition, the Germans were keenly interested in learning anything they could about the role America would play in the war. Pat became convinced that this, more than anything else, accounted for his long two-day ordeal which produced little. Clearly, the entrance of America in the war as of April concerned the Huns.

The panel ordered him to the officer's prison at Courtrai, Belgium. "You will be driven to Courtrai directly. A car is waiting for you out front. You are dismissed," said the lead officer.

Pat exited the room and was greeted by the same driver that brought him in two days before. They walked to the waiting car where Pat met a young pilot awaiting his arrival. It was not unusual for German intelligence to provide prisoners in transit with a peer such as a fellow pilot. It was thought that their common experience could dislodge a nugget or two not attainable in the formal setting of a hearing.

"I am Voss," said the young twenty-year old man, extending his hand to Pat.

"Pat O'Brien," Pat returned shaking his hand slowly wondering if he might be the famous Hun pilot.

Pat settled into the back seat of the German convertible which would take him to German field headquarters. He still felt feverish and pulled his coat across his lap once again stuffing his belongs between himself and his escort.

"Are you Werner Voss?" asked Pat.

"Yes, I am he," Voss responded.

His escort was none other than Werner Voss, considered one of Germany's top aces. He was a close friend of Manfred von Richthofen, the Red Baron. Pat was surprised that Voss was escorting him to the prison. Having joined the German military at age 17, Voss was already credited with 38 confirmed victories and would eventually add another ten before his death in September over Flanders. He was a gifted pilot and second only to Richthofen, himself.

Voss was not in uniform. This was a common practice of the young German ace who was considered, even by his own pilots, to be a loner and rather mercurial. Pat learned that Voss was recovering from wounds suffered on June 6 during a dogfight against the 6th Naval Squadron and that Voss was also testing one of the latest tri-planes at Courtrai. Pat was surprised that Voss revealed such things but the German Ace was anything but regimental.

"I understand you were shot down just over one week ago," said Voss.

"Yes, I believe it has been about a week," returned Pat.

"Your voice has been affected?" asked Voss.

"It is improving," said Pat in a quiet and obviously raspy voice. "Your doctors feel I will completely recover in due time," said Pat.

The two men discussed flying extensively. Despite his condition and captivity, Pat was glad to be talking to a pilot again rather than orderlies, doctors and intelligence officers. He was careful not to reveal anything important, however. After about one hour, the car pulled in front of the prison at Courtrai, Belgium. Voss and Pat exited the car following the driver. Once at the front door, Voss wished Pat good luck and the two pilots shook hands.

The prison was in the center of Courtrai. The large facility was comprised of a number of buildings and a spacious courtyard surrounded by twenty-foot brick wall. Pat and his guide approached a three-story building which formed the main entrance to the prison complex. In the center was a large archway entrance with a sentry box posted to the left. The sentry halted them both and checked papers before pounding the large door knock on the double door entrance.

The door opened and two guards with rifles guided Pat O'Brien through the archway of the prison and into the interior courtyard where dozens of allied prisoners were walking for exercise. They looked oddly at Pat who, despite wearing a British uniform, had a bright red German cap on his head, the one given to him by the German pilots on his first day of capture.

The star which had been on his right shoulder-strap indicating his rank had been shot off, cleanly. The ones on his left had been taken as a souvenir as well as all his RFC badges which Pat had given to the German pilots at their request. They had allowed Pat to keep his "wings" that he wore on his left breast for every pilot knew that these were the proudest possession of a British Flying officer. Pat did not look much like a British officer when he arrived at Courtrai.

Though battered and wounded, Pat O'Brien was alive and was among Allied pilots once again even though they were all surrounded by the significant castle-like structure that was Courtrai Prison.

Pat was wondering if he'd ever leave Courtrai. He knew one thing. Being taken to Germany would end his war and possibly his life.

Chapter 25

Courtrai

The prison at Courtrai was a significant complex. It had served as a civil prison before the war and was quite secure. Pat was escorted to his second floor cell where he found bars on the window overlooking the prison courtyard. All of the prison buildings faced the courtyard and were heavily barred. He placed his hat on a small table and checked his pockets. He had several hundred francs in his back pocket folded in a clip, the photo of him and Paul on the Megantic, a few other papers with notes and some fresh gauze issued to him at the field hospital to attend to his wounds.

He removed his coat and draped it over a small table along with his uniform jacket then walked to the mirror to check his bandages. Pressing the edges of his throat bandage to assure it was firm, he looked at himself for the first time since the crash. "I look rough," he thought. "Seems like I might be a little thinner in the face," he whispered to himself as he slid his fingers down his cheek. "I have to concentrate on eating as much as I can and getting healthy."

Exhausted, he made his way to the simple bed along the wall, sat down and dug the ball of one foot into the heal of the other kicking one shoe off, then the other. He turned to adjust the small pillow and laid back. The bed was not much softer than a table but felt good against his body. He was asleep the moment he closed his eyes.

Discomfort and pain woke him three times in the night. At three in the morning, he pushed up from his bed and gingerly stepped to the door to get the attention of the guard. "Could I have some water?" There was no response. "Wasser?" Pat repeated in the German he had learned running errands for the German baker Oscar Conrad in Momence. The sleepy guard rose bringing him a tin cup, half full. Pat sipped and swallowed carefully. It stung but felt good once down. Pat handed the cup back. "Thank you," he said, not making eye contact but returning to his bed.

The next morning a different guard came to Pat's cell about 06:45.

"Let's go," said the German, sporting a handlebar mustache. "It is walking time now." Pat's wounds were bothering him and the last thing he needed was a stroll through a Belgian prison yard.

He was escorted down the stairs and stepped into the courtyard. A young German soldier, who was mingling with the prisoners serving as an interpreter between non-English speaking guards and the men, approached him. He notice Pat as someone new.

"Good morning, Lieutenant," stated the young soldier in perfectly good English. Pat was surprised to hear him speak English so well and even more surprised to hear the young Gemeiner's New Jersey accent.

"Well, you're the last person I thought I'd meet in this place," said Pat. "Absolutely clear English and I can even tell you grew up on the east coast by your accent. What a surprise. What is your name?"

"Walter Brunner," he said putting out his hand.

"How did you get here?" asked Pat.

The young lad paused and looked away as if he was wondering how he got there himself.

"Well, I was born in the states then when I was fifteen, my folks moved back to Hanover, Saxony. When I turned seventeen, I was drafted by the German Army. It didn't take long for them to assign me to special duty once they heard my English. So they sent me here." Again he paused and looked way. "My job is to accommodate our English speaking guests!" he said then looked back at Pat with a smile.

Pat told him a bit about his hometown and was generally friendly to him. Being nearly twenty-seven, Pat seemed much older to Brunner. Margaret had sent her boy off to Wyoming at about the same age so Pat had a keen sense of how displaced the young soldier felt. The two hit it off. Furthermore, Pat clearly understood that young Walter Brunner could be a tremendous asset. Brunner expressed hope Pat would soon heal from his wounds. He then asked how Pat came to be wearing a German issued hat.

Pat explained to him how German pilots had given it to him in the hospital. "It's from the Bavarian pilot I shot down before I crashed," he said.

As Pat spoke to Brunner in his long coat, wearing the German hat, two German guards wondered who the "tall Hun" was talking to Brunner. They approached and Brunner said something to them in German.

Pat opened his coat showing his British uniform. The two grumbled something in German, scowled, then turned and walked back to their post. Pat grinned as he watched them snarling back in forth as if each was accusing the other of assuming O'Brien was a Hun.

Pat shook Brunner's hand and thanked him, then fell in with a group of men walking the yard all wearing different uniforms. There was a French Marine and a French flying officer. There were two Belgian soldiers, a soldier from Canada and another from the United Kingdom. Three Irish pilots welcomed him almost as family after hearing his last name and the two Scots in the group were cordial. There was a man from Wales, South Africa, Algeria, China and a New Zealander. It was Edgar. Lt. Edgar Henry Garland!

"Pat O'Brien!" shouted Garland as he turned hearing the men behind him welcoming Pat to the group. Though Garland had not been on any of Pat's patrols he was with the 66th. They knew each other well. He was in Pat's group of eighteen who regularly ate meals together at Estree'-Blanche. Garland turned and walked briskly to the back of the pack where Pat was shaking hands with his Irish "cousins."

"I thought you were dead for sure, Pat!" said Lt. Garland. "Didn't you go down on that late afternoon patrol that got ambushed? At least the talk was that you got ambushed." Garland looked at Pat's bandaged mouth and throat with concern.

Pat was so glad to see someone he knew. "Edgar, so good to see you," pausing a second, "I think. Too bad it has to be in a place like this, huh? Well, at least we are alive, right?" Edgar nodded still shaking Pat's hand. They turned and walked together.

"Yeah, we were ambushed alright. Those damn Huns," said Pat. "They set us up. We had a fighting chance going in. Eight against nine, mind you, but we had a chance. But there were other planes along the coast. They were laying in the weeds for us. It was a deathtrap. The Germans are rapidly earning their reputation with me, that's for sure." Pausing again, "How did you get here?"

"Well, I crashed and was captured on the 22nd, you know," said Garland. "I've only been here since yesterday. You?"

"Just got here myself – last night," answered Pat. "I hear that they keep you only a day or two and then you're shipped to Germany."

"It's true, Pat. I heard that myself. Hell, my guard already told me I'm destined for Holzminden near Hanover. It's a huge place. He said it holds over 500 officers. I don't know if the guard was giving me hell or if he really knows something but the prospects of being in prison in Germany, doesn't sit well with me. Doesn't sit well at all," he said looking away in reflection.

Prison in Germany didn't sound good to Pat either. During his first stroll in the courtyard at Courtrai, he discovered that everyone was talking about two topics, how to escape prison and how to get more food. No one wanted any part of prison inside Germany but neither had any of the prisoners thought of a way out of Courtrai. As far as food was concerned, there simply wasn't enough of it and what there was of poor quality.

Edgar explained the food situation. Breakfast was scheduled for 08:00. It would consist of a cup of coffee, that's all. There was never milk or sugar. Some prisoners would save a little bread from the previous day for breakfast but Pat wouldn't find the war bread appetizing at all. It was heavy, black and sour. Lunch consisted of boiled sugar beets or a substitute vegetable with an occasional pickled meat or some soup. Dinner was at 05:30. If they were lucky, it sometimes featured jam made from leftover sugar beets and a preparation called tea which required regular shaking and disturbed the British to no end.

For a wounded prisoner like Pat trying to get well, the lack of food only curtailed his ability to heal. Food and escape dominated the first day's conversations. Little would change in the days ahead.

Pat had received a full orientation from his fellow inmates on his first day. More than the information, however, he valued seeing English speaking gents once again who were on his side. The next morning, Pat visited the prison doctor who examined and redressed his wounds. The Hun doctor was thorough but rough and did not speak English. A smaller bandage was placed on Pat's upper lip. It made it easier to speak. From the doctor appointment, Pat entered the yard where the morning walk had just begun. He walked alongside Edgar Garland. Walter Brunner was also with the group.

"Hey, Kaiser, where can a guy get a little steak and potatoes around here?" quipped Pat, flashing his famous smile at the young Brunner. Garland chuckled, shaking his head in anticipation. He'd see this act before.

"Steak? Holy Jesus, Lieutenant! I haven't seen a steak since I left New Jersey," he responded. "You're not serious, are you?

"Well I figure a guy like you, tight with the Huns here, speaking their language? Why, getting a little beef for your fellow American and my friend here from New Zealand ought to be as simple as finding honey in a bee hive!" said Pat.

"Yes, honey, right!" repeated Garland.

"Why don't you check around with a few of your chummy Hun friends and see what you can scrape up," said Pat.

"You'll get what you get," said the young interpreter. Brunner had been there long enough that he had had his fill of ribbing from Allied troops. Somehow, hearing it from Pat, the first American he had met at Courtrai, stung a bit more. Pat worked him over a bit, jabbing about abandoning his U.S. home and turning traitor on the good ole' U.S.A. and all. The young Brunner took it in stride, the two laughed it off and then Brunner dropped back to speak with another group of prisoners.

Now, it seemed unusual to Pat that the Germans would have an American-born German mixing with the prisoners so and apparently allowing him to be openly friendly with them. But, in fact, the Germans viewed Brunner as an asset, someone who could perhaps lower the guard of a prisoner and entice him to reveal information. After all, no one inside was getting out so why not let Brunner mix freely. As Pat thought of it, he turned a bit sour on Brunner, seeing him more as a willing accomplice. He kept his conversations with Brunner light but one could hear a cynical tone to the ribbing he applied to the "Hun spy," as he referred to him.

At lunch, Pat and Edgar were joined by six others. There was James Dickson and his two fellow Irish Fusiliers, George Devereaux the French Flyer, Smith the South African and Arnold Jacob, the Welsh Lieutenant.

"This food is horse crap," said Dickson, returning his soup spoon to his bowl. "I say we tap that New Jersey Hun for some decent food. I can't survive eating this bog."

"It's called prison, James," retorted his fellow Irishman Chase Kavanagh in a sarcastic tone.

"No, really!" responded Dickson. "If we worked together on this I think we can do better than this Hun grub."

Pat spoke up. "One thing that seems easy enough would be to use our afternoon walk in the country to snatch something from the outside. This afternoon there's a planned walk outside the prison. The walk goes right past a potatopatch, right?" All nodded. "So, when we go on our walk today, we pretend to be tired just as we get to the patch, request a rest, sit down, start digging and take a few with us. That would take care of the potatoes.

"You Irish always start with potatoes," joked Smith. The Frenchman chuckled under his breath.

Pat went on. "There's usually some extra jam at dinner and if we trade a few cigarettes we could probably get enough for the eight of us. These Hun guards look easy to bribe and not too smart at that." Pat had a convincing matter-of-fact tone to his voice.

"That, gives us potatoes and jam," said Chase.

Then more plotting from Pat, "Chase, tonight when the Hun cook comes out to check for leftovers at dinner, Chase, you impose on him to play us a tune on his zither and Smith you sneak into his kitchen and grab us some bread. Simple as that! I'll bribe that tall goofy cook for eggs. A few francs should do the trick. The rest of you save your butter the rest of the day."

Pat was always good with his money and probably had more than most of his fellow prisoners. As usual, he was stirring enthusiasm for the scheme. The group was now convinced. It was like Pat and the old Quarry Gang back at Momence all over again.

The walk past the potato patch that afternoon was a huge success. Each man was able to scavenge one or two potatoes and Pat actually nabbed six. They bribed the prison cook and the eight men had a real feast the following night, August 29th. The meal consisted of scrambled eggs, fried potatoes, bread and jam and a pitcher of beer, which the prisoners were able to buy.

They had plenty for eight but an English officer who had just been brought in on a stretcher joined them and they shared their festive meal with him. The officer had lain in a shellhole for seven days with no food and the group was more than happy to share their dinner.

There were speeches and a few "prison gifts" like the check given to Pat by Dickson. It was for twenty-four francs and was made payable to Pat O'Brien, drawn on a London Bank. Naturally, it could never be cashed but it added to a night of light hearted fun.

After the "banquet" broke up, Pat and Edgar decided to walk the perimeter of the jail yard. It was a warm clear night and the two men wanted to talk further about the second most popular topic in camp after food....escape.

Suddenly, they could hear a distant humming and the German guards began stirring in anticipation. "Sounds like we've got visitors, Pat," said Garland, craning his neck to see any sign of the escalating drone. Suddenly, there were explosions at the far end of the prison, then huge guns hammering away from outside the prison to keep the planes as high in the sky as possible.

"I wonder if this goes on every night?" shouted Pat as the two moved up against one of the building's sides looking up at the action.

"Courtrai gets bombed constantly according to my prison guard," yelled Edgar. "Apparently, we're not the only attraction in town. The Germans have thousands of troops concentrated in Courtrai and don't forget, Pat, the staff headquarters for the region is here as well."

Pat and Edgar watched the bombing with great interest, but also at great risk. The German guards and a few of the prisoners scampered inside to avoid being hit. Pat and Edgar were of the mind that the same bombs falling in the courtyard could just as easily drop on their cell so it mattered little where they stood. Neither could resist witnessing the skill of allied pilots battling the Hun machines. The bombing raid and accompanying dog-fight lasted forty-five minutes and provided a great diversion for both men. After the bombing stopped they went inside to Pat's cell where they talked until two in the morning.

The next morning the head guard announced that a group photo of the prisoners would be taken at 09:00. The group of eight, plus twenty-two others from Pat's prison building, posed under a small tree in the prison yard. The guard arranged a table and chair for himself and men posed sitting on the ground in front of the table with an equal number standing in back. Pat was one of the taller men so he stood in back directly behind the guard.

His lip wound was closed enough that he was able to remove the bandage for the photo. Few men smiled. Pat had his natural grin, as did the guard and one or two others, but it was a somber group and more than a few had headaches from the night before.

"I will have copies of the photo made for those who would like one. It will cost you one mark," stated the German guard. He had a thriving business in conjunction with his guard duties. "Come by later today, and I will have photos ready for you," stated the entrepreneurial German.

Later that morning, Pat decided to check on the photo. Edgar was sitting on the edge of his bed playing Patience, an old German solitaire game. With no reading materials allowed in the prison, card games were but one of the few diversions.

"I'm going to see if the photo is ready, Edgar. I'll be right back," he said walking past his friend's cell. "Right, then," responded Edgar. "Do you need some money, Pat?" Pat waved him off and headed for the administration building.

"Here," stated the guard, exchanging the photos for money. Pat added his photo to the cherished picture of Paul and himself on the Megantic then put it in his back pocket. He placed Edgar's in his shirt pocket. He was glad to have a record of the poor souls that he'd likely never see again. Men arrived and departed continuously at Courtrai.

He hurried back to the prison house to show Edgar the photo. Garland was gone. He had been taken away to be placed on a train and was, indeed, headed straight for Holzminden. This stunned Pat. It happened so suddenly. It struck him how quickly war's evaporation could occur once captured by the enemy. He knew now that he had to become focused on escape or he'd be trapped in a German prison in no time.

Pat began to communicate constantly with the men who were there and particularly new arrivals. Each time a new prisoner arrived he would interrogate him for news from the front, movement of troops and anything that might teach Pat something new or expose an opportunity. Pat probed to find out if the new arrivals knew how prisoners were transferred out. Had they seen any prisoners being moved as they were being brought in? Did they travel in vehicles or by train? Were prisoners transferred in groups? How many guards per prisoner? How were the guards armed?

By September 1, Pat's seventh day at Courtrai, the group of eight, minus Garland but now including the English officer, gathered daily to discuss, among other things, the possibility of escape. Though wounded, Pat was their leader if for no other reason than the fact that he was the oldest in the group. In reality, his natural leadership ability was anything but tarnished by his injury. It was embellished particularly by the very fact that he survived at all. To a man, prisoners were stunned listening to the casual way Pat told the story of his last fight, by his wounds which were obvious, and by the story of his miraculous survival falling from 8,000 feet. Even among battle experienced men in prison under dire conditions, Pat O'Brien's story was exceptional. He was not, however, exempt from being the butt of a joke.

"I think we should disguise ourselves as women and simply walk out of the prison," said the Irish Fusilier James Henry Dickson as they drank their breakfast. That brought a huge laugh from the group. "I'm dead serious!" said the poker-faced Irishman which only made the group roar further.

"O'Brien would stand a better chance as a horse," added Walter Smith from South Africa. "The man is six feet two for Christ's sake!" More laughter ensued. Among the group, discussions about escape were more entertainment than strategy but it filled the day and kept everyone's mind at ease. That evening the men were enjoying some beer.

As the evening went on, the men talked less of escape and more on such topics that seem vital only to men under the influence of alcohol. Odd as it was, prisoners were able to buy beer, yet couldn't get a good cup of coffee in the morning. Pat, having the most money in the group, bought more than he drank. The "official meeting" broke up at around 22:00.

That night Pat did not sleep well. He was thinking of Edgar Garland. His wounds were healing but he was experiencing "healing pains," as he called them, which kept him up at night. No doubt the extensive conversation that night was causing the irritation in his throat. The late hour was probably good for his spirits but a strain on his body. He watched the night air raids accompanied by German searchlights, artillery, intensive bombing and streaks of "flaming onions" punctuating the dark sky. Watching the planes maneuver overhead cause Pat to long for flying. It depressed him that he might not get a chance to use his piloting skills in battle ever again.

Like all prisoners of war, uncertainty was the nag that distracted each day. Pat wondered if he would ever be transferred out. He had decided that escape would have to occur during a transfer. Transfer was, indeed, the vehicle of escape. Reflecting on the evening's "discussions," Pat determined that each man had to organize his own escape and such group plans served little purpose beyond entertainment. "After all," he thought, "the likelihood we'll be transferred out together is nil."

As the late night fighting subsided, Pat left the window and sat on the edge of his bed, kicked off his shoes and stretched out for the night. "Hum," he thought. "Tomorrow is Sunday." He pictured his mother and others arriving at the Methodist Church in Momence for a relaxing day at church. It was so far removed from the prison at Courtrai. He thought of Agnes for the first time in a week then drifted off to sleep.

Chapter 26

Calculated Risk

Anytime prisoners were taken outside the prison, it was the practice to parade them through the streets of Courtrai to create the idea with the locals that the Germans were capturing a lot of prisoners. There were always plenty of German soldiers along the route to jeer and make fun of their captives, as well. Sometimes on Sundays the Germans would parade prisoners through town for no reason at all. The Belgians were always curious and turned out in large numbers. It was common for German guards to strike women and children that got too close. On the morning of September 2, Pat was part of a "happy parade" through the center of town.

As the group passed the Church of our Lady in the center of town, Pat smiled at an attractive young Belgian girl who was standing on the curb across the street outside her home. He said hello to her in English and she replied in her native tongue. A German made a run for her to stifle such social graces but she quickly stepped into the house and the Hun passed her by.

A block later they came upon a number of homes destroyed by allied bombs. "Halt!" shouted their guard. He reprimanded them in French for destroying private Belgian homes. His comments were obviously intended more for the locals than the English speaking prisoners. The French among the prison group later told the men what was said. The walk was about one hour on this day. There was plenty of gawking, jeering, and displays such as the one in front of the bombed out homes along the way to publicly humiliate the prisoners.

The tour group was back at the prison in time for lunch. It was announced that an afternoon of games were planned for everyone's enjoyment after lunch. At about 13:00 Pat and his friends were escorted to the prison yard where three or four prisoners were plucked from the crowd and forced to defend themselves against an equal number of hungry German Shepherds that the guards had avoided feeding for three days.

The starving hounds lashed at the men's legs, which had been prepped for the event by dousing blood and gristle from beef scraps so as to entice the hounds. It was a brutal and savage game of torture that had its roots in old Roman games of slaughter and by the time the hounds were done, the men's pants and legs were shredded from vicious dog bits. It delighted the Huns. It infuriated Pat and his fellow inmates.

These and other antics of the Huns increased Pat's hatred for his captors. The German guards were often seen as cowardly during night bombings raids only to brag the next day about the ineptitude of enemy bombers. Most of the guards were easily bribed and had few scruples. The German medical staff was particularly brutal and often refused to assist newly arrived wounded soldiers, sighting "orders from above." Men full of shrapnel often lay for days in their beds in great pain. A good number did not survive.

Each morning in good weather, the entire prison population was taken to a large swimming pool and was allowed to bathe. There were two pools, one for the officers and the other for the men. Guards sat at each corner of the pool with rifles across their laps and watched carefully as the men dressed and undressed. Interpreters were always with the men so conversations could always be monitored.

Sanitary conditions at the prison were generally good but in the middle of the night Tuesday, September 4, Pat was awakened by an ungodly irritation all over his body. He banged on his cell door to get the attention of the guard. Pat had a bad case of what he referred to as "the cooties." It was lice and it attracted the attention of the guard immediately. The guard was very perturbed fearing he might be blamed for Pat's condition. The commandant was summoned and was extremely angry, cursing the guard and calling for assistance.

Pat was taken from his cell by a guard with a rifle and walked about a quarter of a mile from the prison to an old factory building that had been converted into an elaborate fumigating plant. There he was dipped in a pickle bath of some type of solution. Pat's clothes, bedding and everything in his cell was being fumigated, as well. Once "dipped," he sat nude with over one hundred German soldiers who had become infested in the trenches and were also waiting for their clothes.

Pat thought it odd that even though there was no way for anyone to know he was the enemy, since none of the men were dressed, no one spoke to him. They were talking about Pat however and made no attempt to conceal it, laughing at him though they were certainly in a similar condition. It was just one more irritating thing about the Germans that stuck in Pat's craw and drained his opinion of them. Clinching his teeth in anger, he held a firm gaze attempting to show no anger or mockery so as not to egg them on.

He arrived back at his cell at 05:30 exhausted. The Germans had done a thorough job of fumigating his cell and he was never bothered by "visitors" again. Pat imposed on his guard to let him sleep through breakfast and skip the morning walk, which the guard agreed to do. Pat slept most of the morning.

There were some moments more pleasant than his fumigation the evening of September 4. Once in a while the Belgian Ladies' Relief Society visited the prison bringing handkerchiefs, American soap, tooth brushes and other small items that were American made. The gifts were so appreciated that some men would cry upon receiving them. One day, Pat was caught giving a button off his uniform to one of the Belgian ladies for a souvenir in gratitude but was reprimanded by his guard and never allowed to go near visitors again.

The men held lotteries each day for the extra bread left over from dinner. Hardly a grand prize in Pat's mind but it stirred the interest of the men. They were allowed to buy pears and Pat's throat felt good enough that he bought one for himself at the end his second week in prison. He had regularly purchased pears for his friends who had little or no money.

Pat began hoarding his food. He was planning for his eventual escape attempt which he knew had to be soon as he entered his second week. He stuck to a pear diet and stashed all his bread and anything else that might keep, should he successfully escape. Most of his thinking involved stealing a German plane one way or another and flying northwest to Holland and freedom, but the prospect of walking to Holland did enter his mind. The conditions under which he would elude his captors were hard to determine until the opportunity presented itself but he always pictured himself flying to freedom. All he could do now would be to store food and be ready at any moment to take advantage of an opening, likely while being transferred.

One thing he knew he needed that he did not have was a map. During one conversation with Walter Brunner, the young man revealed that every interpreter had a number of maps in their possession and that an impressive collection of maps were stored in the interpreter's quarters. Through the use of some diversionary conversation one day, Pat had gotten the young Brunner to brag about his responsibility and status as an interpreter and Walter had volunteered the map information. When he had mentioned it to Pat, he suddenly clammed up realizing the value of such information. But Pat's skill with the language of enticement, had duped yet another unsuspecting participant.

On September 7, Pat had a conversation with his Irish buddy James Dickson over breakfast.

"Look Jimmy, all we have to do is start a conversation with the young Brunner and one of his fellow interpreters about some German landmark" explained Pat. "Say, you and I pretend to have an argument that only a map can solve. And it would have to be something very obvious. I'll be adamant about the wrong position and you accuse me of being foolhardy."

"Yeah, Yeah, I follow you," said Dickson, nodding his head.

"Brunner goes in to get a map to prove me wrong, then when he goes to put it back, you make note of where he stores his maps. Then later in the day, we return when they are not there and swipe the map." Pat looked for a reaction. It was positive.

The next day, September 8, Pat and the savvy Dickson performed their stunt "to a T." The young Brunner was adamant that Heidelberg was on the Rhine and he'd show Pat a map to prove it. Dickson had great fun calling Pat a buffoon as part of the whole stage play but the scheme worked. Returning two hours later, Pat and James Dickson successfully nabbed two maps of Germany, one for Pat and one for Dickson.

The map heist couldn't have been timelier. On the morning of September 9th, Pat and six other officers were told that they were to be transferred to a prison camp in Germany. His day had come. Pat slipped a few Francs to one of his guards who revealed that they were heading for a reprisal camp in Strassburg, Germany some 250 miles southwest into the heart of Germany.

"My God," thought Pat. "This is it. If I get that far in, I'll never escape." Then, sitting on the edge of his bed, he began plotting. "Clearly, they will take us by train. But which train? Which station? How will we get from here to the station?" All this thought proved little until specifics were known. Pat would just have to act when he saw the opportunity. He checked all of his personal items and fashioned a bit of a knapsack from a gas-bag brought to Courtrai by a British soldier who had died. Pat slid his precious map into the sock of his left leg beneath his boot.

Suddenly there was a stirring at the door and two guards slid open his cell door.

"O'Brien, we go now," barked the expressionless Hun guard.

Pat rose, walked between the two guards to the jail yard, then to the prison's side exit. There were five British officers and one French officer standing at the same gate, each guarded by a single German guard. The party was escorted out of the prison and pushed immediately into an awaiting truck where guards stood over them with rifles. Pat quickly determined that there was no opportunity to escape in this setting.

"We're going to Ghent first," said one British officer to Pat.

"Halt den Mund!" barked one of the guards turning his rifle in the direction of the Brit. There would be no talking on this trip and it was apparent that these Huns were selected for prison transfer because of their lack of tolerance. It is during transfer that risk of losing a prisoner is greatest.

Ghent was the biggest city of East Flanders province at the confluence of the Scheldt and Lys Rivers. It was about twenty-five miles for Courtrai. Pat was reminded how saturated Belgium was with rivers and canals as they passed over many on the way to Ghent which itself was a significant inland port. It struck him that a walk through Belgium would mean a significant portion of swimming, as well.

When they arrived, two other prisoners were added to the group and the eight were locked in a room at a rundown hotel with a guard sitting at the door, rifle across his knee. Pat strongly considered a break at this point but the guard was so obviously alert and capable that Pat thought better. Thirty minutes later, there was a knock at the door and a garrison of troops, one guard for every two men each. They were marched to the train station where they would board for Germany. Again, Pat saw no opportunity. There was too much firepower to attempt an escape through the streets of Ghent.

In short order, they arrived at the station and halted alongside a twelve-car German train. Eleven of the cars were full of troops and the twelfth was reserved for Pat and his fellow transports. It was fourth-class, old, hard wooden seats and a filthy floor, no lights but a single candle placed on a table in the middle of the car. The car held eight prisoners and four guards.

A superior officer stepped into the car and barked orders at the four guards who would make the trip. He then conducted a weapons inspection in full view of the prisoners so as to demonstrate to them that the guards on this trip were fully armed. It made an impression.

Pat sat next to one of the British officers, both facing to the rear of the train where their guard sat facing them both. The guard was so close that his feet sometimes touched Pat's and he held a rifle between his knees, the butt of which occasionally struck Pat's foot, as well. This arrangement hardly seemed like an opportunity.

As they sat waiting to depart, a crowd of curious onlookers gathered outside their coach.

"Hope you have a nice trip!" one of them shouted. "Drop me a line when you get to Berlin," shouted another in broken English. "When shall we see you again?" asked a third. "Remember me to your friends, will you? You'll find plenty where you're going," shouted an old women.

The German guards made no to attempt to silence the hecklers. The whole scene seemed rather odd if not trumped up to Pat. "Why would these occupied Belgians have such animosity for Allied troops", he thought. "Obviously, a trumped up episode," he concluded, "one more poisonous practice of the evil Hun."

Never to be outdone and seldom fearful of consequence, Pat took his shot at charade. "You're an officer, aren't you?" he shouted out the window of his car to an officer standing at attention.

"Yes, what of it?" the officer responded.

"Well, in England we let your officers who are prisoners ride first-class. Can't you fix it so that we can be similarly treated, or be transferred at least to a second-class compartment?" shouted Pat.

"If I had my way," he replied, "you'd ride with the hogs!' He then turned to the crowd and told them what had been said and they all laughed hilariously. Pat's Irish temperament kicked in.

"That would be damned sight better than riding with Germans!" Pat shouted back. The German guard didn't bother to repeat Pat's final retort to the curious crowd. Just then the train jerked forward and they were off. Pat looked out the window and saw the crowds that had just heckled his group turn away almost on cue with heads down. This was proof that the local Belgians were staged at the train station to heckle the Allied prisoners.

"Unless I escape before we reach the reprisal camp, the war will be over for me," thought Pat.

A reprisal camp is where enemy prisoners are placed near vital resources such as a factory or nearby key personnel so as to deter the enemy from bombing. Any attack on the German assets near these camps would result in the deaths of many Allied officers. Pat and his fellow officers were being taken to this particular camp to reduce the potential bombing of Strasbourg where many German military vehicles were manufactured. Strasbourg also had numerous military forts going back to Napoleon's day that served well as prisons.

"Perhaps we can just jump these guards," Pat thought. "But how would all eight of us escape unnoticed even if we did?" He reflected further, "I can't worry about these other chaps. I'm in this for myself now. Group escape might work for tunnel digging but it's every man for himself at this point."

They passed through village after village and Pat realized that he was getting closer to Germany and an uncertain future.

"The window! That's it! I'll jump while the train is moving. That will give me time to run before they stop and search for me," he thought. "I'll need time to run." It was his only option. Pat would wait until the train was out of the city. That would give him cover in the woods and be in a place where few people would spot him.

Pat looked at his guard and gave a signal with his right hand indicating he was warm then gestured toward the window. The guard understood and nodded affirmatively that he could open the window. Pat rose slowly, reached down and opened the window fully to determine clearance. Taking his seat, he gave the opening a glance and determined he could fit through. The guard was reading a magazine and made no fuss.

Spurred on by the now audible and rhythmic "clickety clack" of the train, Pat determined that the train was likely moving at about thirty to forty miles per hour.

"Let's see," he thought. "I wonder how fast Gus traveled back when I used to leap from his train." He pictured it for a moment. "It must have been fifteen miles an hour or so. It wasn't that bad. If this is thirty, then I just need to move my legs quicker and roll.

Men like Pat, who spent their life on trains, often heard a language in the gears and track sounds of a moving train. Trains would seem to speak to those who spent hours on long runs. This train was imploring Pat to jump. Jump from the train and escape even if it meant dying in the attempt. He had no chance inside Germany. He had a slim chance by jumping now into the Belgium countryside.

"You're a fool if you do, you're a fool if you don't! You're a fool if you do, You're a fool if you don't!" came the train's utterance urging him to act.

Pat stared down, his mind racing in rapid debate. "Should I jump or wait," he thought. But in an instant he no longer debated if he should jump. He was only debating when. "Was the train picking up speed? What it slowing down or staying the same," he asked himself. He determined that the more trees he saw passing by, rather than buildings, the faster the train would likely go. He needed to jump before it was moving too fast.

"You're a fool if you do, you're a fool if you don't," went the clanking train.

Suddenly, Pat's guard rose and walked a few feet to the center of the car where he dipped a tin cup into a bucket of water for a drink. Pat leaned over and told his fellow officer of his plan.

"For God's sake Pat, chuck it! Don't be a lunatic. This railroad is double-tracked and rock-ballasted and the other track is on our side. You stand every chance of knocking your brains out against the rails, or hitting a bridge or a whistling post. You have one chance in a thousand of making it!"

Pat lost his nerve and sat back in his chair. He lowered the window halfway. His guard returned to his seat and turned to his fellow guard across the aisle making a short statement in German that seemed to be about the bitter water in the bucket.

By now the car was full of smoke from the cigarettes of five guards who had lit up. Pat looked across at the elderly guard and smiled. The guard seem preoccupied and wasn't particularly suspicious of Pat. Pat smiled at him and he smiled back.

"No, I'm going!" thought Pat and he started to cough as though the smoke was irritating his throat. The guard looked up in disgust but said nothing. Pat reopened the window fully.

It was four in the morning. They had traveled all night and a number of prisoners were drifting off to sleep. Pat had on his long trench coat. His knapsack contained two pieces of bread, a piece of sausage and a pair of flying mittens. He estimated that the train was still traveling between thirty and thirty-five miles an hour.

[315]

"Now! Go Now!" he thought to himself as his eyes opened wide looking down at his knapsack on his lap which he firmly clutched in his right hand. He glanced up at the overhead rack running the length of the coach. It looked similarly anchored as had been the rack he stretched from on his way to San Diego months ago. "Go!" he thought.

Standing up on his bench, taking hold of the rack with his left hand and a hanging strap from the top of the car with his right, he tucked and shoved his feet and legs out of the window, pulled himself through and let go! He was out.

He landed on his left side and face, burying it in the rock ballast, cutting his entire check and gashing his left eye. The impact drove air from his lungs in a loud "huh" that expelled when he landed.

His hands and shins were skinned on sharp rocks and his left ankle was wrenched making twisted contact with the irregular surface of the rail-bed. He was knocked out cold but regained consciousness in no less than ten seconds. Ignoring his pain in his ankle, he jumped up and ran straight into the woods only to run headlong into a barbed-wire fence along the right-of-way thirty feet from the track. "How stupid!" he thought. "You'd think I've never worked on a railroad in my life. Everyone knows there's fencing aside tracks! Keep your head on, will you!"

Pat negotiated the fence and got on the other side. He didn't realize that the collision with the fence caused one of his two pieces of bread to fall to the ground. A loud squealing sound of metal on metal could be heard up the tracks as the train broke hard. He ran as far and fast as he could. He was out. He was free and he was alive. But they would be coming and soon. He needed to hide.

PART SIX

SEVENTY-TWO DAYS

Chapter 27

Mud, Blood and Stars

Pat was bleeding profusely. While running he reached in his pocket and grabbed one of the handkerchiefs given to him by the Belgian Ladies Relief Society. It was his upper lip injury, ripped open again when the left side of his face slammed against the large rock ballast. Pat grabbed the tail of his coat and held it at his waist to catch the droppings of blood for fear he'd leave a trail leading to his capture. He could hear the squealing iron wheels grind to a halt in the distance. Being a life-long railroad pro he sensed that the train was likely one-half mile up the track. Though he could not hear much else, he could picture Hun guards, likely leaping from the train in pursuit. They were.

Pat hurried through the wooded area for a mile before he stopped, turned, and listened intently. Were they coming? The crack of a twig? A distant voice? There was nothing. He checked his handkerchief, it was soaked. Not wanting to leave evidence behind, he stuffed the blood soaked rag in his pocket and got out a second handkerchief. He spit out a good amount of blood that was dripping into his mouth from his ripped upper lip.

"My ankle!" He had a bad sprain. Adrenaline had pumped through his body for the last mile and it was not until he stopped that the pain shot through.

"I wonder where I am?" It was still fairly dark, about 04:20. He checked the sky.

"Damn, I've turned." The train was heading southeast. Pat had essentially run away from the tracks to the west and then somehow hooked to the southeast and right back in the direction of the train.

"Hell, if, in fact, that train has gone another half mile south, then I'm probably lined up with it now. I need to get west and quick." He looked up again to find the North Star.

"Ok, I'm right now." And so he headed west, away from the train again and did not stop for two and a half hours. Pat's loss of blood had finally worn him down so he stopped and sat down against a tree surrounded by hedge. Then, he listened.

The Germans had become confused as well. The old German guard, who had sat across from Pat, rose in shock when he witnessed Pat's disappearance out the window, right in front of him. No German guard welcomed the wrath he'd receive from his superiors reporting that a prisoner escaped right from under his nose and from a moving train, no less!

As a result, the old German sprang to his feet and caused a tremendous commotion throughout the car and the car adjacent to his. He was yelling chaotically, "Amerikanischen entgangen!" (American Sprang!) As a result, it took some time before the train engineer got word to brake.

Additionally, in all the confusion, the old man had directed armed guards down the tracks toward Strassburg rather than west or back north in Pat's likely direction. After a frantic search up and down both sides of the tracks, the German guard called off his search and the search party boarded the train once again.

As the old Hun prepared to take his final step onto the train he paused and took one last look over his left shoulder. "Was eine gewagte Sache zu tun!" he said to himself. What a daring thing to do, indeed.

Unknown to Pat O'Brien, he had become the first British pilot to escape German hands. He was sixty miles inside Germany when he jumped and he was a long way from freedom. Pat took stock of his wounds. He felt safe, removing the blood-soaked handkerchief from his pocket and pushed it deeply into a hedge so as not to leave any evidence. He reached up carefully to touch the left side of his face, then his eye. He was stunned to feel such a deep laceration over his left eye that was now more painful than his newly opened lip wound. Dabbing it softly with his new handkerchief he could tell is was swelled shut which explain why he could only see out of his right eye. "That damn thing is really swollen. Hurts like hell!" he said to himself.

By now daylight had begun to make its appearance. He saw, for the first time, a canal about three hundred feet away blocking his chosen path. He would have to cross it. Pat walked north to the edge of the canal. "Maybe I'll get some of this mud and blood off my coat, at least," he said as he lowered himself in and swam across, keeping his head above the waterline. Reaching the other side, he lowered his head under a few times hoping he could wash away the grime and blood that was caked on his face. His wounds stung but he sensed that they would respond positively to the cleansing.

Pat had forgotten to remove his wrist-watch before entering the canal. The glass crystal of his watch had cracked when his plane crashed twenty-four days ago but he had it repaired at Courtrai. When he leaped from the train it had broken again but was working fine until he swam across the canal. His map in his sock was damaged as well, which really angered him. It would still function to a degree but Pat felt the mistake was so unnecessary. He vowed to sharpen his focus, think through his options and remember to protect his assets better.

Just then the morning sun landed on Pat's face. "I can't travel in daylight, my British uniform will surely give me away," he thought. And so he decided to hide during the day and travel by night. Not far from the canal he saw a wooded area and headed in its direction. He found a thick brush area where he could hide and removed his long coat. He exposed it to the sun so it might dry.

The swim across the canal soaked the bread in his pocket. He pulled it out, placed it in his mouth and swallowed. It went down with less irritation. "So bitter and soaked in a German canal water. What a hand I've been dealt," he thought to himself. Pat scanned his surroundings then leaned back to relax.

"Thank you, God for getting me this far," he prayed. He was fortunate to be alive. He asked the Good Lord to heal his wounds and give him spiritual and physical strength to find freedom. He cried for a short spell, overjoyed that he had gotten away. Setting pity aside, he thanked God one more time, then laid back and tried to sleep.

He was glad to rest his left ankle but morning clouds covered the rising sun and a slow drizzle kept his coat and other clothes from drying fully. He knew he had to sleep but as much as he tried he could not. He was caked in mud and blood and his clothes were soaked through. It was a very long first day. "I have a lot to learn about keeping my head clear and surviving outdoors," he thought.

As he lay back trying to rest, he thought of the men of the marsh who spent days on end hunting and fishing outdoors. Pat's time in the Kankakee Marsh, like all boys of his age, was usually limited to day outings. He tried to think back. "I should have watched those old trappers more closely. They knew how to survive, how to plan. I was always eager to jump on a train I guess. Now, I've jumped off one and have so little to draw on for my outdoor survival. Well, I'll have to learn."

Night came and he had not slept more than one hour but he dragged himself together and headed northeast. His possessions included his uniform, two shirts, no underwear, leather leggings, heavy shoes he had paid nearly twenty-five dollars to repair while in prison, a good pair of wools socks and a German cap. He still had several hundred water soaked francs in his wallet and other papers. He had stolen a jack-knife at Courtrai from a property-room where prisoners' personal items were kept.

About midnight he came upon another canal. It was smaller and Pat practiced his new techniques by stripping down and placing his clothes and some of his belongings on his head. Around three in the morning there was another swim. He moved swiftly, figuring each water barrier would delay his progress but during the first night he traveled about ten miles based on his faded map.

Morning came and he found some low bushes where he made a bed, removed his wet clothes and ate the last of his rations, the sausage. He relished the taste. "I've got to figure out what the hell I'm going to eat." Lying back in his makeshift bed he thought about food for the next day. "With all the farming in my family I ought to be able to find food somewhere in this Hun countryside. That will be tomorrow's project." He fell asleep.

Pat awoke midday to the sound of a large flock of geese honking across the treetops on their day's mission. It reminded him of home. Though a different breed, there was no mistaking the sound. He fell back asleep until dusk. Awaking just after dusk, he headed in the same direction but his mission was clearly food and drink. He was hungrier than he had ever been and hoped a canal or stream would appear soon to quench his thirst.

For the next three nights he scavenged for cabbage, sugar-beets and carrots. They seemed to be the most abundant. "You'd think these goofy Huns would consider growing an apple tree or two along the way for a guy like me," he quipped, instinctively inserting Irish irony to every situation.

His planned routine of sleeping days and walking nights was logical and necessary so as not to be discovered but his body strongly disagreed with the plan. The only sleep Pat was getting was from sheer exhaustion and it often overtook him at dusk, just as he was scheduled to walk again.

On the evening of the sixth night he was fully spent by 23:00. He found a thick brush that he hoped might shelter him from the continuous drizzle that had not eased all day. Pat fell into a deep sleep. When he opened his eyes at daylight some eight hours later he found himself in the back yard of a German family.

"Holy Jesus, I've got to get out of here!" Pat looked carefully to make certain there was no one up early. Seeing no one, he lost no time sneaking away and vowed he would never give in to the temptation of sleeping nights again.

Every day and night in Germany it rained. "These bastards, I'll never be dry again!" He did everything he could to keep his shoes and socks dry, always tying them onto his head when swimming the rivers and canals which crossed his path the entire trek north. Germany had miles and miles of forests with young pine trees around twelve feet high. They were so close together it became difficult for Pat see the night sky, critical to following his beacon, the North Star.

On his ninth day, he perceived he was close to crossing the German-Luxemburg border. By his calculation, Pat estimated that his jump must have occurred thirty-five miles from Strassburg. If he traveled north in a straight line, which he knew was not likely, he was probably one-hundred and fifty miles from the Holland boarder. Being neutral, Holland would mean freedom. The challenge, which was known by most, was the electrified fencing all along the Belgium-Holland border built by the Huns to keep the Belgians in and the Dutch out. "I'll figure that out when I get there," he thought. "I need to get there first."

On the morning of his tenth day he checked his faded map. By best estimates he had traveled seventy-five miles in nine days. Miraculously, his upper lip was healing, but he was still unable to see out of his left eye. "I may never see out of this eye again," he said out loud as he dabbed his wound with a clean corner of his handkerchief. "Tonight I will begin to go northwest. I can't wait to get out of Hun territory. At least if I get caught in someone's backyard in Belgium, they will view me as a friend." Luxembourg would be no safe haven, as most spoke German and were Hun sympathizers.

Pat's first night trekking through Luxemburg was uneventful. At dawn, he came upon a small woods with plenty of low underbrush and selected a location away from any paths and lay down to sleep. Rain had finally ceased and the woods were such that the sun shone on Pat's "bunk" while the brush kept him hidden. Hoping to fully dry his clothes, he removed them all except his shirt, draped them over a secluded bush and fell asleep.

"This is the best set-up I've had thus far," he thought. It will be nice to wear dry clothing for a change." Through the morning he awoke each hour to move his clothing as the narrow band of the sun's rays moved through the day. Around noon he was startled to hear a man speak not more than fifteen feet away!

"Wenn wir hier geschnitten, hat der Baum einen klaren Weg in diese Richtung."

"My God, I'm done!" thought Pat. "Maybe I should just stand with my hands up and hope they will leave me alone. After all, I have no uniform on. Oh, that's insane. How can I explain my condition? Wait, don't move."

Pat decided to peek through an opening in the brush. There were two men swinging axes against a large tree discussing the job as they worked. They did not know Pat was there. He lay still. The men continued to talk, unnerving Pat.

"Where the hell will this tree fall? My God if it falls in my direction, I'll be crushed. Let's see. Where are they cutting? I can't tell." Pat could only see the heads of the two woodsmen and was unable to determine the flight of their axes. "Who would want to trim a tree that lands in thick hedge? I'm sure the tree will fall away. It's only logical."

But he couldn't be sure. Pat lay watching the top of the tall tree for an hour as the men swung their axes and held a discussion that Pat new for certain would reveal the planned direction of the tree, if he could only understand German. Then, all of a sudden, "Crack" and Pat watched with great relief as the big timber fell away from his brush.

If the wait wasn't torture enough, two children arrived about one hour later with full baskets of food for the two men. Pat agonized watching the men enjoy a bountiful lunch of real food. He almost burst from his hide out and begged for food but kept his wits about him. At around four in the afternoon the men completed their work and left. Pat hurriedly got dress and scampered to the "picnic site" hoping to find a scrap or two. There was nothing. It began to rain. "Of course," he complained under his breath. It was time to walk, no food tonight.

Around midnight, Pat approached a large river. It was wider than the canals he had traversed thus far. "You might know it. This is the first time I've had dry clothes since my first night. It figures I'd run into a river." Being a strong swimmer he knew he could easily cross it in two heats. He could remove his clothes and transport them across in two bundles. "After the first swim, I'll rest a while then head back. I sure would like another day in dry clothes."

He removed all his clothes, including his shoes and tied the first bundle to his head. His first swim was a success. After drinking a good amount of water from the fresh water river, he headed back. He gathered the second bundle and ten feet from completion one of his shoes slipped off. "Damn it! I was so close." Pat completed the run and placed his second bundle on shore. He spent an hour diving over and over until he finally stumbled upon the water soaked prize.

"Boy, and we used to play these goofy diving games at The Quarry for kicks!" Pat never expected back then to use his diving skills in such a desperate situation. "I win!" he boasted as a joke tossing his wet shoe up on shore. He maintained his mood with humor and self-criticism. Still and all, the double crossing and time spent diving for his shoe consumed over three hours. Again, he criticized his tactics and learned the hard way. The entire effort weakened his condition. He was exhausted. He rested for about fifteen minutes and then continued his journey.

Less than one mile later, another river occurred. "Lord have mercy, another river. There's got to be a bridge or some low spot somewhere along here. I'm not up to swimming again." Pat had decided he would not take his shoes off again. He's feet were beginning to swell anyway and he feared he'd not be able to get them back on. He walked up and down the banks of this new river for thirty minutes but found no way to cross. He had to swim it. How did he miss it? Looking at his map in the moonlight he determined the river was not on his map. He made a bundle of most of his clothes, kept his shoes on and dove in.

Had the river appeared on Pat's map he would have seen its shape. It had a camel's hump shape that created a salient bulge. It flowed straight then seemed to reverse direction cutting back and continuing in its original direction. The odd curving shape of the river caused Pat to cross it once and then cross it a second time thinking it was a different river! Exhausted, he was back where he started before he realized what had occurred.

Once he figured out the dilemma, Pat was disgusted with his fate. He jumped in, clothes and all, and swam the river a third time. He vowed to never remove his clothes again. It wasn't worth it. It was nearly impossible to stay dry in the fall of 1917 anyway. "God, what a horrible place this is!" he said to himself as he lay down finally at 05:00. When the sun rose, he could see that his choice was not good. There was little ground vegetation and a Hun could easily see him through the trees where he was planning to rest for the day. The rain began again and Pat spent three hours in the woods looking for a better place to hide. Again, no luck.

[325]

Reaching the edge of the woods about noon he overheard two men talking. They were riding in a wagon up the road. The woods offered little cover but he found a low spot, likely dug by irrigation crews, where he lay low and silent until they passed. Pat was awakened all day by noises in the woods and had one of his roughest days sleeping. When night came and it was time to move there were more clouds and rain and no stars. He had lost his bearings so badly during the day that he really had no idea which way was north. "Hell, I can't stay here. I've got to move and get out of this area." He took a wild guess as to which way north was and set out.

He crossed more rivers and canals than any night previous. The highlight of the night was his discovery of an extensive celery patch. "What glorious food!" he thought. He laughed once again at his desperate situation.

"Anything but carrots, cabbage or beats." He stocked up on celery and when dawn came saw a wooded area to his right where he hoped to dry off once again. The skies looked clear but it was not light enough in the early morning to find a suitable bed. He sat at the edge of the woods to watch the sun rise. When light came, Pat entered the woods and roamed for one hour until he came upon a very familiar and depressing site. His bed from the night before! He had circled the woods all night only to return to the same depressing site that had drained him the day before.

But the sun came up and warmed Pat's body and dried his clothes. He slept and became refreshed. Despite his wasted efforts over the past twenty-four hours he found a new spirit that only a warm day in the sun and dry clothes can create for an isolated man in a strange land.

His friend, the North Star, appeared strong and bright that night as did all the other stars across Europe. Pat was energized to make up time. Tough luck and discouragement were harder on him than a steady diet of vegetables. Lack of food and continuous stress drained his strength and his weight dropped significantly. Fortunately, his wounds were stabilizing. He marveled that his body had the strength to cure his injuries.

Pat thanked God a number of nights despite his troubles. There were times when he was furious with himself for stupid mistakes. He survived frustration with humor and an acceptance of the "gift of fate" that all Irish use when life deals such blows. He was also quite lonely. He thought of his mates back in prison and Estree'-Blanche more and more each day. He thought of home, of Paul, of Richmond and of course of Agnes. Some of those memories were too painful to recall in his current state but he grew in affection for everyone he knew, his family and those he loved.

He thought he'd see more animals in the countryside but only saw an occasional cow. He once tried to lure a stray goat that might provide him goat's milk but the animals were always too close to farms and potential exposure to the German-loving farmers of Luxemburg.

But the cost of so many days outdoors was taking a toll on Pat. Blisters formed on his legs and his knees were quite swollen. His appearance was far from any he had his whole life. His eighteen-day beard presented him as a shaggy transient to anyone that might see him. But no one did see him, until his last day in Luxemburg.

Walking a path close to the Belgian border, he suddenly saw a local who clearly saw him as both came to an intersection. Pat stopped, stooped over and pretended to tie his shoes. Even if the stranger turned onto Pat's path, he would not see his face but the local passed and Pat proceeded.

Eighteen days after leaping from the train Pat crossed into Belgium. Luxembourg had taken nine days. It should have taken two but calamity crossed his every path in the tiny country.

"Finally, Belgium," Pat said as he recognized a road sign in French. For eighteen days he avoided all human contact, ate from the land and swam miles of rivers, canals and lakes. The whole trip seemed to take month. He entered Belgium with one friend. The North Star. Not only did it guide him, Pat eased the devastating effects of loneliness by conversing with the beacon for days on end. It kept him sane.

Chapter 28

Belgium

On his third day in Belgium, Pat could tell that he was moving farther north, closer to the German line. About 03:30, as he approached yet another canal, he suddenly heard a German yelling violently. For the first time, he knew he had been spotted by the Hun. Instinctively, he hunched down in the tall grass, looked back and listened.

"Gehen Sie weiter weg von mir spazieren!" came the shouting voice. Pat could not make out fully what was being said but it indicated to him that there were at least two German soldiers in range. He could see the tall Hun pointing to the west as if to direct another to take a wider path.

"Da drüben in der Nähe von den Bäumen!" shouted the deep-voiced German with the spiked helmet.

Pat recognized the word "Bauemen." "Trees" he thought. It was evident that whatever size scouting party was tracing him they were spreading out in the direction of the tree line.

Pat ran to the edge of the canal hunched over then in a flanking direction to the east. He hoped there were just two Germans on his tail and he'd distance himself before crossing. He went quite a distance and saw no one then eased his body into the canal and swam to the opposite side. There he found a sheltered clump of growth and hid. He decided not move until the Hun gave up looking for him, no matter what. He thought it unlikely that they would cross the canal as they were fully armed, in uniform and would not suspect that anyone would attempt to swim the canal.

The sun came up two hours later and warmed him, drying off his top layer but adding to the tension when he heard German voices again talking on the opposite bank. Had more come? Were they considering crossing the canal?

They seemed so close and their coarse German conversation sounded urgent. The natural way sound travels across water made it seem that they were closer than they actually were. Needless to say, September 29th was looking like it was going to be a nerve-racking day. If he were caught, it could be Pat's last day alive. Germans shot escaped prisoners.

The same two Huns across the canal searched the bank for about thirty minutes. The sound of their voices suddenly had a distinctively new direction as had they had turned and given up the chase. Pat slowly, and as quietly as he could, exhaled as he had been holding his breath subconsciously the whole time while he listened.

"I've got to change my direction, even if it delays my progress north," thought Pat. "I can't just walk straight north through the middle of Belgium right into the heart of the German lines for Christ's sake! I need to move more to their flank where lines are thinner and I might slip through."

And so he did. He proceeded due west for four straight days hoping to find a route less populated with Hun forces. If his estimates were correct, he could then move north again and avoid heavy contact. Due to his weakened state he could only cover five miles a night. He avoided roads and did all his journeying through fields, beet-patches, woods and swamps. The German troops and locals would be less likely to appear in these areas but it made Pat's trip exceptionally difficult.

Concealment was more important than food to him now that he was closer to the front. "I'll get food when I get food. I can't plan my route around food. I have to avoid the Hun at all costs or I'm dead." This strategy would continue to emaciate him in the days ahead.

Heading north again, he came across the biggest obstacle of all. It was the Meuse River, Belgium's largest. Pat knew exactly where he was now. He squatted down observing the great waterway from one hundred yards away in a spot somewhere between the towns of Namur and Huy southwest of Brussels.

"I can't do this!" Pat said to himself in his first state of deep despair. "The damn river is half-mile wide." It was. Clearly, the Meuse was the widest and deepest obstacle Pat had encountered thus far. It was as wide as the Hudson River near West Point, he thought. "If I wasn't so damn exhausted, I'd not give it a thought." Pat had swum the San Diego Bay during his Signal Corps days and that was one and one half mile across. "Hell, the San Joaquin was the same distance as the Bay and I used to swim that for daily exercise when I visited Elmer!" he said to himself.

While Pat was a strong swimmer, he was twenty pounds lighter since the crash, exhausted with wounds not fully healed, and had weakened legs. The Meuse looked like the Atlantic Ocean to him. He searched unsuccessfully for a boat or a large piece of wood that could ferry him across. Nothing. "I have no choice, I have to swim it." It was two o'clock in the morning. The skies, and the river in front of him, were both pitch-black.

After wading in a short distance, the depth forced him to swim. He swam an hour and still had not reached the other side. He floated to rest then resumed once again. Not thirty feet from the other side, he doubted he could make it. His legs and arms were finished. He chose to sink to the bottom, push up, then spring forward again. But the bottom was beyond his reach so he relaxed his body and let natural buoyancy bring him to the surface again. Reaching the surface, he gasped for air and nearly passed out.

"Dear God, please give me just a bit more strength to make it. Please don't abandon me now. All I need is a bit more help from you, I beg you." Oddly, his mind flashed just for a second to the interior of the Momence Methodist Church as his short desperate prayer reminded him of the formality of the good pastor's intonements he had heard as a boy.

Pat mustered every bit of will power he could, pumped and dug in one final spurt. The last thirty yards seemed to take forever but suddenly he felt a muddy bottom. He could barely see the grassy bank within reach in the darkened night. Gripping the tall grass in his hands, his arms shook violently and he lost his grip. Grasping one last time, pulling his limp, exhausted body upon the bank, he fainted from exhaustion. It was three-thirty in the morning and still dark.

About two hours later, the rain did him a favor and woke him up. He was fully exposed and would have been easily seen in the day's light. A towpath nearby would surely bring visitors when the first boat of the day pass. Finding a hiding place in a nearby shrub he slept the entire day with no food or drink. It was a deep physical sleep. Pat literally did not move the entire time.

At dusk he awoke stiff and sore but rested. He noticed his face felt warm despite the cool rain and his stomach was queasy. Having an upset stomach was nothing unusual, he thought, but when he sat up the full effects of an infection flashed through him and he knew he was sick.

Despite feeling ill, Pat had to move again. He rose to his feet and looked back toward the river. All was quiet. Turning forward again, he took a deep breath and walked away from the Meuse River. "I'll walk as far as I can. How the hell did I get across that river?" He started to grin over his success but suddenly his stomach took over, forcing him to stop, bend over and vomit bile from his empty stomach. Once settled, he moved on. "Holy Jesus," he said under his breath taking steady paces to the north.

An hour later he was delirious and carrying on a conversation with the North Star. If overheard by German soldiers, his English would surely give him away in an instant. While his physical routine drove him forward with each step, his fever put his mind in another place.

"There you are, you old North Star," he said pointing and squinting as he looked up. "You want me to get to Holland don't you?" Then driving his finger into his chest, "But this Pat O'Brien – this Pat O'Brien who calls himself soldier, he's got a yellow streak – North Star and he says it can't be done! He wants me to quit - to lie down here for the Huns to find me and take me back to Courtrai – after all you've done, North Star, to lead me to liberty."

Pleading upward with both arms as he walked, he continued to talk aloud. "Won't you make this coward leave me, North Star? I don't want to follow him - I just want to follow you, because you – you are taking me away from the Hun." Again pointing the center of his chest he confessed, "Pat O'Brien, this fellow who keeps after me all the time and presses on my neck, wants me to lay down- this yellow Pat O'Brien wants me to go back to the Huns!"

As so it went all night as his fever came and went. Around one in the morning he had sweat off a good portion of his fever. Pat decided to make what he considered his first bold move since jumping from the train. He would approach a house for food. He had to. He felt he could die if he did not eat. Food became his priority again. He just needed to find a friendly Belgian who would sympathize with his situation, he thought.

At one o'clock in the morning, Pat came upon a small isolated hovel with years of overgrowth wrapping its exterior. The moon's light made it look like a picture postcard. He decided to stir the inhabitants. It did not seem likely that German soldiers would hold up in such a meager place.

He was right. After Pat knocked nervously on the front door a seventy-five year old woman pulled back on the curtain in her small window to the right and peeked out. She was startled and called for her husband and son. The door opened slowing and both men were clearly ready to defend their home, the son carrying a walking stick of some proportion. As was his practice, Pat had a large rock wrapped in a handkerchief for his protection.

Pat smiled but didn't realize how little effect it had on the encounter since his extensive beard fully covered the patented O'Brien smile. His taut face looked unconvincing and there was no sparkle in his eyes. The two men stared at him and were apprehensive but they didn't close the door, Pat thought.

[331]

"Fleger, Fleger, Fleger," Pat stated pointing to his flying coat and alternately to the sky. "Fleger, he repeated. Emphasizing in a raised and more desperate sounding voice once again, "Fleger!" Somewhat convinced, the tension in the old man's face eased and he motioned him inside. Pat was ecstatic and relieved. Assured by her husband of her safety, the old woman showed Pat a seat at the table.

"Sit, sit, be warm, you will eat. I will feed you," said the old women in a Flemish lilt.

Pat watched closely as the elderly woman lit a fire in her stove. The two men took seats and stared at him from both sides. The grimy pot was filled with water and had four potatoes remaining from dinner which she proceeded to heat with a fresh flame. The kettle was hardly sanitary but a pot of warm potatoes and a table and chair was so welcoming to Pat.

"Do you have any bread?" asked Pat, showing her a breaking motion and placing his fingers to his mouth. The old woman shook her head. Pat stared at the pot and the two men stared at him. After long frozen moments, Pat would break his fix on the pot, exhale and smile at the two men who, after the third time, finally smiled back. They could see this man was no threat to them.

After fifteen minutes, which seemed like fifteen hours to Pat, the old woman lifted four steamy potatoes from her old pot onto a tin plate and Pat watched the artistry with intense anticipation. "Warm food!" he thought. The son made a comment to his father and the two laughed.

Pat ate faster than he had at any time in his life. He drank four glasses of water which pleased him to no end as if French champagne had been served a king. He even managed a good belch when finished. When he did, the old woman put her fingertips to her lips, turning away with a grin in embarrassment and all three men laugh. Pat teared up.

"How good it is to be with people again," he thought. He lowered his head and it quivered and tears fell on the table. The old man placed his right hand on Pat's shoulder comforting him for a brief second and the woman had turned back to see the moment. Pat raised his head, looked at the man. A smile of gratitude cut through, warming the entire room, as the old woman stood watching, drying her hands in a tattered towel.

The three men rose from the table. Pat asked if they might spare an old suit or jacket by pointing to his tattered clothes and lifting the lapels off his chest indicating he sought a more protective replacement. The woman shook her head apologetically. The old couple was clearly too poor to produce an extra piece of clothing for Pat. He suddenly sensed that and thanked them, bowing to the woman and shaking the men's hands with his two.

As he approached the door, he caught a glimpse of himself in the mirror. He was shocked to see how awful he looked but noticed that his eye was better. Earlier that day he had just started to see out of his left eye for the first time. It gave him a small amount of renewed hope. Stepping down off the small wooden porch, Pat pointed in the direction he planned to walk, showing the three his planned route. To be safe, when the door closed behind him, he went in the opposite direction. He had sharpened his decoy skills after nearly a month on the run.

Over the next few days, he made it his focus to shed his old clothes and do all he could to acquire civilian clothing so as to blend into the general population with more ease. He shed his long overcoat to relieve him of its weight. He would later regret it when the weather got cool in the evening. He discarded everything in his pockets including his wrist-watch which was not working anyway. He decided to toss one of his two shirts which were both wet and never seemed to keep him warm. One of the shirts he had purchased in France, the other he bought in America. He decided to toss the French shirt for nothing more than sentimental reasons.

He finally buried the Bavarian cap that had served him well, particularly when crossing rivers and canals where he had stored his map. Digging with his hands in soft ground near a huge fallen tree, he thought some day after the war he could actually identify the spot and retrieve his cherished souvenir. The length of time he had spent outdoors had modified his sense of feasibility and little things such as the hat met a lot to him in isolation. Some of the simplest experiences and minor possessions sustained him as they so often do when men are imprisoned or surviving alone.

He knew he had to remove anything that would indicate he was not a Belgian. He discarded his flying mittens received at Camp Borden that were frequently the target of ribbing from his fellow pilots. Pat loved those mittens and had a hard time letting them go. He dug a hole along his path and buried them. The next morning he hovered over a two foot opening in the forest floor he had prepared for the rest of his uniform. To the left of the hole he had placed his wings, now tarnished. He had removed them from his jacket. Without thinking, Pat had carefully folded his uniform coat as neatly as a San Francisco department store gift wrapper. Holding it respectively in his extended forearms, he paused before placing it in the hole.

Looking at the jacket and then back at his wings, it took him about ten minutes before deciding to bury his wings with the jacket. They were the only connection he had to the Royal Flying Corps. They were the only link to his years of flying. They were, in fact, his only link to anything outside Belgium. But he knew he could not carry them with him. There would be no explanation should he be caught by the Huns.

Invading barns at night, he continued to search for discarded clothing and finally acquired a coat. On his fifth day in Belgium, Pat peered from a clump of bushes where he was holding out for the day. In the distance was a small house that appeared to have a piece of men's clothing hanging from a single rope stung between two trees. At dusk, he crawled out of his hiding place toward the cabin and found, to his great joy, a pair of men's overalls which he snapped from the clothesline. They were a bit short for Pat's six foot two inch frame but they were the nicest clothing he'd worn since entering prison.

With his new persona, Pat began to feel a little safer traveling during the day, as well as, night. What burdened him most was the constant presence of ditches, canals, and rivers. Belgium was as waterlogged as any land on earth. He crossed water nearly every half-mile, some days more frequently. The ditches proved to be the most agonizing. They were too narrow to swim and too wide to jump. Most had two feet of water and three feet of mud. A few times Pat tried jumping smaller ditches but his fatigued state would land him knee-deep in mud three feet short of the bank. Getting out was a real mess and he was covered in mud continuously as a result.

There were marshy areas, as well. It was not unlike sloshing through the Great Kankakee Marsh and Pat constantly worried that the Hun would hear him noisily dragging himself through the swampy terrain. Any man traveling through such marshy lands would surely be perceived as an escapee, he thought. "Then again, what goofy ass Hun is likely to be crossing through this mess anyway?" Pat chuckled to himself one cold, wet night in the mud.

As Pat continued north, the density of villages and towns increased and he was increasingly passing between villages, able to hear church bells toll on his left and his right. A different village appeared nearly every mile. When he crossed a cobblestone road, he would often lay in the ditch and watch motor trucks race noisily by sporting steel rimmed wheels rather than normal rubber due to the scarcity of war. "Pretty damn handy, these steel wheels," his quipped to himself. "At least I can hear the bastards coming!"

Pat considered making a fire at night but that made little sense since he had nothing to cook and would only attract attention. There were few horses and only and occasional dog. Most had been taken by the Germans. Experiencing the loneliness of isolation, Pat thought about befriending a dog but gave up that thought realizing he had little to feed it. Donkeys were often paired with cows to pull carts oxen and bulls had been put into the service of the German army all across Belgium.

In addition to his avoiding the Hun, Pat's nights were spent constantly hunting for food. Fishing was out of the question, because he had no way to prepare it. Berries and fruits were rare as the prime season for fruit had passed. The dreaded sugar-beets, turnips and cabbage continued to be his staples. Celery was a real treat and Pat always took as much as he could carry when he came upon the rarity.

His dreams were increasingly about food as he felt himself slowly weakening due to a lack of nutrition. When he could not sleep, he thought of Courtrai, his leap from the train, his last flight and, of course, he wondered if he would ever see home again. He purposely brushed away thoughts of home, his family, Agnes, Richmond and Momence. It was too painful and caused him despair. The most important thing was freedom. Without it, there was no chance he'd ever see any of them again.

But as he approached his second month on the run, it was apparent that if he did not acquire food, he would not make it to Holland. Hunger pangs were even beginning to interrupt his sleep and he was getting weaker each day. He needed to get stronger and that meant he needed to eat. He needed to eat more than turnips.

On his thirty-second day on the run, he decided to approach someone for food. About eight o'clock that day he bound a heavy stone in his kakis handkerchief and approached a small house. He timidly knocked on the door and a Belgian peasant, about fifty years old opened the door. When asked what he wanted, Pat shrugged his shoulders as if daft, then opened and closed his mouth several times indicating he sought food.

The man welcomed him in, sat him at a small table and placed a plate, knife and fork on the table. Pat stared at the utensils in amazement. A month in the wilderness made such accepted practices novel. Cold potatoes, several slices of bread and something Pat nearly choked gulping as fast as he could, warm milk!

Suddenly, the man leaned over, positioning his mouth not two inches from Pat's ear.

"You are an Englishman. I know it. And you can hear and talk if you wish. Am I not right?" said the man in broken English.

Pat turned and saw the man smiling. He trusted his instincts. "You have guessed right. Only I am an American, not an Englishman," said Pat softly.

Suddenly, Pat became concerned, not with his own fate but the likely fate of his host, should the Huns ever discover he helped an allied pilot. The Belgian understood and spoke enough English that Pat was able to relate a bit of what he had been through in the last month. The man quizzed Pat a number of times, to assure himself that he had not welcomed a German spy into his home. Once he felt confident, he decided to help.

"What is your name?" asked Pat.

"I am Leclercq," said the kind Belgian. "Alard Leclercq."

"Well, Mr. Leclercq," said Pat, "I am viewed as a high prize among the Huns. Not only am I an American flying for the Royal Flying Corps, but I am an escaped prisoner. Certainly, my life is worth little to the Huns and yours would be threatened as well should you choose to help me."

"I am aware of these," said Leclercq. "I know the Germans will kill me but what do I have now? I am a prisoner in my own home and all Belgians must drive out the Hun in any way we can. They are bastards!"

"Indeed they are!" agreed Pat.

"You will never be able to get to Holland without a passport," he said with a new confident look on his face. "The nearer you get to the frontier the more German soldiers you will encounter, and without a passport you will be marked man."

Sensing that the middle-aged man knew more than his simple lifestyle suggested, Pat asked, "How can I solve this? Can you help me?"

"Not me. I cannot help you but I know a man who can." Taking out a short pencil sharpened roughly with a butcher knife the man wrote down a name and city. "If you call on this man, you will be able to make arrangements with him to secure a passport, and he will do everything he can to get you out of Belgium."

Leclercq drew a rough map showing Pat the best route to Brussels where the man lived. To keep his contact anonymous, the Belgian indicated that he would respond to the name Huyliger though it was not his real name. "If you go to his location and ask for Huyliger, he will know why you came," stated the Belgian who Pat now perceived was quite knowledgeable and likely part of an underground network within occupied Belgium. Pat had just gotten his first break, he thought. "Thank God someone wants to help me." he said, taking the paper from the table.

"Please, let me pay you for your kind help," said Pat, shaking the man's hand over and over again. Pat still had money in his pocket despite his water soaked journey thus far.

"I would not. I would not take your money," said the kind man.

As midnight approached, Pat prepared to depart once again. He thanked his host many times over. Feeling full for the first time in a month, he took one last sip of warm milk, shook the man's hand and departed into the night.

It was apparent now that if he were to make it to Holland, he'd have to do more than sneak around at night in marshy backwoods. It would require that he make use of his friendly Irish charm to convince strangers he was safe but dole it out in an artful way so as not to reveal his true identity.

Chapter 29

Imposter

Walking through the rural fields of Belgium with its numerous ditches, canals and rivers was one thing. Entering the more populated areas of the north was quite another. Since discussing the need for a passport with Leclercq, the urgency of acquiring official papers pressed on Pat like never before. He had discarded all of his British clothes. He had begun to extend his traveling times into the early morning and occasionally started out before dusk. But he still did all he could to avoid contact with humans – unless, of course, he viewed them as safe enough and likely enough to give him food.

After talking to Leclercq, however, it was clear to Pat that he was certain to not only be spotted by the Germans but questioned and challenged to prove his artificial identity. He had already decided to be more cautious about his routine. But as he walked toward Brussels just after midnight, Pat was baffled.

"How in God's name am I going to be able to speak to anyone that confronts me, whether German or Belgian, without fully revealing my slangy English tongue?" he said quietly to himself, while gesturing with both arms.

After weighing a number of extemporaneous ideas in his mind, he suddenly recalled an old story grandpa Hathaway had told him one day while the two were fishing on the Kankakee. Hathaway told him of the old Pottawatomi Chief, who when confronted by an impetuous Federal Marshall, pointed to his mouth and two ears while shaking his head. The Marshall instantly ascertained that the Chief was deaf and dumb, though he was not.

"Hell, that's it!" Pat exclaimed. "I'll just pull the old Indian trick!" It made Pat laugh from his gut which simultaneously mixed with a surge of melancholy about his grandfather, his home and his sweet life as a boy back at Momence. It wasn't the first time that a humorous thought on his long isolated journey triggered an emotional surge and a few tears.

He felt the two sizeable tear drops scale over his cheeks. "I wonder if I'll ever see anyone from home again. How long has it been?" He tried to calculate the weeks and months since he had said goodbye to Al the day they registered for the Army at home. He pictured that last good-bye stepping up on Gus' train, waving to Margaret and his sister Clara. "Egads! That seems like such a long, long time ago."

Feeling resolved, Pat returned to the practical matters at hand. Though he sensed conditions were about to change for him, he was unaware how dramatic his strategy would be altered. In the days ahead, he would go from a hiding strategy to one of deception, cunning, strong will, and conjecture. It would require the most sophisticate skills of an enemy imposter.

A full moon lit his pathway as he headed toward Brussels after giving leave to Leclercq. In no time he came to a river about seventy-five yards wide. "Hell, I don't feel like going for a swim already!" he said to himself. "I've finally got dry clothes. It looks like Belgium is just going to be one big swim," he said to himself, grinning. Pat decided to walk the bank a few hundred feet in search of that elusive bridge or boat.

"Damn, a boat!" Pat was thrilled and there was no one in sight. The boat was chained to a post but the softness of the bank allowed him to yank it out of its moorings. He pulled so hard it made him dizzy. Then suddenly, it shot out of the ground, tossing him on his backside and implanting an impression of his shrinking buttocks muscles in the soft mud. He giggled like a young toddler, thrilled he jarred it loose and giddy over his improving prospects. Clearly, the food and clothing he had acquired in the last forty-eight hours had lifted his spirits.

Resting a second, his giggles turned to tears. It hit him how beaten down his spirits had been. "That's not me," he said wiping the tears with his sleeve while sitting in the mud. "That's not Pat O'Brien," he repeated. It was the kind of melancholy regret reserved for middle age men who suddenly discover they have lost their youth. "The tough part is behind me," he assured himself. "I'm going to get through this and make it home. I've come too far to fail now."

Pat took some long draws of water from the fresh stream, climbed in the boat and shoved over to the other side. As he pushed the stake into the opposite bank, he looked around again to make sure he had not been seen. "Imagine when those poor bastards come back to find their boat on the other side," he thought, laughing at his own comment.

He was able to travel several miles that night and found safe cover just before sun up. From his hiding place he noticed a large grove of trees that extended in the direction of Brussels. "Great, I can start early and walk inside the woods." Pat had found that he could travel through thick forests during daylight undetected. The large trees shadowed his movements and there were plenty of places to hide should an unexpected human cross his path.

About three o'clock in the afternoon he emerged from a comfortable sleep and hurried to the woods' edge. Half-way through the woods, he crossed a railroad track, further evidence that he was working his way closer to Belgium's main city of Brussels. He came upon a clearing in the woods containing a single house and a large garden being manicured by an elderly man. Going around back to avoid being seen he knocked on the door and an old woman answered. Though surprised, she was not as startled as Pat's earlier host had been days before. The woman called to her husband in French as Pat stood near the hearth eying the ornate interior of the life-long habitat.

He was again successful begging for food with hand signals and even managed to communicate his interest in spending the night, but the couple balked at that request. Pat estimated that both were nearly one hundred years old. The whole scene had the look of Grimm's Hansel and Gretel, he thought, recalling the story he read back at the Momence School. The woman wrapped two small pieces of bread in a cloth and Pat went on his way.

As he worked his way north, it was less likely he'd be able to pass between two villages and stay a safe distance between chiming bell towers. Every mile required two and sometimes three detours to avoid the increasing number of people. After three days, in this more dense area of the country, it was apparent he would make little progress zigzagging around towns. He decided to try his luck going straight through the next village in his path. It was not long before he approached Lonzee' southeast of Brussels. It would be his first opportunity to appear as a Belgian peasant. "Think poor!" he thought, humoring himself.

At the edge of town Pat passed small groups of peasants ambling into town and chose not to join them as a means of cover for fear they might reveal him as a stranger. It was about nine o'clock in the evening when Pat approached the center of the small village.

A Belgian police station was on the right and two German sentries stood across the street on the left. This would be the first test. "Now, what?" he thought, realizing his path would take him no less than ten feet from the Hun guards.

If he turned back he would be suspected. If he crossed the street to the police station side he'd look suspicious. "I'll just march right by them," he thought. "Perhaps the good Lord will keep them talking and they'll hardly notice me." He hoped his peasant look would blend in with the rest of Lonzee's locals. It worked.

They never noticed him. "I'll be damned," he thought. His gut stirred with excitement and he wanted to yell out in joy. Not until he exited the town at the other end of Lonzee' did he feel safe. A mile out of town he couldn't help humming one of the new patriotic songs they had sung back at the aerodrome at Estree'-Blanche. A mile later in the middle of nowhere under a pitch black sky he broke into a soft falsetto having remembered the words:

Land of Hope and Glory, Mother of the Free,
How shall we extol thee, who are born of thee?
Wider still and wider shall thy bounds be set;
God, who made thee mighty, make thee mightier yet,
God, who made thee mighty, make thee mightier yet.

Pat stopped singing and in one hour covered three miles, passing boldly through the main streets of each town. About fifteen feet past three Hun guards in the third village his heart was stopped.

"Hault!" came the command from the tallest German guard.

Pat felt his stomach flip. His heart nearly stopped. He was convinced he had gotten too brave and pressed his luck. As the soldier walked toward him, Pat had a rush of anger overcome him. "Damn it!" he thought. In an instant, Pat pulled a piece of bread and bottle of water from his pockets holding them up in clear view. It worked. The Germans were stopping peasants randomly who were smuggling potatoes from the fields and selling them in the city. Regular inspections added to the intimidation level of local Belgians. As it turned out, Pat's instinct to empty his pockets played into a common peasant pattern of showing "no potatoes" to the Hun guards. The Hun stopped five feet from Pat, nodded his head, turned and returned to his fellow guards.

Two hours later, Pat would shuffle into Gembloux amid a group of peasant women. As they passed three guards, Pat held his handkerchief to his mouth, faking a nagging cough. He purposely adopted the slouching gait of the old peasant women and successfully passed through around midnight. He walked the rest of the night and rested outside Overijes the next day. Departing again at dusk he entered Brussels around eleven o'clock that evening. He was more exposed in this large city than ever before and he felt he needed to find Huyliger's place, immediately.

Pat walked the streets of Brussels for about half an hour following the various landmarks Leclercq had described to him. With surprising ease he found himself at the door of Huyliger's house. When the door opened Pat observed a man in his forties in his dressing gown. Instinctively, Huyliger stepped back and Pat stepped in. Huyliger was an active resister. He only received visitors sent to him by others and purposely stayed anonymous in town. If a man knocked at his door, Huyliger knew the visitor had been sent.

"I am O'Brien. I was sent by Leclercq," Pat whispered

Saying nothing, Huyliger gestured for Pat to sit down and proceeded to place a literal feast in front of Pat. Blood sausage, potatoes, waterzooi' soup and real cheese. Pat was practically frozen with delight then dove in, being a bit cautions with his first taste of meat in over a month. "Go easy, young man. The taste of real food can shock your system if you have not eaten for days," said Huyliger having seen famished escapees before.

Huyliger spoke fluent English and Pat spoke rapid English between large bites. He told the Belgian of his experiences since jumping from the train but revealed little of his role with the Royal Flying Corps, still being cautious.

"O'Brien," said Huyliger, "I am going to help you. It may take several days, perhaps as long as two weeks, but eventually we will provide the means to enable you to get into Holland."

Pat nearly choked on his food and thanked him a dozen times. "I just don't know how I can repay you for your kindness!" expressed Pat with gratitude for the generosity of his host.

"Don't think of that," said Huyliger. "The satisfaction of knowing that I have aided in placing one more victim of the Huns beyond their power to harm him will more than repay me for all the risk I shall run in helping you. You better turn in now, O'Brien, and in the morning I'll tell you what I plan to do."

Pat rose from the table and shook Huyliger's hand. "Thank you, again. I appreciate your help." With that, Pat stood and turned toward the stairs.

"My God! A bed!" thought Pat. "A real bed!" Tears welled up in his eyes once again as he took deliberate step up the stairs. Huyliger showed him his room on the second floor. For the first time in nearly two months, Pat O'Brien was about to lie down in a real bed and sleep safely through the night.

As he removed his clothes, he noticed his knees were still quite swollen to twice their normal size. His left ankle was still black and blue from his leap from the train. When he flew to France in his Sopwith Pup months back, his weight was one hundred and ninety pounds. Looking at himself in the mirror he estimated his weight to be no more than one hundred fifty pounds.

Pat eased into the soft bed giving out sighs of relief, feeling weeks of pain slowly giving way to the comforting recline. "For the love of God," he said enjoying the once fundamental experience of lying in a bed. He slept until noon the next day when Huyliger knocked on his door waking him from a deep sleep.

"Come in," said Pat, still drowsy.

"Good morning, Lieutenant," said Huyliger. Pat was stunned to see him enter with a large tray of breakfast. Coffee – real coffee, slices of bread, hot potatoes and a dish of scrambled eggs. Pat had nearly forgotten about eggs. What a joy!

Sitting at the edge of the bed, Huyliger watched Pat eat and revealed his plan for Pat's escape. "My plan, O'Brien, is to conceal you in a convent until things look right to make your way to the border. During your time in the convent, you will dress as a priest."

"Ha! That's a laugh," bellowed Pat nearly projecting his eggs on the bed. "I can't imagine what my good Methodist mother would say if she saw me in a priest's collar." "I'm a Methodist!" Pat exclaimed laughing. "And old Father LeGreis would surely get a laugh out of it, too!" Father LeGris was the pastor back at St. Patrick's Catholic Church in Momence during Pat's time at home. When Pat and his buddies drifted by the church during the summer, LeGris would spend time talking to the boys. The good priest used to always ask Pat, "Are you sure you're not Catholic?" convinced his Irish name dictated he was. Pat found the idea quite amusing. He bellied again and Huyliger didn't quite get the humor but laughed at Pat, nonetheless.

"When it's time to leave the city you will pose as a Spanish sailor complete with a made-up passport," Huyliger informed. "Posing as a Belgian would be complicated once you had to speak." Huyliger had asked Pat if he spoke any other languages. Pat told him of his years in California which exposed him to a good amount of Spanish. His work on the Santa Fe taught him a few Spanish phrases used to supervise Mexican crews. "Spanish makes the most sense," said Huyliger.

"You will also be given enough money to bribe the German guards at the Dutch frontier," said Huyliger. The Belgian had obviously done this before. Pat was gaining confidence in his ability to finally escape to freedom with the help of his gracious host. "You are not the first, O'Brien. We have done this many times before and it works."

"I will follow your instructions and do whatever you say Huyliger," said Pat. "I just want to rejoin my squadron as soon as I possibly can. But I realize it will take time to prepare my departure," he added. Pat was clearly feeling positive now though much more lay ahead before he would taste freedom once again. They reviewed the safest route out of Brussels. "Basically, you need to go straight north in the direction of Tilburg. You want to avoid Antwerp. There is a real concentration of Huns throughout that area. Still, you'll cross some major roads that lead to Antwerp and they are always full of German troops," said Huyliger.

Following breakfast, Pat and his host sat at the kitchen table. Pat watched as the Belgian carefully filled in the blank passport copied from a genuine passport. Huyliger had mastered many counterfeits. He had also retrieved a damaged rubber stamp tossed out by a German official and had completed the missing half of the stamp with the use of a wine cork and a penknife.

It was such a masterful job that German guards were regularly fooled. Huyliger procured a camera, took Pat's profile photo and outfitted him with a typical hat worn by the Spanish. Pat trimmed his beard to look more authentic. His dark hair and beard made the photo look convincing.

On his third day in Huyliger's home, Pat was having breakfast with his host once again when the man brought up a change of plans. "We've changed our mind regarding the convent." Pat paused and thought to himself, "We?" Looking up over his fork full of eggs he asked about the change. Huyliger offered no reason. "I will take you to a large empty house where you will stay until it is safe to depart," he said.

Pat took a bite and sat his fork down across the plate. He liked that idea of a house better, though he told Huyliger he was willing to convert to Catholicism if even for two weeks under false premises. It was another bit of Irish wit that seemed to sail over Huyliger's head. The Belgian was a serious man. These were serious times in Belgium. Pat saw no reason to be concerned about the change of plans.

That night, Huyliger escorted Pat to the rich part of town where they came upon a twenty room estate. Once owned by a wealthy Belgian, the home had been abandoned since 1914 at the outbreak of the war. Huyliger used it as a hiding place. He had a key, opened the large front door and let Pat in.

"I'll come by each morning to bring you breakfast. Don't leave this place until I tell you." Pat nodded and turned to inspect his new surroundings as Huyliger exited, locking the front door behind him.

Most of the contents were still in place but a quarter inch layer of dust covered everything inside. Pat did his best to explore the house in the dark. Despite its mammoth size, four stories and a cellar full of wine, there wasn't a mattress in the whole place. Pat was forced to sleep on the floor.

The next morning after Huyliger dropped off a light breakfast, Pat watched the streets of Belgium from the fourth floor windows. He stood back a bit so that no one would be able to see him from the street. Though the house had hundreds of books they were written in Flemish or French, offering Pat no diversion. Knowing he would be idle a few days, Pat walked within the house for exercise. He spent time distracting a cat across the street with a piece of broken glass by reflecting the sun's rays at the cat's feet much to the cat's delight. He caught flies, placing them in a spider web, and then watched the spider approach its prey only to set the fly free at the last moment.

On his second morning in the house he found a four year old New York Herald on a mahogany desk. It was dated 1914 and had been delivered at the start of the war. Pat read it dozens of times until he had practically memorized its contents, particularly the sports section. He particularly enjoyed the story about Heinie Zimmerman of the Cubs who was benched for arguing with the ump.

Being indoors that long bored him to no end. Pat's worse day came on his third day when German soldiers stormed the house driving him to the far recesses of the cellar. He was almost certain they had discovered him or were, at least, after the supply of wine in the cellar. After two hours of banging and noise from the Huns they left and Pat discovered they had simply visited to pull as much copper and brass pipe from the plumbing of the house as they could find. It struck Pat that perhaps the Huns were finally stretched thin, resorting to scavenging for much needed metal and other supplies. It reminded him of the steel wheels he had seen on motor trucks in the forest. Were the Huns finally stretched beyond their available resources? If they were, the end of the war could come soon now that America and its ample resources were pouring into the European theater.

On the fourth day, Pat sat finishing his last cup of coffee following breakfast and Huyliger suddenly asked Pat whether he had any money in either France or England. "Well I bank at Cox & Company in London, why?" Pat asked.

"What I want to know is how far are you prepared to go to compensate me for the risks I am taking and for the service I am rendering you?" Huyliger's tone had suddenly changed.

Pat was taken aback by his sudden change of tone. "I would be happy to pay you for your troubles but I could only do so after I escape," said Pat. "If I escape!" Pat added. Huyliger would have nothing to do with a delayed payment and suddenly the trustworthy Belgian seemed to possess mercenary motivations.

When Pat explained that he only had a few hundred dollars on him, the Belgian stated he wanted more. When Pat asked how much Huyliger demanded, the amount was clearly an indication that Huyliger planned to extort. He suddenly produced a note and asked Pat to sign it promising the exorbitant amount. Pat knew he had a problem.

"Huyliger, you have helped me out so far, and perhaps you have the power to help me further. I appreciate what you have done for me, although now, I think I see what your motive has been. But I certainly don't intend to be blackmailed and I'll tell you right now that I won't stand for it," Pat barked a ferociously as he could.

"Very well," he said. "It is just as you say. But before you make up your mind so obstinately I would advise you to think it over. I will be back this evening." The Belgian turned and exited the house.

Pat had his passport but Huyliger still held some pictures, papers and other items Pat had turned over to him including his identification disc, his prison picture from Courtrai and the map to Paul Raney's grave. Pat decided to see if he could pressure Huyliger later that night into giving up these items.

Huyliger returned to the house that evening unchanged. "What do you say? Will you sign the order or not?" insisted Huyliger. Pat was so angry that he was being taken advantage of by this man that he refused to give in. He told him he'd pay him a reasonable amount but not the amount Huyliger demanded. "I also want you to return to me at once all the photographs and other papers of mine which I gave you upon my arrival," stated Pat.

Huyliger didn't budge. Pat, being a gambler, played another card. Advancing toward him and putting his hands on the Belgian's shoulders, Pat looked him straight in the eye. Pat barked, "I'll go to the German authorities, give myself up and show them the passport you fixed up for me and tell them how I got it and explain everything! I shall sleep in this place just once more, then at eight o'clock tomorrow morning, I shall go to the German authorities!"

The Belgian paled. He turned, headed down the stairs and out the door. Pat shouted after him. "I'll wait until the city clock strikes twelve, and if you don't show up with those papers by that time, the next time you will see me is when you confront the German authorities. I am a desperate man Huyliger, and I mean every word I say!"

Going to the Germans was a bluff but Huyliger bought it. Pat sat on the stairs wondering what his fate and next move might be. Two hours later, Huyliger opened the door.

"I have brought you your belongings, O'Brien," he said. Pat looked at the pile. The only items missing were a few photos. He had his disc back and, more importantly, he had the map to Paul's grave. Huyliger so much as apologized for his behavior and indicated that someone else was giving him orders to demand more money.

He then stated that "another man" could help Pat get to Holland for less money. All Pat had to do was to go to another house where the Belgian would introduce him. Pat was suspicious but he decided to see it through. He could always refuse and leave. He had what he needed now.

"We will go tomorrow night then," said Huyliger. Pat agreed.

That night, Pat decided to walk the streets of Brussels and determine his best route out. He was pleased that neither Belgian nor German guards even questioned his presence. This gave him confidence he could blend in and leave the city. He noticed Hun guards were stationed at every major road leaving the city. He would need a strategy to get past these guards. The wise choice would be to leave in the light of day when many of the men left town to work in the fields. Few locals were stopped at the start or end of the day.

The following night Huyliger returned. Pat followed him to the other large empty house. Entering, they proceeded to the second floor where two men awaited them. One was obviously Huyliger's relative and Pat concluded it was his older brother. Again they pressured him. They attempted to trick Pat into giving back his passport for a "genuine passport" that was better. Pat demanded to see the other passport but they were unable to produce it. Pat had reached his limit.

"You will get this passport that I have here," patting the side of his breast pocket, "only off my dead body! If you gentlemen think you can take it from me, you are welcome to try!" Pat noticed an extensive collection of pottery along the wall which he calculated would serve as his initial arsenal of weaponry. Pat eased his way toward the large pots and stood with his back against the wall challenging the men. He also reminded the three of his earlier promise to notify the German authorities of their undercover operation.

The three men backed down and left the house. While Pat had great respect for the peasant Belgians that helped him escape, he had little respect for these three and hoped he would never meet them again.

Pat decided to stay in the house another day or two. He wanted to make sure Huyliger was truly finished with him. He decided to use the time to get more comfortable with his alias and get out in the city both during the day in addition to at night. When Pat had arrived in Brussels, Huyliger had told him about a number of places in town including a moving-picture show that was free during the week. It featured a restaurant where patrons could place their order and then watch a full featured silent film from their table. After Huyliger and his brother left, Pat decided to look for the movie house. While the prospect of entertainment was somewhat appealing, it was the chance to order food that really enticed him. He still had money in his pocket.

After about twenty minutes, he passed the place and was tempted to just walk inside but instead walked a half block past and then turned back with a mind to go in. He froze just outside the door after coming face-to-face with a German officer who was coming out. He lost his nerve.

The next night he was determined to go in. It would be his last night in Brussels and Pat knew he would have to confront German soldiers sooner or later. Pat knew that there were more German soldiers between Brussels and the Holland than in any other section of the country. "I need to get my nerve up," he said to himself as he exited the large house and walked toward the movie house.

"My problem is that every time I see a spiked helmet, I panic," Pat said to himself. "Hell, the Belgians just obey orders and seem as calm as if the Hun were their cousins." As risky as it was, he had to challenge his own fears. More importantly, he wanted to hone his skills as an imposter.

The theater was more in the style of a beer garden than a movie house. The entrance was actually off the alley. At the door was a ticket booth but it was closed, this being a free night. Walking in, Pat did a quick canvas of the place. Though it held easily three hundred people, no more than a dozen had arrived. Pat was early and chose a seat at the back of the room directly opposite the stage where he could see every table in the place.

In no time, the place filled in as small groups of German soldiers entered and took their seats amid the local Belgian fare. Pat watched every Hun enter and take their seat, hoping none of them would chose to sit at his back table. After about twenty minutes, Pat estimated nearly one hundred soldiers and two hundred Belgians filled the hall. Suddenly, a Belgian man and his wife joined Pat at his able. The woman smiled at him and Pat nodded. Two seats remained at their table. "God, I hope civilians sit with us. I can't imagine how I'll get through the evening should Germans take these seats!" Pat thought.

Suddenly, two Huns entered the door and canvased the hall for a seat. Looking the place over, they pointed and made a bee-line for Pat's table. Pat quickly picked up a menu and began to read. It was in French. They took the two seats directly across from Pat, roughly slamming their hats on the table and lifting menus amid boisterous chatter. For the most part, Pat felt he was oblivious to them.

"At least this way, the two will likely turn their chairs to watch the film after dinner," he thought. "That will make it easier." When the waiter came, Pat felt nervous once again. "Now what! I can't order anything to eat, I'll give myself away. What if the waiter asks me a question? How will I answer?" Again he felt doomed to failure and how sweet it would be in the eyes of these two German officers to actually capture a British pilot behind enemy lines, he thought.

The man and woman ordered first and Pat heard the man reply, "Bock!" The waiter nodded and made a note. The woman asked a few questions and the Germans were discussing the menu. When the waiter turned to Pat, he blurted out, "Bock!" No food tonight, just beer. When drinks and food came there was the matter of payment. Pat watched the old man pay and offered the same denomination. When the waiter returned with his change, Pat gave him twenty-five centimes as a tip.

The movie started and Pat was still nervous the entire night. "For Christ's sake, there's too many Huns in this place,' Pat thought. "I've got to get out of this place and out of Brussels! It's time to go to Holland, I've had enough."

[349]

The evening passed without event. As the lights came up, Pat rose from his seat, mixed with the crowd and disappeared into the night. He was proud he got through the night and gained a great deal of confidence. It was a night he would never forget. On his way out, he was handed an handbill for next week's show. He shoved it in his pocket and headed into the Brussels night with everyone else.

"Good night, Brussels," he thought to himself. "Tomorrow I'll start for Holland." He was stronger, focused and not that far from the border, a mere sixty or seventy miles. "If all goes right, I could be a free again two days. God help me."

Chapter 30

Last Leg

Pat wasted little time returning to the house though he felt compelled to detour four or five times when a number of Germans in his path made him just too nervous to pass. He entered the big empty house in the back where he had set the door, made his way upstairs in the dark and lay back in bed staring up at a ceiling that he could not see.

"Sixty miles doesn't seem like a lot compared to where I've been for two months," said Pat to the empty room. "Hell, at least I know where I am now! I know which route to take, how far I need to go and what I need to do. If I play my cards right, I may be able to avoid swimming the whole way. What a difference!" he gasped, shaking his head in disbelief a few times. He thought about how many times he had almost given up but didn't. He thought about how far he had pushed his body to keep moving when it begged to stop. And he thought about how he never seemed to have dry clothes.

Nevertheless, his lip wound was finally healed, his eyesight had fully returned, his ankle was stronger and the pain in his knees, though swelled, had lessened, making walking less painful. During his time in Brussels, Pat had certainly gotten a bit of a reprise, physically. He had also gained confidence in his ability to haggle, deceive and otherwise outwit most everyone he encountered. This intuitive nature, first displayed growing up in Momence, had not only survived but was sharpened to a razor's edge. His last leg to freedom would require masterful use of these critical skills.

Pat knew that even the slightest slipup could prevent him from even getting out of Brussels, let alone escaping enemy territory. Leaving required getting past two guards, commonly placed at every exit from the city. There were plenty of deterrents between Brussels and the Holland frontier, as well. The one that loomed largest in Pat's mind was a nine foot electrified fence that kept the Belgians in, prevented escaped soldiers like Pat from getting out, and limited desertions from the Germans themselves! Pat had first heard about the barrier back at Courtrai.

The infamous barrier was actually more than one fence. There were two six-foot barbed-wire fences on each side of the nine-foot electrical block. Pat had imagined using stilts of some form or pole-vaulting over it like a track athlete. He even imagined constructing a catapult that might toss his body over the top. On this unique night, as Pat envisioned his approach to the infamous barrier, he spoke aloud. "I'll figure that out when I get there." He had to get there first.

Still keyed up from the night's events, he reflected on his long arduous trip over the last two months. He had crashed near Roeselare in the Flemish Region of Belgium not far from the field hospital where the Hun doctor had dressed his wounds. After Courtrai, which was one hour away by car, he caught the train at Ghent where locales heckled him from the platform. He rode the train into the early morning hour where he jumped near Rheinstetten, Germany. After five days he entered Luxemburg, passing Schouweller before angling to northwest. Once in Belgium, Pat made the difficult crossing of the Meuse near Audenne, 146 miles from his leap. From there it was another sixty miles to Brussels. And now, in the morning, he would attempt to traverse the last leg of his journey to the Holland border and freedom.

Over the last two months little of the war or world events were known to Pat. The allies were hanging on by a thread. French and British aviators were falling from the skies over the western front in alarming numbers and since entering the war in April, America was clamoring to produce 4,500 new planes as quickly as possible. And there was an additional concern being discussed among Allied generals.

On the same night Pat arm wrestled his personal papers from the Huyliger boys, Vladimir Lenin snuck into the Moscow and took power from the Czar on November 7 as Russian troops revolted against Czarist generals. He would eventually remove Russia from the war in March of 1918 but as Pat prepared to depart Brussels that night the allies feared that the Germans would rush west once Lennon quit the war.

Might it be that Pat would walk another sixty miles to freedom only to be captured by a German army bolstered by a half million troops who would come west from the Russian front? Fortunately, none of these circumstances were known to Pat. It would have only added to his concerns as he contemplated his final walk to freedom.

In September, newspapers in Canada and the U.S. had listed Pat as "missing in action." On October 7 a distraught Margaret O'Brien had arrived in Powell, Wyoming to stay with her sister. Waiting alone in Momence for news of Pat was more than she could endure and Clara had suggested the trip would do her good. Agnes MacMillan had read of Pat's missing in the San Francisco Chronicle merely two weeks after his crash, as local newspapers commonly reported on their boys first. Pat's friends Charles Pearl and John Keeton also saw the news. Charles had called on Agnes to reassure her. Elmer sent word back home that he too had heard and the entire family was experiencing the numbness of the nebulous term called "missing in action."

The next morning, Pat timed his exit to coincide with the departure of hundreds of Belgians walking off to start their day. His plan worked to a tee as he passed out of the city with other local peasants off to work the fields. In no time, he was out in the country where he met a lone Belgium who he approached for food. Thinking Pat was deaf and dumb and perhaps a little loony, the man gave Pat half his lunch and sat with him along the road.

When night came, Pat began to look for a place to rest, but planned only a short nap. He wanted to travel both day and night knowing how close he was to the border. Finding a perfect spot beyond a barbed wire fence, he crawled underneath it. The wire got caught on his coat. Yanking free he shook the fence for several yards and instantly panicked hearing the command, "Halt!" Pat froze and debated the merits of staying down on the ground or running from the scene figuring that darkness and fog would cause the Hun to miss him.

He decided to lay still. He could hear the German speaking something to himself, then called out as if calling a dog. Pat heard a bark and the guard moved on. Luckily, the dog had heard Pat but not the guard. Pat breathed a sigh of relieve then carefully crept under the wire again with care. As he walked a few yards he determined he had entered an ammunition depot. Figuring the fence likely surrounded the area, he walked to his left some distance, returned to the fence and exited under the barbed wire once again. He walked a mile before heading due north once again.

After about one hour, he came upon yet another peasant cabin and pleaded for food in his usual way. The Belgian woman who lived alone brought him a piece of bread and two cold potatoes. She calculated that Pat was a fugitive as he sat at the table downing his food eagerly. He surmised that she had likely experienced a number of escapees since she lived so close to the border.

The woman had, in fact, helped a number of men on their way. Somehow she perceived he was English and before Pat departed, took his arm indicating she wanted him to wait one moment. She then returned with two pieces of fancy Belgian lace. Pat was touched by her simple gesture though he certainly had little use for lace. He instantly thought it would be a wonderful gift for his mother should he make home.

One piece of lace had the Flemish word "Charite" and on the other the word "Esperance." Translated the words meant "Charity" and "Hope." By this gift, Pat knew that the woman understood his mission. He pressed the woman's hand in gratitude and shoved the lace into the back pocket of his trousers. Not wanting to alarm the woman, he chose not to tell her that he would spend the night sleeping in her backyard. Just before dawn, Pat was on the move again. In the afternoon of that same day, Pat approached yet another cabin to beg for food. This time, after enjoying warm soup with the entire family of ten children, he gave the father and mother a mark in return for their kindness.

Pat spent an hour with the family but hastened his departure when a young man arrived to call on one of the older girls. The caller eyed Pat very suspiciously though Pat hardly looked like a British officer. Nonetheless, it urged Pat to get moving, which he did, shaking the hands of all ten children and their parents. It was a joy to see children again.

He walked all afternoon when suddenly, he found himself in clear view of the Holland frontier. Freedom and the nine foot barrier loomed not 500 yards away. Before moving further he felt the impulse to inventory his belongings. He still had a few marks, the lace from the old woman, his picture of Paul, and the map to Paul's grave, the program from the movie-house and various other notes he had taken along the way.

Pat waited 'till dark and then made his way carefully through a field on his belly, stopping just short of the pathway along the barrier. The vegetation was barely enough to cover him which meant approaching and crossing the fence would have to be in the cover of night.

The border was all he had heard about it. Every foot was protected in the same manner with similar fencing and regular guard presence. The 200-volt fence was erected in 1915 and by war's end nearly 3,000 would die of electrocution, not counting those shot trying to escape.

But it was far from foolproof. Spies, smugglers, and "passuerrs" or guides, who helped people and goods get through, found ways to circumvent the structure. Since the beginning of the war, the Belgians in this area had been in a constant state of intense occupation and scrutiny.

As he lay still looking at the fence, Pat suddenly heard the measured stride of the German sentry. Not one hundred feet from the fence, he quickly crawled back into the woods away from the fence to avoid the guard. He decided he'd hide away for the night and make a more careful survey the following night.

He had seen enough to know that the pole-vault idea was ludicrous. The distance from the six foot fence on the Belgian side of the electronic barrier was at least twelve feet. The same distance could be seen to the Holland-side fence once he traversed the electronic nine-footer. There was no timber in the area capable of being honed as a pair of stilts even if he had tools. He spent the night hiding in a clump of bushes, memorizing the pacing of the sentry and racking his brain on how he might scale the barrier. To see freedom so close and yet have no perceivable means of breaching the obstruction was disheartening, to say the least.

He hid again during the next day, at one point retreating further back to beg for food.

Being so close to the border, the locals were clearly more nervous about welcoming strangers into their home and Pat was forced to resort back to raw vegetables in the fields.

All the time, his mind was churning with possible ways to cross. "I'm no farther along in my thinking now that I've seen the fence than I was a while back when I first considered it," Pat thought to himself.

That night Pat made a survey of the barrier a half mile or so in either direction. He saw no difference in the construction of the fence or the regularity of the sentry. He decided to retreat a bit into the woods again and walk west, coming out at regular intervals to inspect the nature of the fence which lay to his immediate right.

"This is ridiculous!" thought Pat. He felt like a tiger in a cage. To be so close yet unable to cross was maddening. The depth of his frustration grew through the night. He found a place to hide and sleep off his frustrations. He spent the next full day in hiding once again, coming out only once to find some tasty wild berries for dinner. Late that night, he struck on the idea of constructing a huge step-ladder. If he could find a downed tree he could use vines and other smaller ripe twigs to tie off the rungs. It was feasible. If he could prop the ladder up against a post, he could scale it as well as the two barbed-wire fences.

He began to construct his ladder that night, finding a number of fallen pine trees from ten to twenty feet long. He broke off the branches of the two best and made rungs between them using small twigs, parts of his Red Cross handkerchief and parts of his shirt. It was crude but when Pat tested it against a tree it worked, though it wobbled more like a rope-ladder rather than a wooden one. He strengthened it then hid it near him in the woods the whole next day while he rested.

"If I fail," Pat thought to himself, "I will be dismissed, summarily. If it works my troubles are over. No use in worrying about failure. I need to succeed," he thought, giving his spirits a good level of encouragement. A number of times during the day, he reinforced the ladder further while he waited agonizingly for the day to pass.

As night came, Pat made his way toward the barrier with his ladder in hand. The clearing near the fence was about one hundred yards which would expose his approach in greater measure. He waited for the sentry to pass, scurried to the first barbed-wire fence, shoved his ladder under it and crawled under the bottom wire, catching his coat. Clearing his coat, he approached the "death-fence," put his ear to the ground and listened. No sound of an approaching sentry.

Pat grabbed his ladder and carefully rested the top rung against the post. He started up, got to the third rung when suddenly the ladder was loosening! He took the next rung and the ladder slipped, coming into contact with a live wire at the top. The wood and ties he used were so fresh that plenty of moisture still existed in the entire ladder. There was a blue flash and Pat was blown from the ladder, falling hard on the trampled ground just inside the barbed-wire fence, knocked unconscious. He had not made direct contact with the wire so he was not instantly killed. He awoke just in time to hear the sentry approaching once again.

"Damn it! I've got to get out of here and hide this ladder," he thought.
He pushed the ladder out of sight under the electronic fence to the Holland side and lay low between the electrified fence and Belgium-side wire fence. He was trapped. The sentry passed less than seven feet from Pat who was lying still and pressed to the ground. The German walked some distance past him which Pat felt would give him more time.

Pat stared intently at the electric barrier. "Ok, I can't go over the damn thing..." pausing. "Well, how about under it!" he thought. The bottom wire was only 4 inches off the ground but if he could dig a hole deep enough he could crawl under it.

"What a risk!" he thought. "But I've got no choice. I can't stay here!"

He dug with both hands. The ground gave way easily, much to his delight. Having dug eight inches quickly, he caught his hand on a sharp object. "Another wire! Damn it!" He dug in haste. Soon he had a thirty inch hole below the buried wire. Being grounded, he new the second wire could not be live. He grabbed it and pulled up with all his strength. It didn't budge. He pulled, rested and pulled again. Suddenly a staple gave way on the nearest poll.

It enabled him to pull the wire through the ground a bit creating more slack. With more leverage, he pulled as he had never pulled before and eventually eight staples gave way as the wire slice up through the soft ground! To Pat, the sound of the snapping wire was as loud as a mandolin. He checked the ground as each staple pulled away and still heard nothing.

Pulling the loose wire back and out of the way he continued to dig, breaking his nails and scraping his bare hands. The closeness to the power wire made him terribly nervous but he kept digging, focusing on the hole and liberty on the other side.

Finally, it looked like he had enough space. He could pass with a few inches to spare. It was then that he noticed that his back pocket was bulging with the lace given to him by the Belgian women. He removed it and tossed it over the barrier. Lying on his stomach he crawled like a snake. He didn't hurry. He used great care to avoid the live wire just above him. Suddenly, he was through.

There was still the second fence and several feet of Belgium between that fence and liberty. He went to his knees first and thanked God for his long series of escapes as tears of joy fell from his eyes. Getting under the second barbed wire fence seemed like child's play compared to what he had just experienced. He rose and ran toward Holland.

He was free. Pat immediately walked one hundred feet into the Holland woods when suddenly he remembered the lace he had thrown over the barrier. He knew it was a risk, but decided to walk back and retrieve it. Holding his breath he stared into the dark night. He heard the sentry coming back again.

"What if he sees the hole?" Pat thought. It was too late to move now, he hunkered down.

The Sentry passed. Pat rose slowly, listened again and then headed for the barbed wire once again. He grabbed the lace, turned and ran once again into Dutch territory.

It was November 19, 1917. Pat had leapt from the train on September 9th. Seventy-two days had passed. He was a free man again.

As he walked forward along a pathway, he felt as though his muscles were slipping off his frame like candle wax down the side of a lit candle. He had no energy but the exhilaration of being free once again drove his gate forward and he sang, once again, Estree'-Blanche refrain only, this time, in full voice:

> Land of Hope and Glory, Mother of the Free,
> How shall we extol thee, who are born of thee?
> Wider still and wider shall thy bounds be set;
> God, who made thee mighty, make thee mightier yet,
> God, who made thee mighty, make thee mightier yet.

Chapter 31

Holland

Pat knew he was in Holland but didn't know exactly where. After walking about thirty minutes in the dark he came upon another fence. "Why would the Dutch have a second fence?" he thought. He had failed to notice his path had mistakenly arced and sent him back into the same fence, complete with three German sentries. He ducked off the path to gain cover. Peering at the three figures, he suddenly saw the speared helmet and was astonished he had gotten so confused. He looked up.

"Damn clouds. The North Star is no help to me here," he thought. Scanning in every direction, he saw lights from a village that he estimated was three miles away. In fact, it was six miles away. Aware Belgium was in full black-out, he knew the village had to be Dutch and so he proceeded on a straight path in its direction.

Unfortunately, the direct path to the village took him through an extensive marsh. "Not again!" he thought. But he did not veer in either direction and forcefully walked through mud knee deep and in some spots sank in clear up to his waste. "Well, this is the same crap I survived in Belgium," he said.

After three hours, he finally reached firm ground. He had walked at least four miles through marsh. "That trek was at least as far as walking from the east side of Momence half way to Indiana," Pat quipped, shaking off wet and mud. He was now a half mile from the small border-village of Stramproy which lay twenty miles south of Einhoffen.

Before reaching the town, he came upon a small workshop with a bright light still burning inside, though it was after midnight. Pat knocked on the door. Getting no response, he pushed open the door. Inside were three men and two boys making wooden shoes. Pat's knock could not be heard over the sounds of the shop.

As Pat entered, the three men looked up simultaneously and knew what he was. He was full of mud, soaked clear through and his face confirmed that he was another refugee. This was common on the Holland side of the barrier fence. Pat's appearance was unique since all other military escapees had always appeared in uniform. The shoemakers took Pat as a civilian escapee.

"I want to see British Consul," stated Pat to the eldest in the group. They could not understand Pat but seemed very willing to help. One of the younger men was engaged in a conversation with the elder, volunteering to take Pat to town in the morning.

"Breetish?" the elder asked, recognizing Pat's English.

"Yes, British!" nodded Pat.

Pat didn't think it would make much sense to state he was American. That would really confuse them. Few Americans were in this area. The U.S. had just joined the war in April. The older man issued instructions and the two boys left the shop, returning in five minutes with others who were obviously stirred from their beds. It was the man's wife and nineteen year-old daughter.

The host family and eventually some neighbors arrived and watched Pat enjoy a hot meal. It was clearly the best food Pat had eaten in two months. He perceived his Dutch hosts had done this a number of times and by now had a routine that included "watching them eat." Pat thought it strangely humorous that he was the object of such curiosity but he found the people warm, friendly and genuinely concerned with his welfare. As the joy of a well cooked meal sank into Pat's body and spirit, he teared up a number of times, up wiping his eyes a few times with the cloth napkin he had been provided. Looking up he saw the women brandish broad satisfying smiles and suddenly it struck Pat why his eating was a site cherished by these caring Dutch.

The oldest man walked up next to Pat and spoke, "I Venansius!" he said.

Then pointing to others in the room he introduced his family speaking rhythmically, "Venansius, Venansius, Venansius, Venansius." The whole group sported a big grin and the humor of the moment stuck them all including Pat who gave out a belly laugh which ignited the other to do the same.

Pat had a little German money left but not enough to buy a fare to Rotterdam according to Venansius, who waved off the amount, rubbing his fingers and thumb together, indicating Pat was short. The mark was half the value of Dutch currency and nearly worthless in the minds of the Dutch. Three or four family members came forward and gave Pat enough change to purchase a third class ticket to Rotterdam. Again the emotion of the moment overtook Pat but he fought to keep it to himself. His Dutch hosts could see he was moved.

Janus Venansius was truly a good samaritan. That night Pat slept in the Venansius home. In the morning, he was treated to a breakfast feast unlike any he'd seen since Richmond. After breakfast, Pat thanked the entire group who had again gathered to watch the British pilot eat. Through hand signals and scraps of English, they learned of Pat's identity and spoke to each other in amazed tones, looking back at Pat numerous times in stunned disbelief.

Earlier that morning, a few of the Venansius family members had been to the village and spread word that a British pilot had found his way to freedom. They were now stunned to learn that he was an American! Venansius directed two of his younger children to go tell the news to the village. Pat glanced up and paused watching the two amazed children rush out the door but knew nothing of their mission.

After breakfast, Venansius and his oldest boy escorted Pat to the train stop that ran to Einhoffen from Stramproy. A crowd, one of the first of many crowds Pat O'Brien would experience in the days ahead, was on hand to see the American-British pilot. "They are intrigued to see an American," said a young educated man who spoke English and who had joined the throng to see Pat off.

"I'm afraid I'm not a very good specimen," stated Pat.

He felt a little embarrassed for his condition and hoped the Dutch would not judge him to be representative of all Americans. As the train pulled out of the station and headed for Einhoffen, a large cheer erupted from the platform and Pat was again moved to tears.

"What a contrast this is to my departure at Ghent!" he thought. "I'm so lucky to be on this train headed north rather than back with my friends to the reprisal camp. Poor souls, I hope they are surviving that hell."

Like all who return from war, a feeling of guilt came over Pat as he thought about his compatriots left behind. For the soldier who returns, the joy of leaving war is always tempered by remorse for those who are not returning. But Pat had paid a hard price for his freedom, stretching his physical and mental limitations to the breaking point. Relief and exhaustion was the dominant feeling Pat felt on his first morning of freedom.

As the train picked up speed, Pat saw the men and woman of Stramproy going about their daily routine unencumbered. A strong feeling of excitement overtook him. He thought how wonderful it would be to send home the joyful news that he had made his escape.

At Einhoffen, two Dutch officers entered his compartment and looked at him with disdain. There was no way they could recognize Pat as a British officer. His clothes were ragged and, though he had scraped a good portion off, he was still covered with dry mud from head to toe. His unsightly beard added to his vagabond appearance but Pat was so happy, his appearance didn't matter and he flashed the two men his patented Irish smile. Embarrassed at being caught, the two gawkers looked down quickly and Pat chuckled as he gazed out the window at the passing landscape.

The trip from Einhoffen to Rotterdam included a few stops where others boarded the train, a number of them entering Pat's compartment. A few attempted to speak to him but did not speak English. Rather than spoof the old Indian deaf and dumb trick, Pat simply said, "American, American," gesturing as being verbally helpless. Finally, the train slowed as it approached Rotterdam. Pat couldn't help thinking of the thousands of train rides he'd taken in his life. None seemed as exhilarating as this short trip to Rotterdam. He exited onto the platform along with the others and paused, watching waves of passengers hurry down the platform along with men pushing hand trucks with small cargo, and in the distance, the flurry of Rotterdam, awake and teeming with the activity of a major port-city feeding the European war.

Pat walked up to a policeman monitoring the large crowd. "Hello? Can you direct me to the British consul? British Consul?" asked Pat.

"Wat wilt u man? Ik spreek geen Engels. Ik kan niet u helpen," stated the flustered officer. He was unable to understand enough of Pat's words to help him and pointed to the end of the platform encouraging Pat to follow the other passengers out.

Walking to the end of the platform, Pat approached a row of taxicabs and spoke to the lead car attendant. "English consul – British consult – American consul – French consul!" he pleaded, hoping one may be recognized by the driver. The driver looked Pat up and down, uncertain about his appearance but finally waved him in. They drove for about fifteen minutes. The taxi raced through the many twists and turns of downtown Rotterdam then took a final left turn and stopped. "My God! The Union Jack!" exclaimed Pat. Seeing the British Flag had such a profound impact on him and he leaped from the cab.

"Please, come. Come and they will pay," said Pat. The driver was confused but seeing Pat's condition and the sincere tone in his voice convinced him that Pat was sincere. He put the car in reverse, turned off the engine and gave a hard tug on the lock brake. The two men approached the front door of the stone embassy.

"I need your assistance," said Pat to the officer at the door. "If you pay my taxi fare, I will tell you who I am. I assure you that the consul general will want to hear my story. I have just escaped Belgium."

"Indeed, my good man," stated the guard at which point he discussed the fare with the taxi driver in Dutch and handed him currency. The driver tipped his hat bowing slightly to the guard then nodded to Pat and departed.

"Welcome to the British embassy. How can assist you, sir?" stated the guard.

My name is Pat O'Brien. I am an officer in the Royal Flying Corps and have just escaped out of Belgium. I was shot down nearly two months ago," said Pat.

Seeing no uniform and Pat's condition, the guard knit his brow in an unorthodox way. The guard was almost urged to bust out laughing.

"Look, sir!" said Pat. "You let me tell my story to the consul general and I guarantee you, it will cast a totally different light on my appearance and credibility!"

As was his knack and despite his disheveled appearance, Pat O'Brien had once again pressed his point and convinced the skeptical guard.

"Step inside, Mr. O'Brien," said the sergeant guard.

"Lt. O'Brien," said Pat firmly but with a joyful pride.

"Yes sir, Lieutenant," said the guard, accommodating Pat. "Step this way."

The guard showed Pat into an anteroom and invited him to take a seat. "Can I pour you some tea, sir?"

"Yes, thank you," stated Pat. The guard poured a cup and handed it to him. Pat took a sip and found it bitter. Though the tea was fine, he had not fully reacquired a taste for all foods. As the guard exited the room Pat placed it on the table. Shortly after, three men returned with the guard.

"The sergeant here tells me you wish to speak with the consul general and you are a British officer?" asked a well-kept official reaching for Pat's hand. The guard pointed out that Pat sounded American to him. Pat gave him a glance of impatience. The official silenced the guard saying, "Hold fast, Anderson. Let's hear what the man has to say directly."

As the men took their seats around Pat, he told them his story. To a man they were quickly convinced and amazed, regularly glancing down at his tattered clothing attempting to do the mental gymnastics required to believe that any man could possibly survive such an ordeal. But the days and nights outdoors had worn down Pat in a very convincing way. As the group studied Pat's face, his physique, clothing and his hands it was very apparent that this man had just spend two months living outdoors. Yet, the eloquence with which he told his tale, the detail of each episode and his obvious knowledge of the Royal Flying Corps left little doubt. Lieutenant O'Brien was authentic.

"Alert the Consul General," said the lead officer. "I want him to hear Lt. O'Brien's story immediately." Turning back to Pat he asked, "So tell me Lieutenant, how did you, an American, come to fly for the Royal Flying Corps?" Pat told him a brief synopsis of his pathway to the RFC. Entering the room again the orderly announced, "He'd like to see you now."

Pat was escorted down the hall by his now admiring interrogators. When the group entered, Consul General Mr. Ernest Maxse screwed a monocle into his right eye and viewed Pat from head to toe. Pat could see the man's cheeks flush and sensed that he was ready to burst out laughing.

"Go ahead and laugh!" said Pat. "You can't offend me the way I feel this blessed day!" he said with a big smile.

Indeed, Maxse burst into laughter and gave Pat a firm slap on the back. "My good man, one might know that only a bold Yank like yourself with discipline of our fine British training could beat such odds as you have, my boy!"

The others joined in a hearty chuckle and from a distance the whole room sounded like a room full of groomsmen ribbing the groom at the last hour. Maxse was so taken by Pat's appearance that he took his seat gasping for air.

"So tell, son. Tell me your story," said Maxse. And so Pat, for the second time, gave his account. He would tell the story many times over in the days ahead. The consul general was stunned by the achievement.

"Lieutenant," said the consul general, "you can have anything you want. I think your experiences entitle you to it."

"Well, Consul, I would like a bath, a shave, a hair-cut and some civilized clothes about as badly as a man ever needed them. I suppose, but before that I would like to get a cable off to America to my mother, telling her that I am safe and on my way to England."

"Take care of that, Emerson," barked the monocled Maxse waving his eyeglass as he gestured. "Get the Lieutenant a pen and paper so he can write down the address. Let's get it sent immediately." Pat was gratified. "Wright, contact London. Make sure Lt. O'Brien is accommodated fully upon his arrive there. Oh, and make sure our own people are present to greet him when he arrives and take him to his quarters."

"Lieutenant," he continued, "I'd like to introduce you to Sub-Lieutenant John Shevington of the Royal Navy." Shevington saluted Pat and Pat returned. "Sub-Lt Shevington will be your guide while here in Rotterdam once you've freshened up. He speaks Dutch and will take good care of you."

"An honor indeed, Sir!" said Shevington saluting Pat a second time.

Pat spent the next hour turning himself into a human being once again. He maintained his mustache but shaved his entire face smooth for the first time in two months. His mustache covered the scar that was still present on his upper lip from his bullet wound. Even being able to comb his hair with a brand new comb brought him joy. The most glorious hot bath nearly put Pat into a deep sleep. Looking into the mirror he noticed how pale his face had become where his beard had been. The rest of his head and face was weathered considerably and darker from exposure to the sun.

"Lieutenant! I have your suit," came a shout from Shevington in the next room. Shevington placed it on the valet. Shouting again he continued, "I've wired London your dimensions, sir, and you will have an officer's uniform issued to you when you arrive!"

Entering the room from the bath, Pat was toweling off his arms, "How wonderful it will feel to be dressed smartly and looking more like myself once again," he said. "You're a handsome fellow cleaned up, I'll give you that, sir!" said the sub-Lieutenant. You know sir, "We all thought you to be quite the vagabond on first sight," he said respectfully.

Pat took a seat at the edge of the bed where Shevington had laid out new shoes, socks, boxers and a fresh undershirt. "My God, brand new, dry socks!" said Pat. "You have no idea how wonderful a fresh pair of socks is, Shevington. How many days I longed for dry socks!" he said shaking his head. He placed his feet squarely on the floor and looked down at the thick cotton socks that adorned his feet. "Fantastic!" he said.

Once Pat was fully dressed, the two men walked up the street to the nearest barber shop where Pat received a long awaited haircut. He and Shevington then walked the streets of Rotterdam for three hours and Pat's spirits were higher than at any time in his life. For lunch they stopped at Café 't Bolwerk in the center of town, quayside on the inner harbor, where Shevington had arranged for Pat to meet a number of soldiers and sailors who had escaped from Belgium when the Germans took Antwerp. Both Pat and the others found exchanging stories to be quite stimulating and an instant bond formed between them all.

After lunch, they returned to the consulate where arrangements had already been made for Pat to leave for England that very night. He thanked his guide and was able to visit Ernest Maxse and thank him for being so helpful. He was issued money, a wallet, and a small satchel for his personal effects.

About the time Pat was leaving the British consulate office in a taxi, young Glenn Hess, who regularly delivered telegrams around Momence, was jumping on his bicycle in a hurried state. It was noon and there was a special telegram had arrived at The *Progress* for Margaret O'Brien that needed to be delivered "post-haste." The boy pedaled extra hard and upon arriving at the O'Brien home, remembered Margaret was not home. She had been in Powell, Wyoming since October 9, staying with Hatte Belle and John Hansen awaiting word on Pat since receiving word of Pat's missing. Hess quickly headed to the home of Clara Clegg.

"Mrs. Clegg, there's a telegram from the British Consul in Holland. Mr. Howk thinks it could be about Pat." Lewis & John Howk owned the Momence paper and also maintained the local telegram office in town.

Clara Clegg, Pat's sister, quickly opened the envelope. "Thanks, Glenn," she shouted at the boy as he sped away on his bike. "Oh good Lord, let it be news of Pat," she thought, her hands shaking. It read:

Office of the British Consul General
Rotterdam, Netherlands

21 November 1917

To: Margaret O'Brien, Momence, IL
From: Mr. Ernest G.B. Maxse, C.M.G
               British Consul-General
               Rotterdam, Netherlands

Dear Mrs. O'Brien,

I have received Lt. Pat O'Brien, your son and member of the Royal Flying Corps yesterday. He crossed the border of Belgium into Holland and is now under the care of the British Empire here in Rotterdam. More information will follow from Pat.

Respectfully yours,

Consul-General Ernest G.B. Maxse, C.M.G

"Oh my Lord God in heaven!" shouted Clara. She immediately ran to the shoe store where her son Jack was home from the University of Notre Dame on a short break before finals. Her husband, Matt had, died in February and Jack tried to be home as much as he could during, his first term. She shouted the news to everyone she passed on her way. Within twenty minutes, every shop owner in town got word as it spread like wildfire. As the Clegg store filled with well-wishers, Clara sat exhausted from exuberance and nearly passed out. Jack, "we must wire grandma," she said out of breath. "She will not believe he's alive." Suddenly overcome she lowered her head saying, "Oh, my poor baby brother. My, what a wonderful day this is!" She then broke down and sobbed covering her face with a handkerchief as her son, Jack comforted her. Others did, as well.

"Did the telegram say how many German prisoners Pat took out of Germany with him?" said Chuck Astle, always the one to break the ice. The whole room erupted in laughter. Clara laughed as well while she cried, dropping her hands from her face.

Random conversations erupted in the room. All were aghast over Pat's escape. Boisterous comments could be heard followed by laughter which punctuated the certainty of Pat's escape.

"I told you Pat would turn up!" shouted Fred Sandstom to Bob Wood and Bulah Nichols.

"What made the Kaiser think he could keep young Pat against his will?" said Frank Riker, slapping the back of Henry Davis.

A number of women stopped by Clara to offer comfort and congratulations.

Mayor Tiffany had already gathered a small group of prominent citizens in the corner of the room including Arden Sherwood, Harry Exline, Charles Hess and Ed Chatfield. Bertha Thomas and Helen Kirby also joined the group. The mayor would form a committee to organize a major homecoming event for Pat. They agreed to set a meeting date for all parties interested in putting on the event. It would likely be the biggest celebration in the history of Momence.

After about forty-five minutes, the group began to disperse and Mayor Tiffany spoke a short time with the Clegg's on his way out. Clara decided to close up the store for the day. The news was spreading through town rapidly as Clara and Jack walked to The *Progress* to wire a cable to Margaret.

"Let's stop at the house then go to grandma's," said Clara. "I'm sure people will be stopping by. Not everyone knows she is in Wyoming. Bring some coffee with you and our extra pot.'

Clara went to Margaret's house to give it "a good dusting." Neighbors and friends came by the rest of the day. It was the beginning of a whirlwind never witnessed before in the City of Momence. The story of Pat O'Brien was about to stir the entire nation.

Chapter 32

London

About the time his sister Clara was locking up the shoe store in Momence, Pat's boat pulled out of the Rotterdam port. His heart suddenly sank as the vessel accidently rammed a destroyer escorting the ships across the channel. Luckily, there was just a short delay and Pat was on his way again, arriving at Harwich, England after an uneventful trip. He switched to the train at Harwich and continued ninety miles to London. It was late in the evening when Pat arrived at the Liverpool Street Station in central London. He was gratified to see that Consul General Maxse had made full arrangements for a car to meet him.

"Are you Lt. O'Brien?" asked a short driver holding up a sign that read "O'Brien."

"Yes, hello," said Pat. "Are you looking for Pat O'Brien?"

"Lt. Pat O'Brien? Indeed I am. I'm to take him to the Savoy," said the driver.

"Well, that's me!" Pat responded.

"Follow me," said the driver as he turned toward the row of taxi's on the street.

Pat stared out at the London streets as his taxi made its way to the Savoy Hotel in the City of Westminster, central London. To go from the muddy woods of Belgium to the elegant Savoy Hotel, with its hot and cold running water, lavishly furnished rooms complete with private baths, was almost more than Pat could imagine. It was November 21, 1917 and it had been a very long day. Pat lay in bed trying to get his bearings. He found it hard to believe his newly acquired good fortune. The consul-general had provided him with money and the room and amenities at the hotel were also arranged for in advance.

The next morning, Pat spent a good portion of the day sitting in the lobby, doing some people watching and reading every square inch of The London Times. He was amazed to see all that had changed during his time in isolation from the rest of the world.

He spent the afternoon walking within the vicinity of the hotel, eating lunch alone in a local pub and window shopping in area shops. He sat for two hours and nursed two tall mugs of beer and thought of his days at the Ivy back in Richmond. After enjoying a hearty beef dinner at the Savoy, Pat spent the evening in the lobby bar and had some wonderful conversations with the local clientele, never revealing his true identity other than what he couldn't conceal, which was his American accent.

The following morning a message appeared under Pat's door. He was to meet Captain J.S.H. Moore for lunch. The RFC had been alerted to Pat's arrival and Moore would conduct the first formal interrogation of the escaped officer. After reading the note Pat quickly bathed, got dressed, and went downstairs for breakfast. Following breakfast, he decided to venture outside again for a walk.

He was surprised how unnerved he became approaching Regent Street at Piccadilly Circus. The large circle intersection that is Piccadilly Circus is certainly a unique convergence of urban congestion, but Pat was jarred by the confusion that seemed to bombard him. He found it impossible to cross the street, frozen against a lamppost and unable to move. He feared being trampled or run over. Suddenly a London Bobby, recognizing his condition, came up to him.

"You alright, young man?" the tall officer asked, glancing at Pat's rank indications on his coat.

"I'm afraid I suddenly can't move," replied Pat.

There were a great number of English soldiers back home in London suffering a similar neurosis, trying to "get back their nerve." Pat's condition was easily recognizable to the officer. He took Pat's arm and helped him cross the street. The Bobby offered consolation and thanked him for his service to Britain.

"This is not unusual, young man," said the kind Policeman. "It will fade in time."

The officer spoke from experience. He had served in the Second Boer War in South Africa in 1902 and had been hospitalized for two months following an explosion. Veterans are the first to recognize the conditions that plague any returning vet be they physical or mental.

"Thank you, sir," stated Pat. "Did you serve?"

"Yes, son," responded the officer. "Take care of yourself, now. And good luck," he said shaking Pat's hand.

Pat entered the Electric Telegraph Company. Though the consul-general had sent a cable home to Margaret, Pat wanted to be sure he sent one personally. It read:

> Mrs. M.J. O'Brien, Momence, Ill., U.S.A:
> Just escaped from Germany
> Letter follows.
> Pat.

Pat sent a second telegram. It was to Agnes:

> Life's fate has given me a second chance.
> I've escaped German prison camp. In London.
> I'll be home soon.
>
> Love Pat

He headed back to the hotel where he met with Captain Moore for lunch. Moore found Pat's story fully believable. Moore's orders were to write just a small report vouching for Pat's authenticity. When Pat finished the details of his adventure, the Captain put down his pencil, folded his arms, and leaned back in his chair. Pat's story frankly stunned the normally callused officer.

"Lieutenant, how are you feeling?" asked the Captain.

"We'll, as you can see, I am quite thin and my strength is much less than I'd like it to be." He sipped his tea, still not fully acquiring the taste. "I've been aching for so many days, I do believe that I've forgotten what it feels like to feel good!" The Captain chuckled at Pat's wit.

"Well, I can certainly understand that, Lieutenant. You are quite an inspiring man. Let me also say to you," he said pausing second, "In my role with the British Army I have interviewed many war-battered men in the hospital and have also met a few of our boys that escaped from behind the lines." He then leaned forward. Folding his hands and planting his elbow on the table he looked Pat squarely in the eye and said, "But I do not believe I have ever heard a tale of such magnitude. I do believe your story is the most inspiring one of the war I've experienced."

Pat set his tea down and looked hesitantly at the Captain.

The officer continued, "You know Lieutenant, if you don't mind, I'd like to mention you to a contact I have in the promotions business. His name is W.C. Glass and he represents the Keedick Agency in the states. New York, I believe."

"Go on," said Pat.

"The RFC has scheduled you to meet with Corps doctors on Monday morning. This being Friday, I'd like you to just relax over the weekend, eat and drink as much as you can and rest. After next week, I'll bring Mr. Glass to see you. You'll be going home soon to America and he is interested in creating a speaking tour for you – once you feel up to it, of course."

"Well, I might," said Pat. "But I want to spend time at home with my family and get my strength back."

"Indeed, Lieutenant, indeed," assured the Captain. "But if you are amenable, I'll arrange the meeting. All you need to do is tell me what you feel is acceptable and Mr. Glass assures me that he will arrange the agreement to your liking."

"Alright then, Captain," said Pat. "I'll meet with the man."

"If you can come to terms, you would meet with him again in New York when you return to the states along with Lee Keedick. Keedick is a major promoter and is often in London looking for talent. I do believe you are about to embark on quite a reception at home. That's what Mr. Glass believes. Your story has been appearing in the papers throughout the entire United States, I'm told."

Pat was rather stunned that his escape, which had just occurred a few days before, was already making such news back home. He took one last sip of tea and looked surprisingly at Captain Moore.

"Yes indeed, Lieutenant," said the Captain. "I'm told there is quite a stir in the States over your achievement and naturally Pat there are always men who wish to capitalize on such things. Let me advise you, O'Brien to be conservative with your willingness and take care of your own financial wellbeing in this matter. Keedick is an established promoter with a good track record, but like all agents, he will not be forthcoming in his first offer. So bargain your best position."

"Thanks, Captain," said Pat. "I appreciate your advice."

"Here are some additional pounds that should give you plenty of money for the duration of your stay in London." The officer handed Pat a brown envelope with a significant amount of cash. Pat nodded and slid the envelope to his side of the table without opening it.

"There will be a car here to pick you up at 07:00 on Monday. He will take you to the Royal National Orthopaedic Hospital on Great Portland Street in London. We'd like you there so we can look at your knees, as well as give you a good physical. You should expect a full day. If you get tired, just tell them and they will adjust for you. The medical people want to spend a good amount of time with you which could extend into the next day. I apologize in advance for saying so, Lieutenant but you are somewhat of a specimen as well to these folks. They are very interested in determining the long term effects of your diet and exposure etc. It's not often a man survives such a long isolation and it helps us understand how to prepare other pilots who may experience a similar fate."

"I understand, Sir," Pat replied. "However I can help, sir."

"Also Lieutenant, do not be surprised that the psychological doctors will want to speak with you extensively. They are generally quite good. Just talk to them as you would anyone. They will be able to assess what they need to understand without much contrivance on your part. Just be yourself, lieutenant. They are also very good at advising you what you might experience now and in the future due to your experience."

With their formal work completed, the Captain and Pat enjoyed their lunch and had a casual conversation. Most of the time Moore updated Pat on matters of the Royal Flying Corps, the war in general and events in the world that Pat may not have heard about. Pat asked a number of questions about the 66th Squadron but Moore had little knowledge regarding their specific activities. Pat was particularly intrigued by the discussion regarding the Russians and the very recent takeover by Vladimir Lenin and his new Communist Party.

"What condition are they in now?" asked Pat.

"They're still battling there. We are having a hard time determining who's on what side," said the Captain. "Worse yet, there are still a large number of Allied troops in Russia and Lenin does not seem interested in battling the Germans. I'm afraid the war in the east is dissipating. We need to keep the Huns engaged in Russia or they will come west," the Captain said earnestly. "But you shouldn't concern yourself with all this now. Our goal for you O'Brien is to get you on your feet again and send you home. You'll be given a three month furlough to recuperate."

"That's appreciated, Sir," said Pat. "It will be good to be healthy again and spend time at home."

The two men finished their lunch and talked about lighter topics such as family and personal history. After about three hours the Captain took leave of Pat, warmly shaking his hand and thanking him for his dedication and valor which had impressed him greatly. The captain's report to the war department was short and indicated he was convinced of Pat's story. Still, a casual read of the report revealed that Moore's job was primarily to determine if Pat, himself, was a spy. It read:

NOTE ON THE REPORT ON THE EXAMINATION OF
2/LT. P. A. O'Brien,
No. 66th Squadron, R.F.C.

In view of what I was told concerning 2/Lt. P. A. O'Brien, I was careful, in my examination of him to give him no idea of the state of our knowledge. I consider, however, that his is a genuine case. The following points struck me:

He states he jumped from a train when in motion and showed me two cuts near the left eye which he states he received on this occasion. This could no doubt be verified.

He was anxious not to discuss the name of the people with whom he stayed in ANTWERP, but as he said he had given it to the landing officer at the port of disembarkation, I did not press him.

His very short stay in HOLLAND is unusual: but if he is being sent to this country to obtain information, it is unlikely that those responsible for sending him would let him do a thing of this nature, which would at once arouse suspicion.

He informed me that as he had a fairly large sum of money on him, he prevailed on a civilian to take him to a railway station where he bought a ticket to ROTTERDAM and reported to the British Counsel.

J.S.H. Moore, Capt.

On November 26, Pat was moved to the Regent Palace Hotel, a more convenient location for the planned daily interviews. For the next five days, he was kept busy answering hundreds of questions posed to him by various branches of the military.

He answered questions regarding methods and tactics behind the frontline trenches. They quizzed him about the morale of the German troops. Aviation experts asked him about all he had seen of the German flying-corps methods and equipment. Food experts interrogated him as to the food conditions in Germany, Luxembourg, and Belgium. They pressed him to go into as much detail as he could about Courtrai, the train, his escape, his survival techniques, Brussels and, of course, the barrier fence at Holland.

On the evening of the 28th, Pat enjoyed a private dinner with a small group of fliers who like so many friends along the front, believed Pat had been killed when he was reported missing. These small private events were orchestrated, in some cases to help Pat transition back to present reality. It was important that individual and small group reorientation be part of his readjustment. Military doctors understood the importance of such meetings for men isolated under dire conditions and out of touch with the real world for such a long time.

In addition, Pat asked for and received a few breaks during the five-day session. Overall, he was quite willing to tell all he could about his experience. "Anything I can do to defeat the Hun," was his reassuring response each time his interrogators thanked him for the giving of his time to their investigations.

On Monday, December 3, Pat heard a knock at the door at 9:30 p.m. "I wonder who that could be?" he thought. Upon opening the door, a uniformed telegram delivery boy handed him an envelope. Pat signed, tipped the young man, and closed the door. "Perhaps it is from home. They must have received my cable," he thought. He opened the cablegram.

"What the hell!" he exclaimed. A chill ran through Pat as he glanced in disbelief the following message:

Office of Origin and Service Instructions: Buckingham Palace
Number of words: 52

To: 2nd Lieut P.A. Obrien, Royal Flying Corps, Regents Palace Hotel

The King is very glad to hear of your escape from Germany and if you are to be in London on Friday next December 7, his majesty will receive you at Buckingham Palace at 10:30 a.m. Please acknowledge. Cromer
After feeling somewhat stunned a moment, Pat sat down and composed a response which he would send in the morning:

To: Earl Cromer, Buckingham Palace, London:

[375]

I will attend Buckingham Palace as directed, Friday December 7th, at 10:30.

Lieutenant Pat O'Brien

Pat found the wait until December 7, as nerve racking as anything he had experienced sneaking around Brussels. On Tuesday morning, he walked to the telegram office and sent his response. He then decided to go to his bank, Cox & Company, and inquire about his personal trunk. Pat had put his large trunk in storage before leaving for France. It was the practice of the Royal Flying Corps, when a pilot was reported missing, to have two of his comrades assigned to go through the missing pilot's personal belongings, check them over, destroy anything that might be incidental or a security risk, and send it all home or to his established bank.

Every letter was read and never afterward discussed or revealed. If the pilot had been reported dead, the items were sent to the next of kin. As soon as Pat was reported missing, Paul Raney, and another member of their squadron checked over Pat's effects and made a list. Little did Raney realize that, days later, he would die over France. Pat had a hard time convincing the bank teller that he was Pat O'Brien since the bank had him officially listed as a prisoner of war in Germany. The teller was not convinced and indicated he'd release the trunk if Pat could demonstrate proof that he was a relative and that O'Brien was dead!

"Well, I can't very well present proof to you that Pat O'Brien is dead, but I will do the best I can to prove to you he is alive, and if you haven't quite forgotten his signature I guess I can write you out an order that will answer all your requirements and enable you to give me Pat O'Brien's belongings without running any risks," said Pat. He scribbled his signature on a piece of paper and handed it to the bank official.

"Good Heavens, Lieutenant!" shouted the official as he aggressively pumped Pat's hand up and down for the longest time. "How did you ever get away?" Pat was invited to sit down and a dozen other people in the bank soon joined them to hear the story in stunned amazement.

The next day, on December 5, Pat got up early and penned a quick letter to his sister, Clara. It read as follows:

Regent Palace Hotel, Piccadilly Circus, London, Dec. 5 1917
My Dear sister:

Just a few lines, as it is a very great job for me to hold a pen.

[376]

I am still in very bad shape, but will soon be o.k. My wound is all healed up and I am able to talk again, I am glad to say. I am not going to tell you the awful experiences I had as I have three months leave and am coming home.

I will not get there for Christmas, but near New Years. A good ocean trip is just what I need. It was seventy-two days from the day I escaped till I crossed the line into Holland. You would never have known me if you had seen me.

Friday, the 7th of December, I go before the king. Then a week or so I will be on my way home. Tell Buck, Jack and all my friends, hello for me.

I can't turn around but what some newspaper man is taking my picture or trying to get a story from me. But I am too glad to be alive and free to have every one bothering me. Will be glad to get on the ocean, for then I can pick up a little fat.

Well, Clara dear, I must close as it is hard work for me to hold a pen. When I see you will know why.

Lots of love as ever,

Pat

A public relations officer from the Royal Flying Corps arrived to pick up Pat at 10:00 in the morning. Pat was having his photo taken at the Beddington Aerodrome in south London. There would be a publicity photo taken in front of a Sopwith Pup and other shots that both the military and others could utilize. Even the Royal Flying Corps knew that Pat would need a professional public persona. The interest in his story was immediate and extensive. The photo of Pat in front of the plane was immediately sent over the wire in conjunction with press releases that were flooding much of free Europe and North America.

On the morning of December 7, Pat climbed into a cab at the Regent. "Buckingham Palace!" he stated as calmly as he could. The cabbie looked in the rear view mirror as Pat took his seat and they drove off. They arrived at the Palace gate where the sentry asked who he was. When Pat told him, he let him pass immediately to the front entrance where he was met by another elaborately decorated official. When Pat entered a man took his overcoat, hat, and stick and Pat was escorted to a long stairway only to be handed over to another guide.

"Might I have my cane, sir?" asked Pat. "I don't think I can get up these stairs without my cane."

[377]

"Indeed, sir," said the aid. "My apologies sir."

Once up the stairs he was led to the Office of King's secretary, Earl Cromer.

"Welcome, Leftenant O'Brien," said Cromer as he shook Pat's hand and introduced him to two additional men of title. Pat fully expected to be briefed in advance of meeting the King and he anticipated a rather sterile and quick official visit. Cromer and the other noblemen chatted with Pat a short time, inquiring as to his adventure. They had unusual interest, thought Pat. Suddenly, the door opened and he was announced!

"The King will receive Leftenant O'Brien!"

Pat was as nervous as if he was about to meet the Kaiser himself rather than his Commander in Chief. "And with no preparation!" he thought. Cromer beckoned Pat to follow and they entered a large room, where Pat assumed he would be prepared finally to meet the King. To his shock, there stood King George V himself and Pat watched as Cromer bowed.

"Your Majesty, Leftenant O'Brien!" stated Cromer stepping back and out of the room. The King had Pat's hand before Cromer had exited and before Pat could offer his own respects to the King. King George stated he would be very pleased to hear Pat's story in detail and the two sat in highly ornate stuffed chairs set closely for a nearly face-to-face discussion.

At one point the King asked, "Were you treated any worse by the Germans, Leftenant, on account of being an American? I've heard that the Germans have threatened to shoot Americans serving in the British army if captured. Did you find that to be the case?"

Pat indicated he felt no unusual treatment, as such. The King stated he felt Pat's escape was due to Pat's determined will power and that it was one of the "most remarkable escapes" he had ever heard of in the war.

"I hope that all the Americans will give as good an account of themselves as you have, Leftenant," said the King. "And I feel quite sure they will. I fully appreciate all the service rendered us by Americans before the States entered the war."

Pat, sensing he had been there nearly fifteen minutes, asked the King if he was taking too much time.

"Not at all, Leftenant, not at all!" he replied. "I was extremely interested in the brief report that came to me of your wonderful escape, and I sent for you because I wanted to hear the whole story first-hand, and I am very glad you were able to come."

Pat told as much as he could to the King who interrupted him only intermittently to ask a question. He laughed quite loudly when Pat related his experience at Ghent when he departed from the train and shouted his comment about "riding with pigs" rather than the Huns. Pat innocently called the King "sir" throughout, forgetting the formalities of "Your Majesty." The King did not express concern and as Pat would surmise later it was not all that inappropriate since King George was his superior officer, as well as, the King of England.

After fifty-two minutes Pat rose to depart and the King asked, "What do you plan to next, Leftenant?"

"Why, sir, I hope to rejoin my squadron at the earliest possible moment!" said Pat.

"No, Leftenant, that is out of the question. We can't risk losing you for good by sending you back to Germany. If you were unfortunate enough to be captured again they would undoubtedly shoot you."

The two men rose, shook hands, and said "Good-Bye" simultaneously. In the anteroom, Cromer greeted Pat stating, "His Majesty must have been very must interested in your story."

"I was very surprised, myself," said Pat. "He is genuinely a fine man."

As the two men made their way down the stairs, Pat glanced in every direction to soak in the interior view of Buckingham Palace. He knew it was a unique moment in his life, one that he would want to tell his children and grandchildren someday. As they reached the exit door, a young man handed Pat his hat, coat, and cane.

"Congratulations, Leftenant and thank you," said Cromer shaking Pat's hand.

"Thank you, sir," said Pat flashing his contagious smile.

Pat decided not to catch a taxi right away. It was a cool day and his knee didn't feel too bad so he decided to walk a bit. He exited the gate on the northeast side of the Palace, past Queen Victoria Memorial where a number of Londoners, tourists and men on leave were milling about and taking pictures. He glanced down Constitution Hill on his left then decided to walk down the Mall toward Whitehall, the Admiralty and other government buildings. When he got to Horse Guards Road, he took a right and enjoyed the dignity and beauty of central London.

About half way down the street he heard a noisy but synchronized group of six horses with their riders on way to a formal ceremony near the Palace. Pat stopped to watch them pass and was stirred by the great presence of the guard horses in full trot. He felt a good deal of pride in his service to Britain. He also felt great appreciation for his American ingenuity that had gotten him through the last two months of hell.

That night, a banquet was held in Pat's honor at the Hotel Savoy. One of his friends, Louis Grant, from his days at Central Flying School had won a wager among the pilots that Pat would show up someday. Pat had sent him a wire on his first day in London that read:

Lieutenant Louis Grant:
War-bread bad, so I came home

Pat

About the same time Pat arrived at the Savoy for the dinner banquet, residents of Momence were gawking at a large photo of well-dressed Pat O'Brien on the front page of The Momence *Progress* with headlines leading the Friday edition:

"Famous Momence Aviator who escaped from Germany. Lt. Pat O'Brien of the Royal Flying Corps"

"Pat of Momence is again in London, England after having escaped from Germany, where he was a prisoner."

The people of Momence hung on every word. Most read the story two and three times. W.W. Parish was reading the paper aloud to a group of old timers sitting at the Central House hotel having lunch. Interestingly enough, the front-page photo of Pat showed him out of uniform. Glass had pressed Captain Moore to take some photos of Pat out of uniform in addition to his officer's uniform. He figured Pat's fame would create a demand for public appearances beyond Pat's time in the service and, likely, the war itself. Glass' hunch would be proven true.

[380]

The following day, December 8, Pat's story, complete with the publicity photo taken in front of the Sopwith Pup at Beddington, appeared in the Oakland, California newspaper:

Oakland Tribune, Saturday Evening, December 8, 1917

Richmond Birdman Visits King!
Made Three Escapes!
Lieut. Patrick O'Brien in England;
May Return Home

Flight Lieutenant Patrick O'Brien, of Momence, an American member of the British Flying Corps and a former Santa Fe employee at Point Richmond, who arrived in London several weeks ago after a sensational escape from a German prison camp, was received by King George at Buckingham Palace today. The king congratulated O'Brien on his escape. O'Brien is expected to come to America from England to visit his mother, Mrs. Margaret O'Brien

Agnes MacMillan stared at Pat's photo and read the story. Though she had heard the news from Pat's cable, seeing it in the newspaper was overwhelming and removed any doubts she may have had that the cable could have been a cruel joke. She had to wipe her tears repeatedly to remove her blurred vision. If ever anyone was in a fog having heard such news, it was Agnes. She had convinced herself that she would never see Pat again and yet there he was, handsome as ever with that big smile looking right at her and news that he had survived and was coming home was hard to believe. The joy was more than she could bear. The prospect of seeing Pat again after all he had gone through caused her fear. "How had he changed?" she thought. "Would he see her? More importantly, would he still feel the same way toward her?" She asked for the rest of the day off and walked home conjecturing all the way. She would be in an emotional turmoil for the rest of the week.

Pat was not the first man to escape during a war but the odds of being shot down, wounded, escaping from a moving train, walking for days undercover and breaching a nine-foot electrified fence to freedom was something few, if any, had experienced in the Great War. Pat's story was certainly interesting but it was his visit with the King that fueled electrifying publicity about him at home and across all of Europe. In the days immediately following Pat's visit with the King newspapers all over the United States, Canada and Europe were headlining his story.

On Monday, December 10, Pat met W.C. Glass in the lobby the Regent Hotel and agreed he would sign a speaking agreement with Keedick that would begin with a speech at Orchestra Hall in Chicago and then take Pat east for a tour. Pat would stop in New York to sign the agreement on his way home from England but only after paying a very important visit to the Raney's in Toronto. Keedick spread the word of the agreement and calls poured in from around the United States to book Pat even before he left England.

On December 13, Pat walked to the U.S. Foreign office and picked up his updated passport for the trip home. It was his 27th birthday. That evening he appeared at the largest banquet held in his honor since arriving in London. Over 1,000 officers, enlisted men and pilots were captivated by Pat's uncanny and yet penetrating story of his escape from German hands. Captain Moore who had first interviewed Pat was asked to introduce him to the troops. Pat was seated at the head table with a number of dignitaries and when dessert had been served, Moore approached the microphone and the entire hall went silent.

Captain Moore proceeded. "Gentlemen, as you know we are honored tonight by one of our own. Indeed, we know he is an American. Yet, how much more could he demonstrate his commitment to Britain's cause than to put his life on the line on behalf of the Crown.

"Hear! Hear! Hear!" came the customary shouts from the large audience.

"Tonight he will tell you his story for the first time. He was shot down over Germany in his Sopwith Pup, wounded, and captured behind German lines. Second Lt. Pat O'Brien, of the 66th Squadron will tell of his escape and how he came to be with us tonight after 72 days walking through Germany, Luxemburg, and Belgium. He is an example for all of us. He is a man who puts humanity's cause above his own life and welfare. Gentlemen, Lt. Pat O'Brien of the Royal Flying Corps."

A roar went up in the hall that stunned Pat as over 1,000 of his comrades leapt to their feet and applauded him for nearly three minutes. Pat walked gingerly to the podium with his cane sporting a somewhat nervous smile and nodding his head. He was rather stunned by the reception and stood at the podium for what seemed like a day, before the men in the hall finally took their seats. Pat had not prepared for the speech. He just spoke off the top of his head and told his story. Everyone in the room discovered that night that Pat was an enthralling storyteller. When he finished, there was a quiet in the room for five seconds as most in attendance were stunned by the tale.

Then, "Whoa!!!!" a roared the thousand strong now moved by emotion as well as pride, jumping to their feet once again. Pat held form and again nodded this time with a look of determination and pride. It was a night that all would remember for the rest of their lives. Pat took his seat as the cheers went on. Hearing of his birthday the men sporadically and then in full voice sang "Happy Birthday" to Pat followed by "For he's a Jolly Good Fellow," ending in another loud applause. Following the invocation, a number of men came to the head table to shake Pat's hand and thank him for his inspirational presentation.

Seven more banquets, receptions, and luncheons were scheduled around London in the next few days. Military and civilian groups all sought the opportunity to hear the young Irish-American of the Royal Flying Corps in person. Pat could hardly walk the streets of London without numerous requests for autographs, photos, and confirmations that he was the "real Lt. Pat O'Brien." It did wear Pat down a bit.

In just a little over three weeks since arriving in London, he'd spoken at two banquets, given five full days of detailed testimony to British military officials, received daily therapy and medical treatments for his injuries, spent a morning sitting for a significant publicity photo session at Bennington and turned down a number of less credible promoters seeking his endorsement or appearance. Like all in London, Pat was still experiencing the war. Hostile Hun aeroplanes were bombing London daily and British officials continued to enforce blackout periods requiring Londoners to shutter or paint over windows.

Private citizens were instructed not to use the telephone during or immediately after a raid but to await the "all clear" sirens that rang though London on a daily basis. On one day, during Pat's last week in London, ten people were killed and seventy injured as a result of German bombing. A lot was swirling around the young Pilot who had just walked 250 miles through three countries living off sugar beets, cabbage, potatoes, and handouts. His weight gain had plateaued.

Back home one news story after another was appearing about the young man from Momence, Illinois who flew for the Royal Flying Corps and had achieved the impossible. Though Pat had little sense of it yet, a whirlwind of anticipation was stirring up around his remarkable escape.

On December 14, the Momence *Progress* newspaper wrote an editorial about the importance of giving Pat a hero's welcome in his hometown.

"One hundred thousand dollars wouldn't pay for the worldwide publicity given to this small town of potential possibilities by the phenomenal exploits of Pat O'Brien, now made famous by his daring escape from German captors.

"Perhaps the appeal is unnecessary. The *Progress* hopes so. But the city cannot afford to be dilatory in the matter of immediately arranging a suitable welcome for Pat upon his return to Momence."

On Saturday morning, December 15, Pat was walking along the Thames Path toward the Parliament Building. It was a pleasant day for December with temperatures near 40 degrees Fahrenheit. Two men walked past and Pat recognized one of them as Doctor Charles Nelson. Nelson served with Pat and Paul Raney at Estree' Blanche and had gotten to know them both quite well in a short time.

"Doc!" shouted Pat. The doctor turned and looked in Pat's direction but kept walking and looked forward again. "Doc Nelson!" Pat shouted again. "It's Pat O'Brien."

Charles Nelson turned and paused as Pat caught up with him. Nelson was having a problem recognizing Pat but after an exchange of information and careful study of Pat's face, he was convinced that that pilot standing before him in London, who he surely believed was dead, was Pat O'Brien. Having just arrived from the front two days before himself, Nelson had not yet caught up with news of Pat's escape.

"Extraordinary, O'Brien, truly extraordinary," said Nelson in a muffled tone as he examined Pat's profile and physique. "How in God's name did you come to be alive?" Pat just smiled. "Come, Pat. Let's find a place to sit down and have some tea. I must hear about how you came to survive your crash," said the doctor taking Pat's arm.

Pat, Nelson and the doctor's colleague, walked about five blocks to a small restaurant. Pat proceeded to tell Nelson about his experience in the field hospital, his witness of Paul's death, leap from the train, his walk through Germany, Luxemburg, and Belgium, and his meeting with the King. They visited for three hours. Nelson was on his way home to Canada and would leave in two days. Pat told him he would be in Toronto also in a matter of weeks to visit Paul's parents. The talked about looking each other up in Canada if there was time. Shaking his hands as the men departed, Nelson said, "I'm sure your hometown is planning a wonderful welcoming home."

"I suppose they might," said Pat, still unaware of how dramatic his story had impacted everyone back home.

The City of Momence was, indeed, planning for the big day. On Monday, December 17, at the City Council meeting, Mayor Tiffany appointed a committee of three to prepare for the event that included Henry Halpin, James Cleary, and W.W. Parish. Two days later, the three appointees met dozens of business and professional leaders from town at the Commercial Club, which was currently headed by Owen Bigelow. Ed Chatfield, J.A. Mayhew, and E.M. Logan combined with the city council committee to lead the effort. Since hearing the news at Clegg's store days before, planning had already begun. Clearly, the largest building in town, capable of holding an event of this magnitude was the Wennerholm's garage, the former livery stable, now garage, where Pat had ribbed the old mechanics about the future of flying. The entire building would have to be cleared and made ready or a large banquet affair.

Tickets would be required and surely not everyone wishing to attend would get in. The committee estimated that the garage could hold 600 people for dinner. Press coverage would be heavy and officials from Illinois, Indiana and, indeed, other parts of the U.S. would likely make requests. A large committee of townswomen stepped up to prepare the meal. Mesdames Riker, Sherwood, Nichols, Demack, Hess, and Astle were among the long-time Momence citizens that stepped up to help. Committees on Music, Decorations, Invitations, Governor's Reception, and Pat's Reception were all formed in one week.

Pat reported to military medical staff for his regularly scheduled visit on the morning of December 17. Doctors informed him he needed to be stronger, put on weight, strengthen his legs, and acquire a normal diet. In short, they advised Pat that he needed to "slow down." In total, he had recovered only ten of his lost fifty pounds. "I want you lying low as much as you possible while on that ship, Lieutenant," said his doctor. We need to get you healthy before everyone has their piece of you."

Two days later, Pat received a note form Captain Moore to meet with representatives from Harper & Brothers, New York who had offices in London. The representative would meet him for lunch and, if Pat agreed, arrange for a writer to spend the afternoon with Pat to discuss writing a book about his experiences. Wishing to tie the book's release to Pat's planned tour of the United States, it was agreed that the Harper & Brothers editor would travel with Pat on his steamship home where there would be time for both Pat and the writer to complete the manuscript. With his publishing agreement in place and an extensive promotional tour planned, Pat was assured that 1918 would be a busy year.

On his final evening in London, Pat spent time doing what he enjoyed best, sharing a good meal and conversing with the patrons of a local pub. He was sad and happy at the same time. Many of his mates were gone. To his best knowledge, only three from the original squadron were still alive. Lascelles, Stedman perhaps, and Captain Moore had reported that Keast was likely in Italy. The one on his mind most tonight was Paul. In an ironic twist Pat now had Paul's belongings in his trunk and would visit the Raney's first thing upon his return. As well-wishes and good cheer wafted against the ceiling of the old central London pub, Pat O'Brien had a deep sense of departure, leaving his best friend Paul who lay in Faubourg-d'Amiens Cemetery near Arras, France across the British Channel with countless others laid to rest.

PART SEVEN

HOME AGAIN

Chapter 33

Atlantic Crossing

The next morning, Pat rose early to pack. He placed most of his belongings in his large trunk but kept a small leather case for items he wanted to keep close. In addition to letters, official paper work and a copy of the London Times, there were two very important items for his attaché.

The first was a small gift box for Margaret containing two pieces of lace embroidered with the Flemish words "Charity" on one and "Hope" on the other. Pat carefully folded each cloth, laid them both in the box, tied the box with a string, and placed the package at the bottom of his bag. After retracing his steps in Holland to retrieve the handiwork of the Belgian peasant woman, the last thing he wanted to do was to risk losing it in shipment. The second most important item was a portfolio that contained personal letters and small items belonging to Paul Raney. As Paul had done for him, Pat was the one chosen to inspect and deliver his friend's belongings to Mr. and Mrs. Raney in Toronto. The conveyance of these two articles would be his primary objective upon returning home.

Pat checked out of his room, had the bellman deliver his trunk to the concierge, and met Captain Moore for breakfast. Moore reviewed the procedures Pat was to follow regarding Allied secrecy and the limitations on what Pat could discuss in his planned speaking tour and forthcoming book.

"I understand the editor from Harper will meet you in Liverpool for the trip home. His name is Ivan Livingston. You will sail to St. John but under no circumstances should you mention your destination or departure date to anyone during your two days in Liverpool," said Moore. "Livingston has been cleared by the war department and knows your limitations but ultimately it is you, Pat, a British Officer, who is responsible for maintaining our level of security regarding what you know.

"I understand, Sir," said Pat.

Moore reviewed the official documents that verified Pat had been granted a three-month furlough to "regain his health." There were a few papers to sign and updated credentials for Pat who was still a subject of the King.

"I suggest you keep possession of these documents at all times," said Moore. "Ultimately, under your commission as a 2nd Lieutenant of the Royal Flying Corps, you will maintain uniform dress while in public and adhere to the same practices prescribed as such, though you will have no official duties during your furlough. I know you will be a credit to both England and the RFC," he said extending his hand to Pat.

At noon, Pat was scheduled to take the train to Liverpool in northern England where his ship would depart for North America on the 23rd. Before departure, Captain Moore agreed to escort Pat to the U.S. Embassy where Pat would meet with U.S. Ambassador, Walter Hines Page. In that meeting, Pat asked Page for advice on how to transfer to the American Flying Corps, should he decide to do so. Naturally, the Ambassador advised Pat to focus on getting strong again but promised Pat that if in three month, his doctors were in agreement, and he could also resign his commission with the RFC. The Ambassador closed by telling Pat that he would help him as best as he could.

Both Moore and Paige were struck by Pat's weakened physical appearance, contrasted by his passion to stay in the fight. It was inspiring to them both, though secretly they hoped Pat's fighting days were over. Still, neither was prepared to doubt Pat's capacity of spirit to return to battle. Like his father, uncles and grandfather on both sides, Pat O'Brien had that deep sense of purpose that often freed men from fear in the face of deadly battle.

Captain Moore and Pat were driven to the Liverpool Street Station by a young private. The captain, whose respect and admiration for Pat had grown since meeting him days before, was genuinely moved by their departure. After shaking Pat's hand, he took a step back as both men executed an ardent and spirited salute. Though he did not show it, Pat felt a wave of emotion wash over him. While he was still a 2nd Lieutenant, he sensed that this moment could be his farewell to military life. Who could predict what the world or Pat's physical condition would be like in three months? He hoped it was not the end.

Pat boarded the train and saluted Captain Moore again through the window as the train pulled away. He traveled through Northampton, Coventry, Birmingham, and Manchester, then finally arrived in Liverpool three hours later. During peace time there is no city in England quite like Liverpool. During war, Liverpool is bedlam. The influx of men, arms, and equipment through England's primary port choked its harbors and filled every primary street.

As the train slowed into the Lime Street Station, Pat could see smoke stacks and the cantankerous activity of Liverpool industry churning out intensity that would ultimately be dumped in the lap of the evil Hun. The Americans were well into the war by now and ships from the U.S. arrived daily at Liverpool all designed to bolster the Allies and finish the Huns. After securing the transfer of his trunk to the Canadian Pacific Railway Company who operated his ship to Canada, Pat made his way to the Adelphi Hotel in the center of town and checked in. As was his practice, Pat had dinner and drinks at a local popular pub.

Few places in Liverpool had the tradition or atmosphere of the Crown Pub which was located near the train station. A good number of American servicemen were present and Pat enjoyed the evening with his fellow military confidants. Most of the men were unaware of Pat's achievement but three seemed to give him a double take when they heard his name. Most, however, were on their way to France, enjoying their final few days of freedom or preoccupied with their recent war experience, looking to go home on leave. The conversations changed depending on whether the men were "on their way in" or "on their way out." After asking a man his name, the inevitable second question was always "where are you heading?" Everyone in a uniform was either "heading in" or heading out." During wartime, the conversations in watering holes like Crown were all the same.

On the morning of December 23rd, Pat picked up his claim ticket from the bell captain who had shipped his trunk. He hailed a cab, and made his way toward the Mercy River where his ship, the SS Metagama, was docked. At just over 500 feet, The Metagama was one of the largest ships sailing on the Atlantic. She accommodated 520 first-class and 1,200 third class passengers and was making continuous runs between Liverpool and Canada since being commissioned in 1915. For the most part, it was a "ghost ship" kept under the radar as much as possible due to its role. Today, the Metagama would carry returning Canadian officers, NCO's, naval officers, nurses, and Canadian soldiers on furlough. While designed to carry both passengers and freight for the Canadian Pacific Railway Company, the Metagama was almost immediately pressed into service as a troop carrier in 1915.

Around 10:00 in the morning, Pat made his way on board. He was directed to the interior stairwell leading to the first class deck. Reaching the top of stairs he exited on to the promenade deck, walked past the reading room and the first class lounge, then finally arrived amid a cluster of first class cabins.

Finding his room, he entered, removed his hat, placed his attaché on the bed and checked himself in the mirror. He looked a far site better than he had in the cracked mirror of the old Belgian cabin. He ran his hands briskly through his jet black hair and exited back onto the deck to view the departure. After a few minutes watching longshoremen load cargo below, he decided to sit a while since departure was an hour away. He made his way to the first class lounge where he sat in a high-back leather chair and read a copy of the Liverpool Echo newspaper.

The Metagama was a very accommodating ship with extensive, yet conservative, woodworking throughout. It felt more like a cruise ship than a military troop ship because it was. Pat sipped an ale and felt relaxed, looking forward to his long trip home. He sat back a moment, imagining what it would be like to see home once again. Resting his head against the back of the chair he dosed off, only to be awakened by a fellow officer who touched Pat's arm saying, "We're departing chap, would you like to go on deck?"

Pat set his paper down, exited the lounge, and joined the officer on deck, watching the huge ship pull away from the Liverpool calamity. They engaged in light conversation, talked about their experiences and ultimate destinations. The man was a Canadian Army officer who was heading home to Ottawa for two months to recover.

About one hour out of port, Pat received a note at his cabin to meet Livingston in the Reading Room at noon. When Pat entered the lounge he was greeted by a short yet distinguished looking gentleman who recognized Pat from his picture.

"Lieutenant O'Brien?" said Livingston extending his hand.

"Yes, are you Livingston?" Pat responded.

"Indeed. Shall we sit?"

"Sure," Pat said.

As they took a seat around a small round table, Ivan Livingston placed a note pad and pencil to his right then folded his hands. "I apologize for not having found you yesterday in Liverpool. I had some problems with my passport and did not get on board until nearly a half hour before departure. I was quite concerned I'd not make the trip," he said.

The two men ordered some lunch and talked about how they'd proceed. Livingston was quite organized and explained to Pat that the book could be a combination of Pat's pen, his pen, and oral dictation. "I'm not quite up to doing a lot of writing yet, Mr. Livingston," said Pat. "I don't mean I'm uninspired, I mean physically," he said holding up his right hand as if holding a pen.

"That should not be a major issue, Pat. What often works best is for you to talk through the experience front to back which will give me a good general outline of the book. From there you can elaborate and I can ask questions to fill in the storyline. I can actually perform 90% or more of the physical writing itself. You can determine how much you want to actually write. You can even dictate specific verbiage to me. I take dictation. We'd like to initiate the book at the point of your crash, spending most of the time relating your experiences on the run and ending with your time in London this past week."

"That sounds fine, Ivan," said Pat. "When do you want to start?"

"Well, if you're up to it Lieutenant, I thought we could have lunch here and work through the afternoon. Do you think you could outline the experience in that time?" said Livingston.

"I don't believe so," Pat responded. "It may take a few sessions. Keep in mind I walked for two months. A lot happened in that time. But I do like the idea of dictating much of it to you."

They agreed to start over lunch. Pat began his story and the two men actually worked through supper, ordering food again about seven in the evening. Livingston's enthusiasm for Pat's story grew. He knew it had the makings of a very successful book.

"You know, Pat, tomorrow is Christmas Eve. If we can work until nine or so tonight, and then retire, we could continue first thing in the morning, end by noon, and just enjoy the rest of the holiday from there," said Livingston. "I believe I will have what I need to outline the book with one more four hour session."

"That sounds good," said Pat. "We've made a lot of progress."

They ended the day with some quality whiskey and idle chatter about family, the war, and differences between American and British ways. Being British, this discussion of cultural differences, along with an occasional "Americanized word" from Pat, as Ivan called it, helped Livingston understand how to represent Pat better in the book.

As was always the case when people first meet Pat, Livingston took to him quickly and as the third glass of whiskey took hold, the rather straight-laced bookworm, sported hearty laughter, witnessing the humor and spunk of Pat O'Brien for himself. Livingston gained additional insight that would form the mortar around the factual bricks that comprise Pat's book.

The next day, as planned, they worked 'till noon. By the time they finished, Pat was more than willing to forget about the war for a spell. As they left the lounge to join the Christmas festivities on board the ship, Pat felt as excited as a kid realizing it was Christmas and he was a free man.

Pat spent Christmas Eve with various officers who celebrated the day as anyone would when away from home on the holidays during war. Pat purchased a nice pen for Livingston and gave it to him as a gift for which the writer was genuinely moved. As usual, the light hearted nature of Pat drew increased numbers of revelers to his table and by dinner it felt like the old days at the Ivy Inn.

On Christmas Day, the ship was full of spontaneous and raucous feasts. The Canadians on board seemed to be always organizing impromptu clusters of singers belting out brash versions of Christmas carols for their fellow passengers. Pat spent a good portion of time with the Canadians and felt quite at home with them. But as jovial as the ship was the entire day, Pat's thoughts continually drifted toward the small house in Hill Street in Momence where he was quite certain the O'Briens were having the happiest Christmas ever.

Unknown to Pat was the fact that Margaret was not home. She was spending her last day in Powell, Wyoming and planned to depart for Momence the next day. Margaret couldn't get home soon enough. On December 26, Buck prematurely headed for Toronto to meet his brother and Margaret was riding the train home to Chicago. On the 27th, the committee that had been appointed by Mayor Tiffany met for the first time at the Commercial Club in Momence to make plans and assign dozens of volunteers who had stepped forward to plan Pat's homecoming day.

Pat's trip home would take longer than he expected. Two days after Christmas, almost on cue, German U-boats made their first appearance in the icy waters of the North Atlantic and the Metagama began regular zigzag motions designed to avoid tracking by the Hun ships. All traffic between the U.S. and England required such diversion during the war. The German ships would continue to create havoc throughout the voyage. During one particularly agonizing night Pat had more than a few moments of terror imagining he'd come so far and yet could go down with the Metagama in the middle of the Atlantic.

On Saturday, December 28th, Pat was standing on the officer's deck looking out to sea when suddenly he heard a familiar voice of a man fifteen feet aft discussing the evil Hun with another passenger. He was shocked. It was Evelyn Lascelles. He looked again. "Yes, it's him," he said to himself.

Pat walked over to the two men extended his hand and said, "Hello." Lascelles turned and stared at Pat for what seemed the longest time.

"My friend, you certainly look like Pat O'Brien," he declared, "but I can't believe my eyes. Who are you?"

"No, Evelyn, it's me. Pat! Pat O'Brien!" extending his hand deeper into the space between them. "I know who you are. You're Lascelles. We flew together on my last flight!'

Pat was so convinced that he was looking at his friend Lascelles, that it unnerved him to see Lascelles so confused. Lascelles stared at Pat for another minute, shaking his head every few seconds in denial.

"My God, man! The last time I saw Pat O'Brien he was going down to earth with a bullet in his face and spinning like a top," said the startled Lieutenant. "He was one of my comrades in the flying corps. I read he was missing in action but I never believed he survived that crash. It's not possible!"

Then the Aussie grabbed Pat's hand and suddenly became convinced he was talking to his friend. Lascelles apologized to his casual acquaintance for interrupting their conversation and bid him "G-doy." Then the two pilots turned and walked along the deck to the lounge, talking feverously all the way.

Lascelles had seen extensive action. He was first wounded in February of 1916 as a member of the Kings Royal Rifle Corps. With the 46th Squadron he was wounded again in January of 1917 and again in February of the same year. The men of Pat's flight had great respect for Lascelles bravery and longevity. He was one of the few men alive that had seen Pat crash to the earth and through some amazing twist of fate was sailing home on the same ship with a pilot he thought surely had died in battle.

"It is really incredible that we are here on the same ship! Where are you going?" Pat asked as the two men took their seats in the lounge.

"I'm on my way home to Australia to recuperate. I've not been home for over two years and my furlough is for two months," said Lascelles. "What about you?

"I escaped the Hun," said Pat. "I jumped from a train and walked to Holland," Pat said very matter-of-factly.

"You jumped out of a train in Holland?" asked Evelyn.

"No, Germany," said Pat. "I walked to Holland."

"Holy Christ!" said Evelyn. It shocked Lt. Lascelles and he implored Pat to tell him the all that happened, which he did. Like all others who heard it, Evelyn was amazed by the story.

"So what do you know of our old chums?" asked Pat. "I know about Raney. I saw him crash while I was in the field hospital in Germany. He put up a tremendous fight but was outnumbered, you know."

"Indeed. We heard the report of his dogged resistance. He was a natural dog-fighter," said Evelyn.

"I have his belongings, you know," said Pat. "I trained with him in Toronto at Borden. He was a dear friend. I dread my visit to his parents but I must do it. I plan to go to Toronto as soon as we arrive in Canada." Both men paused a second looking out at the sea. "So what of the others?" asked Pat.

"Keast, you know…" Evelyn began looking down.

"No, what? Gone?" asked Pat.

"Yes, He was killed in August, about the 21st I believe, not more than a week after you went down. It was another ambush".

"Others?" asked Pat.

"Well, Edward Bacon, he was the fellow that ran into engine trouble on our last flight, remember?

"Yeah," Pat replied.

"He died in a bad ambush the last day of August."

"How about the Captain?" asked Pat.

"Bell-Irving I lost track of. I know he transferred to the 88th in September. Last I heard they were planning on assigning him to the Training Depot Station but I don't know for sure," relayed Lascelles.

"You remember the doc, don't you, Evelyn?" said Pat. "Doc Nelson was a Canadian that served at the Estree'-Blanche' Aerodrome and became good friends with many of the pilots, particularly Paul Raney and me."

"Of course!" said Lascelles.

"Well, I saw him in London walking along the Thames. I called out to him and he looked but turned and kept walking. He didn't recognize me. Eventually, like you, he realized it was me and we had dinner at the hotel one night. I told him about Raney and my time at Courtrai and walking to Holland. He saw some tough action in the last two months and headed home to Toronto on furlough before I left Liverpool. If I have time, I hope to look him up in Toronto but my first priority is to visit the Raney's before heading home.

The two recovering pilots spent the rest of the day and evening telling stories of their war as only two comrades can. Pat would spend a lot of time with Livingston and Lascelles the entire trip. He sat with Livingston almost daily as they fine-tuned Pat's book. Naturally, he met many others soldiers, ate well, rested, and put on a little weight. But the U-boats agitated the Metagama most of the way, unnerving Pat when reports came in or the ship took an obvious new direction. Though he was on a free ship, Pat didn't really feel as though he had fully escaped the Hun. Not yet. Nevertheless, the Metagama was undeterred and each day Pat was closer to home.

The City of Momence was also undeterred in its plans for Pat's reception. All anyone knew, however, was that Pat left London, and would arrive at an Atlantic port somewhere someday soon. On the 28th the committee put tickets for the planned banquet on sale at Burdick's and Jensen's Pharmacy but no date was printed on the ticket. There would be 450 seats available for the banquet at Wennerholm's and 250 invitations to the evening dance at the South Side Hall were sent out without a date. It was decided to get Pat a gold watch. The women pressed their point that it would be impossible to hold an afternoon meeting for Pat on the day he arrived and then turn the room around for a dinner banquet that night. The men succumbed and no afternoon meeting was planned. The dinner banquet would begin at 5:30 and the dance would follow at the South Side Hall.

Meanwhile Pat's brother "Buck" was already in Toronto. He spent all day on the 28th looking for Pat in with no luck. He had no idea that his brother was still en route dodging Hun U-boats in the North Atlantic. Buck was not giving up hope that Pat would soon arrive but at the end of the second day he sent a telegram home that simply read, "No Pat."

Buck took a break from his hunt and celebrated the New Year with the many Toronto citizens reveling downtown. It would be a joyous New Year for the O'Briens. As he downed his fourth drink just past midnight, he kept looking at the door expecting his brother walk in at any moment. He never did.

On the January 2, Buck decided to look for Pat at Spadina Military Hospital where 900 Canadian soldiers were recovering from war wounds suffered in France.

"Can you tell me how to determine if my brother is here?" asked Buck to a young nurse at the front desk.

"What is your brother's name?" she asked.

"Lieutenant Pat O'Brien of the Royal Flying Corps," responded Buck.

Overhearing the conversation a doctor stepped forward before the nurse could respond. "Are you looking for Lt. Pat O'Brien, the American?" said the doctor.

Buck was surprised. "Why, yes! Is he here?"

"No, but I do know him. I served with him in northern France. I had lunch with Pat in London a few weeks before Christmas. He told me all about his escape.

"You did? Oh great," exclaimed Buck. He's supposed to be here, in Toronto but I haven't found him yet."

"Yes, but the trips length is unpredictable due to the Hun U-boats that constantly harass you across the Atlantic. I'm sure he'll show up soon. I recall he told me he would come to Toronto to see Paul Raney's parents. I'm afraid Paul did not make it out of France. They were two great friends, you know."

"I vaguely remember Pat speaking of a buddy from Camp Borden. They went to England together last year but I know little else," said Buck.

"Well, that's him," said the doctor. "Raney was a fine pilot also but never made it back. Your brother saw him crash from his prison hospital. What is your name?"

"Merwin. They call me Buck. Buck O'Brien. I'm Pat's older brother." Though Buck was only five years older than Pat, subconsciously he was feeling rather protective about him now, and used the word "older" to describe his relationship with Pat for the first time. He noticed it as soon as he said it and realized the deep caring he had acquired for his younger brother over this whole affair. There are moments when we learn what people really mean to us. This was one of those moments for Buck.

"Charles Nelson, Mr. O'Brien. Happy to meet you," said the physician.

"Glad to meet you, too. I appreciate any help you can give me," said Buck. "Our whole town is waiting to hear word that Pat is home and safe. I hope I can locate him. I came here the day after Christmas from Illinois and have had no luck finding him."

"I have a suggestion, Mr. O'Brien. Why don't you come back here around two o'clock this afternoon and we'll go have a lunch. In the meantime, I can check with authorities here and see if there has been any word regarding Pat. Do you know what ship he is on?" Buck shook his head no. "Meet me here at two and I'll make arrangements for lunch. Suit you?"

"That would be very helpful, Doctor Nelson. I'll return then."

"Finally, someone who saw Pat," thought Buck. "And in London no less!" Buck was getting excited at the prospect of seeing his brother once again.

Buck met Doctor Nelson at a local restaurant and learned many details of Pat's ordeal. Even Buck was amazed at his brother's accomplishments. Pat's determination was no surprise to any member of the O'Brien family. Not even Buck, however, could imagine such a challenge would befall his brother.

"I will warn you though, Buck," said the doctor. "You may not fully recognize him. He's lost a lot of weight and you can imagine what a toll living outdoors in solitude for two months does to one's mind and body. He's still a little nervous."

Nelson was able to inform Buck that the next ship from Liverpool was en route but with the threat of U-boats assured, no one could predict an arrival date. Nor could it be said which port would be his destination but Nelson said it was likely to be St. John.

"I came in at St. John," said the doctor. Buck decided to stay a few days and see if Pat might show up the next few days. He didn't.

In Momence and within the O'Brien household, anticipation was building around Pat's arrival. But over the next two weeks a series of ironic miscues and unexpected events added significant tension to the wait. On January 4, the *Momence Progress* reported "no word" regarding Pat.

On Sunday, January 6, Pat's ship pulled into port at St. John. Neither Buck nor anyone in Momence had any way of knowing that the ship had landed or that Pat was on it. In Toronto, Buck decided it would be best to head home until some word came.

Buck planned to relate Nelson's story to his family and wait until word came that Pat was, in fact, on Canadian soil. Ironically, as his train pulled out of the Toronto station, Pat was boarding a train leaving St. John for Toronto. They would miss each other by two hours. There was no way to know in those days, particularly during war time.

As Buck made his way west to Illinois, the largest blizzard in fifty years was blanketing the area around Lake Michigan, including Momence. Not only were roads closed but nearly all trains were delayed due to heavy drifting.

During that same afternoon, the Associated Press sent out a wire reporting that Pat O'Brien, the American, flying for the Royal Flying Corps that escaped German hands and had met with the King, had arrived "at an Atlantic Port." The headline arrived at the Momence Progress newspaper over their wire. Margaret was informed immediately but still no one actually knew where Pat was. It added to the tension.

On January 8, Buck was still enduring a slow and arduous train ride through northern Indiana, notorious for excessive blizzards as much as two feet high caused by northwest winds across Lake Michigan.

Buck arrived home early on the 9th. He informed Margaret of his failed trip, then was surprised to hear her say, "It's alright, Buck, he's home. We got word yesterday." These untimely and disjointed events simply added to the adrenaline everyone was feeling in anticipation of Pat's homecoming. The whole town of Momence was nervous and excited.

Buck told her much of what he had learned from Doctor Nelson, avoiding the more painful parts. He then went directly to the *Momence Progress* office and related Nelson's story to Lewis Howk, owner and publisher of the Momence Reporter.

"We need to find out where Pat came in," said Lewis. "I have an idea. I think the Hearst Newspaper folks can help us," he said to Buck.

[400]

Once finished, Howk immediately sent his story and a message over the wire to the Chicago Examiner requesting that the paper send a notice to their Hearst office in New York and try to locate Pat. The New York office sent a wire to every deep water port on the Atlantic coast to find out where Pat had arrived.

Had Buck met his brother in Toronto, he would have seen how the war had taken its toll on him physically. Short of that, Buck related an additional stunning report to Lewis Howk of the casualties he had seen at Spadina Hospital. The paper published his comments in detail. It read:

"Few people in the middle west realize the significance of this war. It was brought home to me when I visited a military hospital at Toronto and saw hundreds of returned soldiers, crippled and maimed and talked with returned men. Nine hundred were quartered at the institution. When you gaze at men with part of their face missing, others with a nose and ear severed, and many who will go through life without the use of their limbs, the horror of war is made apparent and it is easy to hate. I pray that every imperialist responsible for this wholes murder may meet their deserved fate before the conflict ends."

Word came back from the Hearst wire rather quickly. While Buck was still finishing up at the newspaper office, Margaret and Clara heard a loud knock at the door. It was the young Hess boy, with a telegram. He gave them a copy of the one just received from Hearst Newspapers, sent to Lewis Howk. It read:

"Pat O'Brien of Momence arrived at St. John, N.B. Leaves for Toronto."

Later that afternoon Margaret received a telegram from Pat. It read:

"Will be home in a few days," Pat

This last telegram had been sent from Toronto, confirming his arrival in that capital city.

Right after Buck got back to the house, a winded Charles Hess delivered another telegram that arrived for Buck. It read:

"Come to Toronto at once – urgent." Pat

Needless to say, Buck's head was spinning at this point.

Chapter 34

Buck's Hunt

After spending two days getting home from Toronto, Buck was on the train early the next morning heading back. He repacked his bag, grabbed two ham sandwiches, and ran up to the train station to catch the first train north to Chicago. If the tracks were clear, he could catch the Toronto train in time and be there before the day ended.

At the moment Buck was traveling through the countryside of St. Joseph County in Indiana, a cab was dropping Pat off at the home of William and Jessie Raney in Toronto. Ever since he sat in his wheelchair and watched his best buddy fall from the sky, Pat never let Paul Raney out of his mind. Today however, he dreaded visiting the Raney's. Naturally, with all the time Pat had spent at the Raney home during the Borden days, this visit was much more than a formality. His closeness to Paul's folks made the visit easier and harder at the same time.

Pat stepped slowly up the steps and rang the doorbell. The door opened and he was met by Mr. Raney, himself. "Hello, Pat," said the distinguished, mustached man. "Come in, won't you?

Mrs. Raney met the two men halfway down the hallway leading to the sitting room and embraced Pat as she would have her own son. Pat was carrying his attaché with the personal documents he brought to give to Paul's folks. Pat sat next to Mrs. Raney on the stuffed flowered couch and Paul's father sat in the matching chair opposite them. Pat removed his hat and Mrs. Raney clasped Pat's hand the whole time.

Pat told the Raney's all he knew and all he saw of Paul since leaving Canada. When it came to the day of Paul's death, Pat indicated that he would spare them some of the particulars but both implored him to tell them everything, which he did. It was difficult for Pat to relate what he witnessed on the day Paul fell from the skies but he did so in his articulate yet sensitive style. Mrs. Raney broke down a number of times, squeezing Pat's hand as if it were Paul's. Pat didn't have the heart to tell her how painful her firm grasp actually was.

Pat's closeness to Paul was very comforting to both of the Raney's. They visited for three hours and then had dinner together, ending the day with a very emotional parting. At the door, as Pat held his hat with two hands at the waist, large tears fell from his eyes. He noticed Mrs. Raney grasping the envelope he had given her in a similar fashion. That moment froze in his mind and would reappear frequently in the days ahead. She held it in a way a traveler might hold her purse, having just missed the last train. It was a sad departure but he had brought Paul home to his folks in a way that a telegram could not. Included in the portfolio held by Paul's mother was the map Pat had carried for days showing the location of Paul's grave in Flanders.

An hour after Buck's train left Momence, Emil "Matty" Laird, owner of E.M. Laird Aeroplane Company in Chicago, called Clara Clegg indicating that he had talked by long distance telephone to Pat. Clara was stunned by the call. Laird was an early designer of Aeroplanes in Chicago and knew Pat from the West Pullman Days. Through his contacts in Toronto he successfully tracked down Pat's location and he called the hotel.

Laird told Clara that Pat had told him that he was in good health and "feeling fine," and would be in Momence in a few days. Laird also indicated that Pat was the first officer with a rank lower than General to ever visit the King privately. Clara was ecstatic and after relating everything to Maggie, spread the word through town. Meanwhile, Pat's story was racing around the world driven by a highly energized press.

Buck arrived in Toronto at 6:15 p.m. and though Pat was at the train station to meet him, the two brothers failed to find each other. Buck decided to head for the King George Hotel where he knew Pat was staying. As it turned out, both Pat and his brother walked into the hostelry at the same time.

"Buck!" shouted Pat supporting himself with his cane as he lunged toward his brother. As soon as Buck saw him standing there supported by a cane, tears rushed to his eyes.

"Pat, it's so wonderful to finally find you!" said Buck as the two brothers embraced. Buck cried and Pat was just so overjoyed to see his brother that he couldn't stop smiling. There had been many emotional reunions for Pat thus far along the way since his escape. For Buck, this was his first. The two laughed heartily and Buck stepped back holding onto Pat's forearms to examine him.

"Well, you look a little skinny but I'm sure you're still full of piss and vinegar or did the Borsch drain it all out of you!"

[403]

"You know better than that, Buck," said Pat. "Those bastards couldn't wash the Irish out of my bones! Hell, I'm ready to go back."

"You're still full of bullshit! At least that hasn't changed," said Buck. "Let's sit down, I'm starving."

"Me, too," said Pat.

They made their way to the dining room and ordered drinks along with the best steak in the house.

"The night is young, Pat. If you're up to it, why don't we eat and then go out on the town and enjoy ourselves," said Buck. "There's plenty to do in this town, I hung around waiting for you forever last week so I was forced to partake."

"Hey, don't forget, I lived in this town for a while last year," said Pat. "Of course, I was a little busy out at Camp Borden at the time, but I did get out a bit."

Pat and Buck enjoyed their meal and got caught up on so many topics. Pat wanted to hear mostly about the family and people in town. He asked about Al and wondered if any of the old-timers had passed away since he'd been home. Rather than talk a lot about his adventures he wanted to know more about what he had missed. "All I've done since I got to Holland is tell my story, over and over and over again. It's nice to talk about something else for a change. Buck obliged him though secretly he was dying to hear Pat's stories. "There will be time for that," he thought.

"That's just fine Pat, I know basically what you went through after talking to that Doctor Nelson. I met him here in Toronto at the hospital."

"No kidding?" said Pat. "How did he look to you?"

"He looked fine to me. Like a doctor, that's all."

"Well, he was pretty exhausted when I saw him in London," said Pat as he finished his glass of wine. I hope he's doing better."

Pat and Buck finished supper, went out to see some stage shows, listened to music in various pubs and had a great time celebrating their reunion. Pat couldn't wait to get home now that he heard all that was happening with the family. Buck asked him a number of times if he was tired but Pat had had some good rest in recent days and was feeling strong. "Don't worry about me, Buck," he said. "I'll let you know when I'm done."

At one in the morning they called it quits and were having coffee in a small shop near the hotel. It was an evening that both men would never forget. Pat felt like he was almost home now even though he had not yet stepped onto U.S. soil. He would do that the next day.

"Alright Buck, here's what I have to do now," said Pat. "Tomorrow I take a train to New York to meet with a promoter named Lee Keedick. I'm signing a contract with him to do a speaking tour. I'm also meeting with the publisher of my book in New York. Where I need you next is in Chicago when I come home from New York. It looks like that day will be the morning of January 22. Maybe Bud and some of others can make that trip, too but I know you all have lots to do at home. Based on what you told me, it sounds like everybody is going to be busy in Momence for the next few days."

"You're right about that Pat," Buck said. "I can go with you to the station tomorrow and head home when you leave for New York. I'll bring your big trunk with me. You don't want to mess with that. Just take enough clothes for your trip to New York."

"Great idea, Buck," Pat replied.

The next morning Pat gave Buck a big hug on the platform where crowds were boarding the train to New York City. He told his brother he loved him and Buck did the same.

"You'll be home soon, Pat," said Buck. "It won't be long now. Just be careful in the big town."

"You're kidding, right?" joked Pat.

"What the hell am I thinking? You just escaped Germany and lived off turnips for two months. I think you can handle New York!" laughed Buck.

"Yeah, I think I can handle it," said Pat with a big smile. "But thanks for being concerned."

Pat stepped up with the aid of his cane which brought tears to his brother's eyes once again. As he had done so many times before, Pat paused, turned and gave his brother that big wave across his tall frame then stepped into the first car. Buck watched him walk to his seat through the windows.

"Board!" shouted the conductor who got on the train and signaled to the Engineer. The train pulled away and Buck watched it until the last car was out of the station. His brother was not home yet, but he was clearly on his way. "My, won't mother be excited," he thought to himself, again wiping a few tears with his sleeve.

Nearly every Momence citizen who was home during the day on Saturday January 19, watched impatiently for their newsboy to come by with the Friday edition of the *Momence Progress*. Could it be anymore ironic that the newspaper announcing Pat's arrival was delayed? The weekend snow storm made it impossible for a shipment of paper to reach Momence from Chicago in time and the Friday edition was printed a day late.

Buck had returned home on Tuesday and announced to his mother, family and anyone he could find in town that Pat was really coming home this time. He also told the paper about his impression of Pat since meeting him in Toronto:

"Pat is healing fine. He is still nervous, however, and not yet in normal health. My brother is so happy because of his safe arrival that much of his horrible experience in Europe appears more dreamlike than real. When I spoke of his adventures he was unconcerned, talked little of it at first. Pat's wound is healed."

Word spread in Momence that Pat would arrive on the 9:50 train from Chicago on Tuesday. This created great excitement. Every business in town began sprucing up their storefronts like the Fourth of July. They placed "welcome home" signs in store windows, hung banners adorning their marquis and put up signs indicating that they would be closed all day on Tuesday. Flags of the Allies were mounted on trees and light poles from the depot to the center of town, all flapping rapidly in a cold wind.

Homemade signs of "Welcome Home, Pat," appeared in the windows of many houses and school children were drawing pictures, writing poems and talking feverishly about Pat O'Brien, having never met him.

With over a foot of snow covering the town, young boys hit the streets with their coal shovels offering "professional snow removal services" to any house or store that would pay them a nickel.

Mayor Tiffany's steering committee set the banquet and dance date for Wednesday the 23rd. The paper contained final details of the planned events along with more stories about Pat including his visit with the King, which thrilled everyone. "Momence has a real international hero, now!" was a common statement all over town. Most could hardly believe it was true.

All committees now worked in haste. One hundred people began transforming the Wennerholm Garage into an elegant banquet hall, arranging wall-to-wall seating for 450. The head table would feature men of national and state prominence, as well as military representatives who would be attending. Publisher Houk announced that the newspaper would fully sponsor the Grand Ball after the banquet. It would be held at the South Side Dance Hall. Houk hired the popular Wurlitzer Band for the big event.

A parade was planned to start from the depot, down Railroad Street, west on Front Street through the center of town, to the Clegg Shoe Store where people could greet Pat. The Momence Cornet Band had been in daily rehearsals since Sunday and the superintendent of schools announced that all Momence schools would be closed on Pat's day. Grant Park and the St. George schools also announced closures. Momence had long been a town that always knew how to throw a party – even if during the winter.

Meanwhile, in New York, Pat was meeting with Lee Keedick. The promoter was reviewing Pat's contract with him which included appearances in 40 cities during 1918. Keedick was a major promoter and Pat was surprised at the size and reputation of the venues planned for his speaking tour. "Carnegie Hall?" Pat asked with raised eye brows looking over the list. "Of course!" said Keedick. "You'll fill the house." One week after arriving home, Pat would begin his tour at Orchestra Hall in Chicago and make a second appearance there five days later. Buck had told Pat that Kankakee and Lowell had made requests for speeches in their towns.

"Are these places you know well, Pat?" asked Keedick.

Pat confirmed he consider them all "home" so a clause was written into Pat's agreement allowing Momence, Kankakee, and Lowell to host Pat and keep all receipts. A standard speech was set for all the Keedick events but Pat's hometown presentations could be done as Pat saw fit. Each Keedick speech would last one hour and ten minutes, allowing for questions to complete the two hour format.

The leading speaker in the United States at the time was William Jennings Bryan. He ran for President three times, served as Wilson's secretary of state and was the most popular speaker on the Chautauqua Circuit in 1917. Pat would eventually replace him as the lead money earner on the speaker's circuit in 1918.

Keedick offered Pat a contract that would provide him an income level "just short of what the President of the United States makes," as Keedick put it. After his two appearances in Chicago, he'd speak in a few smaller towns in the Midwest, then head east in February for an extensive East Coast tour including Philadelphia, Boston, New York and Baltimore. He'd be in Oregon and Northern California by June, then Colorado, Texas and Southern California and back to San Francisco by the Fourth of July.

In the evening, Pat sent a letter to Agnes with the dates leading up to his first speech in California.

Dearest Agnes,

What a thrill it is to finally be in the states. I'm in New York now meeting with a promoter who has arranged an extensive speaking tour for me over the next six months. Unfortunately, dear, it looks as though I will not get to California until late summer or fall. I'm sorry.

I know you must be agonizing as I am that I am safe and home, yet we cannot see each other yet. It would be wonderful if you could come east but I know your work schedule does not allow that. Please know that I miss you terribly and have so much to tell you. You're probably reading about my exploits, injuries, and escape in the newspapers. When I see you I will tell you the whole story without the flare that newspapers seem to always add. It was a remarkable experience though. Many parts of it were sad too.

I will write every chance I get. Perhaps also we can plan a phone call in the next few weeks while I'm traveling.

Love, Pat

For Agnes, the letter was full of joy but also much sadness. It hit her hard when she read about Pat's weight loss. That told her more than anything else how tough a time Pat had experienced. She folded the letter and placed it in her purse but only read it one more time. It was a bit too painful to think about. Since Pat was vague as to when he might come west it left her feeling rather helpless, particularly when her friends that knew them both would ask, "Has Pat said when he's coming to Richmond?" She could only answer, "Not yet."

Pat also sent a more cryptic letter to his Santa Fe buddy, Charles Pearl in Richmond:

"Arrived home in the states. Am having an awful-good time. Think I will arrive in Richmond about the 1st of February. Do not expect me till you see me. I will get there as soon as I can. Have a great deal to tell you. Your friend. Pat O'Brien."

On January 21, Pat met with officials from Harper & Brothers in their New York office. He spent some time looking through the draft manuscript that Livingston had done on the ship. Livingston had gone to the New York office from St. John and had been working on the book ever since. Pat was generally pleased. Livingston asked that Pat work on a forward to the book on the way home. Pat suggested a few adjustments in the final draft to Ivan, his editor, and agreed to send the forward to him upon his arrival in Momence.

At 3:00 p.m. Pat's business was done in New York. He signed a good contract with his publisher that would bring great rewards if the book sold. Livingston and his superiors were thrilled. They felt they had a potential best seller on their hands.

Pat stepped off the elevator, proceeded through the lobby and out the door. A chill of excitement rushed through his body. "I'm going home!" he thought. "I'm actually going home now." He walked to Grand Central Terminal where his bag had already been put aboard, checked in at the Pullman counter, walked down the big ramp to track thirty-eight, and stepped on board the Twentieth Century Limited. Five minutes after taking his seat, New York began slipping past his window as the famous express headed west to Chicago.

The Twentieth Century Limited ran as an all-Pullman luxury extra-charge sleeper train with a running time between New York's Grand Central Terminal and Chicago's LaSalle Street Station that was guaranteed or passengers would receive some monetary adjustment for lateness. The train was pulled out of Grand Central by an electric engine to Croton-Harmon at the north end of the Hudson River where the larger single steam locomotive replaced it for the non-stop run to Chicago. It featured plush crimson carpet, rolled out to welcome passengers. The phrase "getting the red carpet treatment" had already entered the American narrative as result of this innovative service.

As the train ran north along the east side of the Hudson River, Pat looked west out his window at the legendary waterway that guided his grandfather Martin into America from Quebec over seventy-five years earlier. Pat studied the Hudson Valley landscape passing Riverdale, Yonkers, Dobbs Ferry, Tarrytown, and Scarborough. Arriving at Harmon, Pat switched to the mighty steam train that crossed the Hudson on a non-stop overnight run to Chicago.

Being a former railroad man, Pat was very interested in the train. He talked to one of the engineers about the use of the "track pan" that allowed the train to replenish its water supply while on the move. The pan scooped up water from a trench between the rails allowing the train to speed non-stop to its destination. Pat's preoccupation with this unique train helped him to keep his mind off the long 960 mile trip home. He got a haircut while on board, another unique feature of the train, and slept in the accommodating sleeper car for about six hours. His trip would take just under twenty hours but Pat O'Brien was, indeed, finally heading home.

Early on Tuesday morning, January 22, Buck met James Kirby, Edwin Chatfield, and James Cleary at the Momence depot on the C&EI. line. Kirby, Chatfield, and Cleary were members of the "O'Brien Steering Committee" and would accompany Buck to the LaSalle Street Station in downtown Chicago to meet Pat's train. It was decided not to meet Pat at Englewood, one of the preliminary stops on the Southside. A number of press would be pouncing on Pat at the LaSalle Station when he arrived in Chicago. Houk had advised the men go there to ease Pat's arrival.

Pat could tell he was entering Northwest Indiana as the Twentieth Century Limited passed South Bend. The snow in some spots was over three feet high but the tracks were clear. About forty-five minutes later, he could see smoke rising ahead and to the right as his train approached Lake County. It was Gary, Indiana. U.S. Steel was belching smoke from its big mills, running full tilt in support of America's effort to dump capacity and strength on the Enemy in Europe.

Pat remembered that the train he was on made use of the New York Central Railroad line through Indiana. As he stared leisurely out the window at the blinding white snow and icy blue Lake Michigan in the distance, it hit him. The New York Central was formerly the old Lake Shore and Michigan Southern Railway line that ran through Gary and right past Miller Beach. "Miller!" Pat said out loud.

Hearing Pat's eruption, gentlemen across the aisle reading their papers looked up. Pat didn't notice and quickly made his way to the exit portico over the coupler area between cars. He earnestly peered out of the tall exit door window.

Suddenly, the beach appeared, then trees flashed by in a blur, then a sand dune far enough away that Pat could follow it with a fixed stare. A split second later the street that led from the tracks though Miller Station and directly to Miller Beach itself appeared clearly, then washed away. It was the street where Octave Chanute had carried his experimental wings through town, startling skeptical locals. It was the beach where years ago Pat stood and lost his hat as the winds gush upward and swept him away into the world of aviation.

Pat stood at the door for five minutes as tears rolled down his face. He had come full circle, from Miller, to West Pullman, to Stockton and the grainfields of California, to North Island and Borden, to England, France and Flanders and then back again, all on the back of a steam train.

Rail, the marvel of 19th Century Industry, had given way to the aeroplane, now mankind's decisive weapon of war. Flight would be the new means of transport for the 20th Century. Pat realized he had played a small role in that transition. He had bridged the two in his life and almost gave up his life doing so. But it struck him that it was his own energy, his arms and legs that walked, swam and climbed through the toughest part of the journey, making his return to Momence ultimately possible.

As Pat felt the tug of the big turn north around the tip of Lake Michigan toward Chicago, he took his seat again for the final leg into the city. His brother Buck and the official Momence welcoming party stood in the lobby of the LaSalle Street Station awaiting its arrival. Buck noticed over twenty men milling around, many were with cameras. Neither Buck nor any of his party revealed who they were at this point. The reporters looked harmless enough.

"Now arriving on track four, the Twentieth Century Limited from New York City. Arriving, track four. Track number four for the Limited," barked the P.A. announcer.

Buck and his party rose and moved toward the doors and onto platform floor to meet Pat. More than two dozen men stood up and followed them onto the platform, as well. James Cleary was startled by their movement and looked back over his shoulder with a confused look.

"I told you it would be chaos," said Buck. "Everyone knows about Pat now." The train pushed into its final position belching a huge amount of steam and hissing when it stopped. Conductors and men with hand trucks scurried about and suddenly, Pat appeared, stepping down off car number two and on to the welcoming red carpet.

"Pat!" shouted Buck as he ran down the platform to greet his brother. As soon as he shouted Pat's name, he knew he'd made a mistake. A crush of reporters passed him up moistening their pencils on their tongues and flipping open dictation pads as they ran.

Pat stood smiling with his cane wedged up against his him, holding his suite case covered full of stickers in his left hand including a large "London" sticker dominating the montage. Buck grabbed Pat's suitcase.

"Welcome home, Pat," said Buck giving his brother a big hug. The two brothers had an emotional exchange then Buck broke the ice saying, "Pat, you know these men, don't you? Chatfield, Cleary, James Kirby?"

Pat nodded, smiled, and shook each man's hand after shifting his cane to his left side, which Edwin Chatfield noticed.

"Welcome home, son," said the distinguished looking Chatfield. "You've got a whole lot of excited folks back home eager to see you."

"Hello, Pat," said Cleary.

As they shook his hand in sequence, reporters started firing questions. Buck held them off and suggested the photographer in front shoot a photo of Pat and his friends from Momence. Buck posed for the photo as well.

Pat answered a few questions for reporters as cameras flashed attracting passengers exiting the train.

"Who is that?" asked a middle-aged woman, walking up from car six.

"It's that O'Brien fellow," said a reporter. "The guy that jumped out of a train and escaped the Germans.

"My word," she said looking back as she kept walking with the throng hurrying off the train.

Pat and the others moved toward platform seven, where the "Nine o'clock C&EI train" was posed to take them to Momence. Reporters followed. Buck hung behind and tipped the Porters telling Pat he'd catch up.

Kirby asked Pat about his trip and how he felt but nothing about his ordeal. The Momence men were sensitive not to bring up what was surely a horrid memory. Pat would reveal those details at the right time and place and thousands of Americans were about to pay good money to hear him tell his story. Momence folk were concerned with Pat's welfare and didn't view him as a celebrity as others did.

"I'll bet you're glad to be home, huh, Pat?" said Kirby, feeling a little embarrassed after stating the obvious.

"Sure am," said Pat.

What was embarrassing to Kirby sounded sincere to Pat. Reporters wanted to know how he escaped as if that question could be answered in one sentence. Friends wanted to know how Pat was faring. Pat appreciated their concern.

When Buck returned, photographers were barking Pat's name, requesting he pose for photos as multiple cameras flashed in irregular sequence. Pat stood motionless with a smile, feeling some discomfort from his long trip. Buck and the others stepped in alongside him. Reporters shouted questions which Pat answered with ease.

"What's your opinion of the Kaiser?" a reporter asked. "He wears a lot of funny looking hats," was Pat's response, which drew a roar.

"What'd the King have to say about your escape, Pat?" asked another? "He said only a Yankee would be a fool enough to jump out of a moving train," Pat answered.

And ultimately, "How did you survive a crash from 8,000 feet?" asked a young reporter.

"I landed on my soft head," retorted Pat with his infectious grin.

The press loved him. Though his physique was obviously ravaged by weeks of eating turnips and living outdoors, his wit, if anything, was sharpened by the disconnection between his weakened appearance and sharp tongue.

After a few more questions and continuous photos, Buck stepped forward, thanked the reporters and steered the Momence contingent onto the lead car. Pat wanted to stretch out and rest a bit so he took a double seat on the right side. Buck sat two seats up on the left. Kirby and Cleary sat across from Buck and Chatfield one seat up from them. They wanted to let Pat rest. Buck was able to sit sideways, converse with the others and keep an eye on his brother. He looked back and Pat was holding his hat, eyes closed with his head resting against the frozen window.

"Board!" shouted the conductor and the train pulled out of LaSalle Street Station on time. The car Pat was riding in was seventy-five percent full. Once the train was rolling nearly half the train flipped up the front page of their Chicago paper and there was Pat's picture. Buck noticed it right away and rolled his eyes. Pat might not get the rest he needed on this trip.
Sure enough the entire car began to stir and Buck could see many looking back at his brother who was still resting with his eyes closed.

Sitting in the front of the car was a woman from Chicago named Mary Helen Bolden. She had read in the Chicago paper about Pat's story and saw his photo. She was able to track down which train he would ride to Momence and was confirming Pat's identity to everyone around her. Whispering and pointing increased until finally two men came over to Pat who sat up noticing them. They extended their hand and congratulated him on his feet. Pat was cordial, smiled, and soon had a number of passengers around him.

"So much for that cat nap," thought Buck. He looked at Chatfield and they both shook their heads and smiled.

Ms. Bolden was in a huddle with three other women informing them of who Pat was. All four were agog with Pat's presence and giggling like the young lasses had in Pat's youth. They debated getting up and meeting Pat when a big man with a cigar overheard their conversation and said, "It's war time, ladies. It's fully proper to pay homage to the young man".

In these days, women were still cautious about "being forward" when approaching men. The man's comments were plenty for them and they rose and walked toward the crowd that had now gathered around Pat. The ladies joined the men in conversation and all of them asked him questions. Pat actually rose and invited the ladies to sit. They insisted he sit, which he did.

At Chicago Heights a pretty auburn-haired gal boarded the train and rushed to Pat saying, "Do you remember me?" Pat smiled and thoughtfully stroked his chin with a smile saying only, "Are you coming down?" The girl responded, "I will if I can. Mother is already in Momence." The young lady could hardly breathe.

At Beecher, a man Pat's age in overalls came on and walked up to Pat. "Hello, Pat, sorry I'm in work clothes," the man said. "Good to see you back," he said. Pat knew the man from his youth and the entire coach enjoyed watching their reunion.

As the train pushed south, word spread of the special passenger on board. At each stop, exiting passengers could be heard telling boarding passengers, "Pat O'Brien's on this train." The result was a constant flow of people through Pat's car slowing only once the train exited the suburban south and crossed into Kankakee County.

Chapter 35

Home at Last

Six miles north of Momence the trained slowed and came to a full stop at Grant Park, Illinois. Buck had received a telegram requesting that the train stop a bit longer so Pat could appear on the platform and speak to locals. The railroad agreed to stop.

The two towns have common roots, not the least of which is the countryside between them which includes Yellowhead and Momence Townships where Martin and Daniel once had farms. Grant Park families had family in Momence and, of course, the reverse was also true. Pat would speak to his Grant Park "cousins" in the same tone he'd speak in Momence.

He walked onto the platform waving to the huge crowd that had gathered to see their local hero. The applause and cheering was the loudest sound ever heard in the small town according to old timers in attendance. Pat said a few words, thanked everyone for coming out on such a cold day and told everyone how honored he was that they wanted to see him. The crowd was perfectly silent and Pat's voice cut through the cold air with emotion. He waved and turned back to the train as applause went up. It was just applause but very full sounding and stunning to the emotions. No yelling, no yelping. In truth, many were too choked up to speak. But for some reason, the pure pulsating clapping in the cold air sounded more authentic than the type of cheer normally associated with political speeches. It sounded very much like a massive flock of mallards had suddenly lifted off the Kankakee River, startled by the presence of danger.

As the train pulled out again, the people in Pat's car took their seats and Pat walked down the center aisle to his seat with the aid of the overhead racks on both sides. He didn't have his cane but the baggage rack was no stranger to Pat. As he took a new grip of the rack with each step he gave it an emotional squeeze reflecting upon how firmly the mounted luggage rack had helped him exit from a German train. Today, it helped him get to his seat and prepare to walk out freely from an American train and see his family and hometown once again.

As the train came into view at Momence almost 3000 men, women and children crushed up against the small station where Pat had once waved goodbye to his mother, sister Clara, and longtime buddy Al Fontaine the previous May when he left for England.

The steam engine drifted to a slow stop and blew its whistle sending up cheers as the Momence Cornet Band struck up "The Empire March." Buck exited first and confirmed with a nod to his mother that Pat was coming. Pat was somewhat stunned and a little embarrassed. He hesitated, then rose and walked to the end of the car preparing to exit the train onto the familiar platform where he had boarded old Gus' train so many times in his youth. Suddenly, the whole scene was as foreign to him as the train stop at Ghent. To see so many people there to greet him was overwhelming and a surprise. Though he knew everyone there, they were bundled up in the face of one of the coldest and snow-filled winters in memory. Pat stood at the door and a cheer when up along with a flourish of flags waving overhead as everyone stretched to see the Momence hero.

Margaret O'Brien, sisters Clara and Lila, brothers Perry and "Bud"(Clarence), Elmer from California, "Mulligan" (Ivan), and the other members of the O'Brien clan had been positioned nearest the train car door and stood eagerly awaiting Pat's appearance. As the brakes squealed their last arrest of the train at the depot, the door opened and there he was. He hopped his way quickly over to his mother with the help of his cane. Only a few did not choke up at this site. He fell into her arms as cheers swelled.

"My big, big boy," cried Margaret. "Mother," Pat responded as both cried during their short, private moment. One could see Pat shaking emotionally and Margaret was also physically shaken. Clara clutched Pat's left arm and the other family members crushed close together as another huge cheer went up, warming the cold January air. Bud noticed the walking stick dangling from Pat's right arm as he held his mother. He quickly grabbed it so it would not fall and Pat was more than adequately held up by loving family. He looked up at Cleary who was standing close by. Pat had a big smile on his face and his eyes were full of tears which cause Cleary to become emotional as well.

The applause and cheering lasted throughout the family embrace and most everyone felt a mixture of joy and pride. Youngsters continued waving their small American flags and glanced up at the parents who were expressing seldom seen and uncharacteristic joy. More than one child was confused by the presence of tears in what was obviously a joyous moment. But such are the lessons learned by youth.

[417]

Margaret and Pat turned and faced nearly the entire town that had assembled. The crowd extended across Railroad Street, up onto the porch of the Columbus House hotel and down 2nd, 3rd and 4th streets trailing away from the rail center. An even louder cheer went up and the Silver Cornet Band of Momence struck up "Hail, Hail, the Gang's All Here" drowning out the school children who has just begun singing "Columbia, the Gem of the Ocean" in honor of the new Momence hero. Pat waved, Margaret was still overwhelmed but had a big smile on her face, dabbing tears all the same.

As the band faded and the kids continued to sing, Momence men could be heard shouting, "Speech! Speech!" Pat turned to his brother Bud, "Tell them I can't talk, Bud, – sore throat, cold, anything." Bud nodded raising his hands to silent the crowd as Pat whispered to him, "Fact is, I'm scared to death."

Bud explained that Pat was exhausted from his trip and would have plenty to say later but, for now, he was nursing a cold and wanted to save the talking for later. Pat and Margaret stood side-by-side and Pat was supporting his weight with his cane again on his right side. The band and others carrying flags walked up Railroad Street a half block to position for the planned four-block parade to the center of town. Dozens of men with shovels, trucks and a few horse-pulled plows had risen at dawn to clear the street of the large amount of snow that had fallen over the last two days.

The huge crowd pushed forward and many of the older Momence residents were crowding up to shake Pat's hand. He smiled his classic smile and tried to answer their questions, with one arm always around his mother. Buck was carrying Pat's bags, while two railroad men loaded other passenger items onto a wagon. The plan was to parade down Railroad Street to Front Street and march straight through town to Clara's store. The Clegg's had a large apartment above the store.

"Durn my hide, ye got a mustache!" said Frank Demack.

"Once I chased you out of my strawberry patch," barked Boula Nichols. "You flew some then, too!" she added as a big laugh washed over those who could hear the comment.

Most quietly shook Pat's hand and spoke affectionately. "Welcome home Pat."

Margaret reached up and patted Pat's cheek, finding it hard to believe her son was actually home. "They said you were killed," she said softly, still amazed he was home. Pat spoke alternately to his brothers and relatives as the crowd pulled back, allowing them to step down from the platform. Just as Pat got to the steps, a big cheer went out from the farmers in horse drawn bobsleds tucked into the parameter of the crowd. Pat waved and they cheered. A few mothers quickly grabbed their overly excited youngsters who were jumping up and down on the bouncy spring seats of the family sled. Suddenly, the band struck up "The Thunderer March" by Sousa and a parade began to form in their wake.

Pat, his mother, and Clara stepped into the awaiting car that would take him uptown. As they pulled away, the entire town followed and bobsleds fell in behind the walkers. When they got in front of the Clegg Shoe Store the procession stopped. Pat and his family went inside the shoe store and most of the parade came through to say hello to Pat. He greeted a number of old acquaintances, shaking hands for nearly two hours.

Knowing Pat was getting tired and seeing the line through the store thin a bit, Clara stood up on one of her checkout counters and spoke to the crowd.

"Hello, everyone, can I have your attention?" she said. "Hello, all!" she repeated. Elmer pressed two fingers against his lip and added a loud whistle. The crowd turned and looked toward Clara.

"My mother and our family want to thank everyone for coming out and greeting our brother today and making it such a wonderful day for all of us. As you know, tomorrow will be a big day of celebration and Pat has been traveling such a long way. So we'd like to thank you all again and ask that you let us retire now so Pat can rest. We will see everyone tomorrow and are so grateful for the expressions of love you have given our brother today."

A large cheer went up and folks began to drift from the store, a few turning back and waving to Pat or touching his arm as they passed with kind phrases and final welcome home gestures. The store was empty in ten minutes and the O'Brien's retired up stairs to relax in Clara's apartment and have some lunch.

After lunch, Pat took a short nap. About 2:00 p.m. he and his brother Mulligan spent a few hours visiting some older citizens who were not up to greeting Pat at the train depot. They were all people that Pat knew well and it brought him great joy to see their grateful reaction to his visit. After their last stop they were greeted by two little girls returning from a trip to the candy store. One had three pieces of candy. She extended her hand up to Pat and said, "Here, Lieutenant Pat, you can have all I got." Pat thanked her but said she could keep her candy. The second more bashful little girl added, "I'd give you mine, too, Mr. O'Brien, if I had any." Pat smiled and thanked the girls and then handed them both a nickel. They turned and ran off, thrilled.

That night, one of the happiest dinners in the life of the O'Brien's warmed Clegg's apartment where all had gathered. It was like a delayed Christmas for the whole family. The bright yellow lights could be seen burning late into the evening and anyone passing by heard waves of laughter push against the walls of Clara's apartment as if the building might burst.

Pat was able to sleep until 11:00 a.m. the next day. The night before Margaret told her family and some close friends to stay home in the morning and "let Pat sleep." He did. Bud and a few other O'Brien grandchildren "stood watch" at the store to gracefully turn away any visitors or press that stopped by to see Pat. Most understood. Just before lunch a big bag of mail was delivered to the Clara's home much to the surprise of everyone. Pat's story was becoming rapidly known everywhere.

Following lunch, Pat sat comfortably with his family and clusters of Momence citizens began to mingle uptown, anticipating the largest community event in the history of the town. Around 2:30, Clara O'Brien Clegg walked steadily down the sidewalk on the north side of Front Street with her head down to brace January's cold western wind. She was carrying a bag of groceries in her right arm, partially blocking the frigid winter from her face. She and Margaret had decided to "pick up a few things" for what would surely be a busy week for the O'Briens

As she stepped past the corner building at Range and Front streets, she could hear the voices of a large crowd to her right. Lowering her grocery bag, she was stunned to see nearly two hundred people all huddled at the end of the block in the cold, waiting to enter Wennerholm's Garage. "My word," she said. "The banquet doesn't start for three hours!"

Scalpers, mostly from out of town, were offering as much as $20 for the $1.25 admission ticket but there were no sellers among the Momence citizenry. There were probably more automobiles in town than anyone had seen since the first Jackson appeared. Strangers in suits with note pads and an occasional camera in tow were quizzing locals about what they knew about Pat O'Brien. Schools were closed for the day so a good number of Momence children were milling about with their intuitive sense of excitement, not fully certain of its source. Businesses opened bright and early that morning to "greet the public" and possibly experience the first boom of Pat O'Brien fame.

Those fortunate enough to have a ticket for the banquet were amazed at the lights and colors which transformed the Wennerholm Garage into an elegant banquet hall. Streamers and banners of red, white, and blue along with a large number of small American and British Flags adorned the entire arched ceiling overlooking settings of silver on white linen table cloths and a beautiful centerpiece on every table. Ladies in gowns from Momence and cities all over Illinois and Indiana adorned the hall that, in the end, welcomed 500 attendees, forcing many to stand and straining the capacity of the big hall.

People were in their seats by 6:15 when suddenly Pat appeared in the back of the Hall preceded by Mayor Tiffany and Margaret on Pat's arm. There was silence for a moment and then a burst of cheering and clapping erupted that seemed to push the walls out. Margaret took a seat up front with family and Pat was escorted to a large head table at the back of the hall where fifteen Momence boys were at attention, carrying the national colors. The banner behind the table had Pat's name followed by a bright star with an American flag on the left end and the Momence honor roll extending to the right represented by 103 stars of the Momence heroes who had died in battle since the great insurrection. Once Pat was seated, Reverend R. M. Wood gave an invocation that most would not soon forget.

Young ladies volunteering from the Red Cross under the guidance of the Momence Women's Relief Corps served a dinner consisting of a Fricassee of Chicken, mashed potatoes, hot rolls, and dessert.

Following dinner, speeches ensued. Mayor Tiffany declared that "Pat O'Brien has brought honor to the city and to the State of Illinois. He proved himself true in all the traditions of his blood and his country." He went on. The mayor read a letter from Governor Lowden who also sent regrets he could not attend. Henry R. Rathbone, notable Chicago attorney and future U.S. congressman gave a stirring speech.

But finally, the crowd became extremely hushed in anticipation of Pat's speech to his hometown. The Master of Ceremonies attorney, E.P. Harney, gave a stirring introduction of Pat saying his "valor has earned him the everlasting gratitude of this country." But then he concluded his lofty words with an introduction that could only be given in Momence.

"Little Pat who carried water for contractor Clark when he built the brick building on Front Street, mischievous Pat who was a lovable trial to his grade school teachers, young Pat who didn't have time to bother much with high school books and who left home at 15 to find his life, Pat who had a way with "Colleen" and manner of respect with gentlemen, Pat, the son of the fighting O'Briens, has returned. Ladies and Gentleman, one of our own, Lt. Pat O'Brien!"

The entire hall rose to their feet in a roar of applause and cheering that was reminiscent of the reception Pat had received from his fellow soldiers in London. After easily three minutes, the crowd hushed again and Pat spoke his first words.

"I am not going to say 'Ladies and Gentlemen' but I am simply going to say 'friends," Pat began as the audience smiled in silence. "First of all, I must say that I am so happy to be back in the best town in the world, my birthplace." This brought emotional applause. "I will not say a lot about the war since time does not allow but I will tell you only of my escape and perhaps that is what you wish." Most nodded in agreement. "I should tell you all, however, that I am restricted to some degree in what I can say in terms of naming names or mentioning some specifics about locations and other matters but for the most part you'll hear how fortunate I am to be back here with you once again."

Pat told of his battle above the clouds, when six machines held off twenty-two and how a machine gun in an enemy plane rattled bullets at him and finally placed one into his teeth. He talked about Courtrai and the conditions of the great prison including the torturous dogs. He gave details of his jump from the train, many swims, close calls, and agonizing errors he made during his long trek to freedom. He gave details of his time in Brussels, though he never mentioned the city, and related his encounters with poor and friendly people of Belgium and Holland. Many would smile and shake their heads as they heard of his makeshift weapons, diving for his shoes, walking for miles in mud and drinking water from dew dripping off vegetation in the fields. Faces were equally stern when Pat revealed his disdain for the Huns and how important Allied resolve must be to finally defeat the enemy.

There was more than one teary eye in the audience as he told the tale of his good friend Paul and the number of pilots who flew into the hell of aerial warfare. In truth, most were saddened just thinking that such a fresh young optimistic "kid" like Pat O'Brien, from their town, could give so much, and brave such odds and pay what was obviously such a physical price for the cause of freedom and peace in the world. For everyone who heard Pat in the hall that night, the realities of Europe were now brought home and made personal.

He also talked about how much he thought of home during his long journey to freedom. In no time, the attentive audience was struck by his gift as an orator. Pat never stumbled or looked confused. He displayed his intuitive talent for storytelling with emphasis and pause in all the right places as if trained in the art of persuasion. "He just has it," whispered James Cleary to his wife. The look on her face was evidence enough that she fully concurred.

Had anyone in the hall that night heard Pat's speeches in London, they would have been struck by how different his language and style was in this presentation tonight. He talked as he would only talk at home, in a trusted setting, in language that he and everyone present fully understood.

"I fought like the devil, for I thought I was a "goner" anyway. I knew if I ran for it I would about fetch up in No Man's Land, which is no place to fetch up, and I was popping it to 'm whenever I could get a line on a Hun, when I got this," showing them his ragged scar hidden by his mustache and for which he wore a gold strip on his sleeve. "Well, I felt the blow all right, and for the millionth part of a second I thought, 'I've got mine." The next thing I knew I waked up next morning in a German hospital just east of Ypres. There was a big push and they had field hospitals everywhere and we were five miles back of their lines."

And finally, he told of the agonizing breach of the dreaded electronic fence, describing his near electrocution when his back pocket, bulging with the Belgian lace brought home to his mother the day before, nearly touched the live wire in his first attempt to crawl under the fence. Margaret gasped, then broke out in laughter with the rest of the hall, demonstrating that while Pat was a natural comedian she was a downright natural as a "straight man."

Once the laughter died down, he went on in a more serious tone. "I reached Holland and then and there knelt and thanked God for His mercy," he said.

It was an enthralling, nearly hypnotizing presentation. More than one caught themselves holding their breath at certain points. Most would say it was the most powerful speech they had heard in their life. Upon the conclusion of his speech, a great pent-up level of awe, enthusiasm, and respect erupted into an outburst of applause and cheering, louder than before. For many, the collective roar of the people in the hall that night not only acknowledged Pat's great achievement but made men and women reflect on Momence itself and how a favorite son sometimes needs to leave, achieve greatness and return in order to teach a small town what it forges in the souls of those who draw from it.

To close the evening the Reverend Fathers J.W. Maguire and W.J. Bergen, both noted speakers from St. Viator's College, delivered short orations. Father Maquire gave a glowing tribute to Maggie saying, "I know that as long as there are women like Mrs. O'Brien, the future of the world is secure!" It drew cheers from the crowd and tears from the O'Brien children including Pat. Master of Ceremonies Harney thanked the speakers, the ladies of the Red Cross and everyone who had anything to do with the magnificent success of the memorial evening. A large part of the crowd left shortly for the South Side Hall to attend the patriotic dance in honor of Pat. Those not attending milled about and a few were able to say hello to Pat before leaving.

"The *Momence Progress* Welcomes Pat!" was the large red and gold banner greeting first arrivals inside the South Side Hall not fifteen minutes after the end of the banquet. The hall was decorated with large American flags and draped tables with patriotic colors lined the parameter of the large dance floor.

The Whirlitzer Band was already playing when the first few arrived. Dancing began right away while Pat and his family were still shaking hands at the banquet. There were fox trots, one-steps, two-steps, circle two steps, and waltzes played one after another to the thrill of all who attended.

About forty minutes into the evening, Pat and his family arrived and the floor was cleared for their entrance. Pat walked in arm-in-arm with his sister Clara as they lead the Grand March into the hall to long applause. Margaret looked on with great joy as the floor cleared and Pat danced with his sister to officially begin the night. Pat requested the one step, mainly because the more rapid dances brought pain to his side. All eyes were on the returning hero and his loving sister. Speeches were over, stories of war's horror mute, and the profound meaning of it all would pause for now. It was time to celebrate one of life's finer moments, the safe return of one once thought lost.

[424]

In the grand tradition of Momence revelry going back to its beginnings, the South Side Hall was engaged until 6:00 a.m. Pat had speeches in the morning in Kankakee so he bid farewell around midnight. Mr. Cleary volunteered to drive Pat and Margaret back to Clara's where the two talked for another hour before calling it a night.

Chapter 36

First Days Home

As treacherous and uncertain as 1917 was for Pat O'Brien, 1918 would be one of the best years of his young life. He would be hailed as a national hero, find his book *Outwitting the Hun* on the best seller list, speak to thousands of people in nearly every major venue in the United States, and become a rich man. Noted Momence citizen Edmond Chipman, who founded the city's first library, stated in the *Momence Progress* that, "Pat O'Brien will make more money in 1918 than I made in my entire career."

Pat's first few speeches at home would be more like meeting old friends than "profiting while other soldiers are sacrificing," as Reverend Alvin P. Howells of Centralia, Illinois would later snipe in his newspaper. Pat O'Brien was destined to become a major celebrity but he was still "Pat" at home.

After a heartwarming and emotional first day in Momence, followed by a late night visit with Margaret and the entire O'Brien family, Pat rose early Thursday morning in Clara Clegg's large second floor apartment over the shoe store. Most of the family was still asleep. He shuffled his way into Clara's kitchen to brew some coffee. Every other step was pulsated with the thud of his cane hitting the wooden floor. Margaret opened her eyes suddenly hearing the unfamiliar sound. After a moment she realized what she was hearing and tears filled her eyes.

Arriving at the sink, Pat began filling the coffee pot with water. He thought of how wonderful the simple joy of brewing a pot of coffee at home truly was. A yellowish-red hue entered the east window of the kitchen announcing dawn and he stood listening to sounds outside. He thought of his youthful days tobogganing the hills at Six Mile Grove. He pictured the crystal glare of frost brought to life by sunrise glancing across the marsh. Just then the first bright light glistened off the edge of the building across the street, catching his eye as water spilled over the top of the pot and ended his thoughts.

"What a day it was yesterday," he whispered quietly to himself. It was the first time he had had a chance to relax since stepping off the train the day before.

"Good morning," said Margaret in a soft tone, tying off her robe as she stepped on to the chilly linoleum floor. She walked over to her son and put both arms around his waist from behind, laying her head on his back.

"Are you sure you're Pat O'Brien?" she said in a humorous tone. "You feel a little skinny for my Pat." Pat chuckled quietly. "I better make some pancakes and sausage and get some meat back on this skinny frame you've got here."

Pat turned and gave his mother a hug and then took a seat at the kitchen table. Margaret pulled her big frying pan from the cabinet and dropped a chunk of lard in the center, turning on the gas. They engaged in idle chatter about the previous day's events while drinking coffee.

"Do I smell coffee?" Buck said entering the room.

"Yeah, and mom's making pancakes," responded Pat.

"Oh, hell, I ate so much yesterday, I don't think I could eat a sesame seed," said Buck.

Buck grabbed a cup of coffee and joined Pat and Margaret at the kitchen table. Soon others were stirred by the smell of pancakes and the kitchen was teeming with O'Briens all chatting about the day before.

"Big day today, Pat," said Buck.

"Yeah, I hope I get through it," responded Pat.

"I wish you could rest today, Pat," added Clara. "I hate for to you rush off already without a day to rest. Such a long day, too," she said rubbing her hand across Pat's back.

After breakfast Buck was to drive Pat to Kankakee for a full day of speeches and appearances. The day was planned by attorney C.M. "Clay" Buntain who founded the Kankakee Rotary Club. He was their first President and also had a hand in forming the Illinois Bar Association. Buntain was originally from Momence and was a logical host for Pat's Kankakee appearances. Pat, Buck, and Al, who planned to spend the day with Pat, left for Momence at about 8:30 a.m.

All of Kankakee was abuzz in anticipation of Pat's appearance. The day started with an informal reception at the Elks' Club at nine, attended by Kankakee's leading citizens. Clay Buntain was a gracious host and felt a genuine pride introducing Momence's favorite son. Pat's first speech of the day was scheduled for 3:00 p.m. at the First Presbyterian Church on Court Street. By two-o'clock there was standing room only available in the church.

When Pat entered the church with Buntain, a respectful standing ovation greeted him as he walked up the center aisle. The folks in Kankakee were excited to have such a celebrity in town but didn't know him as a boy, as did Momence. Pat could tell it was a different crowd than Momence. Something made them feel less connected, perhaps more formal. It instinctively generated in him an urgency to "deliver," a term he had learned from Keedick in New York. As the applause continued, Pat turned and faced the audience, smiling and nodding left and right, occasionally lifting his cane to point to someone he noticed in the hall. Finally, the ovation dissipated and people took their seats. Reverend David Creighton said a prayer and Buntain followed with an introduction.

"Ladies and Gentlemen, today we welcome Lt. Pat O'Brien to our city. It is a special privilege for me to introduce him since he is from Momence. All the country has learned of his fantastic escape from the Hun. It is a miracle that he is here with us today to tell his story. Please welcome Lt. Pat O'Brien."

Pat stepped to the center as all eyes studied his cane and irregular gait. After thanking Buntain and other dignitaries present, he launched into his presentation. As he got to the part where he crossed the Holland border, he noticed how tense the audience had become. For the first time, he noticed their faces, each expressing an intense focus on his words, some shaking their heads. Like any good orator, he toyed with the pacing and emphasis of every word. The Kankakee speech was becoming his first truly professional presentation. He was not distracted by a large number familiar faces, flooding his mind with memories, dulling the focus of his story.

He presented a nonstop, hour and fifteen minute presentation that enthralled every person present. Visible reactions to his speech sharpened his articulation, his pace, and emphasis. His ability to stir the emotions of his audience was something seldom seen in small towns such as Kankakee.

By the end of his presentation, emotions, applause and cheers were equal to any Pat had heard since his first talk to his fellow soldiers in London. His pacing was so well timed that his final "thank you" comment was drowned out by a roar and standing ovation that pressed against him.

It was quite an experience for his audience. It was a learning experience for Pat. As he stepped back, acknowledging the applause, he pictured himself standing on the stage of Orchestra Hall in Chicago in eight days. The audience in Chicago would know even less of him than his Kankakee neighbors. He'd have to really deliver his speech next week. He marked the experience as he exited the church escorted by Buntain and a committee of eight men.

For dinner, Pat was guest of the Kankakee Rotary Club at McBroom's Café across from the Majestic Theater. The evening speech at the Majestic would be his major public presentation of the day. At dinner he made some brief comments, then turned to Buntain to mention he was a little tired. The distinguished lawyer empathetically explained to the guests that Pat would take questions while seated. Following a number of questions, the small group rose and gave Pat a heartfelt ovation. He was forthrightly made a life-time member of Rotary in a formal ceremony and the group headed across the street.

The Majestic was the prime theater in Kankakee and anyone that could get their hands on a ticket to Pat's presentation was there, arriving early as was the case in the afternoon. The theater was busting at the seams. Pat, sensing the serious and anxious tenor of the audience opened with a story about the Kaiser's request in 1914 to the United States War Department to recruit one thousand German American's over to help Germany conquer the French. Most everyone listened intently and Pat knew he had his audience set. Pat went on.

"When the Kaiser received a negative response from the United States, he wired back saying, "Send one Irishman instead!" The crowd roared. From then on Pat had them in the palm of his hand and he tossed emotions back and forth between the intensity of his story and humor that punctuated the tension of his escape.

Prior to concluding he introduced Clara and some of his brothers who were in attendance, then raised his cane overhead saying, "Good Night!" A ten minute ovation ensued, this time many eyes were filled with tears, and men shouted "hurrahs" throughout the applause. Pat had come to Kankakee as a celebrity who happened to be from Momence, considered the second city by those in Kankakee. By the end of the day, all of Kankakee considered him their own. Yet, Pat was more than a local hero. Since the U.S. had entered the war, there were many local heroes. Pat's story transcended all of these. Kankakee came to realize this that night at the Majestic Theatre.

Pat's last local speech before his national tour began was at the Grand Theatre in Lowell, Indiana the next night. Lowell, too, adopted the young hero as their own. To a great degree, Pat's ties to Lowell were stronger than those in Kankakee. He had spent many days visiting his oldest sister Lila O'Brien Worley there. The Hathaways had strong ties to Lowell and Margaret visited often after her sisters moved to Wyoming.

Before the evening's festivities, Pat and his mom visited Lila on her farm six miles southeast of Lowell. Lila was 43 at the time and the oldest of the O'Brien children. Pat's brother Perry came down from Gary where he was working in the tin plate mills. Clarence and Ivan, who lived in Momence, also made the trip as did Clara. Even though a bad storm hit that night, causing Indiana Lieutenant Governor Edgar Bush to cancel the trip from Indianapolis, there was a "monster crowd" according to the local paper.

In a special box draped in flags of the Allied nations sat Margaret, regularly dabbing tears from her eyes. Bert Viant made a miniature Aeroplane with propeller that hung in the middle of the room at the Grand Hotel. Gladys Brown sang "Pat O'Brien," a song she wrote herself, along with two additional local debutants. Finally, A.M. Fuller presented Pat with his third gold watch in three days. The night's event generated $500 for the Red Cross.

Pat mentioned that some of the happiest times of his youth were spent in Lowell and thanked the people of Lowell from the bottom of his heart. But as in his appearances to date, the highlight of the evening came from Pat's words, profoundly delivered in a way that only a tested young man of strong will and patriotism could deliver. All in attendance were equally moved and stirred to patriotism as a result of his speech.

Pat spent the next two days relaxing and visiting friends in Momence. On January 28, he would speak to the school children at St. Pat's Academy. That morning, he and his mother walked up the steep stairs to the convent entrance where the sisters lived. Pat made use of his cane and the handrail and Margaret looked on with some concern.

"Can you make it, honey?" she said.

"Sure, mom, if I can walk 250 miles I can make it up these fifteen steps," he said laughing. Margaret still looked up at him with concern. The sisters were awaiting his arrival and suddenly the door opened. It was the Mother Superior.

"Welcome to St. Patrick's, Lieutenant. Hello, Mrs. O'Brien," she said.

Pat and his mother entered the big parlor on the right and were greeted by a number of senior sisters of the order. St. Patrick's Academy had both high school and grade school students from town but also featured a boarding school made up of Chicago children. After a cordial welcome, the party moved to the recital hall where students and staff had gathered to hear Pat speak.

To begin the program, the entire student body rose and sang the "Star Spangled Banner." It moved Pat to hear the young students sing so well. Ms. Bernadette Suprenant began the program with a welcome for Pat.

"We hail you as a hero of the American Nation. In the ardent manifestation of patriotism which everywhere greets you, we are proud to welcome you in our simple way and we thank you for condescending to visit St. Patrick's Academy."

"We all know that in our land something more is required to constitute a prince than being born under a palace roof. Honorable parentage or wealth is not sufficient to place the royal crown upon a head. It is only by mighty effort and persevering toil that one can reach the heights of fame and hang out his name to shine in the bright galaxy of national glory. Here we have no heirs apparent to the crown. The great men of America are self-made. Nineteen-eighteen may have in store many memorable occurrences but the event which will leave a lasting impression in our hearts is the celebration of the return of our hero – Lieutenant Patrick O'Brien."

After Miss Surprenaut's address, Lieutenant O'Brien was presented a large bouquet of flowers by Bernard Altendorf. Pat also received a box of candy and a Catholic button inscribed in Latin, "Adveniat Reguum Tuum." Translated it means "Thy Kingdom Come." A poem, "America's Call," was then recited by Frank Demack, after which Leonard Burns sang a solo, "America, Here's My Boy." Everybody joined in on the chorus.

Pat told the students of his adventure and all were amazed at the story. Regularly during his presentations, one or two nuns could be seen making the sign of the cross in disbelief. Some of the older girls cried a bit as they gave him a standing ovation. One 2nd grader paused on the way out the door, turning to Pat and giving him a brisk salute. It was the nuns dabbing their eyes at this point.

The next day, Pat walked north up Range street toward the Central School which could be seen towering over the tree tops of all Momence. Even as a man of twenty-seven, he, like most, had a little apprehension returning to the old school where many of his teachers still taught the basics. Had he been an exceptional scholar he might have felt a little different. He was a "loveable menace" as his grade school teachers recounted since he left.

"Who's in charge these days?" Pat said to his brother Buck who was accompanying him to the school.

"Ma says a lady named Hardy," said Buck. "Miss Alice Hardy."

"Is she cute?" Pat asked.

"Oh, hell, Pat, you'd be wise to be on your best behavior on this visit, don't yah think?" responded Buck. They both laughed

"Don't worry, Buck, I'll act like a good soldier," Pat said with a laugh giving his brother a hearty salute. Pat was in full uniform. As he passed the Methodist Church and crossed Third Street he caught a glimpse of the old familiar fenced in playground. The corner "step through," as the kids used to call it, was essentially a "gate" with shoots of pine boards "planted" in such a way to let the kids in and out but keep the animals out.

"Gee, look at that Buck. They still have the 'step through.' I don't see any cows walking the street these days, do you?" said Pat.

"You know how it is, Pat. Nothing changes" said Buck.

Pat looked up as they stepped into the yard. He could see dozens of faces all pressed against the tall glass panes of all three floors where every teacher from 1st grade on had determined it impossible to make the kids sit following lunch. Nearly the entire school was peering out of the windows looking for the almost unbelievable hero from their home town. Pat O'Brien was first on the agenda for the afternoon. As Pat and his brother got closer they could see faces suddenly pull away like targets in an arcade, all obviously hurrying to take their seats, eager to be dismissed to the big room where Pat would speak to the entire student body.

Pat and Buck walked up the steep stairs to the first floor where they were greeted by a few teachers and Miss Hardy. They walked into her office and Pat could see a number of students following each other in an orderly fashion up the stairs to the third floor, all looking back with startled looks to gawk at the famous Pat. Most of the teachers found it hard not to take a peak themselves as teachers urged their students up the stairs at a safe pace.

"Welcome, Lieutenant!" stated Alice Hardy smiling having known Pat most of his life. "Thanks, Miss Hardy," returned Pat equally formally quite tongue and cheek.

"As you can see Pat, the children are very excited to hear you speak. I must say it's been a challenge to teach much this morning, what with all the stir and all," she said.

"Seems like I recall causing the same stir years ago when I was student!" said Pat.

Laughing, Miss Hardy confirmed, "Indeed you did, Pat! Come, let's go. I think they are ready."

The three walked up to the hall where the young students were positioned on the floor sitting like Indians. The older students had chairs and most of the high school age students stood around the perimeter.

"As I said at the banquet to your folks this week, I will not say ladies and gentlemen, but friends," started Pat. "Before I tell you about my adventures in the war, I want to say first that if I had known what was waiting for me at Momence I don't know whether I would have gotten off the train at Chicago or not."

The older kids chuckled but the young ones just kept watching this "bigger than life" soldier in uniform before them. Pat went on, "I want to thank you all for the royal reception accorded me at the depot upon my arrival home." This drew wild applause and even young children joined in with excitement. "Now I'd like to tell you a few things about my time in Europe and how I escaped after crashing my aeroplane."

Pat proceeded to give an exciting account of his experiences. Many times the entire room gasped as he told of the dog fight in the air, his jumping for the train and, of course, his near death experience crawling under the electronic fence. Pat told a few tales of his days at the Central School which thrilled the children to no end. Each high school age boy was in awe of Pat and, as might be expected, the high school girls were all enraptured with his presence.

One of the more touching questions he received was from a tiny first grader sitting on the floor in the front with legs crossed. The little girl asked Pat, "Why do you carry that stick?" It was, of course, Pat's cane which he had to use to get around. "Just in case I run into a skunk on the way home, I want it to whack him before he gives me a spray!" retorted Pat which brought on a burst of laughter from the entire school.

With that, Miss Hardy asked the children to thank Lt O'Brien for speaking to the school on this special day. They all stood and applauded him. Pat asked if he might stand at the door and greet each student. Miss Hardy agreed and he shook the hand of every student as they left the hall. Not one boy or girl at Momence School that day would ever forget the visit of Pat O'Brien.

At 6:15 that evening, forty-five year old Fred Nichols arrived at Clara's apartment to pick up Pat. A group of local men and members of the Medinah Shriners Club in Chicago had invited Pat to have a stag dinner in his honor at the Nichols home. Pat's history of being enamored by both the young lass and men of principle held true. As much as the gathering was comprised of some of Momence's leading citizens, Pat felt relaxed to be with a small group of trusted friends he had known his entire life. He had been a Shriner since his days in California, so natural fraternal bonds were in play as well.

In addition to Fred Nichols, Charles Astle, Clyde Tabler, Doctors Shronts and Bartt, as well as C.H. Hallinger were in attendance. Also attending was seventy-three year old Henry Tallmadge, grandfather of Toby, Pat's newly adopted son. Pat gave Henry a copy of a letter from Toby he had brought with him. It explained the particulars of Pat adopting Toby who was serving for the American Hospital in France, an independent American hospital at the aid of the French. Toby had a strong desire to join the Royal Flying Corps but it required he be a British subject at the time. He had traveled to London to hear Pats' first speech to the troops. Pat understood Toby's motivation immediately and initiated formal adoption papers, allowing Toby to join the Corps. The letter was an explanation to Henry Tallmadge regarding the arrangement. Henry was genuinely pleased but naturally concerned for his grandson. "Hopefully this damned war will be over soon and he'll stay out of trouble," Henry said.

Mary McClaughlin, Mrs. Tabler, and Mrs. Shronts prepared a wonderful meal for the men and following dinner they settled into a long and genuinely heartfelt discussion about Pat's experiences. He felt relieved to have a comfortable conversation with his fraternal brothers without the rapid fire questions that were already accompanying his personal appearances. For the first time, he was able to discuss the impact of the war on him personally. As was the case with his large audiences to date, Pat's comments fully enthralled the men. For Pat, the conversation was without the formality of military repartee or the flair of a speech. His fellow Shriners were mostly concerned about his welfare and expressed that to him directly.

"I appreciate the opportunity to visit with you," Pat said.

"Pat, you know, it is just like the service," said Tallmadge. "You must have confidants. We just want you to get healthy again and be assured that you're going to be ok and can go on to a full and fruitful life. You've certainly earned it."

"Thanks, Mr. Tallmadge, I hope I do to!" said Pat with an appreciative tone to his voice.

"Pat, what do you hear from the British about your future?" asked Astle. "Are they going to review your case at the end of your three month furlough or are you to go back?"

"I don't rightly know," Pat answered. "Naturally, I'm still under the King but I'd like to go back. When I was in London I met with U.S. Ambassador Page. He indicated that at the end of my furlough he'd look into the possibility of transferring me to the American Army. I'd really like to do that. I'm not sure if he really believed I was serious but I am. I want to get back in the fight. The Huns are on their heels now that we're there but I'd like a few more licks at them before it's over."

"You've done plenty, Pat," said Tallmadge. "If we're all fortunate, the Huns will quit soon. That's certainly my hope."

Pat looked at Tallmadge a little surprised. "I was just getting into it when I was shot down. There are plenty of pilots that have given more than me. Even my best friend Paul Raney, gave his life. There are a few buddies of mine I'd like to avenge. Paul, for one. I know, however, that I'll not likely fly over Flanders again, I understand that."

"Why's that?" asked Clyde Tabler, the youngest among them at thirty-nine.

"Well according to Captain Moore, the officer that received me and saw me off in London, they shoot any escaped pilot should he be captured again. Even the King told me it was not in the cards. But there are other ways to fight. If the Army won't have me I could try the French Legion or perhaps fly in another theatre. I just know we're not done.

Like I say, you've done plenty and right now your job is to get strong again," advised Tallmadge.

"Yes Sir, I agree Henry. I understand that," said Pat. "Besides, the doc said I have to get these organs back in place," placing his hands over his abdomen with a smile. The men chuckled a bit and served themselves one more drink.

The group broke up at 11:00 p.m. and Fred Nichols drove Pat back to town. Nichols told Pat that he would do anything for him and that he hoped Pat might look on him as someone he could trust. Nichols remembered the day Pat left Momence at fifteen, four years after Daniel's death.

"I know I'm only fifteen years your elder Pat, but like any of those men tonight we're glad to be available to advise you, as a father would. You're very important to us. I think you know these men would support you even if you weren't a war hero," said Nichols ending with a slight grin of assurance.

"Yes, I understand that Fred. And it means a lot. It really does" Pat responded. "Right now I just want to get healthy, do my part to raise War Bonds and most importantly tell the people I meet how important it is that we push hard until the Hun is well back into Germany. From there, I hope I can get back into the fight. There are too many men that have given their lives for this. We must win."

"You damned right, Pat," responded Nichols. "Now that we're in the fight, I'm sure the war won't be much longer, I'm sure."

The week Pat came home, the *Momence Progress* published a letter of thanks from Pat to the City of Momence and all his old friends for the wonderful reception he had received. It read:

"I take this means of acknowledging my deep gratitude to fellow townspeople and those from the surrounding countryside for the honors with which I have been showered while guest of the City of Momence. To those who have come from afar to assist in welcoming me I also extend thanks."

"Words cannot express the deep feeling that is mine because of contact again with old friends and neighbors of the best little city in the world."

"Suffering has come to me only to be wiped out in a day by such kindness as I didn't know existed. God bless all of you. Pat."

On the morning of February 1, 1918, Pat O'Brien was up early shaving and getting into his uniform. Margaret already had breakfast on the kitchen table and called him and his brother to eat.

"Well, sounds like we're back home like kids again, huh Buck?" said Pat, laughing at how naturally Margaret had slipped into her familiar routine.

"We're comin', ma!" shouted Pat as he shut off the water, tossing a towel back at the sink after wiping his face hurriedly. He quickly proceeded to the kitchen.

Pat and Buck were preparing for their trip to Chicago. It was a big day for Pat. He would make his first public appearance for Keedick, his promoter. Pat's first professional speech was scheduled for that night at Orchestra Hall in downtown Chicago. Keedick had taken the train from New York to handle the details of the day which included a number of interviews and minor appearances downtown before his sold out presentation at Orchestra Hall.

Just before sitting down to eat their breakfast, Al arrived.

"Al," Pat said, "come on in and have breakfast with us. You're just in time."

"Smells good, Maggie! Gee, I'm starved," said Al.

"Al, I wanted to ask you to do me a favor," said Pat.

"Sure Pat, anything," responded Al.

"I wonder if I might store my trunk in your attic?" asked Pat. "There's not a lot of room here and the damn thing is parked in the middle of the living room!"

"Sure, I can put in the attic," said Al.

"Well, I'm goin to be on the road for some time and I don't want to dump it here and have it get in everybody's way for the next six months," said Pat.

"Easy to do, Pat, I'll get a cart at Astle's and haul it home," Al said.

The two brothers and Al gulped down their breakfast and chuckled once again as Maggie gave off vane advice to slow down and "eat a good breakfast." It didn't sway them a bit and after kissing her good-bye, they jaunted out the door and headed for the depot.

"Thanks Al," yelled Pat as they waved good bye to Al who was heading back.

"Knock 'um dead, Pat!" he shouted.

[437]

About the same time Pat and his brother Buck were boarding the train in Momence, Mrs. Jane Sarah Ottis, wife of Dr. Daniel Mortimer Ottis of Springfield, Illinois was watching the snow covered fields north of Bloomington whisk by her train car window on her way to Chicago. Like so many who had read about the exploits of Pat's adventure, she developed a keen interest in his story. She was making the trip to hear Pat speak "for the first time" publically as the Sangamon Journal had reported that week. Sarah Ottis had time on her hands. Her husband had recently gone to war.

In April of 1917, Dr. Ottis was forced to abandon his practice Springfield when the U.S. Army asked him to head up a medical unit from Sangamon County. The unit would consists of twelve doctors, twenty-one nurses and fifty orderlies all recruited from the Springfield area. They were drilled at the State Arsenal in Springfield for two months but had departed for Ft. McPherson, Georgia on January 22, the very day Pat O'Brien arrived in Momence.

The two trains steamed north toward Chicago where Pat O'Brien would make his public debut and Sarah Ottis would hear him speak. Pat was having a lively conversation with his brother Buck. Sarah was staring out at the vast icy white terrain one hundred and twenty miles to the south, contemplating how the last week had been with her husband gone, and imagining what she would do next.

"Oh, hell," she thought. "I'll find something to do. I've never been short on ideas.

Chapter 37

First Tour

The train pulled into the LaSalle Street station at about 9:45 a.m. Pat waited for passengers to pass before exiting with his brother.

"Let's wait till they clear, Buck," said Pat. "I don't need to be trampled on my first day as a professional speaker." "Indeed!" Buck stated in a fake, elevated tone. They glanced at each other and smiled. When the last passenger exited their car the two brothers got up and walked forward to exit the train. Pat stepped down and immediately heard a familiar voice.

"Pat!" shouted Lee Keedick.

"Hello Lee, how are you?" returned Pat, grabbing the promoter's hand. "This is my brother Buck," Pat said lifting his cane slightly to point toward Buck. "I don't know if you two have met."

"How do you do, Buck? It's nice to meet you," said Keedick. "This is Bill Glass our general manager." Glass shook Buck's hand then turning to Pat said, "How are you, Pat? Good to see you. It looks like your starting to fill out. Being home must help enormously."

"It sure does," he said as the four men walked up the platform to the terminal.

"How did the speeches go at home, Pat?" asked Keedick.

"He was outstanding!" inserted Buck as the men approached the door.

"It went very well, Lee," said Pat. "I think I'm starting to develop a pace."

That's good, that's very good," stated Lee. "This is a big appearance for you tonight. It really will accelerate your notoriety. The place is sold out and I've got a huge contingent of press here. We've got a few interviews set up this morning, a luncheon and then some interviews in the afternoon. I've arranged for you to stay in one place this afternoon so we don't have to be walking all over town." Changing the subject he said, "How are you feeling?"

"Not bad. I had quite a first few days at home but got a good night's sleep last night" said Pat, hobbling through the terminal with his cane. The group exited the station and Lee looked east down Van Buren Street.

"Do you feel like walking or would you like us to get a car?" asked Lee.

"Actually, I don't feel bad at all. If you fellows will go a moderate pace, I'd like to walk. I've not seen the city since returning," said Pat. Where are we going first?

"Monadnock Building off Jackson," said Lee.

"Why don't we go over to Dearborn and walk north from there?" directed Buck.

"Great!" said Keedick. "Let's walk."

They walked to Dearborn and then headed north up the cavernous street to Jackson. Entering the Monadnock Building, they went up to the 4th floor where they met with reporters in a large, narrow room. Pat was introduced to the reporters by Glass and took a seat answering a number of questions from the reporters. Some knew the basic story of his escape but very few had heard the particulars. Pat's book would not be released for another month, so most information was from early London reports and the limited number of press that covered his homecoming in Momence.

"Keep in mind, gentlemen, that the Lieutenant's book will be out March 1st. For now, Lieutenant O'Brien will discuss some advanced details planned for tonight's speech but we also want to be supportive of the book publisher's efforts which will have much more," said Keedick.

"Will Pat talk about the escape tonight?" asked one reporter.

"Sure. You'll have a good outline of the story today and I encourage you to be there tonight," Keedick responded. "Don't worry gentlemen, the story is extensive and like none you've heard. There will be plenty to write about after the speech."

Keedick was a pro and one of the best handlers in the business. He was particularly adept at pacing the press. Press conferences like these primed the pump for the major presentations. Keedick was confident that Pat would deliver. The speech would create a burst of publicity for the next appearance.

By the time the book was released in thirty days, there would be a national audience so hungry for anything about Pat O'Brien that financial rewards would be tremendous for both Pat and himself. His story was "a winner," as Keedick referred to it.

Pat proceeded to give some of the key dates of events, a bit on his flying background and he spent a good amount of time talking about the war itself and how the United States had to see their effort through until the Hun was fully defeated. He commented about his physical condition, making light of some of it which brought a good laugh from the group of normally jaded reporters.

By the time Pat was done, he'd convinced the over twenty-five journalists in the room that his story was something special. A dozen reporters surrounded Pat and were writing rapidly on their note pads. Two others were packing up cameras and Buck overheard their conversation. They did not know that Buck was Pat's brother.

"I was going to pass over the speech tonight at Orchestra Hall but after hearing this, I don't want to miss it," said one.

"What the hell, Jerry, I was hoping you'd not show up and I'd get an exclusive on this thing!" said the other.

"To hell with you Bob, I'll be there and plenty early, too!" he replied.

Buck looked back at the reporters surrounding Pat, at the two packing up and back to the group surrounding Pat once again. His brother was more than a war hero from Momence now. Buck understood, for the first time, that his brother would soon be a national hero. He paused to think about how this might wear on Pat and what effect Pat's fame could have on the O'Brien family. It was wonderful to have Pat home and the events of the last few days were exciting. But Buck worried for his brother nonetheless.

After lunch, Pat and the others walked north to the Tribune offices at the southeast corner of Dearborn and Madison Streets where they spent the afternoon doing interviews and greeting a few military officers from Great Lakes Naval Base and Fort Sheridan. Joseph Medill Patterson, part owner of the Tribune Company held a private dinner for Pat and a number of important guests from both the military and the business leadership of Chicago were there. Patterson owned the paper along with his cousin Robert McCormick, but McCormick was engaged in France at the time as a member of Pershing's communications staff.

Pat was very interested to learn from Patterson that McCormick had served under Pershing in Mexico during the Expedition when Pat was in San Diego. McCormick had also interviewed Czar Nicholas of Russia, as well as the First Lord of the Admiralty in England, Winston Churchill. Pat hoped he could meet McCormick someday.

Following dinner, the men took a cab to Orchestra Hall on Michigan Avenue five blocks away. Pat was stiff from sitting all afternoon and when they arrived, entered the stage door on the Wabash side and stretched out his legs back stage in preparation for the speech. He could hear the large capacity crowd, all humming with excitement and then applause as Keedick walked on stage to make the introduction.

"Good evening, ladies and gentlemen," started Keedick. "I am Lee Keedick. Tonight Chicago will be the first city to hear the fantastic story of Lt. Pat O'Brien." Applause washed throughout the hall. You'll hear how this native son from Momence, Illinois, just south of here, flew for Britain, was shot out of the sky, was captured and escaped. Yes, he escaped jumping from a moving train not one month after crashing behind enemy lines from 8,000 feet. Tonight, I invite you to hear the story first hand from the man himself," extending his arm stage left, "Ladies and Gentlemen, Lieutenant Pat O'Brien."

The crowd gave an enthusiastic applause and Pat came out sporting his cane, waving once as he always did across his frame, then shaking hands with Keedick before taking his position center stage. He looked up to the third level balcony and once his eyes adjusted, he could see the entire hall was full. When applause faded, Pat began his planned outline presentation, adding details that few had heard before.

"Usually, when a bunch of fellows get together, they talk about women. But in our first prison, in Flanders, we talked only about escape and food and got very little of either," the crowd chuckled. "There were eight officers going to an interior prison camp and a guard with a rifle for every two prisoners. We rode all day and night. Twice I put up the window to jump and lost my nerve. As I put it up the third time, about four in the morning, the guard gave me an ugly look. I knew it was then or never and dove out."

Pat could hear the audience gasp and many were shaking their heads in disbelief. Pat described those early hours and how the train had stopped to find him but that he had cleared the area quickly, despite bleeding extensively from his wounds.

"Food? Well, for an appetizer, I ate a turnip, the entrée was a sugar beet, and the meal closed with a cabbage stump that even the Germans scorned," said Pat, much to the delight of the audience. "And I never did like vegetables," he said. "I hope I never eat another!" This got a sharp punctual laugh, a sign to Keedick that the audience was hanging on every word.

[442]

He described his swim of the Meuse River as his biggest physical challenge. "When I got up the bank, I fainted. It was the only time I ever fainted. My boyhood on the Kankakee River saved my life."

One hour and twenty minutes later, he was finished and the crowd leapt to its feet for an ovation that seemed to go on for the longest time. Pat nodded in appreciation and occasionally raised his cane, particularly to the upper seats.

Keedick came back on stage and indicated that Pat would be in the reception area of the second floor mezzanine for a while to greet anyone that wished to meet him personally. He also mentioned that Pat's book would be out in a month. There was a huge number of press from all around the country in attendance, many of whom had not been there during the day but had traveled by train for hours to hear the pilot's first public speech.

After about fifteen minutes of answering questions and greeting guests on the second floor, a woman of approximately thirty-nine years old came up to Pat.

"Hello, Lieutenant. My name is Sarah Ottis."

"Hello, Miss Ottis. Glad to meet you," responded Pat.

"Mrs., Lieutenant, Mrs. Ottis," she paused, "from Springfield, Illinois."

"Sorry, Mrs. Ottis," Pat responded. "Very nice to meet you, ma'am."

"I heard about your exploits and immediately got on a train to Chicago" she said. "My husband is a medical officer with Pershing's Army. I look forward to hearing you speak again," she said, nodding and holding her hat with both hands in front of her.

Pat smiled saying, "Thank you very much, Mrs. Ottis."

He reached out to shake the woman's hand but she did not break and he pulled back. For a split second he heard in his head her words "hearing you speak again." He had never considered that people would want to hear him more than once.

"Very nice, Mrs. Ottis. I appreciate your coming all this way to hear me speak," Pat said with his heart-melting smile and tip of his head.

The woman extended her hand this time which Pat shook and then turned to the next couple waiting in line to meet the famous pilot. Ottis moved along but then stood against the large windows located along the exterior of hall across from Pat observing the reception line all waiting patiently to meet him. "This man really has something," she thought.

Following the reception, Pat and his small entourage cabbed to the Union League Club on Jackson for dinner. Keedick had arranged for Pat and his brother to stay there while he and Glass were booked at the Standard Club on South Michigan, the Jewish Club. At dinner, they reviewed the presentation and Keedick was quite pleased.

"Just keep telling the outlined story and add whatever little items you'd like, Pat. You've got all the instincts to read the room," said Keedick.

Pat was scheduled at Orchestra Hall again on Feb 6th. Each day leading up to that speech was filled with smaller appearances throughout the city. On February 3, he was the guest of Mary E. Hall from Momence who was wintering in Chicago. Pat came for dinner with about a dozen people. On February 5, Pat was guest of honor at a "bob ride" given in Chicago by Beatrice Barsalou and a number of Pat's old school chums who had found their careers in the city. Following the morning frolic through snowy Chicago the entire group had lunch for Pat at the home of Evan Beales, another former Momence resident. Pat thoroughly enjoyed these reunion visits and there always seemed to be a large number of young ladies around him at all times. His charms were not left behind in the forests of Belgium.

Keedick's agreement with Pat included transportation while on tour. But beginning with Chicago, Pat was frequently driven to events by willing and often well-to-do young fans. This would continue for most of the tour. One lady frequently seen with Pat escorting him to appearances around Chicago was Sophie Smith, sister of Mr. De Ver Warner who was the wife from the highly successful manufacturer of corsets in Connecticut.

From the very beginning, Pat drew the rich and famous who were enamored by his wit, boyhood charm, and bravery in war. Pat was not indifferent to the lavishness of the rich and enjoyed his first encounters with the well-to-do.

On the 6th, he met with his new doctor a few blocks from the Union League. The physician gave him a complete examination and stated to the press that though Pat was certainly still affected by his war experiences, "he will heal, fully." Pat's internal organs had actually shifted around inside him as a result of the crash. He was happy to hear the diagnosis, however, for he still held out the desire to return to battle and the doctor's report gave him hope. His hip continued to agonize him requiring he use his cane continuously. After his smile, it became a commonly known image of the young pilot hero.

Following a second sold out appearance at Orchestra Hall on February 6, Pat and Buck returned to Momence. Two days later, they headed for St. Louis where Pat was to appear at Odeon Theatre.

About that time, Pat and his brother arrived at the Odeon on North Grand, young Sergeant John L. Brown of Momence was knee-deep in snow on Cass Street with about seven other passengers. They were trying to push their "jitney bus" out of the snow.

"Push, boys!" came the yelp from the driver as the rear wheels lurched up and out of four feet of snow. Brown had taken the train in from Bellville to see Pat speak. He was stationed with the 221 Aero Squadron at Fort Scott.

"Thank God!" he thought and they all climbed back on the bus. A few minutes later, Brown jumped out of the bus, ran into the hall and took his seat just as Pat was walking on to the stage to a roaring applause. It was another stunning presentation and Brown was moved to tears as he stood applauding with the entire hall. To think that this great hero was from Momence gave him a feeling of pride he had never experienced.

Later that night, back at the base, Sergeant Brown wrote a letter to his family.

"I arrived at the hall just as Pat came on the stage. No, I did not miss a word. He spoke for nearly two hours and if the audience applauded once they did a dozen times. His talk certainly was interesting."

He went on. "I saw Pat and shook hands with him after the lecture but did not get to talk to him much as he was in a hurry to get to the depot. I don't know Pat very well, but it seemed good to meet someone from Momence."

Also present at the St. Louis speech was Sarah Ottis of Springfield but she had chosen not to stand in the reception line. She did watch Pat greet well-wishers for nearly forty-five minutes but kept her distance. Pat did not notice she was there.

Severe weather prevented Pat from speaking in Peoria the following day as another snow storm blew through Illinois. At the request of a fellow Mason, Pat spoke at the Auburn Park Mason Hall on the south side of Chicago on the 14th of February. But these presentations were "warm-ups" for the ultimate venue all performers seek and few ever experience - Carnegie Hall.

Keedick, being a master of promotion, saw the February 17 speech at Carnegie Hall in New York as the true launch of Pat's national fame. Even in 1918, New York City was the center of communications and Keedick understood how to use the newspapers to promote his acts. The ripple effect of a story as dynamic as Pat O'Brien's could spread clear to the west coast and all over free Europe in a matter of days. War now had the attention of the public and Americans everywhere were hungry for heroes. Keedick knew how to set the time bomb and he understood that if one is going to make a huge impact, the best place to do that is New York City. The New York Times, in true form, called it "Lieutenant O'Brien's first appearance on the lecture platform." They didn't get the story one-hundred percent correct, informing the New York audience that he "escaped by jumping from a car."

But the New York crowd wouldn't be set afire by patriotic references or folksy anecdotal stories about eating turnips and cabbage stumps. Pat intuitively knew this and stirred the somewhat jaded Manhattanites with a shot to the gut. He told them how the very doctor who removed the bullet from his throat had ridiculed Pat for being an American.

"When I nodded, since I couldn't speak, the Hun doctor said he should take me out and shoot me, for I was just a common murderer, he said. One of the German officers said that it would be impossible for America to play any important part in the war," Pat said. "That same German said that the maximum number of men the United States would ever be able to ferry over the Atlantic was about 250,000." The crowd laughed.

He continued, "I told him that he was in for a rude awakening, and that before it was all over he and that the rest of the Germans would think that all hell had crossed over." The crowd stirred with fervor. Many in the crowd booed at hearing this tale of the Hun. Pat had struck a nerve and the Carnegie crowd was captivated. He then artfully turned their disdain for the Hun doctor into patriotic passion normally found in places like Des Moines, Iowa.

"The Germans constantly complained about America's seizure of the German-made, S.S. Vaterland," Pat said, adding a pause. The ship was the largest ocean liner in the world when launched in 1913 and had been laid up in Hoboken, New Jersey since the war broke out in July 1914, unable to return due to British dominance of the seas.

"I told my captors that they would live to see that ship bring Americans to fight against them by the thousands," said Pat. The crowd offered thunderous applause. He went on. "The day I sailed from Liverpool for America, I saw the Vaterland steam into that harbor with her decks crowded with cheering American soldiers!" This brought the well-dressed audience to their feet in a thunderous applause.

Pat's opening night in New York was an astounding event. The timing of Pat O'Brien on the national scene, it would turn out, could not have been better. He had successfully convinced the New York crowd and more importantly, the attending press that the war was a direct affront to America, despite the fact that no guns had been fired on the homeland. His value to Keedick and to the American war effort rose significantly that night. War Bonds had to be sold and Pat was the perfect motivator.

It was, as it turned out, Pat's firsthand experience with the Hun that made his claims so compelling and built passion for the Allied effort at Carnegie Hall. After concluding his one hour and thirty minute speech, Pat gave a heartfelt thank-you to the Carnegie Hall crowd and raising his cane overhead, paid a final farewell, "Good night, folks!" They rose to their feet in thunderous applause.

Streams of reporters could be seen hunched over, rushing out of the famous venue to immediately file stories with their papers as the crowd screamed with delight. Keedick was ecstatic. He knew what rapidly exiting reporters meant. It was the fuse that would explode Pat O'Brien onto every front page in America. The next day he was proven right.

Philadelphia, Boston, Providence, Baltimore, Toronto, Cleveland, Chicago, Waterloo, Denver, Dallas, San Francisco, Los Angles, and even Calgary, Canada ran stories the next day about the new national hero, Lieutenant Pat O'Brien and his amazing story of escape and, of all things, his visit with the King.

At ten in the morning, the day after his debut in New York, Pat spoke to 20,000 Troops at Camp Dix, near Trenton, New Jersey. In the week following Carnegie Hall, he gave thirty-two speeches in New York alone. On February 24, in Philadelphia, two thousand people stood in a driving rainstorm for two hours awaiting Pat's speech at the Academy of Music, the oldest grand opera house in the United States, built in 1857.

The Philadelphia inquirer stated it was "hardly requisite to remind Americans that it was Lieutenant O'Brien who, after an encounter with aviators of the German army, eight thousand feet in the air, was brought to earth and was made prisoner by the Huns." The paper further stated that "the manner in which Lieutenant Pat O'Brien outwitted the Hun is perhaps the most interesting story yet told by a fighting man."

In one week's time, Pat became a household name and the term *"Outwitting the Hun,"* appeared in newspaper stories two weeks before Pat's book of the same name was released. Either the publisher Harper Brothers recognized the catchy phrase of the newspaper writer or Keedick had planted the thought in a reporter's mind, knowing the planned title of the book. There was no way to know.

"Outwitting the Hun," was a fresh and exciting book that people could not help but read straight through. It was full of tension and intrigue but written in an uncomplicated style. Young school children, as well as sophisticated book critics gobbled it up with excitement. Fueled by extensive printing of excerpts in newspapers all over the country, it would become an additional catalyst for Pat's appearances, drawing overflow crowds seeking his signature. Sales of the book exploded in every city. Pat signed so many copies while on tour that he would regularly complain of "the additional war injury" acquired in his right hand from writing so much.

A train carrying Pat pulled into Boston, Massachusetts on March 19 as he read the New York Times. He had resumed his habit of reading extensively on the train when touring ensued. He had hardly noticed the train had slowed. "Russians sign Brest-Litovsk Treaty with Huns" was the headline that drew his attention.

Since taking over Russia in 1917, Vladimir Lenin was hell bent on removing the Russians from the chaos of the war in Europe. Lenin had other problems, like holding together his fragile new government in the face of the Czarist Whites who continued to hang on. Pat knew what such a peace treaty between Russia and Germany meant. It would mean that the eastern front was no more and his buddies in Belgium and France would feel the entire force of the German Army.

"The boys are in for it now," he thought. "I must get healthy and get back to the front," he said to himself, folding the paper and looking up at Boston for the first time.

Pat's cab approached Harvard Yard up Bow Street. He could see the Old Cambridge Baptist Church towering on the right as his car turned left onto Massachusetts Avenue and along the series of iron gates near Wigglesworth and Wadsworth Halls. It struck Pat that in one month he'd spoken twice at Orchestra Hall in Chicago, at Carnegie Hall in New York and would today make an appearance at Harvard University.

"Hardly worth the price, I'd say." Pat was excited to be in such famous places but would trade them all for a bit part at the Momence Opera House if it meant being able to skip those seventy-two days in the woods.

The car pulled over and Pat was greeted by a number of academic types who extended him a hand. Keedick shook hands with their hosts. They entered Harvard Square through the Widener Gate, past the Widener Library and into Emerson Hall. The first floor was full of eager undergrad students, looking to catch a glimpse of the national hero. As Pat proceeded to room 105 where his speech was planned, at least a dozen students extended a copy of Pat's book under his nose, seeking an autograph. Pat's audience was a mixture of University officials, some privileged students and members of the press. He took some time to stop and sign books.

At the Harvard speech Pat revealed for the first time that he planned to seek a transfer to the American army in order that he re-enter the struggle.

"I want to fight under my own flag," he said. The reception and reaction to Pat's presentation was the same as it had been since New York one month before. Pat expressed desire to return to the fight caught headlines in many morning papers the next day. It raised his stature as an American icon, yet another "never say die" patriot.

Pat was headed back to the Midwest following speeches in Providence, Rhode Island and Wilkes-Bare, Pennsylvania. He arrived in Chicago on March 22 and conducted an extensive interview with the press before heading south for a major appearance in Indianapolis. The rapid fire interview at the train station involved twenty reporters who fired questions at Pat about many of the stories from the book. Reporters were now armed with more information and hungered for additional details.

They learned about the hungry dogs that tore at prisoner's trousers at Courtrai. He expounded about his attempt to traverse the electronic fence at the Holland border which added immensely to the thrill and daring of his escape.

Regarding the King, Pat said "I had a long talk with the King and think he is one of the most democratic men England has ever had on the throne."

It seemed that the female reporters captured more of a glimpse into Pat's condition and demeanor than the factual reports written by many of the men. Norah Meade, of the Fort Wayne-Journal Gazette called Pat "Dandy and Daredevil."

"A tall, slim boy with a lean, twitching face, long nose, mobile mouth at which his fingers pulled nervously; a strong head, crowned by rich and darkish brown hair, an alert gait and a general air of restrained but unmistakable recklessness – that was my first impression of Lieutenant Pat O'Brien." Through reporters like Meade, readers who never met Pat could acquire a picture of him and see signs that the tensions and stress of war were still present.

"He sat beside me, and my attention inevitably wandered to his hands. They were Irish hands – slender-figured, impatient, imaginative. His nails, fantastically long and fastidiously manicured, seemed a contradiction until you had considered the extreme smartness of his attire. A striking combination of dude and daredevil – that was my final summing-up," she reported.

Perhaps it was Pat's inclination to open up more to lady reporters and put up a healthy front with the men, but the reading public got unique insights into the nature of Pat from the female press.

By March, the nation could not get enough of this new, American icon, this modern war-time hero. Every nation needs heroes and countries at war have little trouble finding them. In the United States, admiration came to men of outstanding bravery, with humble beginnings, and a self-effacing personality. Pat fit that bill completely. Plus, he was witty, good looking and at the same time a sympathetic figure made visible by his inseparable cane at his side.

Miss Meade revealed details sought by the public writing, "A small scar carefully hidden under a military mustache, and what looked like a pencil mark protruding from the left corner of the left eye – these were the only tangible evidences of his escapades. Then you marked the attenuation of the six-foot body, and the head continually turning at the slight hint of sound, and you divined that many a day could pass before Lieutenant Pat O'Brien become the man he was before the war."

In fact, reacting to sounds in such a way was common among returning vets whether they fought on the ground or in the air. Pat recognized how his harrowing experiences had impacted his temperament. To Nora Meade he revealed, "I don't know what's the matter with me," he declared. "I can't seem to get any fun out things I liked before. If I go to a show, I keep twisting and turning in my chair, waiting for a chance to get out. And before, when people didn't do exactly as I asked, I let it go. What difference did it make? But now! Lord, you should hear what Cain I raise!"

Clearly Pat was puzzled by these manifestations. "Even before I crossed the Dutch border," he said, "I was getting that way. If that Belgian hadn't given me the muffler I wanted, I think I'd have killed him on the spot."

Reporter Meade provided her reaction to meeting Pat first hand. "His face set for a moment in an ugly, nervous frown, and the long hands began to close and unclose. Then a pretended yawn to change the shadows, and he gripped the sides of his seat. Another minute and the frown was a bright smile."

But it was Beatrice Fairfax of the *Indianapolis Star* who conducted the most insightful interview of Pat O'Brien. The four hour interview had been taken the day after his Carnegie Hall speech and was running all week in the Indianapolis paper as a lead-up to a major two-day series of events in Pat's "home state."

Lowell, Indiana had adopted Pat as being from their town, and so in the minds of all Hoosiers, this gave Indiana the liberty to call Pat their own, as well.

Fairfax began with her impressions. "Across his broad shoulders there is a bar that reads 'England.' But on the cuff of his right sleeve there is a tiny flag that bears the Stars and Stripes. He's proud and he is Irish but when they called him Irish-American on the posters advertising his lecture, Pat made them erase the Irish reference."

"'I'm' American," Pat said to Fairfax. "There can't be any hyphens now."

"You want to fly again?" asked the reporter.

"Why not? The world needs men," responded Pat. "The men who don't feel it their duty to go don't seem real to me. They just glide by like a panorama, a picture, not a part of life at all! I must go back to help. I know it's the right thing for me to do and I have to do what I think is right no matter how anyone else feels about it. It is right for me to fly again. I've got my petition into the medical board to be accepted into the American Air Service"

Fairfax was stunned. She paused and looked up from her note pad. She had certainly heard of men who had sought exemption from service on physical grounds. This was the first time she could remember ever hearing of a lad seeking "physical exemption" to get into military service.

The experienced journalist heard something else that was new.

"The world needs men. Have I ever heard such a statement?" she asked herself. "Had anyone?" Caesar certainly called upon the men of Rome to serve Rome. Every royal king of Europe had declared hundreds of times the need for men to serve the fatherland. And even Lincoln called upon Pat's father and uncles to defend the north. But the idea of the world needing brave, committed men of good will to save it from itself was a new idea, in a new age, personified by new men like Pat O'Brien. In 1918, there were few of them.

"You mentioned you'll be taking the eight o'clock train to Toronto tonight, Pat," said Fairfax. "Are you going to deliver a speech?"

"No, I'm going to attend a funeral. You see they are bringing Tommy Atkinson home to bury him. He was my pal over there. We were together for a long time, longer than most. When you keep seeing new faces you know pretty soon someone else is going to see a new face where yours had been. I felt it was my turn the next day before they got me."

"Were you frightened?" asked Fairfax noticing, for the first time, how Pat was twiddling his thumbs.

"Of the Germans," asked Pat who followed the reporter's eyes to his nervous hands upon which they both had an ice-thawing laugh. "No, I hated them too much."

"I didn't hate the Germans to start with. Of course, I didn't like them or their methods but hating doesn't make you fight very well. You see red when you hate and you can't see through red to do what you want to do. I just disliked them from the start, let's say. I didn't hate them when I woke up in their hospital and they probed the bullet that got me out of my throat. I began to hate them the day I sat in front of the hospital and watched them shoot my friend Paul out of the sky."

Pat ended the interview by saying, "No one who has not actually seen service abroad can have the slightest idea of the immensity of the struggle going on there," he said. "It is simply horrible and I want to awaken my country to the fullest realization of the task before it. Unless we all get together, this terrible slaughter will continue for years. For unless there is an absolute crop failure in Germany, the Huns can go on fighting indefinitely."

Beatrice Fairfax thanked Pat for the extensive interview and watched him walk up the platform to his train headed for Toronto. As he had done many times before, he gave her his patented cross-body wave and broad smile. She would not be the first jaded journalist to be taken up by the spirit of this new young American.

Pat spent the next four days in Toronto. His day with Tommy's parents was as painful as when he related Paul's death to the Raney's. He also spent a day with a young cadet he had taught at Borden who was in the military hospital there.

"Hello, ma?" said Pat into the hotel phone. "Can you hear me ma? It's Pat."

Margaret took the call from Clara's store. "Sure Pat. When are you coming home?"

"Well, I'm heading back today from Toronto. I'll be coming to Chicago where there will be about a six hour wait - then on to Indianapolis. From there I'll borrow a car in Indianapolis and drive to Lowell on Monday so we can drive to Momence together."

"Ok Pat, I'll wait for you," said Maggie. "Better stop now, I know you're long distance."

"Bye ma, see you then," said Pat.

About thirty minutes later, Sarah Ottis turned and exited the Decatur depot stuffing her round-trip tickets to Indianapolis in her purse. She would leave the next day to spend three days in the Hoosier Capital.

[453]

Chapter 38

Hatred for the Hun

Pat had a six hour layover in Chicago on his way to Indianapolis. At the station he was interviewed by dozens of reporters for four hours. Nearly all the reporters on hand were from secondary markets throughout the Midwest. This was the first time many of them were able to meet Pat personally. They worked for small town papers and their interviews brought Pat's story to rural America. His book *Outwitting the Hun* had been out for nearly three weeks and the story was hitting critical mass around the country. Nearly everyone within reach of a newspaper knew something about Pat O'Brien.

When Pat arrived at Union Station in downtown Indianapolis, he was greeted by Major Gearhart who headed the 821st Aero Repair Squadron at Indianapolis Motor Speedway. As soon as America entered the war, the Speedway was closed, allowing the 821st to use it for the service and repair of military aircraft flying within the U.S. A military driver drove the two men to the Claypool Hotel where Pat checked in and they sat down to enjoy a dinner together. Seeing the Major was particularly exciting for Pat since Gearhart was an officer at San Diego when Pat was there in Signal Corps camp.

"Though it's not been that long, it seems that we've not seen each other for ages, Major," said Pat.

"Indeed. A lot has happened very quickly. You've experienced quite an ordeal, haven't you Pat?" responded Gearhart.

"Well as you know, I'm one of the lucky ones who made it home. I've seen a lot of death in Europe. The scale of this war is something that Americans do not yet sense, Major," said Pat.

"I agree, Pat," said Gearhart.

As they enjoyed their meal the two caught up on all that had happened since San Diego and spoke of various Signal Corps men who had moved on to the U.S. army air division. A few were in Europe but very few.

"Well, Pat, are you up for an appearance at the dance tonight?" asked Gearhart.

"As long as I don't have to dance, it will be fine," Pat responded.

"I know a number of my men are eager to meet you and over 200 will likely attend. A local committee sponsors these dances for my squadron every few months. The dance is at the All Souls Lutheran Church tonight. Once we get past the dignitaries, I think you'll spend most of your time talking with the men," related Gearhart.

"I'm always eager to meet fellow soldiers," said Pat. "It sounds like a good time."

The two men finished their coffee and then headed out for the evening's festivities. On their way they passed the State Soldiers and Sailors Monument in the center of Indianapolis. The 284-foot monument anchored the large round-a-bout intersection and was a tribute to all veterans in American wars to date.

"It's a beautiful piece of work, isn't it?" commented Pat as they circled the iconic structure.

"That it is, but it's not spoken of with much pride recently," responded Gearhart.

"Why is that?" Pat asked.

"Well, the whole thing was designed and built by the Germans," explained Gearhart. "A guy named Bruno Schmitz. He's a major architect in Germany. Since the war, folks in Indianapolis don't speak of it much," he said.

"I can understand that," responded Pat. "It does put a bit of a chill over the whole thing, doesn't it?"

"That it does, Pat," Gearhart replied. "These days, a guy like me with such a German name hesitates from time to time, you know?"

"Oh, that means nothing, Major" said Pat. "Nobody thinks that way about a soldier with your background. You shouldn't fret about it."

After five minutes of silence, the two soldiers arrived at their destination. Pat thoroughly enjoyed talking aviation with many of the eager flyers. The pilots in attendance were thrilled to hear about Pat's experience but were equally interested in his keen working knowledge of flying. Talking about flight was a welcomed conversation that Pat had not had for a long time. It stirred his interest in "getting back into the fight." Pat had repeated his speech many times since coming home. The strong desire to "soldier" again increasingly pestered him with increasing nag. He feared becoming a minstrel with only a past to tell. He did not consider himself finished. After all he was only 27 years old. At the end of his long day in Indianapolis he lay in his dark hotel room unable to sleep, resolved to begin his effort to return and fly again.

The next day, Major Gearhart arrived at the hotel at about 2:00 p.m. A parade was planned that would travel through the business district and end at the Murat Theater for his speech. The parade was headed by the mounted police, city-wide Boy Scout Troops, the Tenth Infantry Band from for Fort Benjamin Harrison, The Newsboys Band and the Boy Scouts' Drum and Bugle Corps. It attracted considerable crowds passing through the principle business section of town.

A packed house awaited Pat's arrival. He was introduced by Major Gearhart who related how he and Pat were among the very first flyers to arrive at North Island in San Diego. He also stated how obvious it was back then that Pat was not only an experienced flyer but a determined young man that would do great things. "Ladies and Gentlemen, an American who has indeed done great things, Lt. Pat O'Brien!" were his final words of introduction.

As he had before, Pat walked onto stage to a standing ovation that was warm and lengthy. Seeing the young soldier supported by a cane often brought tears to those who saw him for the first time. But by the end of Pat's speeches it became part of his charisma and as whimsical as an Irish shillelagh.

"Good evening, fellow Hoosiers," started Pat. "Now you might find that odd for me to call you fellow Hoosiers but let me explain."

Pat related his connection to Lowell and his days traversing both sides of the state line.

"Today, my mother lives with my sister in Lowell and if you know most border towns, folks have ties on both sides and often move back and forth more than once in their lifetime."

[456]

After cracking a number of humorous jokes about differences between Hoosiers and folks from the Land of Lincoln, he had the crowd primed to enjoy his two hour speech.

"I have been interested in flight since I was a kid," he stated. "One day I jumped a train to see where the famous inventor Octave Chanute had tested his winged kites on the Indiana Sand Dunes. During flight school in Chicago I flew an old Curtiss that would make you laugh now. And when I was in California a buddy of mine named Hesser and I built our own plane, parts of which are scattered all over California." This drew a big laugh from the Murat crowd.

Pat then began to tell of the day he was shot from the sky, describing in detail his trek through Belgium, his many close calls, and finally his crossing of the Holland border. Like other audiences before them, the Indianapolis crowd frequently held their breath and shook their heads in disbelief as Pat related the threats on his life in such a "matter of fact" way. Pat was animated, well-paced, and continued to gain mastery of storytelling.

"The most thrilling moment of my life was when I had half of me through on the Holland side, half of me in the enemy's country and a deadly wire an inch and a half above my back as I crawled through that hole," Pat said. "There are many more details in my book but some things I cannot tell you or it will put people that helped me in danger."

Expressing his disdain for the Germans, Pat stressed the importance of Allied determination. "I learned there in that Hun Prison that we are fighting every man, woman and child in Germany and not the German Kaiser alone!"

Since the United States had just recently entered the war, most Americans viewed the enemy as the Kaiser and his army. Pat felt it important to impress on his audiences how extensive the war was. He indicated that Americans needed to prepare for great losses.

"For example, I trained with eighteen others in Canada destined for France. Of those eighteen, only three are alive today. One is a prisoner in Germany, the other is in Italy, and I am here." This surprised the crowd and brought a somber tone to the realities of this new global war. "This is what America faces as long as the Hun continues to haunt Europe."

Pat ended his comments and invited questions from the audience, responding for twenty minutes. The audience at the Murat that night had adopted Pat as their own. They felt a special connection to him because of his Indiana roots and his natural Midwestern style of speaking. Pat was proving to be someone who could adjust his style to any audience, but in the Midwest he could speak without imitation. He was one of them.

The Murat Theater crowd brought Pat back onto the stage three times with applause. Each time he smiled and raised his cane overhead thanking the crowd. Finally, after the third time he quieted the crowd and said, "These legs are only good for three encores folks, so I thank you for the last time. Good Night." Applause could still be heard as Pat exited the stage door with Major Gearhart.

The next morning Pat acquired a car with the help of the Major and headed north toward Lowell. It was the first time he had driven in months. He took the time to think about his strategy to reenter the military. "First the U.S. Army Air service," he thought. "If they won't accept me, there's always the French. One way or another, I must return." He enjoyed the peaceful drive alone and the time to think on his own. "How ironic," he thought. "You'd think I had enough solitude after Belgium," smiling as he drove.

Pat got to Lila's home to pick up Margaret about noon. When he arrived he learned that Henry Tallmadge, grandfather of Toby, had passed away early the previous Friday. The civil war veteran was a strong civic leader and once Mayor of Momence. His son, Floyd, lived in Pueblo, Colorado at the time. Unfortunately, Pat and his mother would arrive too late for the funeral scheduled for 1:00 p.m. that day. After a short visit with Lila, Pat and Maggie headed toward Momence.

"How was your speech in Indianapolis, Pat?" asked Maggie.

"It was marvelous, mom. I felt comfortable there. I think they accepted me once I told them of our ties to Indiana," Pat said.

"I'll bet they did like that," said Maggie. "You know how folks are. They feel comfortable with their own. I'm sure you gave a great speech, Pat. You have a natural talent for speaking, son."

"Actually mom, much of it feels automatic now," said Pat. "The main part of the speech doesn't change much. Those are the parts that Keedick and I agreed needed to be part of each presentation. Now I promote the book, have a little room for my own anecdotes and, of course, when they ask questions that makes it interesting."

"You seem to be making good money from these speeches, Pat" said Maggie. "How long does Keedick think your speaking can continue?"

"Well, my contract with Keedick is until July 1st that includes forty speeches. My military contacts are arranging for me to go to the southwest and speak at bases. I've already started making arrangements to speak in California in July. The war department wants me to promote bond sales out west plus I want to go to Richmond and see my old friends. I've promised Agnes I would get their once my commitments to Keedick expire."

"I'm sure she is really dying to see you Pat," said Maggie. "Are you writing her?"

"Oh, sure, when I can. I keep her informed."

"Just make sure you take time to write her. If you care about this girl, she needs to hear from you – and regularly," Margaret said with a rather firm tone.

"I will ma. I will," responded Pat. "It's been quite a whirlwind since I've gotten home. I feel like I haven't even had time to rest."

"After you go to California, you should come home for a while. We'll get the whole family together for a big reunion. You can take a break. The book will continue to sell so you'll have income. You'll be able to take a break from speaking by then," said Maggie.

"That would be nice, ma. To be honest with you, I really hope I can sign up with the American Army and rejoin the effort," said Pat.

"Oh Pat, you're not actually thinking of going back to the war, are you? You've done plenty. Besides, you're in no shape to reenter the service. You're still a British officer, how can you switch to the U.S. Army?" asked Maggie.

"Well, actually mom, I resigned my commission from the Royal Flying Corps on March 21st. My leave was up and after reviewing my doctor reports, the RFC indicated I was not ready to return to service and gave me the option. When I get stronger, then I'll try to serve in some capacity for our new American Flying group," said Pat.

"But you're still wearing the uniform," responded Maggie with surprise in her voice.

"Yes, that's true mom, but the U.S. Army struck some agreement with the Brits. I'm more effective presenting myself as I was under the King. It sells more bonds and that's important right now," he said.

"Well, for now Pat, just concentrate on your speeches and give yourself time to heal," Maggie continued. "After that you can come home for a while, huh?"

"I will ma. I'll be busy in April promoting the Third Liberty Bond Drive which starts April 5th. The country needs $3 billion dollars. Both the British and American services want me to continue as I have and help promote the sale of bonds. For now, this is what I can do but I really want to get back into the fight," Pat said with a rush of enthusiasm in his voice.

"Well, just take your time, Pat. You've been through a lot" Margaret said in a soft, ending tone.

By now the car was approaching Momence south of the marsh and crossed the old upper crossing road. They stopped at the Tallmadge home around 4:00 p.m. after picking up a cake at the bakery. After a short visit with the Tallmadge family, they arrived at Clara's. Pat fell asleep on the couch after dinner and slept for two hours in his clothes and stocking feet. Clara and Maggie visited quietly so as not to stir him.

The rest of the week Pat spent a lot of time visiting friends in Momence, especially Al. On Friday he headed for Minneapolis for a speech. On the same day Toby Tallmadge came home but he missed seeing Pat.

With the launch of the Liberty Bond Drive nationally, Keedick had Pat booked out east in early April. Evidence that the focus of Pat's speech now expanded to promote bonds began with his Harrisburg, Pennsylvania speech. The three-headed promotion now consisted of Pat, his book and the need to buy war bonds.

The *Harrisburg Patriot* headlined Pat's speech on the front page,

"Hundreds line up in rain to hear Lieut. O'Brien's Story of Outwitting the Hun Liberty Loan Drive gets Good Start"

The crowd that jammed into the Chestnut Street Auditorium was clearly the largest ever seen. With the rain coming down in torrents, special police guards at all entrances were scarcely able to control the mob that fought for an opportunity to enter the hall. As the doors opened a crush of people spilled over the sidewalk and far into the street. Clearly more tickets were sold than seats and after a long delay most found their way in with many standing. An overflow room off the auditorium was opened up and the stage crew placed speakers in the adjoining room.

Pat's speech at Harrisburg contained more intense hatred for the Germans than at Indianapolis. Though he continued to pay tribute to the German airman who proved to be expert fighters in the sky, his talk was punctuated by a contempt for the Germans and German methods.

"You may not hate the Hun yet, but if I live to be a hundred years old I will hate him! And when your long list of casualties begin to come in then you will hate him, too!" stated Pat early on in his speech.

He spoke of the death of Paul Raney in a low somber tone that had everyone leaning forward to hear. Then raising his voice he nearly shouted, "It's hard, but it's happening every day and it will continue to happen until we drive the Germans so far back that they don't have anything to stand on except their shadow."

The old hall echoed in a roar. Pat went on. "Don't think we are fighting only the Kaiser. If you think that you are mistaken. We are fighting every man, woman and child of the Fatherland." He related numerous incidents and conversations with Germans while held prisoner convincing all who heard him of the serious nature of the fight.

In the audience that night were over 1,500 Liberty Loan workers. Early in the morning following Pat's speech they hit the streets visiting every industrial establishment and store in Harrisburg. After two weeks of continuous selling, they sold bonds well beyond their assigned quota. Simultaneously, the Red Cross collected $150,000 in donations throughout the town. Patriotism had reached a fevered pitch in Harrisburg and in many cities in the country. Testimonies such as Pat's brought the war home to every American that heard his words. He spoke in a different city every night during the first four weeks of the bond drive.

On April 11 he was on the train heading for Poughkeepsie. He was reading the Pittsburg Gazette-Times about activities in Russia. Amid the torrid, revolutionary battles between the "whites" and "reds" in Russia were the Allied forces, still fighting Germans under a completely different agenda than Lenin's. One of the largest Allied forces in the mix was the Czechs who currently controlled the Trans-Siberian Railroad but would eventually be caught in a vice as Russia unraveled.

The eastern front intrigued Pat, partly because he knew of the impact on France should the Russians quit but also because he sensed that the chaos in Russia could well extend beyond the deadlocked armistice in western Europe which was just beginning to be mentioned as a possibility in the summer of 1918. That meant war might extend long enough for Pat to heal and fight once again.

Pat's final Liberty Bond speech on the east coast was at the Lyric in Baltimore on April 25th. The Baltimore Manufacturers Record paper called it "soul-gripping and intensely interesting." Pat repeated his warnings not to underestimate the Hun and told his audience to expect a hard fought struggle.

"The Huns have at no time, since the war began, conducted themselves in such a way as to command the respect of the American people or that of any of their enemies," he said. "They have at all times and in all circumstances shown themselves to be cruel and barbarous. They have shown themselves to be worse than beasts. They have committed outrages that even the lower animals would not undertake. Instead of developing a higher order of civilizations they have used their brains to concoct diabolical and devilish schemes such as civilization had never before dream that men claiming to be civilized or semi-civilized would be guilty of. It's no wonder the Hun is hated."

The Lyric audience found their feet immediately as Pat concluded. His message resonated that night as it had each night for three weeks. It had been a hard tour but Pat was determined to not only sell bonds but convince his audience of the importance of the persistence required to defeat the Germans. He was tired and was feeling the physical effects of the tour. After all, it was still less than six months since he had crossed into Holland. It was a patriotic effort that was physically hard on his still wounded body.

The next day, Pat stepped up into the first train headed for Chicago on the Baltimore & Ohio Railroad. He would have time to relax at home. His only commitment was a Liberty Loan Parade in Momence and a speech in Decatur, Illinois. He looked forward to being home again.

Pat arrived in Momence on Saturday, April 27. Buck and Clara both greeted him at the train station.

"You look tired," said Clara.

"I am," Pat responded.

"You can relax now. You're home. I'll fatten you up and you can get out of the uniform for a change and take some time for yourself," she said.

"I'm looking forward to that," said Pat. "I do have one commitment this week. I have to speak in Decatur next Tuesday but that should be a one day trip."

"I'll go with you, Pat," said Buck.

Pat spent four days out of uniform, relaxing, visiting friends and even took some time to work some hot spots along the Kankakee River east of town where he caught dozens of rock bass, small mouth, and a few big catfish. It was such a wonderful time, simple as it was. He had time to clear his mind, rest his body, and think about his upcoming trip west.

He'd see Agnes again soon but not soon enough. He wrote her a long letter one afternoon and updated her on his recent tour. But before California, he would make one more trip east, in May, to New England and down the coast to Washington DC.

In June he was scheduled for the Rockies where he would visit Floyd Tallmadge, son of Henry in Pueblo, then speak at Colorado Springs, Oklahoma City and finally a big military tour in Texas and on to Los Angeles. On July 1 he would finally arrive in San Francisco and see Agnes once again. He began to think of her more during his relaxing days at home in May.

On Friday May 1st, the Liberty Loan Parade stepped off from the Central School at 1:30 pm. The parade was led by Mary Louise Vankirk and Mattie Stetson, mounted on two prancing steeds followed by the Momence Band, the high school cadets, various floats and banners and then the school children from Central, St. Pat's and the country schools in grade order. The American Red Cross chapter, the Women's Relief Corps, Women's Club and various lodges and organizations marched carrying American Flags. At the end of the parade Pat and other vets spoke briefly in support of the war and the importance of purchasing of war bonds. Momence purchased a good amount of bonds for the war effort that day.

Most of May was peaceful and without incident for Pat. Clara, however, had decided to sell the store, finding it difficult to manage it since her husband Matt's passing. Son Jack was at Notre Dame so she could not rely on his help anymore. She sold the store to A.G. Grouch, a long time trusted clerk at Jensen's Drug Store.

On May 19, Pat headed for New England. His largest audience was at the Polis Vaudeville Theatre in Bridgeport, Connecticut. At Washington he spoke at the National Theatre, three blocks from the White House. The old theater had entertained every President since Andrew Jackson. But these appearances were different than Pat's earlier tour. For one thing, they were scheduled at 4:00 p.m. before the main attraction of entertainment in the evening. The venues were part of the Vaudeville Circuit and front page patriotic stories announcing him were replaced by three inch ads in the entertainment section of the newspaper. Pat really felt like a minstrel now. Keedick had run out of venues and Pat had become a commercial act in his mind and Keedick's.

Pat returned to Momence on May 28th. He'd have a few days to rest before heading for Colorado. In Pueblo he spoke at the Centennial Auditorium on June 1st for the benefit of the Women's Service Club. The next night he was a guest at the home of Floyd Tallmadge from Momence who had arranged the local speeches for Pat. They had a warm visit and spoke of Floyd's dad with affection.

On June 8, Pat spoke in Oklahoma City to an admiring crowd and then headed to Fort Worth to begin his tour of military bases where he would once again speak to the troops, something he thoroughly enjoyed.

In Texas, Pat was scheduled to not only speak to hundreds of troops but he would demonstrate some of his more sophisticated flying techniques at Kelly Field in San Antonio. This thrilled him to no end.

"I'm flying again," he said to himself as he received the word in a letter from his old friend Edwin Hesser. Hesser was assigned at Camp Dick in Dallas. Pat was thrilled to be flying again. He had no idea that "the impossible" would happen once again.

Pat arrived in San Antonio on Thursday morning, June 13 and checked into the St. Anthony Hotel. That afternoon, five or six reporters gathered outside the hotel in the open air café and conducted an impromptu interview with Pat.

Pat had clearly regained his swagger. The time off in Momence had him feeling stronger, more spirited, and full of mischief. In short, he was returning to his old devilish self. But in his comments one could tell that he wanted to put the past behind him.

He laughed away every question about the peril he had experienced in Europe. He had tired of the formatted presentations prescribed by Keedick for weeks on end.

"Yes, it is true I spent a couple of years in Germany one month, but I'm here now. Many reporters tease me about laughing, say I was born laughing and would die laughing, but this gross exaggeration. I only smile when I have lots of money, or talk to a pretty lady but I'm broke now."

The reporters laughed but felt a little diverted as they genuinely were attempting to get a story. Pat went on.

"The only thing of my old uniform left is this trench cap. When we fly, we wear the helmets of course, and this was left behind with my belongings when I went across the lines that memorable day that I fell. When I got out of Germany it was with the belongings of the dead Pat O'Brien sent to London to be shipped to my next of kin. I hauled it out when I was called to Buckingham Palace and we went to see the king together. We have been through alot together."

Pat absent-mindedly started dusting his boot with it. Catching himself in the act, he laughed again. "That's a good old boot, too. British shoes they gave me in Holland, when I escaped. Looks like it will last, doesn't it?"

"You know, I wonder if people expect to see a man who has been wounded in a big fight, possibly losing both eyes, come home and sit on the streets and beg. They seem to forget that a man has to make his living now when he's not fighting as he did before the war."

"Recently, a lady came up to me and asked in all seriousness, 'What war relief are you lecturing for?' I answered in all seriousness, 'for a wounded soldier.' 'Ah,' she said, 'what wounded soldiers?'

He smiled at the recollection but sobered in a moment to say, "I believe the majority of American thinks the war is a huge movie, maybe a tragic movie but still something that doesn't touch them. I tell you when you see your best friends killed in front of your eyes, you know what war is. And the way some of them seem to think the war is going, it will be over in a few months!"

"We have to keep sending men, keep sending them until we have enough if it means five million from here" – he mentioned the figure as casually as if he had said five hundred. "Then when peace is declared we can demand any terms necessary, with those five million men still in Europe to back up our demands."

Leaning forward suddenly, as he talked smiling again, "I have been trying to get well enough to get back in the fight, with the American colors this time, but for once luck is against me." His injury was bothering him again. He called it his running wound.

"I got it running – but thank goodness it went into my mouth, instead of the back of my head. They took it out in a German hospital, a German doctor, and the only trouble about the whole business was that I was unconscious and couldn't bite his hand."

"And now this thing," he said tapping his heavy cane on the floor, impatiently. "Why honestly, I am scared to death for fear I'll drop some money on the floor, for I know I couldn't stop and pick it up."

Blarneying as only an Irishman could, he teased the reporters with cynical comments throughout, speaking first on one thing and then another, skimming over a subject then dismissing it lightly with a wave of his hand. Only occasionally did he show an unexpected tenseness or a nervous tapping on his chair indicating that he has been through such harrowing experiences.

Pat spoke at Main Avenue High School at 8:30. Major General Willard Holbrook introduced him. Colonel Daniel McCarthy, department quartermaster, got him a car assigned and Pat drove about San Antonio to see the sights.

On the next day, June 14th, Pat arrived at Kelly field. Over 5,000 airmen had gathered around Field No. 1 to hear Pat and then watch his demonstration. Pat was exhilarated to be among so many airman and finally getting a chance to fly again. He spoke to the troops for about thirty minutes. To a man they were all thrilled to hear the details of his experiences in the air, for most of these men were completing their training and had not been to Europe.

After his presentation, Pat donned his helmet and climbed into the two-seater used for training pilots. Pat had not flown such a plane since his days at San Diego. He planned to demonstrate various loops and battle maneuvers which he had just reviewed in his presentation. Pat was used to a much lighter scout or single combat machine.

Being accustomed to a light machine with a velocity of 150 miles per hour, he did not make altitude in the 80 miles per hour machines as rapidly as he calculated, and the machine, being heavy, did not respond as those he flew in France.

At the height of about 2000 feet, he began to demonstrate the spinning nose dive. All seemed to go well and the audience was enjoying the exhibition, until Pat tried to come out of the dive. At about 200 feet from the ground it became evident that something had gone wrong. His plane sideslipped, and he came straight to the ground, driving the nose of his plane a foot and a half into the soft earth.

Fortunately, he was in the rear seat of the plane. Had he been in front he would have easily been killed. His nose was broken and bleeding. An ambulance and about twenty men rushed to the scene fearful that the war hero who had gone through so much might be dead. When they arrived at the crushed aeroplane, Pat was already complaining that the blood dripping from his nose might spot his new flying suit.

"My God, he's alive!" said one of the medics last to arrive at the scene.

"We thought you were dead," said another who had ridden the ambulance out.

"Are you kidding?" said Pat. "This damn machine is so big it took all the blows. If crashing that kite I flew in Europe didn't kill me I wouldn't expect this hunk to do so."

Miraculously, he was able to walk away from the wreck. As he walked away from the destroyed aircraft he expressed concern for his schedule.

"I'm scheduled go to Houston tonight for a speech. Do you think I can get patched up in time, doc?" Pat inquired walking with the lead physician.

"You know about these things Pat," said the military doctor. "You know better than I things can show up the next day when your body has been jarred like this. Besides Pat, you're still in recovering from your last crash."

"Well, you're probably right doc," said Pat. We'll have to get a wire off to Houston. I'll stay the night but I'll be on my way after that.

The impossible had happened. He had crashed again and survived a second fall from the sky.

PART EIGHT

AGNES

Chapter 39

Reunions

Early the next day, Captain Hesser and Pat boarded the train for Dallas. Hesser was assigned as official photographer at Camp Dick located in central Dallas. He was also instrumental in booking Pat at various Air Services bases since Pat had started his military tour. Therefore, the Army reassigned Hesser to serve as Pat's guide while on tour.

"So Hess, what do you have planned for me today?" Pat asked.

"Well, as you might expect, when we arrive we'll have lunch with a bunch of reporters. They'll be a mix of local papers and some military press there. Probably the same basic questions but being at Fort Dick, I would imagine you'll get some technical stuff from the pilots and, of course, they'll want to know about your two crashes!" said Hesser.

"For the love of God, do you believe I lost control of that damn plane?" said Pat. "I should have known. I knew it was a heavier aircraft than my old 'Pup.' What was I thinking?"

As they settled into their seats, the two airmen went into a flying discussion that sounded like a foreign language to the businessmen seated across from them reading the Dallas Times Herald. It allowed the miles to sweep by unnoticed until the train arrived in Austin where a large number of passengers departed and boarded, breaking Pat and Edwin's trance. Ever since their days building planes in California, Pat and his good friend could talk aviation for hours on end. They had not seen each other since Pat joined the Signal Corps.

As the train pulled out of Austin, Hesser went for coffee in the dining car, returning with a cup for Pat who was reading the paper left behind by the men on their left. He pointed out an ad to Hesser promoting the speech planned for the Women's League that night.

"Looks like another ladies night, Hess," Pat exclaimed. "Those are fun. Only problem is I get a lot of autograph requests afterwards. And a few marriage proposals, too! But it's always enjoyable talking to the ladies."

"Did I tell you, Hess?" Pat said. "I booked a whole slug of Chautauqua tours after California." Chautauqua was a nationwide traveling tent circuit with entertainment and speakers that traveled the small towns of America at the time.

"We don't see as much Chautauqua down here as you do in the Midwest. They're here, just not as frequent," replied Hess.

"They are popular with the small towns. Most of those folks have only read about my story. Now that I've appeared in most of the big cities, there's a whole other audience in the small towns, if you don't mind speaking in tents," said Pat. "They pay pretty well, too. You're a bigger draw in the small towns."

"When do you start?" asked Hess.

"Well, after we finish in Dallas I hope to take a week or two off in San Francisco to visit Agnes and my old friends from Richmond. After that, I pretty much spend the first two weeks of July in the Bay Area giving speeches. Then Modesto, near our old turf for a few and then back to the Midwest."

"Have you talked to Agnes?" asked Hess.

"Sure, I called her a few weeks ago and have been sending letters. She's got a new job at a fancy department store now. I think the name of the place is called "Paris something." He paused a moment. "City of Paris," that's it. Very swanky, I guess. I'm looking forward to spending some time with her but I have such a busy schedule during my visit there. Hopefully, we'll be able to go up the Russian River for some relaxing time together. I really haven't been able to communicate with her as much as I've wanted to. I hope she'll still see me. I thought of her alot while on the run in Europe. You know how it is, Hess. People change. It's been a long time. I hope she feels the same."

Hess was aware of Agnes and had met her and Pat's friends from the Bay Area during the time Pat was traveling to Modesto frequently to make experimental planes.

"Agnes is a pretty tough gal. It's been a long time for her but I'm sure it feels longer for you with all you've been through," said Hess in a reassuring tone. "Besides, if it's meant to be, it's meant to be. If I remember Agnes, she's tough enough to withstand most of what gets tossed her way. I'm sure she'll be very glad to see you."

"That bunch sure knows how to have a good time, Pat," said Hess. "I wish I could go with you."

"Yeah, I miss them. It will be good to see them all," responded Pat.

"And after Chautauqua, What's next?" asked Hess.

"Well, by then I will have probably spoken in every city and town in the country." Pat said in an ironic tone. "The crowds will get smaller if I continue to tour. I'm certain of that. A guy can get overexposed you know, Hess."

"But you've always drawn large crowds, Pat. I wouldn't worry about that," Hess replied.

"Yeah, but you will see. It will fade. I'm old news now," responded Pat. "First I spoke in the big halls in the big cities. Now you've gotten me around the military bases. Chautauqua is the like the traveling circus. You roll into a tiny unsuspecting town, set up the big tent, and set their world on fire. After that, after everyone knows Pat O'Brien, I'll become old news. More than that, I didn't get into this war to make speeches. I got into it to fight," he said.

"I start Chautauqua at the end of July and go all the way up to the first few days of October. From there, I'll get off the circuit. I'm ready to shut up for once." Hess laughed.

"I've got some money in the bank. The book is doing very well." Pat paused then put down his paper. "I want to be a soldier again. I want to fly again," he said. "You know me, Hess."

"Yeah, I know. If there are two dogs fighting over a bone six blocks away, somehow, you'll find them," quipped Hess.

"This damn war is likely to end before I get a chance," Pat responded. "The Brits, Canadians, and Americans have already turned me down. One says it's my hip, another that I've done my part and the Brits don't want me in the air for fear I'll be captured again and shot. You know Hess, I think they don't see any logic in putting me back in Europe because they think this thing is close to being over."

"Well, I don't know about that but by the looks of that two-seater back in San Antonio, maybe that's the reason!" Hess said with a smile.

"Oh, now that's heartless! Some buddy you are, Hess." After pausing a second he said to Hess, "So tell me, Captain. How is it that with all your officer flying credentials, they have you doing public relations, taking pictures in the service and escorting me around like a valet?" Pat retorted.

"Now who's being heartless?" Edwin took another sip of coffee. Pat got a good laugh. Edwin actually had quite a talent for photography and it was recognized once he entered the service. It had always been one of his hobbies.

"I've still got a chance, Hess. After the Chautauqua swing, I'm heading to France. The French Legion or the Escadrille might take me. If I could just climb in the cockpit one more time, and give the Hun a little payback, that would be grand."

"I know how you feel, Pat. There's talk that the western front is deadlocked. There's been no movement for months. The air fighter is the one weapon that can break the deadlock. With the U.S. in the war and young fellas like the cadets we're going to see tonight jumping on board, we can break the German's backs and finish this thing. England and France are exhausted. But it could all be over by Christmas. Who the hell knows?"

"It could be over quick all right but not because of our overwhelming strength. If the treaty signed in March between the Russians and the Huns holds, you'll see thousands of Germans head west. That could finish us off. We still need to press on in the west and not wait for the damn thing to stop on its own. Russia is a crap shoot."

Pat had followed the Russian situation closely for months. Czarist Russia had committed eight million men to the Eastern front thus far, which kept a good portion of the German Army out of Western Europe, where Britain and France were bleeding white from four long years of bloodshed. Lenin and the Bolsheviks took power in Russia from Czar Nicholas in 1917 and now had signed a treaty on March 5, 1918 with Germany to cease fighting. The Huns would be free to leave Russia and march into Western Europe.

The old Czarist loyalists, however, were not going away quietly. Unfortunately for the Allies, the "white" armies were more preoccupied with taking back their government than fighting the Huns. The Allied and Central Powers were still fighting all over Russia, a country that was officially no longer at war with Germany or its allies.

Central Power armies from eastern European countries, aligned with the Huns, turned their guns on each other. Some changed sides and turned on the Germans. Bandits and ethnic groups such as the Cossacks clamored for stockpiles of food and war materials scattered all over Russia hoping to establish their independence from a now unstable government.

"The mess in Russia could go on for some time," said Pat. "The problem is if Lenin holds on to power, Germany will have no reason to stay. They'll finish us off in the west. The Allies have so many men and such huge amounts of materials in Russia. It could easily fall into Bolshevik hands and the "whites" would be done. If for no other reason, the Allies need to stay just to get their armies and supplies out. The only way out is to go east, to Vladivostok, on the railroad. If there's one thing I know about Hess, it's escaping and railroads."

"Ah ha, so now I see what interests you about Russia, Pat. You always were a few steps ahead of the rest of us," confirmed Hess.

"If France doesn't take me, I'll go to Russia. It will be my last chance to pay back those bastard Germans," said Pat emphatically.

The train stopped at Killeen, Waco, and finally arrived at Dallas, Texas. Captain Hesser had a car arranged to pick them up at Union Station and take them directly to Camp Dick. Camp John Dick Aviation Concentration Camp, also known as Camp Dick, was on the 227 acre Texas State Fairgrounds in Dallas and had just been taken over in January by the Army. The camp was a personnel holding pool for graduates of ground training schools. Over 2,000 young flying recruits were stationed there awaiting their next level of training and eventual deployment.

When Pat and Hesser arrived, they had lunch in a mess tent where they also met a group of about twenty reporters. Cadet Fay D. Dice of the 11th Cadet Squad was a former New-Democrat reporter that flew as a civilian instructor at Camp Scott and other aviation camps. He started the questioning and clearly had the most knowledge of all the journalists present.

In his notes he wrote that Pat was "a big man, well built and graceful, very polite when a lady is around, but a regular guy with the fellows. He noted Pat's dark hair was ruffled and his boyish eagerness and sincerity of purpose made him a favorite with the men."

A second reporter asked Pat if he was married yet. Pat said, "I have a reputation for being a dare-devil and brave, but I come back home and find most of these fellows I used to know are married. I haven't risked it yet."

Lieutenant Fuller, one of the officers present pressed further. "Really, are you married, Pat?" Pat said "no, no, I got those scars in war." Again, as usual, the reporters laughed and began to be taken in.

After about forty-five minutes of questions, Pat was escorted by post officers to the drill field where he reviewed 2000 aviation cadets of Camp Dick on parade for the first time. Upon completion of the pass and review, Pat spoke to the cadets, complimenting them on their first level of achievement and dignity on parade.

As he had done so many times before, he joked with the men after requesting their drill commander put them at ease. He told them of some laughable days training at Borden, "One of the Englishmen made a remark on the night I completed my training in Canada," said Pat. "He said to me, 'the trouble with you Yankees is that you are too proud to fight.' Well, one wasn't!" Pat barked. A roar went up.

Most of Pat's speech was his standard presentation but, as usual, he got off-script speaking to his military brethren. Pat revealed that not only did the sinking of the Lusitania cause him to "declare war on Germany," he actually purchased a ticket the same day and traveled from California to New York with plans to sail to England and join the British. He reminded the young recruits that America was not in the war at that time. "On the day I was to depart New York," Pat stated, "my boat was delayed one day. That night I read a war bulletin and learned that the U.S. was going to war with Mexico and an air service would be formed to support Pershing. I immediately returned to Richmond and joined the Signal Corps.

Pat spoke to the cadets about flying. He detailed some specific techniques used in the art of air battle that only an experienced fighter pilot would know. It enthralled the young neophyte cadets. Finally, Pat described his last battle in the air.

"Eight of our machines were ordered to go out and pick a fight, and I was in one of them. We ran into a bunch of nine Huns and were having a glorious battle when eleven more Germans came swarming over to where we were, making it twenty to eight. I dove and made an Immelmann turn, came onto a Hun Albatross and he slid through my fire, committing suicide. But I still had three to contend with. We were flying at an altitude between 8,000 and 9,000 feet."

"One of my foes got my range and shot away some of my instruments. One from the other side got better aim and a bullet hit me in the mouth, lodging in my throat. The next I knew I was in a German field hospital. To keep up my Irish luck, when I fell I had landed within 150 feet of the field hospital. They cut me out of my machine, thinking I was dead and wanting to identify me."

"Now, this hospital was an old Belgian home in the middle of a clearing. There were no beds, nothing but cement sacks to lie on and no covering except my coat. There were no nurses, which probably accounts for why I only stayed six days," he said. The previously enthralled and tense group of 2,000 cadets exploded again with laughter.

He talked about Paul Raney. "Imagine my feelings when the orderly brought me a picture of myself and Paul Raney, my dearest friend in the service. They dumped his body in a shallow grave with no honors and no flowers," Pat said. He told of how the British buried noted German aviators including machines flying over the grave and dropping flowers. "The aviation service is the only one that has any courtesy or chivalry left in it today. Until Paul's death, I was fighting because I thought it was my duty. Now it is for revenge, as well. When casualty lists come bearing the names of some of your loved ones, you will know something of how I felt." Two thousand fresh cadets returned to their somber mood.

At the end of the speech the cheer that went up resonated in Pat's ears and took him back to his first presentation to troops in London. His eyes filled with tears. To see the young, inexperienced boys cheering him as if Ty Cobb himself had just hit a winning home run. Though he was only twenty-seven years old, Pat felt extremely distant from the young cheering cadets before him. That thought, his tears and the sudden sensation that he was leaning on his cane jolted him to attention again so as to show dignity and strength in front of the troops. He waved his cane vigorously overhead, extending the cheers another full round.

For dinner, Pat was guest of honor at the Officers Club where he spoke of the intensity of the enemy and the importance of relentless training of all American recruits. He spoke in powerful terms about this commitment and every officer was struck by his sincerity.

That evening over 6000 people heard Pat speak for the Dallas Mothers' League, including the entire camp who was thrilled all over again hearing Pat a second time. Knowing that his appearance in Texas could very well be his final speech to active troops, Pat was particularly impassioned that night. In five days he'd be in northern California for a homecoming in Richmond and a reunion with Agnes.

For the next three days, Pat and Captain Hess spent time at Camp Dick. Pat was able to give some small group lectures about the fineries of flying as a weapon of war. For most of the cadets, having just finished ground school, it was a bit of a leap since none had earned their wings yet but it was obvious that flying was one skill but being a fighter pilot was quite another experience. Pat was in his element and felt great being around aircraft once again. He took a number of solo flights in some of the newer aircraft and flew co-pilot with a few advanced cadets.

Early in the morning on Thursday, June 20, Pat and Edwin boarded the train heading for Los Angeles. Hess would complete his escorting assignment once they arrived and pass responsibilities to Virgil Moore, another old acquaintance of Pat's.

"It sure was grand to spend time with you around aircraft once again. I haven't talked that much about flying for months. Some of these cadets think I'm just a photographer," said Hess.

The two men found their seats on the train headed back to San Antonio where they would catch the Southern Pacific line through New Mexico and Arizona, arriving in Los Angeles in about five hours. There they would hook up with Pat's old Signal Corps buddy Virgil Moore. Hess would "hand Pat over" to Moore who would accompany Pat to Northern California for his Bay Area speeches.

Both Pat and Hess fell asleep as soon as the train pulled out. It had been a busy week. As the train pulled into Austin, the two friends sitting across from each other awoke simultaneously. Holding their gaze a second, half awake, Pat uttered, "Let's eat!"

They took a spot in the dining car, shared a beer, and laughed about making planes from scratch during their time in California. "We had no idea what the hell we were doing, Hess," said Pat. "Why was I always the one designated to make the first run?"

"Pat, of all the pilots I've ever known you have more guts than any of them," Hess said. "Either that or your brains are in your pants. I'm not sure," joked Hess.

About two hours later the train arrived at San Antonio. They switched trains and then talked all the way to Los Angeles. Captain Hess had about two hours before he had to return to Dallas so he and Pat took advantage of the time to have one last beer in the Harvey House restaurant located within the Le Grande Station.

Pat was looking over the beer list when he noticed a lean, uniformed pilot enter the restaurant over Hess' right shoulder.

"Moore!" shouted Pat.

Like Pat and Hess, Virgil Moore was an experienced pilot, and was now training young cadets at Coronado. He acquired a two week pass to escort Pat during his time in California. Since Pat was appearing as a member of the Royal Flying Corps, the U.S. military had agreed to provide escort and logistics assistance during the military tours.

"Pat O'Brien as I live and breathe," said Moore.

"Boy, it seems like ages," returned Pat. "But you must have such an easy life. You don't look one day older than the day I left for Canada!" Moore had been one of those present the night Pat left North Island and the flyboys sang, "Pack up your Troubles" arm in arm. "That seems like a decade ago, doesn't it Pat?" said Moore. "It sure does, Virgil," returned Pat.

"Oh, sorry Hess," said Pat. "This is Virgil Moore. He and I go back to the first days of San Diego. Hell, we were there before Foulois, weren't we Virge?"

"Hi Moore," said Hess said extending his hand. "Old Birdman, huh?"

"Yeah, Pat and I used to fly kites off North Island," said Moore. "Hell, we didn't know any better."

"At least you two had real aeroplanes. Pat and I were making our own back in California," said Hess.

"Oh, I don't know Pat," responded Moore. "Did you think those planes looked real?"

"Hell no!" responded Pat. "We flew two old beat up "Jennys" remember?"

"Oh, those were bad!" confirmed Hess.

Moore sat down and Pat waved the waitress over an ordered a beer for his old friend.

"Gosh Pat, it's amazing to see you," said Moore. "I've read all about your escapades. I remember the day I heard you were missing. It was such a shock when you literally came back from the dead." Pausing after hearing what he said. "Sorry Pat, I didn't mean it to come out that way."

[479]

"Hell, Moore, I was nearly dead twenty-five times. I've got more lives than a black cat," said Pat.

The three men finished a second round while comparing notes about their flying escapades. Captain Hess suddenly realized the time and slugged down a final gulp. He was sad to be parting from his old dare-devil friend. More than any of Pat's flying chums over the years, Hess had a personality closest to Pat's daring way and passion for flying. Hess' emotions were stirred by the parting which was also helped along by multiple steins of fermentation.

"Bye, chum," said Hess.

"We'll meet up again, Hess," returned Pat. And with that, Hess was gone.

About thirty minutes after Hess's train pulled away from the station headed for San Antonio, Pat and Virgil were chatting away in the dining car of their train headed north on the Southern Pacific toward San Francisco.

Virgil got up for a second round of beef. As Pat sat alone it suddenly hit him, "I'm going to see Agnes tomorrow!" He became nervous and set his fork down. He stared out the window trying to picture how he and Agnes would greet each other. "Will she meet me at the station alone? Will the others be with her? Will she see me first or will I step off and have to find her?" he wondered. Like all adults who fall in love, thoughts often become simple and childlike. Profundity departs and youthful whim possesses every thought. It's also that time when goofy nicknames like "cupcake" are used by perfectly grown adults.

"There's fresh beef, just put out Pat" said Moore, totally out of context.

"Train food," Pat responded. "It's like hotel food. It all tastes somewhat similar. You'd think they get it out of the same pot." Moore laughed and took his seat.

"Boy, listen to Pat," said Virgil. "For a guy that ate turnips and cabbage head for two months, you've sure gotten picky!"

"Yeah, I shouldn't complain," said Pat. "But all I can think about is home cooking, particularly Agnes."

"Don't give me that hogwash, O'Brien," retorted Virgil. "It ain't Agnes' cookin' you're thinking about." Pat smiled looking down at his food as Virgil made his point by pointing his fork in Pat's face.

The two Pilots finished eating, ordered another beer, and did some catching up. Virgil had never left North Island. He was there as Lt. Benjamin Foulois slowly but surely built a legitimate air field at San Diego. "Did you ever get out of those canvas tents?" asked Pat.

"Yeah, you wouldn't know that place," responded Virgil. "I've trained a lot of pilots there, Pat, particularly since we've jumped into this fray."

"I know what you mean, Virge," said Pat, setting down his glass. "Can you imagine? When I left Camp Borden we were eighteen men – eighteen! We were nothing more than a spec. I just met over 2,000 American cadets in Texas. Two thousand and that's just at one camp. Hell, there were only eighteen qualified pilots in Canada when I left for England." Taking another sip of beer. Pat went on. "This damn country can really muscle up when it wants to. What angers me is that we waited so long. I guess that damn Wilson thought he could talk his way to victory."

"I agree, Pat" confirmed Moore. "You have no idea how much I envied you leaving San Diego that day. I wanted to go to Canada with you but I just didn't have it in me I guess. I was younger then. It was all like a camping trip to me." Pausing and feeling a bit less of himself he went on. "Sometimes I wonder if I've done enough."

"Don't feel that way, Virgil. What you've done training pilots all these months has more impact on victory than the half-dozen or so Huns I shot out of the sky. Your story just goes untold but your impact is great, too," he said.

"Thanks, Pat. Coming from you that means a lot," said Vigil in a soft voice.

The two finished off their last beer and decided to return to the passenger car. Moore was tired and dozed off in the seat across from Pat. Pat sat against the window watching the length of California go by as he returned his thoughts to Agnes. He pictured her at the end of the platform perhaps, running toward him maybe or standing alone holding one of her hats at her waste, looking unsure, alone, soft and nervous. "Any or all of those possibilities would suit me just fine," he thought. He then leaned his head against the window and dozed off himself.

About an hour later, Pat awoke pulling his face from the window as the heat of the Mojave Dessert woke him. "Tehachapi," Pat said to himself. He had taken the route a number of times and he knew the Mojave Dessert lay just southeast of the Tehachapi Pass and the famous section of "loop tracks" or helix that scaled the mountain by looping back and over itself, lessening the angle of the grade.

[481]

It connected the desert to the San Joaquin Valley where he and Elmer had spent so much time. Every railman found the unique loop of interest. Pat was no exception. It was an engineering feat built forty years earlier. But as Pat watched the train double back on itself it wasn't the engineering complexity that struck him this time.

He was struck how untouched America was from the war. In Europe, all he had seen was twisted and scarred rail lines, destroyed one day, repaired the next but in the end tossed about unable to move trains anywhere across the entire continent of Europe. "Perhaps someday," he thought "when I'm into my middle years, I'll find myself a railroad hand again, reconstructing Europe's rails from the destruction of war. America will be the only country on earth with the capacity to rebuild. It will surely mean "boom-times" for us after the last shot is fired."

The Valley appeared instantly as the last car slipped off the Tehachapi snag. The familiar fields extended as far as Pat could see and all the memories of his time there with Elmer and Hess came flooding back. He felt more fondness for the Valley now then he had during the short time spent there. The train stopped in Bakersfield waking Virgil, who took up site seeing out his window, as well. Then Tulare passed, fostering more memories for Pat. At Fresno, Pat and Virgil decided it was time to eat. The eleven hour trip would get them to San Francisco in the morning.

"Do we want to make use of the sleeping car, Pat?" asked Virgil.

"Well, I don't know about you but there's few on the train. I think I'll stretch out in my seat. I'm likely not to sleep that well either way," he said.

"That was my idea, too," responded Virgil and so the two men spent the night alternating sleep with quiet discussion until dawn. At 7:00 a.m. the next day, June 25, Pat awoke and could see the congestion of San Francisco in the distance. "It won't be long now," he thought. "I hope she is there to meet me," he thought. He pictured her up early, dressing and wondered what she might look like after all this time. He pictured her red hair, petite frame and wonderful eyes that he suddenly missed so very much.

As the train slowed, Pat reached for his small bag and stuffed his newspaper inside.

"Tell you what, Pat. I'll lag behind and let you see Agnes on your own first. I don't want to be in the midst of your reunion," said Moore chuckling. "Once I see you're done manhandling her, I'll walk toward you both," he said in a joking way, giving Pat a bit of a ribbing.

"Thanks, Virge!" Pat quipped, in a tone matching Moore's campy remark.

The train came to a complete stop and an average number of passengers were exiting in such a way that at the far end of the platform, Agnes MacMillan felt nervous that Pat might not be on board. Each time she'd see a gap in the flow of people exiting the train, her heart would sink as if she'd seen the last passenger come off. She had not seen Pat step down but he had. He was in the farthest car and was walking toward her. She could not make out faces but was looking for that aggressive, brisk gate so familiar to her when Pat departed months back. But there was a stagger in Pat's walk now and every other step relied on the press of his cane on the wooden platform. He saw her first.

Agnes wore a fairly tight-fighting dress that flared at the hips. She wore a small hat with just a single ostrich feather to the side that garnished her presence. Pat noticed she had a fashionable umbrella in her left hand that was closed and looked like a cane from his distance. "How ironic," he thought. He could see her craning to see any sign of him from her position at the end of the platform.

Pat raised his big arm overhead holding his cane and Agnes instantly recognized that broad sweep across his body. She saw the cane a split second later. The photos she had seen in the local papers of Pat never included the cane and he had not mentioned it in any of his letters.

Pat hurried toward her. Agnes ran full force. They pause not two feet from each other then clutched in a heavy embrace. In the stillness of their kiss, the umbrella fell to the platform first, then Pat's cane.

A porter pushing a cart full of luggage passed two feet from them and said in full voice, "Welcome home, son." Nether Pat nor Agnes heard him as he passed. Embraces between young men and women were becoming more a common site these days, especially including boys with canes.

"You're here, Pat. I can't believe you're here," whispered Agnes in Pat's ear.

"I thought I might never see you again, Agnes," said Pat, then he kissed her gently but pressed against her red lips.

"You look so different," said Pat. "Wait, that didn't come out right. You look beautiful, hon. And these clothes, so modern. You look like you came straight from Paris."

"Oh, Pat, this is just the latest style," Agnes returned. "You're just behind the times."

Saying nothing but looking down with a gesture, Pat directed Agnes's attention to his cane. "I'm not that good at bending over yet, Agnes. Do you mind?"

"Oh, you poor thing," said Ages. "Of course," and she picked up both Pat's cane and her umbrella. Taking his arm she turned and the couple began a slow walk up the platform.

Pat had fully forgotten Virgil for the moment. His flying buddy was keeping his distance about fifty feet behind them seeing their conversation in full exchange.

"Are you the only one here?" asked Pat. "Did none of my old chums come down to greet me? Boy, how quickly a guy is forgotten!"

"Are you kidding? All of San Francisco is doing nothing but talking about your upcoming speeches. Your book has been running in the paper for the past week," she said. "All our friends, the sweet things, they insisted I meet you here by myself. They'll all be at the Inn by 11:00 and we've got a big lunch planned. Everyone will be there."

This brought a rush of tears to Pat's eyes which Agnes noticed right off. She smiled at him though Pat kept his eyes looking forward as if to hide his emotions. Turning suddenly he remembered his escort buddy.

"Virgil!" shouted Pat turning with a concerned look. Virgil was fifty feet behind them. He waved, stepping it up to join the two.

"Agnes, this is Virgil Moore. He's an old buddy from North Island and he's my attaché while in California."

"Oh my, attaché indeed, aren't we important now!" scoffed Agnes.

Agnes was a sweet gal but never missed a chance to give Pat a little jab every once in a while. Anyone that knew Pat and Agnes knew that she was certainly up to the task. A man with the personality of Pat O'Brien required a strong counter balance and Agnes was that.

"Hello, Virgil," said Agnes. "It's very nice to meet you. I'm sure Pat is a handful but you look up to the task." The three continued up the platform.

"Pat, you'll never guess who's driving us to the ferryboat," said Agnes.

"Who? Jerry Solich?" said Pat.

"No, Chuck Pearl. He insisted," answered Agnes.

"I'll be," said Pat. Turning to Virgil, he continued, "He's my old railroad buddy. He taught me the ropes as a Fireman. Hell, if it wasn't for Chuck, I would have never met Joe Cato."

"Cato?" asked Virgil.

"You remember me telling you about the guy I flew experimental with for months? He went on to the east coast but I cut my teeth on his planes," answered Pat. Virgil nodded.

"There's Chuck," said Agnes waving as Chuck stood outside his car. Chuck ran up and grabbed Pat by the arms unashamed to show the tears welled up in his eyes.

"Damn O'Brien, I thought you were a goner," said Chuck. "It's really hard to believe you are actually here."

They climbed into Chuck's brand new 1918 Chevrolet "490." Chuck Pearl had moved up the ranks within Santa Fe and was doing quite well for himself.

"What did you do, rob a bank Pearl?" asked Pat.

Chuck Pearl drove to the ferry station, parking his car in the public lot. All four took the ferry to Oakland and then onto Richmond. There was so much to talk about between them that the ferry crossing went quickly. Virgil listened mostly and was taken in by the Bay, being an old Oklahoma Boy.

When they arrived at the Ivy, Agnes told Pat to go in first. The entire restaurant was full of people waiting to see him. Chuck Pearl had "bought the place out" for lunch. A big cheer went up as soon as Pat stepped inside. It was an astounding experience for Pat to be back in his old haunt once again. The place hadn't changed. Pat's whole world had changed but the Ivy was the same. Something about it moved him as he fought back tears. All the hell he'd been through and yet the same mugs sat on the same shelves filled by the same bartenders. It just didn't see possible but it was.

Jerry Solich was the first one to shake Pat's hand. There were a dozen firemen from the Santa Fe and even McCracken's secretary Sharon Johansson who first greeted Pat and Jerry was there.

Conductor Joe Thomas, the young pilot Ed Neville who flew with Pat for Joe Cato. Curley McNeil and Claude Craig were there but Tim Reardon, the third of Cato's pilots, had died in a crash while training at San Diego after Pat had departed for Canada. Pat was surprised to see Buster Wolfe and Mike Fisi who were young mechanics on Cato's team but now sported Army Air Service uniforms. Both boys were due to depart in one week.

Pat and the entire group took their seats. Chuck Pearl rose to welcome Pat.

"First of all, thanks to everyone for coming out to greet our old pal Pat, today. I know he appreciates it, as does Agnes. Pat, we were all concerned when we heard you were missing. But we all knew that if anyone had the guts to survive, you surely did. And Pat, when we heard you'd jumped out of a moving train every man at Santa Fe said, "so what's new!"

The room broke out in laughter. "So let's raise our glasses to our friend Pat O'Brien, who somehow has returned to Richmond once again for which we are all so grateful. Here's to you, Pat!"

"Hear, Hear!" shouted everyone in the room all raising their glasses followed by hearty sips. Lunch was served but Pat hardly had a chance to eat as one after another of his old friends came up to shake his hand and say hello. Finally, Agnes began to run interference so that Pat could eat. It didn't matter. Pat was too excited to eat anyway. The celebration went on for four hours. Finally, after an appreciative speech by Pat and another toast to his good fortune, the party broke up.

Agnes pulled Pat aside as the final few exited the Ivy and Chuck Pearl was paying the bill. "I have arranged a room for us at the St. James, Pat," whispered Agnes. "I hope you won't mind." Pat just smiled and nodded to her quietly. He was exhausted but mostly wanted to be alone with Agnes. They had barely had time to talk. Pat told Virgil about the arrangements and slipped him some cash to cover his room. "We'll see you in the morning," said Pat. Virgil winked and gave Pat a mock salute.

The young couple slowly made their way to the St. James Hotel where upon entering the lobby they took the stairs to the 2nd floor. In cahoots with Agnes, Pearl had arranged for Pat's bags to be placed in the room. Agnes had the key but yielding to the etiquette of the day, felt compiled to pass it to Pat who opened the door. Once inside, Agnes turned and latched the door, demonstrating her independence of certain levels of contemporary etiquette. Both were so compelled to be alone with each other so there was little discussion in the first moments. Like so many wars before and after, the pacing of courtship, with its measured escalations of intimacy was washed away in the context of "no tomorrow."

The moment ascribed Pat as the vulnerable one. Only Agnes could take away the days, weeks, and months of pain and uncertainly that hung inside Pat's heart. For weeks he had embodied the classic American hero while on tour, attesting to his ability to stand firm against the calamity of war. In the privacy of this room, however, with the person he trusted and loved, Pat could let down his guard and lay his soul open to Agnes and perhaps free himself of a portion of the remorse bought over him in the last year.

The night contained every emotion and passion that two young people in love could experience when the world collapses around them. How hopeless Agnes felt when so little information was known of Pat's fate. So guilty did Pat feel when thoughts of home and Agnes evaporated in the fields of Belgium. Surely, selfish was Agnes giving up hope and deciding that the loss of Pat would not decay the rest of her life.

Early in the evening both seemed consumed with guilt and many tears were shed, the one comforting the other, removing the pain with tender words and soft kisses. By midnight, there was laughter and a reminiscing of the early days and all that Pat had missed since leaving Richmond. In the early hours of the morning Pat told the full story of his horrible ordeal, not with the flare of Carnegie Hall but with all the pain he had kept to himself for over a year. As the first sign of the new day was barely discernible, all talking stopped and the two lovers gave their bodies to each other, removing the final pains of separation in the bliss of physical love. They fell asleep in each other's arms as the day outside was just beginning.

Chapter 40

Agnes

"Agnes? Agnes, you awake?" whispered Pat just over her right shoulder. She stirred but gave no response. "Agnes, it's 12:30 in the afternoon," he said under his breath, trying to sound urgent. He tucked his chin over her shoulder peering over to see if she was awake.

Eyes still closed, Agnes slowly slid her right hand up and around Pat's neck, holding him close. He kissed her neck. "I'm hungry," he said.

Finally, a whispered response came from Agnes, "You're always hungry. Where do you put it all? I swear, I do not know," adjusting her hand so as to tug on his ear.

"Aren't you hungry, sweetie?" responded Pat.

"Well, let me think. I just woke up. I'm not sure what day it is, let alone what time it is. My hair is a mess. No, I don't think I can tell if I'm hungry or not yet," said Agnes, teasing in her charming way. Rolling over on her back she turned so she could see Pat. He leaned down and gave her a soft and fairly lengthy kiss.

"It's wonderful to have you home again, Pat," she said. "It seems like ages since you stepped on to that train for San Diego."

"Like a lifetime," responded Pat. "But I'm here now, so let's not talk about that. Let's not look backwards." He gave her another kiss on cheek and she returned the embrace, before suddenly sitting up in their bed.

"I need to look much better than this if we're going to go eat." She swung her legs around and off the edge of the bed. Pat lunged and wrapped his arms around her waist, pulling her back on to the bed where they tussled playfully for a time ending it with a loving embrace.

"I need to freshen up," said Agnes as she rose and headed for the bathroom.

"Where do you want to go?" asked Pat, yelling to her from the bed as he slipped on his trousers.

"I don't care, you pick," shouted back Agnes.

"Well, I guess we better have lunch now. It's afternoon already," returned Pat. There was no response from the bathroom. Agnes was focused on her mirror.

Pat continued, assuming she was listening. "I'm in the mood for Italian," he said. "Let's go to the Fior. I have a hankering for their angel hair pasta. The whole time I was eating cabbage heads in Belgium, I always thought about Fior's pasta and Italian bread," Pat touched his fingertips to his lips the pulled away in the classic "voila'" gesture.

The Fior D. Italia was the finest Italian Restaurant in San Francisco and one of the oldest in the country having first opened in 1886.

"Italian is fine," said Agnes hearing him but preoccupied with her primping. Then, when his words finally registered she said, "Wait a minute, you want to go all the way to San Francisco? I thought you were hungry!" she yelled from the bathroom.

"I don't want to stay in Richmond, honey. We can get a quick crab sandwich here and enjoy dinner at Fior's tonight. Bring your things. I'm going to check out of here. I've got plans to stay a day or two in San Francisco."

"Well, I need to dress differently than if we're going to the city," said Agnes. "After all, what if I run into one of the young chaps from work?"

"What chaps?" said Pat quickly. Agnes laughed having gotten Pat's attention.

"Why in the world does a women need to change what she wears based on what she eats?" Pat asked.

"You wouldn't understand. You're a man," quipped Agnes as she applied final touches to her lipstick. Pat tucked his belt firm and ran his fingers through his hair just as Agnes entered from the bath room.

"Stand still, you," she said, running her comb along both sides of Pat's ruffled locks, then down the back. Framing him with her two hands, she leaned back to observed her work.

"There. Better!" she said. Pat rolled his eyes.

They exited the room and walked hand in hand down the stairs to the lobby. Pat was carrying his overnight bag containing their clothes. Agnes entered the adjoining Ivy Inn and ordered two crab sandwiches to go while Pat checked out of the hotel. When she returned to the lobby she saw him standing near the concierge, flipping through the morning paper.

"He's never far from the front," she thought. She could sense that Pat often drifted to Europe and those he left behind. "Perhaps I can get his mind off things over the next two days," she said to herself.

"All set," said Agnes holding up the bag of sandwiches. He put down the newspaper, took her hand and they exited the hotel.

On their way to the train station, they stopped at Stiefvater's Department Store. Agnes added a bit to her wardrobe which Pat paid for. He enjoyed spending his money for once. "You know Agnes, I've been making money all year but never get a chance to spend it! I'm always chasing to the next speech," he said as they walked out of the store.

"Why do you wear those same boots, Pat? You've certainly bought enough new clothes since you've been here but no boots," asked Agnes.

"I shall not part with these as long as I'm in this uniform. These are the boots given to me in Holland when I first escaped. They mean a lot to me. Do they look that bad?" asked Pat.

"No, I was just curious," said Agnes. "I found it funny you've never bought new boots."

They took a cab to the Southern Pacific Station where they rode to Oakland and transferred to the Ferry at Oakland Harbor. Ferries ran across the bay every thirty minutes. They used to run only every two hours when Pat lived in Richmond. He was surprised at the upgraded harbor and the huge increase in activity compared to just two years earlier.

"People are starting to work and spend money again, Pat," said Agnes. "We've notice it in the store also. The war has made money for many people."

Upon arriving in San Francisco, Agnes took Pat to the City of Paris Store where she worked. She was quite tickled to "show off" her boyfriend to her girlfriends there. Actually, Agnes had only recently revealed her relationship to Pat which stunned her friends.

Pat was well known throughout the country but though she certainly grasped the extent of Pat's celebrity, she never thought of him that way. Agnes began working at the City of Paris Store eighteen months previous so none of the girls knew Pat before he left for war.

They shopped a bit more, said good-bye to the girls and then headed for the elevator. Nearly every clerk stared enviously as the elevator doors closed. Pat had charmed them to no end.

"Agnes is so lucky," said one.

Reaching the first floor, Pat turned to Alice and said, "We're at the Palace."

"Oh my, Pat, that's so expensive!" responded Agnes, generally surprised.

"It's fine, Agnes. I'm not the poor boy you knew two years ago," he said. "If I don't spend some of my money, I'll get robbed on the street," he joked.

The Palace was commonly referred to as the "New Palace Hotel." The first hotel had been destroyed, much like Potter Palmer's Palmer House was lost in the great Chicago Fire. The San Francisco earthquake in 1906 forced owner William Chapman to redo the interior. Though it was one of the few buildings standing after the quake, the interior was destroyed by fire. As with the Palmer House, the second version of the hotel far exceeded the first. The property contained 755 rooms, all with individual bathrooms. Its main feature was the "Palm Court" on the first floor which anchored a towering atrium through the landmark's center core. There was nothing more elegant than the Palace.

Once checked in, Pat and Agnes headed for the Fior. They walked one block north then west to Stockton Street where they caught a street car heading north. The Fior was about ten minutes away in the North Waterfront area. They were given a secluded private table and enjoyed a wonder five-course Italian meal with wine that raised the eyebrows of even the wine steward due to its price and rare selection. It was an elegant dinner with intimate and heartfelt conversation. Pat was truly relaxed and glad to be with Agnes again.

"What's today, Thursday?" asked Pat.

"Yes, Thursday," she said. "I have all of this week and next week off. It's going to be wonderful. Is your first speech on Tuesday?" she asked.

"Yes, on the 2nd of July, then Oakland on the 3rd and I'm off on the 4th," said Pat. "I was hoping we could make a day of it."

"Me, too," responded Agnes. "I know the gang talked about plans for a picnic up the Russian River. They asked about us coming along."

"Sounds like fun," said Pat sipping a fine desert wine as they spoke. "Let's see how next week develops. I thought we could stay in San Francisco a few days then head back for the weekend. What do you think?

"I think it will be wonderful, Pat," responded Agnes, also enjoying the fruity desert wine.

Pat and Agnes spent Thursday and Friday alone in San Francisco. They shopped, returned to the City of Paris Store a few times, visited many of the scenic waterfront areas in the city, and went to the theater at night. They spent hours talking about all that had transpired the past two years and shared stories of their days growing up at home. Their late evenings were spent relaxing at the luxurious Palace Hotel each evening. On Saturday morning they went to Agnes's apartment in San Francisco where she gathered clothes for the weekend. By noon they were back in Richmond and checked back into the St. James Hotel.

That evening their entourage of friends gathered at the Ivy. Jerry Solich, who was now married, came with his wife. James McCracken, who had hired Pat at the Santa Fe, joined the group. McCracken had not seen him since Pat left for San Diego. Pat enjoyed catching up with his old Santa Fe buddies.

"What ever happened to young Chip Walker?" asked Pat. Chip was the understudy that had taken Pat's place the day he first met Joe Cato on the Stockton Run.

"Unfortunately, after he was drafted and went to basic training, we heard less than one month later that he was shot up by strafing German planes near St. Mihiel Salient south of Verdun," reported McCracken.

Pat went cold. The thought came to him, "Chip took my place again." Then another thought, "Why did I think that? I was almost killed, myself"

"It's a hellish place, Verdun," said Pat. "He was such a nice kid, just wanted to be a railroader, I remember. When the young ones die so early it hurts. I saw a lot of young boys go quickly like that."

"Yeah, nice kid," repeated McCracken, looking up suddenly. "Look there's Hanson."

"Nice kid?" thought Pat, "as if Chip simply took a job with another railroad! Oh well, they can't know, not really," he thought. As with every other veteran of war, the casual response of those that were not there reminds vets of their responsibility to those left dead on the battlefield.

Frank Hanson, the engineer on the Stockton run, had just arrived. Agnes was engaged in conversation with some of the wives and girlfriends but had a distinctive ear to Pat's warm greeting for Hanson at the same time. She was enjoying hearing Pat interact with his close friends.

Otto Stevens from Stockton and wife arrived.

"Hi, Pat," said Otto extending his hand. "Hello, Agnes," he said turning to her. "This is my wife, Arlene," he said gesturing toward her. Agnes knew Otto but had not met his wife yet.

"Hello, Arlene," responded Agnes. "Join us girls, here. The men are just talking about trains, you know. We have more important matters to discuss."

"That's certain," responded Arlene, relieved to see that the gathering included the ladies. She took a seat next to Agnes. "Looks like we will be hosting Pat in Stockton next week," said Arlene to Agnes. "Will you be with him?"

"We haven't talked about next week yet," replied Agnes. I have the week off but his speaking schedule is busy. I think he's in Stockton the following week, isn't he?"

"July 10th – yes," confirmed Arlene.

"Then probably not. I'll be back at work that week," replied Agnes.

The ladies carried on their conversation and men talked war, railroad, and any number of humorous mishaps that had occurred during Pat's time with the Santa Fe.

Pat learned from Buster Wolfe, who was a mechanic at Stockton and was not eligible to serve due to his poor eyesight, that Curley McNeil, Claude Craig, and Tim Reardon, the three test pilots who worked with him at Cato's field, were all aviators in the U.S. Air Service. Sadly, Reardon was shot from the skies over Flanders and Ted Neville, who had asked Pat about Sarajevo the day Pat walked in to Hanger #2 at Stockton, had perished during a training session at Coronado, never having seen action.

The evening went late. Pat wasn't about to let his close friends toast him once again, so at one in the morning he hoisted his glass to the entire group giving an emotional and heartfelt toast to his friends who cared enough to welcome him home after his long two years away. It was a night that all would remember for a long time.

On Sunday morning, Pat and Agnes decided to go to church. They rose early, had breakfast at the hotel, and headed for the First Methodist Church in Richmond. They almost entered Our Lady of Mercy Catholic Church which was, oddly enough, right next door. Agnes snickered with embarrassment as they backed down the steps in the face of the good Father, whose collar indicated the wrong church.

"I can't imagine St. Patrick's Church and the Momence Methodist Church side-by-side," said Pat as they hurried next door. How odd."

The Richmond Methodist church was built into a steep hill at the bottom of West Richmond Street on the corner with Martina Street. Pat found it an unusual looking little church with three distinct architectural structures, forced together as if designed by a committee. "It likely was," he thought.

The service was simple, lasting about one hour. There were familiar hymns and a sermon that stressed the importance of commitment. Somehow it rang true for Pat. Though the preacher was speaking of religious commitment to the "holy Lord Jesus," Pat couldn't prevent his thoughts from drifting to his flyboy mates in France, the relentless Hun and how he, somehow, had not completed his task. It haunted him most idle hours of the day of which he had few. But every inactive moment of his day was filled with these thoughts.

As the service was drawing to a close, a man about thirty years old tapped Pat on the right shoulder. Pat looked behind and greeted the man. "Hello," said Pat.

"Are you the aviator, Pat O'Brien?" the man asked.

"I am," said Pat. "How did you know who I was?"

[494]

"Well, I noticed your cane during the service and, I apologize, but I peered around and noticed you looked a whole lot like Pat O'Brien," he said. The man in church had seen the same ad that all of San Francisco had seen, promoting Pat's upcoming appearances the Allied War Exhibition. It showed Pat standing in front of an aeroplane using his cane. Pat was out of uniform and surprised he was recognized. "Damn cane," he thought.

"Do you mind terribly if I point you out to the congregation?" asked the man.

"Sure, I don't mind," said Pat.

During final announcements, Pat was introduced and the small church rose to give him a warm ovation. On his way out, many hung back to shake his hand and congratulated him. Pat had "left the war" over the last three days. Due to his state of mind following the sermon, he felt a bit uncomfortable receiving accolades once again. He understood, however, that it was important to be living testament to the relevance of the Allied effort. He began to gear up for the next two weeks which would be full of major speeches, book signings throughout the Bay Area, and appearances at the Exhibition.

The Allied War Exposition was a two week event, sponsored by the U.S. Government. It consisted of a parade and fourteen exhibitions illustrating American, British, French, Canadian, and Belgian war efforts. It included a number of German "trophies" captured by the Allies including downed planes, tanks and artillery. The San Francisco show was the first and only complete exhibit of its kind. Los Angeles, Waco, Texas, Cleveland, Cincinnati, and Chicago would all host portions of the exposition after San Francisco.

Edwin Hesser had made all arrangements for Pat's appearances and would arrive from Dallas on July 7. Until then, Virgil Moore would handle details before returning to Coronado.

Pat was scheduled to have lunch with Virgil Moore Monday, July 1 to review the upcoming schedule. Pat and Agnes stayed close to the St. James Hotel that morning, then met with Virgil Moore for lunch.

"Hi Virgil," said Pat as Moore entered the dining room of the Ivy.

"Hello Pat, Hi Agnes," said Virgil. The three sat down, looked quickly at menus, and then ordered food. Once the waiter stepped away, Virgil reviewed the schedule.

"Tomorrow you'll speak at the Dreamland Roller Rink on Fillmore, Pat," relayed Virgil. "It's quiet a large venue and we expect a big crowd. This will be your first appearance in the Bay Area and everyone has followed your story so closely here. Frank Hanson would like to tag along so I told him the other night it would be fine. I could use an extra man in case I get pulled away. There will be a lot of press, I'm sure."

"Do you plan a formal press conference beforehand?" asked Pat.

"Not beforehand but after," suggested Moore. "That way you won't have to answer 1,000 questions that will likely be answered in your speech. It will be more efficient."

"Great idea, Virgil," agreed Pat. "The other way seemed to be repetitive."

Virgil went on. "Oakland Auditorium Wednesday, another big venue. Then you're off July 4 and up to Berkley on Friday. That will be a challenge, Pat. The Hearst Greek Theatre at Berkley is actually an outdoor facility. It sits about 6,500 with lawn seating for about 2,000 but will probably be overflowing. I'm told their amplification system lacks a bit so you'll have to be in good voice that night."

"I feel great, Virgil," said Pat. "I've had some nice rest these past few days." Agnes kicked him under the table.

"Saturday you get a breather" he continued "The Exposition opens Sunday. They requested you ride a tank for the parade. I told them you're a pilot for God's sake! They agreed you should ride in a car." Reaching into his stack of papers, Virgil pulled out a program. "Here's the schedule for the War Expo. Looks like you'll be busy.

"Agnes will be back to work then, will I have help?" asked Pat.

"Sure, Hess will arrive on Saturday to replace me and Hanson will stay on" Virgil replied. "I'll be heading back to Coronado on day three of the show."

"That's grand, Virgil," responded Pat. "I appreciate all the arrangements you've made. It's a big help."

Pat and Agnes turned in early that evening. Both could sense that their time together was reaching the halfway point. They began to cherish each minute alone.

Pat's presentation at Dreamland on July 2 was a roaring success. There were six ovations and the cheering echoed extensively off the high ceiling rafters creating the loudest response yet to Pat's speech. Virgil, Hanson, and Agnes were struck how free and easy Pat was speaking to such a large audience and how entertaining his delivery was. Pat's extensive speaking experience was evident, his timing and ability to manipulate the audience had become intuitive. "You're a real pro," said Frank Hanson as they exited the building. "Thanks, Frank," said Pat.

Local publisher and book seller Paul Elder was the promoter of Pat's speech at the Oakland Auditorium the next night. It seated over 5,000 but Pat spoke to a standing room crowd that neared 6,000. Agnes really enjoyed this second presentation because she could hear Pat much better than in the cavernous Dreamland Rink. Pat sold over 400 books that evening, a lot due to Elder's abilities as a master promoter of authors at special events. Pat could only sign 250 copies. His hand became too sore to continue. The press gathering was smaller than the night before since many of the Bay area press had attended his speech in San Francisco.

The next day, Pat, Agnes, and the entire entourage of "Ivy Inn Group" headed north to the Russian River for a full day of picnicking, games, swimming and the beauty of the Redwoods. More than once during the day, Pat shook his head, hardly believing he was celebrating the Fourth of July in Northern California in arguably the most beautiful spot on earth.

Agnes' girl friends from work came along with their boyfriends, husbands and, in a few cases, children. Pat had invited them to join the group when shopping with Agnes at the City of Paris Store the week before. Agnes was surprised that he had actually gotten them to come, but Pat could be convincing, she thought.

After a long and enjoyable day, Pat and Agnes found themselves along the Russian River at the secluded spot where they had their first picnic together two years previous. They were sitting on a bench in silence watching the waters drift by.

"I wonder where the gang is," said Agnes.

"Oh, they'll be along," responded Pat.
Pat reached into his pocket and concealed a small jewelry box in his two hands.

"The past week has been pretty wonderful, Agnes. I never thought I'd experience life like this again. It's taught me how much I need you and love you. Will you have me?" he said opening the box to reveal a diamond.

[497]

"When did you do this?" she gasped. "I was with you all week, when?" Agnes reached out drawing the ring and Pat's hands closer. Pat removed the ring from its container, placed the jewelry box to his left on the bench, and slowly slid the ring on Agnes's finger.

"That's my secret, Agnes," laughed Pat. "Don't forget, I snuck out of Germany. I can certainly handle sneaking a ring out of a jewelry store without you noticing!"

"Pat, it's beautiful!" responded Agnes while looking at her left hand. "I love you Pat O'Brien," and she embraced him with a long kiss. Intuitively, they both looked at the ring a second time.

"I hope you like it, honey. I worked with your girlfriends selecting it. They were very helpful," he said. "I had no idea where to start."

"Wait a minute," replied Agnes, "so they know?"

"Well, I had to tell them if I was going to get their help," said Pat.

Suddenly, it became terribly apparent why every girl in the women's lingerie department had seen fit to participate in the Ivy Inn Picnic.

"O'Brien, you slay me!" laughed Agnes.

Pat and Agnes rose and walked up the path to a clearing where the group had decided to meet up for the trip home. All present were now aware of what had just transpired thanks to Agnes' girlfriends who revealed Pat's plan. As Pat and Agnes appeared, exiting the tree-lined pathway into the clearing, a cheer went up and the girls ran toward Agnes to admire her prize, pulling her aside.

Pat was left unattended and just laughed. "I guess I'm just Swiss cheese now, huh fellas?" walking toward them. As he shook hands with his buddies, they were extending a combination of congratulations and "fair warnings" as men do whenever the most eligible bachelor among them gives in.

The group made its way to the pick-up point, then to the train depot where they boarded and headed back home. The women sat in one section of the car and talked all the way while the men sat at the other end working two different card games and chewing on cigars.

The next day around 4:30 p.m., Pat, Virgil, Agnes, and Frank Hanson were headed south on 23rd Street toward the shoreline which would take them to Berkley, a mere ten miles south.

"You know, Pat, this could be one of your biggest audiences ever," said Virgil. "I spoke to my contact there and requests for tickets have far exceeded their capacity."

"Yes, but you know how it is there," said Agnes. "They'll be up on the grass, hanging off to the sides of the pit area. I've seen as many as 12,000 cram in that space.

"You're right, Agnes," responded Virgil. "Being an open outdoor area there's room for overflow crowds.

The driver turned onto Hearst Street which wound through campus, and finally Gayley Road which brought them to the arena. There was already a churn of activity in and around the theatre. As planned, the press conference was scheduled for after the show but a dinner with various university, military and local officials was set up in the large open area backstage.

Pat offered a short thank you after dinner by saying, "And so, I want to thank all of you for welcoming me here to Berkley tonight. I have a few surprises planned for this evening, one of which is sitting to my right. I would like to introduce you to my fiancé of just one day, Agnes MacMillan." Pat gestured toward Agnes who nodded to the guests. They applauded enthusiastically. It was a private affair and there was no press in attendance so word did not get out that Pat was now engaged. Such news would have most certainly tweaked the social pages of newspapers nationwide.

The open-air Hearst Greek Theatre was built in 1903 as a gift to the university from the noted newspaper publisher. President Teddy Roosevelt addressed the graduating class there in May of that year. A tall, ornate concrete wall fifty feet high ordained with Greek columns provided the backdrop to the large stage which was over 125 feet wide. The wall featured a large door opening in the center with two smaller entrance doors to either side.

Following a rousing introduction by the President of the University, Pat stepped forward out of the shadows through the large center door. A cheer washed over Pat that sounded like a football game at its peak. There were 10,000 people crammed into the famous theatre that night.

Pat's speech followed a similar pattern as all the others had, receiving the same reactions from the large audience, including those tense quiet moments where no one stirred. In this outdoor arena the silence revealed chirping birds accompanying Pat's serious moments as the audience listened intently.

As his speech wound down, Pat went off script.

"Now being from Richmond, I am well aware of the great traditions of this University and, in particular, the large and famous "C" made of concrete on Charter Hill," he said pointing east with his cane as he spoke. A large "whoop" when up from the audience which included a good number of college students.

"You may recall a St. Patrick's Day some years back when all of Berkley occupied a week's time trying to determine who the evil bandit was that painted your golden "C" a bright Kelly green in honor of the Galich feast. Well, it can now be told that is was I, Lt. Pat O'Brien of the Royal Flying Corps, and a small band of Irish lads who climbed the famous hill that night and stained your cherished golden icon to a Leprechaun's delight!"

A huge swell of laughter went up, filling the night skies, and stirring a number of birds form their observation perch on the tree tops. It was the story that filled the papers nationwide. Somewhat ironic, was that quips of such an unusual nature were now more newsworthy than the two hours of substance Pat had delivered on patriotism, commitment and the importance of American resolve.

Following eight standing ovations and pep rally-like chants from the college-aged induced crowd, Pat raised his cane overhead, said good night for the final time and walked through the big center door at the back of the stage. He did his press conference standing up as a clutch of journalists pounced on him with a wave of questions about the St. Patrick's Day prank. It was somewhat disappointing to him though he conceded it was news. It was just more evidence to Pat that his story was now told and other than the awaiting small-town Chautauqua crowd back in the Midwest, he had given his final major speech.

A good portion of the Ivy Inn crowd attended the speech. It was a thrilling night for all of them. To a person, they were startled at their friend's aplomb.

"We had no idea you were such a dynamic speaker, Pat," said James McCracken. "I congratulate you, Lieutenant."

"Don't forget James, this is not Pat's first speech," said Agnes coming to his defense.

"Well, he certainly surprised me," repeated McCracken.

The last night for Pat and his friends at the Ivy Inn was that evening after the Berkley speech. There were no speeches but lots of heartfelt goodbyes, hugs, and hearty handshakes that ended the evening. Though Pat would not leave until July 14th, his entire week ahead would be spent at the Allied War Exposition.

The next morning Pat was up reading the paper in the lobby of the hotel. Agnes was tired and slept in. She had risen and was bathing in preparation for the day, when Pat flipped up the front page of the San Francisco Examiner. He was stunned.

San Francisco Examiner - dateline: Washington July 6, 1918.

"Wilson signs order to enter Siberia"

"About time," whispered Pat as he poured over the story. Pat knew that the struggle for control of Russia was far from over. Furthermore, recovering the men and material of interest to the Allies would be a monumental task.

With echoes of the Berkley speech fading in Pat's mind, he felt a more powerful pull toward the war again. In was unsettling, gnawing and began to occupy his consciousness more each day.

"Good morning, dear," said Agnes who had finished her bath and came down to meet him for breakfast. It broke Pat's spell and he hesitated before blurting out, "Good morning, honey."

The two had breakfast at the hotel. Pat spoke about the story he had just read. While he never actually said anything about returning to action, Agnes had an uncomfortable feeling. He discussed the article with such passion and at some length. It felt as if he had turned a page with the Berkley speech. His relaxed demeanor of the past two weeks seemed to be fading. There was intensity in his voice again she had not heard since their first night together in Richmond ten days before. It unnerved her in light of his commitment at the Russian River just a few days before.

The next day, the Allied War Exposition opened. Agnes was able to attend since it was Sunday. The entire week was a whirlwind of activity for Pat. Frank Hanson and Edwin Hess kept Pat busy and before the public, signing books, speaking about the war and posing for photos. Though the Exposition wouldn't close until July 21, Pat's final presentation was on July 13. He would travel to Modesto the next day to visit his brother Elmer. Both men planned to return to Momence on the 18th for a family reunion planned of the O'Brien's.

The night before Pat left for Modesto, he and Agnes spent the evening at the Palace in San Francisco. It was their last night together and the young couple got little sleep through the night which was filled with a mix of tears and affection till dawn.

The next day, Agnes, Frank Hanson, Jerry Solich and Captain Hesser saw Pat off to Modesto on the Southern Pacific out of Richmond. As they had before, Pat's friends said good bye to him in the terminal. Just before Pat stepped away with Agnes for their final goodbye, Hess pulled Pat aside for one last moment.

"Pat, when you return from France, look me up. I'm starting to find some very lucrative work in the film industry these days," said Hess. "You know taking pictures of starlets and all that. I'm building quite a collection of contacts in the movie picture business. You might look at that as a possibility for you."

"The movies?" responded Pat.

"Sure, you're a good looking lad, you can obviously speak articulately and you're a known entity, Pat. Everybody knows who Pat O'Brien is," Hess explained. "You'd be a good match. By the time you return, I'm likely to know a whole lot more people that could put you in the pictures. Think about it." Hess slapped Pat on the arm, not wanting to hold him back form Agnes who was tugging on Pat's hand to say good bye.

Pat and Agnes waved one more time and stepped down the platform toward the boarding train.

"Just remember, Agnes. My final speech will be in mid-October in Wisconsin," said Pat as he held Agnes before departure. "I don't plan to book any further speeches after that."

"But what will you do from there, Pat?" asked Agnes.

"I don't know yet. I just know my speaking days are over. My story has been told," said Pat. "I have time to think about what comes next. Perhaps I will find something back here in San Francisco or we may have to look at relocating someday."

"Well, I'm certainly not chained to the City of Paris Store. That's for sure," said Agnes in a somewhat pitiful way that brought tears to her eyes. She could not get the feeling out of her mind that Pat was preoccupied with war again.

As is the case with goodbyes, the conversation started to sound like chatter as the departing couple attempted to hold down the emotions they are feeling inside. Suddenly, the steam train signaled its eminent departure and their talking stopped. Pat pulled Agnes toward him and gave her a forceful and passionate kiss that lasted for some time. Fittingly, the same stevedore that had passed their way pushing cargo when Pat arrived weeks before passed them once again.

"Time to board young man, better hurry," he said.

And thus came the end of their embrace. Pat walked up the platform and characteristically paused before stepping up, turned back, and swung his arm across his body to wave goodbye. Needless to say, Agnes' eyes were full of tears and she could only muster a flicker of her handkerchief but Pat saw it. He turned and stepped up and into the awaiting car.

Chapter 41

Return to France

Pat arrived in Modesto at dusk where Elmer greeted him with open arms. The two brothers had a robust dinner and caught up on weeks of activity. They spent the weekend enjoying food, drink, and festivities which Pat gladly paid for.

On Monday morning, July 16, Elmer had to work so Pat walked a few blocks to the nearest restaurant for breakfast and a morning paper. Elmer would work until Wednesday. On Thursday, he and Pat would head home to Momence.

The headline on the front page of the Modesto Bee was startling news for Pat.

"Russian Czar and his family murdered by Bolsheviks"

"My God, all hell is going to break loose now!" said Pat under his breath.

Though the Czar was dead, Pat knew that control of Russia would be a long, drawn out affair. Some Russian troops, now loyal to Lenin, comprised the Red Army and had little interest in fighting the Germans. After all, Lenin and his Bolsheviks had already sued the Germans for peace in March. "White" Russian troops, prevalent throughout all of Russia and still loyal to the Czar, were resisting the Reds. They were in a precarious dual war against the invading German-led enemies on the Eastern Front and the revolting Reds within their own ranks.

"Who is Germany to fight?" thought Pat. "Furthermore, who are we fighting?"

Germany and the other Central powers of Austria-Hungary, Bulgaria, and Turkey advanced on Russia only to find their enemy retreating to join Lenin's Red revolutionaries. Allied Armies in support of Russia witnessed the same mutiny. It became apparent to all foreign armies fighting for and against Russia that they were caught in a quagmire which shifted every hour.

President Wilson moved to send American Troops to Siberia as part of the Allied initiative to capture the Trans-Siberian Railroad so thousands of troops and material could exit Russia.

"What an opportunity," thought Pat. "But I'll try France first."

On the long train ride home, Pat told Elmer of his visit to Richmond, his engagement to Agnes and his plans to end touring after his Chautauqua tour. He also told him about his plans to go to France. He'd leave after his last speech scheduled for La Crosse, Wisconsin on October 14th. Like the others that knew of Pat's desire to return and fight, Elmer was confused and concerned about Pat's desire to return to war.

"You've done enough, Pat," he repeated a number of times on the way home.

"Until it's finished, I must give what I can," said Pat. "If France does not take me, I will look to Russia."

You're out of your mind, Pat, stay home! The war could be over this year, you don't know," pleaded his brother. "Let the young ones finish. You're twenty-seven years old for Christ's sake!"

"My age means nothing in this case, Elmer," responded Pat. "I must do what I am capable of doing."

They arrived in Momence on July 22nd. The next day, the entire O'Brien clan was home for the first time in many years. Elmer's son Elmer Jr. was even in town for the gathering. Clara arranged for a family photo at Frank Lane's studio on the second floor of the Ganeer Township Hall in the morning. Pat wore his British uniform. Food and festivities were on hand the entire day at the island park. Margaret was feeling wonderful to have her entire family together once again. After dinner, while the children and their parents were feeding ducks along the south branch, Pat sat down with her to visit.

"I've decided to end touring after my final bookings, mom," said Pat.

"That's fine, Pat," responded Maggie. "You've traveled long enough, and you've done well. It's time you settle down."

"But I'm not planning on settling down quite yet, ma. I'm heading to France before November 1st. The French are the only Army that has not turned me down. I have to make an attempt."

"Oh, Pat," responded Margaret, "that's so unnecessary. You've more than done your part."

"Everyone tells me that but it is not my motivation," said Pat. "If I'm capable of aiding the Allied cause, I want to do that. It's important mom. The war is not won yet, by far."

"I know, Pat, but we just worry about your welfare so much," said Margaret. "For the life of me boy, I don't know what there is in you that causes you to be so drawn to action."

She paused and looked down for a moment, neither one of them speaking. Then continuing in deliberate and soft tone, she went on.

"But you've always been that way, so I don't suppose any of us, not even your own mother, can change what's in yuh." She paused again. "Just use your head, Pat. We all love you and want you home safe."

"I know. I will, mom," assured Pat.

The day ended over a warm fire and even the young O'Brien grandchildren lasted well past their bedtime, toasting bread over the fire then flavoring it with drops of honey.

The next day Pat played with some of his nieces and nephews, taking a well-earned break from his hectic schedule. For the next few days he had time to visit his friends in Momence, do some fishing, and venture out one day to the marsh to hunt and take in the abundant habitat. It gave him time to think through his options following his final tour.

On July 27, Pat gave his first Chautauqua presentation at Freeport, Illinois. He made a swing out through Ohio the first week of August including Marysville where he appeared with numerous of other acts and speakers. By the end of the week, he was in Iowa again, then did a series of speeches in Central, Illinois including Pana, Danville, Connersville, and Sullivan, Illinois.

It was the Sullivan appearance that Pat found the most memorable, not because of its overflow crowd, the packed the house at the Jefferson Theatre, or even the number of autographed books he signed. He met someone that triggered a memory back the very first speech public speech he gave in Chicago.

"Well, hello Lt. O'Brien," said a woman extending her hand. "How have you been?"

Pat greeted her as he did all those who lined-up to meet him, but asked the woman, "Do I know you?"

"I'm Sarah Ottis. I met you at your very first appearance in Chicago, Orchestra Hall, do you remember?" she asked.

"I do remember the speech but I've seen so many since then. It's hard to remember every......" Cutting him off, Sarah Ottis when on.

"My husband is Lieutenant Colonel Daniel Ottis. He is a medical officer with Pershing's Army in France. Remember? You and I spoke at Orchestra Hall in Chicago."

"Yes, I do remember now. You are from Springfield, is that right?" asked Pat.

"Well, it's interesting you remember that Lieutenant," she said. "As a matter of fact, there are a number of folks here from Springfield to hear you speak. Are you returning to Chicago tonight?"

"No, my brother and I will spend the night. We plan to be up early fishing on the Kaskaskia River," answered Pat.

"That's perfect," said Ottis. "We were wondering if you might like to join us this evening for a few drinks and meet some of our Red Cross volunteers. There are also many prominent citizens of Springfield who are interested in meeting you. We're walking over to the Jefferson Inn."

"I'd like to check with my brother first," said Pat.

"Fine, fine, check with your brother," responded Ottis. "You have a lot more people to greet. I'll stand over there so signal me once you have checked with your brother."

Just then Elmer unknowingly stepped up having existed from the hall into the lobby, "Well, that went well, huh Pat?" he said.

"Oh, is this your brother, Pat?" asked Sarah. "Hello, I'm Sarah Ottis," she said reaching her hand out to Elmer, not waiting for a confirmation from Pat who turned to greet the next person in line.

"I was just talking to Pat and he indicated that if it was alright with you, you both might join a number of us from Springfield for a quick drink at the Jefferson Inn," she said to Elmer speaking rapidly.

"Well, if it's alright with Pat, I will go, certainly," said Elmer not exactly certain what just happened.

"Wonderful!" said Sarah. "I'll be standing over there with the Springfield group so when Pat is done greeting his fans, just come over by us and we will show you the way to the inn. It's not far. We can actually walk there."

Pat finished the receiving line, signing copies of his book and thrilling those who got to shake his hand. The head of Chautauqua for Decatur asked Pat if he wanted to stop a number of times but Pat indicated that he would stay and greet everyone, despite the cramp in his hand. He enjoyed meeting small town folks. They were like people from home, genuine, respectful, and admiring.

Pat and Elmer joined the group from Springfield at the Jefferson Inn a few doors down from the Theatre of the same name. Both buildings were on the Sullivan town square which tonight was teeming with patrons late into the evening. Pat's appearance was a major event for the small town. He and his brother spent an hour being introduced by Sarah Ottis to each one of the Springfield contingent. She introduced Pat as if he was an old friend. Pat was cordial and genuinely enjoyed meeting the group. They were thrilled to have a private gathering with such a known celebrity.

As the night went on, Pat's first meeting with Sarah Ottis in Chicago came back to him. "She was the woman that didn't shake my hand and the one that said she looked forward to seeing me, again." He remembered that. Something about her gnawed at him but he couldn't put his finger on it.

The night ended around half-past eleven and the two brothers bid the group good night.

As they headed for the hotel on foot, Elmer turned to Pat and said, "Who is that woman?"

The two brothers laughed.

"Now you know why I want to get off the road," said Pat. "There are people like her everywhere. I think I'm ready to get away from people for a while, aren't you?"

"Yeah, I'm ready to go fishin'! I don't know about you," said Elmer putting his arm over Pat's shoulder.

The two brothers could be seen laughing and somewhat stumbling their way all the way back to the Savoy Hotel. Halfway there Pat started, softly at first, with his brother blending in half way. Soon they were belting the song Pat first sang with his buddies on North Island. It had become a regular duet for the two brothers since Pat returned from oblivion. As the strains of "Smile, Smile, Smile" echoed off the small brick facades of downtown Sullivan, Illinois, Pat thought about how he had changed since his long isolated walk through Europe. There had been many lonely nights walking alone, dying for the chance to talk to anyone. Tonight, after nearly continuous contact with thousands of people for six months, he'd had his fill. The pain of enduring isolation suffered in Europe seemed finally removed. He was ready to take a break.

They were up early and met a local guide in front of the hotel. He drove them southeast of town to the Kaskaskia River and indicated he'd be back around noon. Pat and his brother fished all morning until the driver returned. They then headed back up route 121 stopping at the Masonic Home where Pat spent an hour visiting with the thrilled residents living there. At 2:30 they were back in town and had a bite to eat at The Ideal Restaurant in Sullivan which featured a "lunch room and short order service." They boarded the train bound for Chicago at 3:30 p.m., arrived around 7:00, transferred to the Momence train and slept all the way home. The two brothers had grown close since their days in California. The two days in Sullivan further secured the bond between Pat and his oldest brother, twelve years his elder

.

Other than a few Chautauqua presentations within a half-day's drive, Pat was able to stay close to home where he immersed himself in the day-to-day "events" of Momence. He was able to visit people and places he knew as a boy. There were the old-timers at Worcester's store telling stories of Momence that seemed brand new to Pat this time. Old schoolmates welcomed Pat daily into their homes for a meal, talking well into the evening about old times. And packs of young kids followed him around town as if he were the Pied Piper. But the four weeks among life-long friends and family had little of the wrenching he'd experienced on the road. The whirlwind around Pat's tumultuous return had finally subsided. For the first time, he finally felt like has was home.

But on September 15, he was back on the road again heading for Danville, Illinois, located eighty miles south of Momence. He told the opening day audience at The Greater I. & I. Fair that he planned to go to France. The national press ran short "filler stories," regarding the announcement, demonstrating continued national interest in Pat's affairs.

.

After Danville, Pat spent two days visiting Maggie in Lowell, She was ill. He took care of her and engaged in long conversations at her bedside covering many topics. On September 21, he kissed his mother good-bye and headed for Momence for the big Bond Rally scheduled for that day. The nation's fourth, and final, bond drive was underway to raise $6 billion. As usual, Momence would do their part. The parade and celebration was a huge success and featured speeches by Pat and other Momence vets.

His next trip was to Cedar Falls, Iowa on October 3 where he spoke in the auditorium at Iowa State Teachers College. The next night he appeared in Waterloo, Iowa at the Waterloo Theatre where eighty-five fully dressed nurses from Presbyterian Hospital served as ushers for the evening. They all got to meet Pat backstage following the speech and were thrilled.

The next two days he made multiple appearances at the Dairy Cattle Congress held in Waterloo. On Saturday night, October 5, Pat was asked to join 150 Red Cross ladies on Dairy Show Park stage, and lead the audience of 5,000 in singing the Star Spangled Banner before presenting his speech. At this event he was just one of the many attractions that included musicians, actors, comedians, military bands, acrobatic acts, cattle from 20 states, elephants and other zoo animals, and one of the biggest attractions of the week, "The Spirit of 1918," a life size statue of a liberty woman made totally from butter. Pat was fully immersed in show business, now.

On October 14, Pat's train pulled into the St. Paul and Pacific Depot at La Crosse, Wisconsin. His speech at the La Crosse Theatre that evening would be his final Chautauqua appearance and he felt it could possibly be his last appearance, period. The final Allied push towards the German border would begin on October 17, 1918. As the British, French and American armies prepared to advance, the alliance between the Central Powers was beginning to collapse. Turkey would sign an armistice at the end of October, Austria-Hungary would follow on November 3.

No one in La Crosse or the rest of the country knew that the war would end in exactly four weeks. But Pat's promoters had sensed over the summer that selling Pat O'Brien on patriotism alone might not stir enough interest, even in La Crosse, Wisconsin. They understood that suspense and humor had to replace the fervent patriotism once used as the primary draw for Pat O'Brien. Pat understood this before anyone else. He knew what worked on stage and what did not. He was first to understand the interests of the public in the many questions they asked over and over again.

The La Crosse Tribune and Leader Press ad read, "One minute he thrills you – the next he has you doubled up with laughter." The description was true and had certainly been so since Pat first spoke to the troops in London three days after his escape. What was different now was how Pat was being "sold."

Across the top of the ad the paper used a "catch-line," borrowed from one of Pat's comments following his Texas crash. It read, "Someday I'll Stub my toe, fall down and break my neck." Below the ad a short promotional story about Pat's speech was bannered, "Pat O'Brien, too real for the movies." Unrestricted movie producers had already developed a reputation for exaggeration in portraying the fantastic.

Pat would leave for France in eight days and try to get in on the final push against the Hun. While he had mentioned his intentions at Danville, only Margaret knew exactly when he planned to leave. He told her during his visit to Lowell.

On Wednesday, October 16 he stopped over in Chicago to update his passport papers on the way home, arriving in Momence that evening. He spent one final day at home and then headed to New York on Friday. On his way to New York he spoke at New Castle, Pennsylvania to promote bonds. On the same bill with Pat were heroes of the French Foreign Legion who were touring the United States at the request of the government to promote the sale of war bonds. Needless to say, Pat was thrilled to talk with them.

"Where is the best place for me to enlist?" ask Pat.

"You want to join the Legion, even though you have served so well already for the British, Pat?" said Captain Charles Lefebvres, thick with French accent.

"Yes, I have plenty of fight left in me," said Pat. "I can fly even with my bum leg. I just want one more chance at the Hun."
"But why not fly for the RFC?" Lefebvres asked

"They will not take me," Pat responded. "Neither will the Canadians nor the American Air Service. Two of them don't want me captured and shot and the U.S. has so many young pilots now, there is no room for an old man like me. I'm hoping either the LaFayette Flying Corps or the French Foreign Legion might consider my services."

"I am certain the Legion would value a talent like you but not as a pilot, Pat," said Lieutenant Baudin. "As for the Lafayette Flying Corps, they were absorbed just last February into the American Air Service as the 1st American Squadron. It would appear that your only way to fight is with the Legion."

The first Americans to fly for France were the original LaFayette Escadrille, later referred to as the LaFayette Flying Corps when they peaked at nearly 300 American pilots. Like Pat, they flew for France before the U.S. had joined the fight. In February of 1918, with the United States fully engaged in the war, they were brought into the American Air Service. Pat had already been turned down by the AAS so he knew his only chance was with the Legion now.

Stunned that he missed the transformation of the LaFayette Flying Corps, Pat did what he could to hide his disappointment and went on. "My ship will arrive at Bordeaux. Should I travel to Paris or is there a closer location where I can enlist?" asked Pat. "Will they send me to Algeria?" Legion headquarters was based at Sidi-Bel-Abbes, Algeria at the time.

"No, there are recruiting offices throughout France," responded Lefebvres. "I suggest you go to the enlistment office in Paris, though."

"Right, then," said Pat. "That's what I'll do."

Following Pat's final speech, which the Legionnaires enjoyed hearing, he said good bye to them and he thanked them again for their help. "Good luck to you, Pat," said Lefebvres as Pat jumped into an awaiting car headed for the New Castle train station.

Once in New York, he had lunch with his old promoter Lee Keedick. Though Lee pressed him to sign additional appearances on the Vaudeville Circuit in New York, he was not successful. Pat told him he'd consider it once the war was over. The two men shared "stories of the road" and had a few good laughs over incidents that always occur when traveling in haste from one town to the next.

The next afternoon, he called Agnes at The City of Paris Store in San Francisco. A secretary from in the office came running onto the floor to alert Agnes. She added, "I think it is Lieutenant O'Brien." Agnes was surprised by the call but glad to hear Pat's voice on the other end. He had written her about every three days since his departure but it was not the same.

"Hello, Agnes," he said. "It's Pat."

"Pat what's the matter, has something happened?" returned Agnes. Long distance generally carried bad news in 1918.

"No, everything is fine," said Pat. "I wanted to let you know, I'm departing for France tomorrow." The line went silent. "Agnes? Did you hear? I'm leaving for France."

"Yes, Pat, I heard you," returned Agnes. "It's just a surprise – so soon."

"I know dear but I must do it now while the war can be won. I hope you forgive me and understand that as soon as I am finished I will be back in San Francisco," said Pat.

"Please be careful Pat and if they won't let you fight, come home. We're all praying the war will end soon," said Agnes rather choked up at this point.

"Well, I better hang up now, Agnes," he said. "I sail tonight. I love you... and I will be back soon."

"I love you, too," said Agnes. Both hung-up their phone but Agnes did so a bit slower than Pat. She looked at the calendar hanging above the phone. "The twenty-first," she said under her breath. "That's a full three months since my last period." It concerned her for a moment but it was too early to check anyway so she put it out of her mind. She dabbed at her eyes, took a quick glance in the mirror on the way out, and returned to the lingerie department.

Pat's ship would sail for Bordeaux, France on Tuesday, October 22. Prior to boarding he sent a telegram to his contact in Kalamazoo, Michigan, cancelling his planned speech there. He also sent a note to "Clay" Buntain in Kankakee and asked him to make an appearance on Pat's behalf at Manteno, Illinois. The small town had planned "Pat O'Brien Day" for November 28. Pat had ordered a plaque of gratitude for the school there but knew now that he could not make the appearance.

He also sent a long letter to Agnes just prior to boarding the ship. He assured her he would be safe and return as soon as the war was won, "provided," he wrote, "they consider this old hobbler capable of flying a plane." He tried to sound as upbeat as he could though he had doubts about his chances and was certainly unsure of the current conditions in France.

Pat had not forgotten what war devastation looked like but he was surprised to see how extensive it was all across the countryside in France as his train made its way north out of Bordeaux to Paris. A year ago, battlefields could be identified from the air. From Pat's train car window it looked like the entire countryside of western France was chewed to bits... It was.

Pat stepped off the train at the Gare du Nord station in the center of Paris and waved for a cab to take him to Fort de Nogent, the recruiting office for the French Foreign Legion. When he arrived he entered the large archway gate and was escorted to the recruitment office within the compound. The courtyard was meticulously kept. Pat showed his passport to a century guarding the door to the main administration building who sized up Pat.

"Are you the pilot?" asked the guard.

"Yes, sir, I am," responded Pat.

"My honor to meet you sir," the guard responded and gave Pat a salute, which he returned. "Come, I will show you."

The guard instructed his back-up to take his position. Pat heard his name through the barrage of French and figured he was explaining who Pat was. The replacement smiled, saluted both Pat and his superior, and took the century post.

Sitting behind a large mahogany desk was Captain Charles McClelland. "Welcome," he said with a thick Scottish accent. Pat was surprised to meet a Scot in the French Foreign Legion but the Legion was made up of men from all over the world.

"Thank you," said Pat. "Are you a Scot?"

"I'm an American but was born in Scotland," said McClelland. "Surely, I'd be with the British Army were I still living in Scotland, but short of that the Legion is perfect for me. I entered before President Wilson saw the light." McClelland put his pencil down and leaned forward, "You're the American pilot that flew for the RFC, aren't you?" he asked.

"Yes, I am," Pat said, "We both got impatient. I joined the Brits and you joined the French."

"Indeed," said McClelland. "I was there."

"Where?" Pat asked.

"In London the night you spoke," he said. "I was on leave and went to London. I heard you were speaking and attended with a few other Legionnaires in my group. It was quite stirring, indeed.

"How extraordinary," responded Pat. "You were there. You heard the speech then. Good lord, I was only free of the Hun less than a week at that time. I am a much more polished speaker today."

"You were pretty good then, O'Brien," responded the Captain. "I must say, however, you look much better today than you did then. You've put on weight. You needed to."

"Sometimes I think back at the whole thing and it seems like a dream and then it seems like yesterday, the next minute."

"I know what you mean," he responded. "I spent nearly a year at Verdun. It was hell. After the tough knocks I took, they gave me this desk job."

"Verdun was much rougher on the ground than in the air where I was," said Pat.

"Say, O'Brien, after we do our business here, what say you and I go have dinner somewhere and talk about our days as mercenaries?" said McClelland.

Pat laughed, "Right, mercenaries aren't we? I know regular troops that think we don't bleed when shot up like they do. What a crazy war." They both laughed.

"So what can I do for you, O'Brien?" asked the Scottish Captain.

"Well, I'd like to get back into the fight and this seems like the ideal place for me," responded Pat.

"You?" said McClelland sounding shocked. "Why you've given already. Why do you want back in?"

"I just know the job is not done and I want another shot at those Hun bastards. That's all," said Pat.

"Pat, this war will very likely end soon and the Legion doesn't need to put soldiers like you in the ranks. You and I have both done our part. Every soldier has his time, you know. Ours has passed."

[515]

Pausing shortly he went on, "You could probably enter as a 2nd Lieutenant but you'd be a ground soldier, neither one of us want that."

Pat understood that the Legion was not the place for at twenty-seven year-old limping pilot.

"No, Pat," said McClelland in a soft tone. "I couldn't sign you. After all, it's a five year contract. I'm due to see the end of my stint in eight months. I say you and I both go home. This mess is going to end soon. All I hear tells me that both sides will just quit even if the Allies never get to Berlin. It's locked in stalemate. Anyone that's been to the front can see that."

Pat knew his opportunity in Europe was now dead. It helped that he was turned away by someone that, like him, had a passion to beat the Hun, had done his job, and understood what drove Pat to stay in the fight.

"Ok?" asked Charles.

"You're right. I don't quite fit the need right now," said Pat pausing a moment. "I will take you up on the dinner offer, however. What time are you done?"

"We can go now," said Charles. "I'll get my understudy to cover the last half hour.

And so Pat O'Brien, an Irish-American who fought for the British and Charles McClelland, a Scottish-American under the same flag who fought for the French, walked out of an old French fortress graced by Napoleon himself. They were two men on the brink of ending their military careers. But as they ordered their first glass of wine and toasted to each other's honor, Pat looked McClelland straight in the eye and said, "There's always Russia!"

"Oh, Christ O'Brien," said Charles with a hearty laugh. "Let's eat some of this fine French food. I'm starving."

"Me, too," responded Pat.

The two men visited well into the night. Their respective heritage armed them with plenty of ideas regarding refreshments after dinner. They promised to keep in touch with each other and meet again once the war was over. Charles had a home in Connecticut.

Pat made his way to the Hotel Edouard where he would stay. The next morning he was up early and entered the coffee shop with an English language paper under his arm. More news from Russia landed on the front page.

> "Germany Cancels Brest-Litovsk Treaty
> Seeks removal of Allies from Russia"

Germany had had enough of Vladimir Lenin's feet dragging. He promised the Hun a significant amount of land in western Russia in exchange for peace. It required he complete the takeover of Russia from the old Czarist regime and drive the Allied forces from the countryside. Neither was happening. The Germans could not be assured that their eastern flank was protected. Meanwhile, the Western Front was frustratingly stagnant but since the entry of the United States in the war and the extensive resources they brought to the fight, the trend was going in the wrong direction for Germany.

Germany began to crumble from within. Faced with the prospect of returning to sea, the sailors of the High Seas Fleet stationed at Kiel mutinied on October 29. Within a few days, the entire city was in their control and the revolution spread throughout the country. On November 9 the Kaiser abdicated; slipping across the border into the Netherlands and exile. A German Republic was declared and peace feelers extended to the Allies. At 5 a.m. on the morning of November 11 an armistice was signed in a railroad car parked in a French forest near the front lines.

Eight days after Pat O'Brien arrived in Paris, all sides laid down their arms, and the war ended. Pat had come to France to get back in a war that suddenly stopped. From the upper floor of his hotel he heard a noise from the street swelled from below. Word of peace was spreading through the streets of Paris.

"Well, I certainly can't miss this," he said to himself as he watched the throngs gathering below. He suspended his personal ambitions and joined the celebration well into the evening. The war was over, but every experienced solider knew it was not resolved. Exhaustion stopped the hostilities of the Great War and the war dubbed "the war to end all wars," was ironically the least likely to resolve Europe's indigestion once and for all. No one in 1918 thought war would return to Europe ever again but in slightly more than twenty-one years, it would start all over again.

Chapter 42

Pulling Away

Pat spent the next three weeks in France watching peace relentlessly force its way back into the streets of the victorious Allied capital. Peace was also returning to the hearts of Parisians, who seemed to have no need for sleep. Watching a four year war unwind in the capital of the triumphant nation is a stunning view of human passage.

Paris, as much as any city in the world, with its radial boulevards extending outward to distant battlefields, coerces returning armies to its center. It provides a mammoth turnabout for mechanized and horse-drawn armaments, blocks of infantry and elevated heroes, all welcomed in and then pushed through by throngs of admiring civilians waving their kerchiefs one moment, then wiping tears with them the next.

On Armistice Day 1918, in the Compiegne Forest thirty-seven miles north of Paris, the Allies and Germany signed an agreement that ended the fighting. It marked a victory for the Allies and a devastating defeat for Germany, although it was not technically a surrender. Additionally, Germany had been left physically untouched by Allied efforts with the exception of some far eastern areas damaged by early Russian victories. President Wilson fashioned the terms with his "Fourteen Points" but the actual document was written largely by French Marshal Ferdinand Foch who commanded the Allied forces.

In the agreement, hostilities would cease and German troops would withdraw to behind their borders. There would be a full exchange of prisoners, preservation of standing infrastructure, and a promise of reparation. The disposition of German warships and submarines, along with specific conditions to hold the peace, were other conditions of the settlement. It would not be until June 28, 1919 that the Treaty of Versailles would put the final stamp on the war and, simultaneously, breed enough resentment in the Germans to resume hostilities in twenty-one years hence.

On Sunday, November 29, Pat exited his hotel and crossed the Seine River over the bridge at Pont Royal. He crossed Georges Pompidou road and took a slight left, then right into the Tuileries Garden.

Before him convulsed a congregation of humans that took his breath away. He could hardly see anything but a flurry of excited French all clamoring to get as close to the Arc de Triomphe as they could. The cheers came in waves as full companies of Allied military passed under the historic archway from Greece, Italy, Portugal, Canada, the United States, France, Britain and other victorious allied countries.

After about an hour colliding with throngs of revelers, Pat pushed his way out of the crowd onto the concrete walk that cut through the Garden. He circled around the first large fountain pool, through the manicured gardens, and past clusters of infantry awaiting cue for their opportunity to experience passage through the great historic arch.

He had made arrangements to meet McClelland and a few of his friends from England at the Obelisk within the Place de la Concorde, on the west end of the Garden. The tall spire given to France by Greece in the 19th Century was an ideal meeting spot and Pat found the group at its base as soon as he worked his way through the crowd.

"Hello, Pat. We meet again," said McClelland with a hearty handshake.

"Everyone, this is Pat O'Brien, aviator extraordinaire," he said trying to sound French, which was tough through his Scottish brogue.

"Hi, all," said Pat shaking hands with the men and tipping his hat to the two ladies in the group. They turned and headed west for the most famous street in Europe, the Champs Elysees.

One would be hard pressed to find a more dramatic or enchanting boulevard anywhere in the world than the Champs Elysees in Paris. It runs from Napoleon's Arc de Triomphe all the way to the Louvre lined by characteristic Parisian houses and luxurious shops. The group of six men had a hard time keeping things moving as the two female officers were regularly held back by the fashionable curiosities that lined this famous thoroughfare.

The group spent all afternoon taxiing from one end of the Champ Elysees to the other, down the Rue de Rivoli and across the famous Alexander III Bridge over the Seine. They saw the Palace of the Luxembourg, Luxor, Boulevard de l'Opera, Notre Dame, Napoleon's Tomb, and numerous sites off side streets. Even though the threat of German occupation and bombing had ceased, all these famous sites were still covered with sandbags, as were statues on the Arc de Triomphe.

In the evening, Pat and his friends dined at Maxim's and ended their day at the Folies Bergere where they saw Maurice Chevalier, home from London where he had been a smash hit at the Palace Theatre.

At the end of the day, Pat said a final goodbye. He and McClelland reaffirmed their plans to meet again in the U.S. when McClelland returned home. Pat jumped in a cab, passed late night revelers, and went on to his hotel for a final night in Paris. He came to France to fight but war was not to be had. There would only be Russia now, and he lay in bed most of the night, contemplating his next move.

Pat was in Bordeaux again on December 5 where his passport was validated for the trip home. He would sail on the La Lorraine which had already begun bringing throngs of American troops home from Europe. There were other vets Pat met returning on his ship – Pilots Charles Chapman of Cambridge, John F. Connolly of Dorchester and Johnny Evers, a former Boston Braves star. Evers was part of the famous "Tinker to Evers to Chance" double play combination made famous with the Cubs in 1907. Pat took a particular interest in meeting Evers who would go on to manage the Chicago Cubs and White Sox after the war. Like many ball players during war years, Evers career was broken up by service to the country. Finally, Two Knights of Columbus workers, James Brelin of Providence and John T. Starks of Lowell, Massachusetts, were part of the group. They spent most of the trip home humorously attempting to convert Pat to the Roman Catholic Church. "It's only right, with a name like yours, O'Brien!" they kept repeating.

But in a fortunate twist of fate, there was one man on the ship that was equally captivated with Pat as Pat was with him. It was Harold N. Willis of the French Flying Corps who escaped a German prison camp after being reported "dead." A Harvard architectural graduate from Boston, Willis was the twenty-fifth member of the original LaFayette Escadrille. His experience was so like Pat's that the two men could hardly find enough time in the day to talk and compare notes. In the ship's messdeck on day two of the voyage, Willis came up to the table where Pat and the others were having breakfast.

"Are you O'Brien?" asked Willis.

"Yes, Pat O'Brien," responded Pat standing to shake the man's hand.

"I'm Harold Willis of the French Flying Corps, from Boston."

"Yes?" responded Pat still shaking the man's hand.

[520]

"I escaped Villingen," said Willis.

"My word," said Pat, startled and slowing the pace of his handshake to a crawl. "You were in the Escadrille, were you not?" asked Pat.

"Yes, I was number twenty-five," Willis responded.

"Take a seat, join us," responded Pat with great enthusiasm, pulling out a seat for the pilot. Pat and Willis immediately became absorbed in an intense, quiet and fairly private conversation as the others looked on while finishing their breakfast. They eventually bid farewell to the two escapees leaving them alone at the table.

Willis was shot down near Dun-sur-Meuse while flying as part of a fighter escort mission with a bomber squadron attacking German positions near Verdun. He began to explain the battle in terms that only a fighter pilot like Pat could understand.

"Albatross D.IIIs and D.Vs jumped us and broke us up," said Willis. "We were all instantly involved in dog fights, as you can imagine, and all of a sudden I'm on this Hun's tail and I shoot him up. Not three seconds later I've got a D.V on my ass, I pull back on the stick, of course." Pat interrupted him.

"An Immelmann!" Pat exclaimed well in tune with the loop performed by Willis.

"Right!" Willis responded with increased excitement. "But I didn't shake him. All I got accomplished was to isolate myself from everyone else and he got my tail again."

"What were you flying?" asked Pat.

"Nieports," responded Willis as Pat nodded affirmatively. "But the guy was skilled. He was a hell of a pilot. The son-of-bitch shoots up my engine and I decide to ditch. I figured 'get your ass on the ground and you might have a fighting chance, right?"

"Of course," said Pat, hanging on every word.

"So I see this small hill and head right for it," Willis continued. "The Huns follow me down and land close enough that they beat the infantry to me. Lucky for me."

"Same with me, Harold" said Pat. "Thank God pilots found us first. At least there's a chance of not getting your brains kicked in." Pat was referring to the uncanny respect early pilots had for each other regardless of the uniform they wore.

"Exactly!" confirmed Willis.

"So here's the good part, Pat," said Wills. "The Huns take me to their airfield and underneath my flying suit, all I have on are my pajamas."

Pat busts out laughing, knowing full well that pilots regularly refused to wear their uniforms under their flight suit substituting warmer clothes.

"I tell them I'm an officer!" says Willis. "Hell, with no uniform, I figured, why not get better treatment? And they buy it!"

Willis and Pat talked for three hours until the deckmess steward came to wipe tables for lunch. Willis described his first attempt to escape with nine others at Eutin in March of 1918. Though the escape failed, it taught Willis some critical lessons that he and a group of thirteen prisoners used to escape Villingen three prisons later. Willis walked eighteen miles to freedom over the Swiss border. He was stunned to learn of Pat's 250 mile walk to Holland. Willis was the first and only member of the Escadrille to escape the Hun. Pat was the first member of the RFC to escape German control. They were inseparable the rest of the trip home. Pat drew a renewed spirit to fly from their visit.

The La Lorraine arrived in New York on December 10. Pat gave a hearty handshake to his shipmates and an emotional hug to his fellow prisoner-pilot. He had wired Lee Keedick of his arrival date and Keedick was there to greet him at the dock. Pat introduced Willis, Evers and the others to Lee who was particularly glad to meet the two celebrities.

"Here's my card," he said to Willis. Evers was well known already as a ball player. "If you don't go back into baseball, give me a call," said Lee. After about ten minutes they all went their separate ways.

Keedick and Pat had dinner that evening and Pat agreed to make a few appearances on the Vaudeville Circuit. There would be time before a trip to Russia, he thought. He decided he'd spend Christmas with the family, do the Vaudeville dates, deal with some financial matters at home, and visit Agnes sometime before departing for Russia. One way or another, Pat was going to fly again. His time with Willis solidified his decision. He had not felt his passion for flying since Estree Blanche.

Meanwhile, on the opposite coast, Agnes MacMillan was also having dinner with her good friend. The topic of conversation was quite different, however. Since their first meeting at the Ivy Inn, Arlene Stevens and Agnes had lunch regularly and had become good friends. They just hit it off as soon as they met. Being new to California, Arlene appreciated having a friend that had lived there her whole life. Agnes liked having a confidant that didn't know everyone at the store and was new to town. It allowed her to seek confidentiality which Arlene promised.

"It's for sure, then?" asked Arlene as she and Agnes awaited their order in the City of Paris Store café.

"I'm afraid so. I know I'm not showing much yet Arlene but the doctor is certain" responded Agnes.

"Well, you're fortunate," assured Arlene, always the optimist. "You have Pat's ring. He's on his way home now from France. You need to tell him. He loves you. He'll marry you, Agnes. When is he due to arrive?"

"He arrives in New York today," she said. "I'll wait to hear from him. If he tells me he's coming to see me, I'll tell him when he's here. I don't want to tell him on the phone or, God forbid, with a letter. But I must hear what he has to say first. If I tell him I'm pregnant before he expresses his interest in settling down, I'll never know how he truly feels. He's still a wanderlust and gnawed by what he sees as his incomplete effort at war."

"That's ridiculous," stated Arlene. "Look at what the man has been through Agnes! He needs you. My God! It's his baby, too. You have to talk to him. He needs to know."

"I know, Arlene, but I know him. He needs to be ready to call the war over," said Agnes.

"But it is over, Agnes," responded Arlene, somewhat confused.

"Not his war," said Agnes. "His war is not over yet. Nothing would please me more than to know he has finally reconciled all his regrets, whether valid or not. I need to hear him say he's ready to settle down and start his life with me and our baby."

Two days later, On December 12, Agnes received a telegram from Pat.

"Got home safely. Will call you at work this afternoon around 3:00 your time. Pat"

On that day, the phone rang promptly at 3:00.

"Thanks, Ethel," said Agnes as the office clerk handed her the phone."

"Hello?"

"Hi Agnes it's Pat," came the voice on the other end.

"Pat, dear. How are you? How was France?" asked Agnes.

"Paris was unbelievable Agnes," he said. "Can you believe the war is over? How's San Francisco? Did they have a huge celebration?"

"Well, on the day they announced it there were a lot of spontaneous celebrations in the streets for the whole day and we had a parade last Sunday. Pat, there were so may military here. I think all of Presidio was in the parade. There are still many boys not home yet but they say they will be coming."

"Oh, they're coming Agnes," said Pat. "You should have seen the packed ship I came home on. Guys were sleeping anywhere there was a space. I thought we'd sink!"

"Incredible, Pat," said Agnes with other thoughts rolling around in her head.

"So, Pat, when will we be able to see each other?" she said, finally asking the question. He didn't hear her and went on.

"You won't believe who I met on the ship coming home," said Pat. "I met Johnny Evers. Oh, I know that probably doesn't mean much to you but he's a former baseball player for the Cubs and Boston Braves. He's real famous. He's been serving in the war for a year. But the person I met that really amazed me was Harold Willis. He's an original member of the Escadrille and the only one to be captured and escape. Agnes, you would not believe how close his experiences were to mine. I spent a lot of time with him on the way back. I told him my whole story and he told me his."

Pat was noticeably excited. Thinking that perhaps, Willis was therapeutic for Pat, it gave her some hope that he may have worked through some things by meeting this fellow Willis. But she sensed it could have pulled him further in the wrong direction.

"That sounds wonderful, honey," she said with genuine empathy. "Do you know when we might be able to see each other?

Pat heard her this time. "Well, I'll be in Momence for Christmas and I'm looking to earn a little money before I come out west," he said.

"Good Lord, Pat! You know you've got plenty of money with the year you've had. What, did you do buy the Eiffel Tower while you were in France or something?" she responded, trying to keep things light.

"No, but I did see Maurice Chevalier," he said also trying to keep things light. "It's just that I had dinner with Keedick in New York and he wants me to do a short Vaudeville stint, so I'll do that in February. That will give me January to look for some real estate. I need to do some investing."

"I see," said Agnes, not liking the tone of the conversation but hiding it well.

"Here's my plan, Agnes," started Pat. "Mom's talking about visiting her sisters in Wyoming in May. Her sister Hatte Bell is not doing well. In fact, Aunt Arletta is talking about moving to Cody from Ralston. I think Mom wants to spend some time there, particularly if Hatte is as bad as it sounds. It's her heart, I guess."

"Uh huh," said Agnes, starting to drift toward her worst fears.

"Anyway, I thought I could make the trip with her, drop her off, and then come to Richmond for a while so we could see each other then," said Pat listening for her response.

Pat was coming to see her, thought Agnes. That, in and of itself, was good news but something about his lack of urgency and the level of excitement she heard from him about his adventures unsettled her.

"But I'm the one that has the urgency," thought Agnes. "If he knew I was pregnant he'd understand that."

She was terribly confused and very anxious. How should she handle this? The baby would be born two months before Pat would even show up in Richmond following his Vaudeville dates. She promised herself she would not tell Pat over the phone. She had to tell him face to face. Then again, she pictured how it might be if she greeted him at the train station with a baby in her arms.

She'd decided she'd greet him alone, without the baby, when he arrived and hope he might suggest settling down, ending his elusive dream to fly again.

[525]

Pat rattled on, regurgitating agonizing details about dates, options, reasons, conditions forcing his hand, and placations about how quickly the months would pass before May. Agnes heard him but was not listening to a word he said. She was dizzy with conflicting thoughts.

"Does he want to see me? Did something happen on the trip? Did he forget our discussion about seeing each other right after he returned from France? Then again, he didn't expect to come home so soon? But, why the Vaudeville dates? Well, maybe he does have to take care of some business. He's been traveling continuously for a full year," she thought.

"Honey?" said Pat, hearing no response on the other end as he talked rapidly.

"Huh?" responded Agnes. "Oh, I'm sorry. Someone was talking here." She paused once again.

"So? What do you think?" Now Pat was confused.

"What, dear?" she responded trying to recover the conversation.

"So, don't you think the idea of me visiting in May when I bring mom to Wyoming makes sense?" said Pat.

"Make sense? Is that all he's thinking? Of course not, nothing makes sense right now," Agnes thought.

"Sure, Pat. May's fine," responded Agnes, her head still spinning.

"Ok, good," said Pat. "I'll write you and call periodically as we make plans. Where will you be around Christmas?"

"I'll be around, getting together with family and friends like everyone else," she answered.

"Ok, Agnes," Pat said. He was feeling suddenly far away and disconnected. "I'll talk to you soon."

"Ok, goodbye, honey," she said hanging up the phone slowly as she had following the phone call before France. She paused one final moment, touching her handkerchief to her lips.

"I will not tell him about the baby unless he agrees ahead of time to marry me," she thought.

Agnes would rather spare Pat the conflict than force his hand before he was ready. Additionally, it would be a true indication of his love for her if he acted on their plan to marry not knowing of their child. She would wait to hear his thoughts, then react in the best interest of herself, Pat and their baby.

If Pat had marriage on his mind, it was not evident in the days following his phone call to Agnes. He did some things that he hoped could lead him back into the cockpit once again. The December 29 issue of Flight Magazine listed the newest group of men announcing they'd take up the challenge of the Daily Mail to cross the Atlantic in a plane. The London newspaper was offering 10,000 pounds to the first team that could successfully fly "from any point in the United States of America, Canada or Newfoundland to any point in Great Britain or Ireland" in 72 continuous hours."

While in France, Pat had announced his plans to enter the contest. He had not decided on a plane yet but would work with Captain I.F. Fuller and fly with Lieutenant C.C. Robinson to achieve the feat. C.C. was one of the original eighteen from Borden. This story was reported in Europe and across the United States. Agnes just happened to read it in the San Francisco Examiner.

After reading the story, Agnes called Arlene and asked her to have lunch with her again, on December 30. After they placed their order, Agnes handed Arlene the paper.

"Did you see this?" she asked.

Agnes took the paper from her and saw the small article circled numerous times.

"Well, just because he says he'd like to fly across the Atlantic doesn't mean he doesn't want to settle down," said Arlene. "It is a nice prize and he's probably also thinking about bringing in some income. After all, you told me how he was done giving speeches. Even Pat said that to me once, America has heard his story, right?"

"No, you're correct Arlene," responded Agnes. "The real issue right now is that I've got to leave the store. I'm entering my sixth month and I can't work anymore. I've got some money saved up. With Christmas over, it's a good time to take a leave. I can always go back at some point. I'll tell them I need to take a leave. They'll agree."

"Your right, Agnes," confirmed Arlene. "Right now just deal with the job issue. Let's see how Pat is after his Vaudeville shows. You need to take care of yourself and stay confined until you have the baby."

Unwed mothers in those days had few choices and were not expected to be seen much in public, let alone working in a highly visible position of a fashion store.

"Thanks, Arlene," responded Agnes. "I'm glad I have you as a friend. I want to have this baby and make sure everything goes well. I can't control what Pat ultimately does. I need to take care of myself right now."

There was no doubt in Arlene's mind that Agnes was a strong and self-confident woman. After all, like Pat, Agnes had been on her own early in life and worked hard for everything she had. She loved Pat and wanted to be his wife but she also knew that his life's ambition had yet to be met. She had little doubt Pat would "do the right thing" and marry her. But she did not want the baby to be the reason for marrying her.

Her pregnancy drove a new timeline now. And yet, she could not explain the urgency of the situation to Pat without revealing she was pregnant. If she did that, Pat's decision would forever cloud his genuine love for her for the rest of their life together.

Unexpected pregnancies bring on instant responsibilities regardless of circumstance. She knew those responsibilities fell on her and Pat. As the child grew inside her, she began to feel that her strategy to assure the authenticity of Pat's love was secondary to the care and stability of the child. She decided that whatever decisions she made, they would be made with the baby's best interests in mind.

The baby was due about the same time as Pat's last Vaudeville appearance. In fact, by Agnes' calculation, the baby was conceived on July 4. Pat's final speech was April 4 at the Majestic Theatre in Chicago, exactly nine months to the day. She would do what she had to do now, then make future decisions when the time came.

After they finished lunch, Agnes and Arlene walked out of the store together and gave each other a long hug.

"Thanks again, Arlene," said Agnes.

"Anytime, hon," responded Arlene. With that, they headed up the street in opposite directions.

As 1919 began, circumstances began to reshape the lives of the O'Brien family, as well. Pat's brother "Buck," interviewed in Chicago on January 14 for a position with a major shoe manufacturer in San Francisco and was hired to start March 1st.

Having come home for Christmas, Elmer was still in town. It was decided that he and Buck would travel back to California together. With little farming to do in Modesto until March, Elmer would be able to help get Buck acclimated.

Lee Keedick booked Pat for a speech at the American Institute of Mining Engineers Convention held at the Biltmore Hotel in New York City on February 18. Trade association conventions were a new market for Keedick and he wanted to book a solid presenter for his first view events.

The event was very much like Pat's early speeches, complete with questions from the audience that went as long as the audience desired. He'd not had a presentation like it for some time. Those in attendance had interest in Pat's story from a historical point of view. They expressed their appreciation for his patriotism and his bravery in battle. Pat enjoyed the presentation and reception which followed. Vaudeville was different.

Pat's first Vaudeville presentation was on February 24. He hated it. He appeared with other acts in a two hour variety show. His portion of the program was a strict 20 minutes.

"How the hell am I supposed to do anything in twenty minutes for Christ's sake," he told Keedick more than once during the first week.

Though Pat felt terrible about the Vaudeville format, the crowd cheered him so enthusiastically that the director of the show moved Pat's position up in stature from 6th to 9th, three before the final act. On the bill was Ruth St. Denis, famous dancer and teacher of future dance icon Martha Graham, Louise Dresser a singer-actress who would later go on to star with Buster Keaton in film, vaudeville hoofer George White who would later star in movies, and Frank Fay, the Irish actor, singer, dancer who hit it off with Pat quite well.

Many of these vaudevillian regulars would build significant movie careers in the years ahead. Pat was quickly becoming well known among the "sawdust crowd." He enjoyed them and they found him to be witty and quick. But Pat's focus was not on show business at the beginning of 1919, not yet anyway.

Pat and Keedick had breakfast one morning after a week of shows. Pat had the New York Times open and searched for the review. It read as follows.

"He gave a snappy anecdotal monologue. Opening at the Keith Palace New York, he made a cheering hit and the vaudeville powers got his name to a contract that insures added fame and far more lucre than his actual heroism earned."

"What a pile of horse manure this is," Pat said to Keedick laughing.

"Yeah, I saw it," said Keedick. "Don't pay attention to those critics. I don't give them any thoughts." Keedick returned to his breakfast, glancing up to see if Pat was really bothered by the review.

"The guy that wrote that article is one of many young journalists that barely know we fought a war, Pat. He has no idea what you went through," said Keedick with empathy.

It struck Pat that perhaps Keedick was less of a charlatan than he'd expected. Despite their business relationship, Pat and his manager had a personal friendship that included great respect for each other. Keedick understood the monetary value of Pat's story but never disrespected it. Pat never let Keedick sell him short but understood that Keedick had to make money too.

"These Vaudeville jobs are strictly for the money, Pat. Take them for what they are. Don't even worry about what the papers say. The journalist that wrote that review just doesn't think anyone should make more money than he does, which isn't very much, by the way," assured Keedick.
"Well, they sure are rude," said Pat. "I'd like to pop this guy."

"Like I said, let it roll off your back. We're both going to make a lot of money in the next few weeks," said Keedick. Pat agreed, tossed the paper on the empty chair to his left and resumed breakfast.

Pat was able to come home after appearing at the Palace in New York. His next Vaudeville speech was actually in Chicago. It gave him an opportunity to visit family and do some personal business.

On Wednesday, February 25, Pat bought a farm outside Morocco, Indiana. He was looking for a real estate opportunity and his brother Ivan, who was struggling at the processing plant in Hammond, wanted to farm. Pat figured he'd buy the place for an investment and Ivan could reap the profits from the crop each year. Ivan was only 22 and his wife and he were starting a family.

On the same day, Buck, who was thirty-four at the time, and Elmer, now forty-one, left Momence for northern California. There was quite a gathering at the local tavern for Buck in the afternoon and Pat was happy that Buck had found an opportunity in California.

Pat headed back to New York on Sunday, March 2. He worked the week in New York making reappearance at the Palace on March 9th. He was moved up on the bill again to the 11th position. When he walked off the stage to a roaring crowd, Keedick was off stage. He smiled at Pat, who was smiling, rolling his eyes with ironic acceptance.

"Remember O'Brien," said Keedick, "Money, money, money!" as he rubbed his thumb against his fingers.

Pat was back in Momence by March 13 and helped Ivan and his wife move into their new farm house. Pat thoroughly enjoyed the change of pace and Ivan was thrilled to be farming again. Pat purchased the 280 acre farm from Frederick and Anna Madsen for $21,000, cash.

Meanwhile, Agnes was in her last month of pregnancy. Arlene was proving to be a loyal and trustworthy friend. She stopped by to see Agnes three to four times a week and generally stayed with her weekends to help out. Late in the evening on March 21, Otto Stevens arrived to bring the two ladies to St. Mary's hospital on Hayes Street. It was time.

Early in the morning of March 22, Agnes MacMillan gave birth to a baby girl around 2:45 in the morning. By 4:30 a.m. Agnes was fast asleep in her bed. Arlene was sleeping in the chair next to Agnes. The baby was sleeping in the nursery with ten other babies, fast asleep. The small pink tag attached to the headboard read, "Carol Ruth MacMillan."

Pat was standing in his bathrobe looking out of the second floor window of Clara's apartment. It was just 6:35 a.m. He had awakened around 4:45, about the time Carol Ruth was born. He was unable to sleep and was now sipping on a freshly brewed cup of coffee. The eastern sky was just showing signs of daylight.

Two weeks passed and Pat did his final speech for the Vaudeville circuit at the Majestic again in Chicago. Jack Clegg had not found the shoe business pleasant and decided he wanted to become a pilot like his uncle. He had announced plans to join the Air Service by May 1. Clara was saddened about Jack's decision and sold the store to A.G. Crouch, a clerk at Jensen's drug store. She maintained ownership of the building and continued to live upstairs. Somewhat distraught and suffering from her rheumatism she was confined to her home for a few weeks following the sale.

[531]

Arletta and Theodore Hansen, living in Ralston, Wyoming at the time, had finished their packing for Cody, Wyoming on April 11th. Belle Hansen needed help as she had been ill for some time. Her husband John was still working and needed help with his wife. The two sisters decided it would be best to be together. Unfortunately, John Hathaway who was living with them at the time injured himself loading up when a horse broke and pulled him some distance.

Pat made a big splash when he brought some of his Vaudeville "friends" home with him on April 15th. The troop appeared at the Majestic Theater in Chicago along with Pat on April 1st and Pat convinced them to travel with him to Momence, which they all enjoyed. Towns like Momence instantly know when "city folks" are in town.

"They dress different," said one old timer when he saw world famous comedian John McCormick and actor Walter Weemes following Pat around town for two days. Weemes was a "black face" comedian and considered the world's greatest ventriloquist. Pat made a point of bringing them to every watering hole in town and the local folks were thrilled to have such entertainment "right here in Momence."

On April 19, exactly four weeks since the birth of the baby, Pat sent a telegram to Agnes from the shoe store indicating he'd call around 3:00. She never got it. About five minutes to five Momence time, he went downstairs to the shoe store and called the City of Paris Store in San Francisco.

"Hello, is Agnes there?" said Pat in routine fashion.

"No, she's not working," said the office clerk who had catered Agnes' previous calls from Pat. "Can I help you?"

"I sent her a cable," said Pat. "I'm Pat O'Brien." he said thinking she might recognize his name.

"She's not working here anymore," said the clerk. "She took a leave."

"Leave?" sounding a little shocked. "Do you know where she is?" asked Pat.

"Not really," said the clerk. "I don't think she's working anywhere else. I think she just took some time off."

"Thank you." Pat was stunned. This time, he hung up slowly "What happened?" he thought. "Damn it, I should have called sooner." Immediately, he called the St. James Hotel in Richmond and asked for the concierge.

"Listen, Bobby," he said to the longtime concierge, "I need you to ask Otto Stevens or anyone that you know from our group to call me tomorrow between 10 and noon. I need to talk to someone right away. I'm looking for someone. Here's the number." He gave the concierge Clara's number.

"Sure, Pat," said Robert Jones who knew Pat well.

The next day, Pat was camped out at Clegg's hoping for a call. The phone rang about 12:30. "Hello!"

"It's Agnes, Pat."

"Agnes, how did you find out I called?" said Pat, relieved but startled.

"Otto came by with a message from the hotel that you had called and were looking for someone," said Agnes. "I figured you might be looking for me?"

"Are you ok?" asked Pat. "I called the store and they said you're not working there anymore. What's going on?"

"I just took some time off," said Agnes. "I had some time coming and with the holiday past, thought it might be a good time for a little rest."

"Sure, I can see that," responded Pat but clearly confused. He went on.

"I just wanted to let you know that mom and I are leaving for Wyoming May 19. It will take us two days and then I'll stay and visit until the 24th. I will arrive in San Francisco on the 30th."

"That will be grand, Pat," said Agnes in a rather flat tone but not too revealing of her frustration over how things had gone with Pat the past two months. He had not talked to her on the phone for over a month. It was becoming terribly obvious to her that he had his priorities elsewhere but she understood also that her situation was accelerated due to the baby.

"Ok, Agnes. Are you sure you're ok?" asked Pat, sensing her lack of enthusiasm.

"Yes, I'm fine," she said. "I'm just a little tired today. Write me, particularly if something changes."

"I will. I will, Agnes," said Pat. "You take care of yourself, ok?"

"Sure, Pat, talk to you soon" Said Agnes.

"I will. Good bye," returned Pat cautiously.

"Bye," she said.

Agnes hung up the phone and not slowly, this time. She had made a decision about the baby already. It needed a proper home. If her next visit with Pat did not go as it should, she would give the baby up. In reality, she was no more ready to raise child than Pat but for different reasons. She was not in a financial position to raise a child by herself and had little family available to help raise the child while she worked. There was no way to survive without Pat's help. She had discussed the whole thing with Arlene.

"I think I know of a perfect couple," Arlene had told her.

"Don't tell me now," said Agnes. "Let's see how my visit goes with Pat. I'd rather not know who they are quite yet."

"I've not even mentioned it to them, Agnes." Said Arlene "But they are perfect."

George and Vesta Hughes were from San Bruno at the far south end of San Francisco. Arlene new them because they lived next door to her sister-in-law, her husband's sister. They were in their upper thirties and over cards one night, Vesta had mentioned the couple's difficulty having children. Arlene kept their identity to herself and Agnes kept her decision in limbo until seeing Pat again.

Pat felt that Agnes might have had a bad day. She didn't sound the same. He bought the "needed a break" story she gave him regarding her job and never suspected anything else. He felt detached from her though and uneasy about the tone in her voice but, as men so often do, worked through it in his rational and mistaken mind.

Agnes was pulling away. Pat was making plans to update his passport. It was hard to predict how their next scheduled meeting would turn out. Even Arlene was not certain. None of Pat's friends knew the situation.

Not yet anyway.

Chapter 43

Conversations

On Thursday, May 8th, 1919, Al Fontaine came home from war. Pat, Clara, and members of Al's family greeted him at the train depot. Pat found great comfort in being able to welcome home his childhood buddy. He had not spoken to him in over a year.

The Fontaine house was jammed with people the entire day as friends came to welcome Al home. Al had lost his father a few years earlier so his mother had been taking in borders to make ends meet. She was relieved to have her son home and Al welcomed the chance to live a normal life once again in Momence.

That same day, The *Momence Progress* reported that Jensen's Drug store had just installed its first soda fountain. Though insignificant against world events, it was big news in town. It would be open to the public on Saturday morning. That morning, people were standing in line for twenty minutes just to get a seat. Like everyone else in Momence, Pat and Al were also eager to see the new convenience.

The two friends stood in line at Jensen's waiting for a booth seat. Pat was so happy to spend some time with his friend. He would have hated to leave for Wyoming, California and Russia without welcoming Al home and spending some time with him.

Al figured that with the end of the war, surely Pat would stay home for a while. That was not going to be the case. The two veterans were engaged in a vigorous discussion about America's newly acquired leadership on the world stage and Pat was as passionate as ever. Victory in Europe was already driving economic activity along with product innovation in the United States, just as it had done following their father's wars.

But this war also placed the United States squarely in the role of a required participant in global affairs. Men who come home from war knew these things first. Those at home felt things change not knowing the cause. Veterans always change the character of their home towns and the trajectory of their country once home from war.

Pat related all that had transpired in France and how unpleasant his Vaudeville experience had been. Al told of near-death experiences and the squalor that was northern France. Their conversation was not unlike so many other men before them, sharing intimate stories of horrific days at war and the lagging effects that continued to be present in them though they were removed from battle and home again.

After nearly an hour discussing Europe, Pat shifted the conversation to Russia. He talked fluidly about the recent history there and gave an amazingly clear overview of the highly complex forces weighing in on the Allies: White Russia and Lenin's led Red Army. As Al listened, he was struck about how much more Pat seemed to know than the average American about the conditions there.

"We have a lot of resources and Allied troops trapped in the whole mess, Al," said Pat. "There's only one way out and that's the railroad to Vladivostok."

"You're going, aren't you?" Al asked.

"Who knows more about sneaking out of a country and using the railroad to do it than me, Al?" he said with both hands raised upward, flashing his famous smile.

"You're crazy," responded Al, dipping into his second ice cream sundae with a grin. Though he hated to see Pat risking his life once again, Al knew there was no talking Pat out of it. "What about Agnes?" asked Al.

"She seemed rather distant on our last phone call," said Pat. "I think our time apart has given her cold feet. But I'm sure she'll be ok. I just need to spend time with her, that's all."

"Have you told her about your planned trip to Russia?" asked Al.

"No, something like that, I need to tell her in person," responded Pat. "I'm sure she'll be concerned but by the time I return, it will be about a year since we got engaged. That's a fairly normal length of time these days. I'll wait till I see her in a few weeks."

Had Pat known of the circumstances facing Agnes he'd likely have a different view. Not knowing of the baby, he felt it reasonable to take one last run at the war and return to marry the woman he loved.

"Well, good luck with all that, chum!" Al said, adding a slightly cynical tone. They both laughed and Pat animated a fake smack to the side of Al's head.

As they walked to the Fontaine home, Pat offered to help Al financially if finding work turned out to take some time.

"Not only that, Al," said Pat, "you should take some time off and try to unwind. I never had much of a chance when I came home. I was on the road the same week I arrived in Momence. You need some time to get your feet on the ground. Take it from me, I know."

"Pat, I really appreciate your offer to help me financially," said Al. "I hope I don't need it, but I do appreciate it."

"Well, don't hesitate Al," responded Pat. "I've made a lot of money this year while you were still finishing things off in Europe."

"Thanks, Pat," said Al.

"There is one thing I need your help with though," Pat said.

"Name it," responded Al.

"I need to get my trunk. I'll need it for Siberia. That place ain't Hawaii you know," Pat said smiling. "I'll need plenty of warm clothes. I hear its cold at night even in the spring. I'm going through the Gobi Desert and it turns to ice once the sun is down."

"Sure. I'll help you carry it to Clara's. I hope mom hasn't stuffed it with my clothes," said Al. Al had first stored it when Pat came home from England after his escape.

They arrived at Al's house and dug out Pat's trunk from the attic. It was in the same spot. They carried it to Clara's place where Pat would prepare for his big trip.

After visiting a bit longer with Clara, Margaret and Pat, it was time for Al to head home. The two women did not notice the intensity of Al's good-bye to Pat, but Al knew Russia was a risk and choked up a bit as he said good-bye to his buddy.

"Be careful, Pat," said Al, shaking Pat's hand and grabbing his forearm with his left. "You always scare the hell out of me with your crazy escapades. I don't know how, or for that matter why, you do it."

"I'll be back before you know it," Pat said as he handed Al an envelope with cash.

"What's this?" asked Al.

"It's a little cash," said Pat, "just to tie you over."

"Pat, I'll be fine," pleaded Al, trying to hand it back.

"Consider it a loan then," said Pat pushing his hand back. "Besides, what the hell am I going to spend it on in Siberia?"

"Thanks, Pat, I'll only use it in a pinch," returned Al.

On his way home, Al opened up his envelope. There was $1,000 in cash inside. He was stunned and quickly folded the envelope, stuffed it in his pocket and instinctively looked around to see if anyone had seen him looking. He then laughed to himself. There was no one in sight. The trenches of France had not left his subconscious yet.

"I do need a break," he thought.

Al placed his hand once again into his pocket to be certain his envelop was still secure. He felt sad thinking of Pat. Had he just seen his lifelong buddy for the last time? Al shuffled home, hid the envelope under his mattress and took a long time to fall asleep. It had been an emotional day. If he could only sleep, he thought.

"Here I am, finally home," he said to himself. "Pat runs off once again on one of his adventures and I really have no one to talk to. He's the only one that understands what it's like over there. Why couldn't he stay another week, anyway? Russia's a long way. I probably won't see him for at least six months, if he makes it back at all." Al liked to be home. Pat loved home too but "for some reason," Al thought, "Pat needs to go away regularly in order to forge a longing to be back once again."

After about an hour he whispered, "I'll start fresh in the morning," then dozed off.

On Monday the 12th, Pat took a morning train to Chicago to get his passport arranged for his planned trip. Before departing he received a call from the *Momence Progress*. They'd heard he was leaving soon and wanted to hear his plans.

"I'll give you a call this afternoon from the train station," Pat told them. "I've got to catch my train now and then I'm heading for New York later today." The paper agreed.

After completing his business at the consulate's office, he walked to the LaSalle Street station to wait for his train to New York. He made his way over to a large bank of phone booths to give Agnes a call.

"Hello Agnes," he said when she answered the phone.

"Hi, honey, surprised to hear from you. Has something happened?" she said with genuine concern.

"No, everything is fine," said Pat. "I was just waiting for the train and wanted to call you to let you know everything is all set and I should be in San Francisco around May 30th."

"That will be fine, Pat," responded Agnes. "Are you heading west already?"

"No, I'm downtown Chicago, getting my papers in order," responded Pat. As soon as the words came out, he realized he may have said too much.

"Papers? Do you need papers to come to San Francisco, honey?" responded Agnes attempting to insert some light humor.

"No, Agnes." He paused to think a second. "I didn't want to tell you on the phone, I planned to tell you when I saw you but after we visit."

Agnes did not responded in sequence. "Visit!" she thought. "He calls it a visit?" She rolled her eyes upward, sensing the worst may be happening. A chill ran through her body. She knew what this meant.

"I'm heading to Russia on a project. It's very important," he said with caution. Hearing no response he went on. "You see, Agnes, there's one final push to get out of Russia before we're caught up in the mess the Bolsheviks have made of things. There are still many Allied troops there. I'm going to do what I can to help them out," said Pat.

"Pat, I'm just so shocked that you still feel that you must end the war all by yourself," said Agnes in a somewhat raised voice. "What about our future, Pat? I just never know what you're thinking. I feel like I've barely seen you since you've been home. When do you plan to stop?" she asked.

Pat was right. Telling Agnes over the phone was not a good idea. He'd just slipped up and had accidently revealed his plans. His mind was racing. What could he say next that could ease the situation?

"I'm sorry, Agnes," he started. "I really didn't want to tell you over the phone. I understand why you're angry. Let's talk about it more when I see you. I'll spend a few days visiting the family in Wyoming and then get to San Francisco as soon as I can, ok?" He held his breath waiting for a response.

"Pat, I know you need to do what you need to do," she said. "I understand that. I need to get on with my life, too, Pat."

Her words sounded like a break-up. She didn't intend that so she added, "Let's talk when you get here."

"Yes, let's," responded Pat. "I'll see you in a matter of days, hon."

They hung up simultaneously and both regretted the call, for different reasons. Pat took a seat in the lobby of the LaSalle Street Station and waited quietly for his train to New York where he had three days of business scheduled. Suddenly, he remembered the newspaper in Momence. He walked back to the phone banks and took an interview then came back to his seat quietly where he stared out the window thinking about the call with Agnes the whole time.

Meanwhile, Agnes began a long walk to Arlene's. She determined that the time was right to meet Mr. and Mrs. Hughes and talk about the baby. She cried most of the way, not out of self-pity but for her baby whom she loved.

"Thank goodness for Arlene," she whispered aloud crying as she walked briskly for twelve blocks to the house. "It's so sad. I hate to give up my baby."

For Pat, there was no way to change his plans even if he wanted to. For Agnes, she knew she needed to carry out her plan though she didn't want to. She still felt forcing his hand and telling him about the baby created more uncertainty. Baring some dramatic change of plans on Pat's part, she'd go forward with the idea of giving up her baby. "Let's see how our visit goes," she thought to herself, not fully willing to give up hope.

Pat boarded his train and after about twenty minutes it was making the wide turn around Lake Michigan, heading east for New York. He would have a late dinner with Keedick when he arrived. It was primarily a social visit but Pat was also eager to tell Keedick about his planned trip to Russia. Pat was also scheduled to visit Mitchel Field on Long Island where the Curtiss Company had hundreds of JN-4s in use and an equal number of American pilots still training despite the end of the war. He'd been invited there by one of his old Signal Corps buddies to inspire the new pilots, something he always enjoyed doing.

On the 14th, Maggie went to Lowell to visit Lila and Ben before her big trip west. "Tell them we love them all," were Lila's last words as she kissed her mother good bye. Then she added, "Spend some time talking with Pat, mom. I worry so much about him. I wish he would slow down."

"You know how our Pat is, Lila," said Margaret. "He just goes and goes. Thank God for that in one way, honey. He would have never come back to us if he wasn't so determined."

"Yes mother, thank God indeed. Enjoy your trip mother and be careful," said Lila.

Margaret stepped up into Ben's car. Ben waved to his wife, then put the car in gear and headed for the train depot in Lowell. Margaret turned back once to wave a final time to Lila and was particularly chatty with Ben on the way to the station. She asked for his thoughts on Pat. Ben felt Pat was still on a journey to complete "his war," as Ben called it and that people around Pat would have to give him the time he needed.

"Unfortunately, Maggie, Pat is on his schedule, not ours," said Ben.

"You are right, Ben," responded Maggie. "I guess we all want Pat to be as we would like to see him."

Back in Momence, Al sat at home reading his copy of the Progress. He read the short clip regarding Pat's planned trip to Russia.

"Pat never mentioned that he could be gone for such a long time," he thought. "I certainly don't remember him saying, 'possibly two years.'" The two friends never held back anything. What he didn't know was that Pat had spoken to the newspaper after their final visit and, furthermore, had made the comment to the paper less than five minutes after his uncomfortable phone call with Agnes. He was quoted in the story as saying he'd be gone for "six months, possibly as long as two years."

"Let's hope things calm down and he's back sooner rather than later. I wonder what happened since Tuesday," he thought, folding the paper in half and tossing it on floor next to his chair. "I can't believe he didn't tell me everything."

On Friday the 16th, Pat boarded an early train in New York and headed home. He would spend the weekend visiting friends in Momence. He and Al did find time to talk again about the war and discussed additional horrifying experiences they both witnessed in Europe. He was also able to explain to Al what happened regarding the newspaper story. Al was grateful for this. The two men experienced a second goodbye and a second treat at Jensen's on Pat's final day in Momence.

Margaret and Pat departed Momence for Wyoming the following Monday. On that same day, 8,000 British troops left New Castle, England headed for Vladivostok. It would take a few weeks but eventually Pat would be in Vladivostok too. He decided to put Russia and the war out of his mind for now. It would be a long, wonderful train ride to Cody. He'd finally get the chance to talk extensively about his experiences with the person who knew him best, his mother. He'd also see the Hathaways for the first time since his escape and this thrilled him to no end. Naturally, they were tremendously excited to see him.

There's an enchantment about the great prairie in America. Its lure is its miles and miles of sameness. Other than the dramatic crossing of the Mississippi, the route west of Chicago on the Chicago, Burlington and Quincy Railroad is not one to distract. In settings much more diverse and enchanting, passengers, determined to fill long hours of travel with conversation, are constantly drawn to the window, distracted by natural beauty and a divergent landscape. Such is not the case across Illinois, Iowa and Nebraska. As its sparse landscape persists, the mind clears clean, ceding space for thought. Margaret initiated the first extensive conversation.

"Pat, how do you feel now after all this time?" asked Margaret. "What have your doctors told you?"

"Well, I do what I feel I can do," responded Pat. "But they tell me my internal parts may never be in the right place. I think my second crash set me back more than the first."

"But are you in pain? I mean, other than your hip?" asked Maggie.

"The most irritating thing is my hip. I don't really feel uncomfortable anywhere else but every once in a while my whole body feels suspended or just out of synch, as if I may fall apart or as if pieces of me are about to fall off," Pat said.

"You need some extended time doing nothing, Pat," advised Maggie. "You don't realize it but you've been going and going ever since you've gotten home. An experience like the one you've had can add ten years to your life, Pat."

"It already has," he responded. "Some days I feel like an old man and then the next day I feel great and my energy takes over and I just want to do everything I can, all day, until I physically can't do any more."

Maggie continued her inquiry. "You've always liked to go and go Pat, but don't you think you're more urgent about it now or maybe you just seem to be in such a hurry? You're home now and you're safe. You've got the opportunity to live a long life, thank God. Why not take time to give your body a rest and let life come to you a bit. There's no need to be so rushed about living. You're young."

Pat was quick to respond.

"Mom, I've died so many times in my short life, I'll never know how much time I may have on this earth. I had no business surviving a bullet in my throat, no business jumping from the train, no chance I could bargain my freedom from that crook in Brussels and few odds I'd escape into Holland. Heck mom, I was so used to calamity by the time I crashed in Dallas, I barely paid attention," he said with certainty and a bit of humor. "There's no reason in life to go slow. Only people who believe that life is long, days drag on and God gives us plenty of time, go slowly. I can't do that. I've never done that."

Maggie went silent. As parents sometimes do, she'd gained a life lesson from her child. It's so common for parents to teach their children about living that it is an odd feeling indeed when the reverse holds true. Pat was unlike anyone Maggie knew in her life. He was unlike nearly everyone in the town of Momence. She could see every pattern of Pat's youth now in his twenty-eighth year of life. Many of his traits were noticeable as he was growing up. The full breadth of his driven nature had not been fully visible until this day.

[543]

"You are right, Pat," she said quietly. "We are all different. All of us are. You just happen to be one amid thousands of other people on this earth who see life in a different way. Be proud of that, sweetheart. God gave you a gift to stand out. To be an example for others and show all of us what can happen if we hope." She paused again.

"All I ask is that you just take care of yourself, Margaret replied. "I mean physically and mentally. Don't drive yourself too hard. God intended us to rest, too, you know, Pat. You're important to everyone that knows you. You're even important to people that do not know you but only know about you. Ok?"

"Thanks, mom," Pat said. "But I enjoy what I do now. I'm not driving myself to despair. Why would I do that? I don't do things I don't want to do. No one is forcing me each day. I just do what I enjoy. Why can't people just understand that and let me be?

Feeling a bit bad for raising his voice, he went on.

"I know I can cause people to worry but it's not my intent. Even Al seemed to be in a worried state this week. I think if he felt it would make a difference he'd tell me to stay home and stay out of Russia. But he knows better. I was probably a little arrogant with him but I'm glad we got to visit one more time after my trip to New York. He's a good soul and has been my friend my whole life. But he's not like me."

"Very few are, Patrick. Like everyone else, Al loves you like a brother and just wants you to take care of yourself, that's all," she added

.

They both went silent for a while, content with the exchange. Most of Iowa went unnoticed until the train slowed at Des Moines.

"Let's grab some lunch, mom," said Pat. "I'm starving."

"Ok, honey," said Maggie.

Pat and his mother visited the rest of the afternoon. Overnight they both experienced a comfortable night's sleep in the sleeper car. As the sun came up the next day, they were having a hearty breakfast in the diner car when the train pulled out of the Casper station and traveled toward the Bighorn Basin. Pat looked up and could see the Tetons some distance away. The Plains were behind them now. Between Casper and the great mountain range lay Cody, Wyoming, along the Shoshone River. Pat was flooded with memories of his two years in Cody. It had been a long time since he'd thought about the place.

"I'm very excited to see everyone, ma. Who's going to be there again?" asked Pat in an inquisitive and boyish tone.

"Naturally, John, your Aunt 'Hette' and their kids, Ruby, Edith and Ellery," said Margaret. Hette was Margaret's closest sister Hattie Belle. She went by 'Hette' and was also called Belle.

"Of course those kids aren't kids anymore," responded Margaret. "Why, the youngest boy Ellery must be fifteen by now.

"They had another baby about my age that died, right?" asked Pat.

"Yes, dear, Florence," responded Maggie. "She was beautiful child. She died in Momence. It was the fever…very sad."

Pat glanced out the window and reflected about how it might be to have a cousin his age had Florence lived. He thought about his near death experiences and the length of his father's and grandfather Perry's long life. The roulette of birth and death came to him in this flash of insight. Leaving his thoughts, he returned to Maggie's comments.

"Wow, I've lost track," said Pat. "I remember Ruby and Edith were small, cute kids. I'm sure they're much older now. It will be fun. How old is Belle now?"

"She's around fifty-two as is John," responded Maggie.

"Do their kids all live in Cody?" asked Pat.

"Ruby lives in Powel. She married Sam Lanchbury about three years ago. I don't think you've met him yet. Edith is still at home, nineteen or twenty by now and of course young Ellery is only fifteen. Hette told me he's very excited about meeting you.

"What about C.C?" asked Pat.

"C.C and Ted are in Cody, too. Hette just can't keep up on her own with all her rheumatism and such," Maggie responded
.

Ted and C.C. had lived in Powell which was about twenty miles northwest of Cody. Maggie's brother John, 'Uncle Jahnke' as Pat called him, lived with C.C and moved to Cody with them.

"But it hasn't been that long since you've seen them Pat. Why all the questions?"

"It seems like a century since I saw them last," said Pat. "So many details washed out of my mind during the war and my long walk. I guess I just suspended a lot of thinking about the normal things in life. I tried to think about home when I was hiding in Belgium but it was hard. The few years I was gone feel like a decade. I'm sorry."

"That's ok, Pat," responded Maggie. "I was just surprised that you could not recall their age."

"Either way, I can't wait to see them all," said Pat. Pat looked out the window once again, sharing his thoughts with Maggie.

"It's always despairing to see people complain about their lives and yet that poor baby never got a chance to live at all," said Pat. "I feel lucky, for some reason, thinking of her."

"I know dear, life is so precious. If the good Lord gives us a long life to live we owe it to him to live every day to the fullest," she said. "You've certainly done that, sweetheart."

Margaret paused a moment, noticed Pat still staring out the window, then continued, "Don't let anyone tell you how to live your life, Pat. Only you can determine that. You've earned that right. Just remember that we all love you and you can always come to family whenever you need help."

Pat took Maggie's words to heart. It was special to hear her express love and support. He reached out and took her hand, looked her in the eye and gave her a broad smile. The ride to Cody was well worth the trip to both of them.

"You know, mom," Pat said softly, "I remember a night in Belgium when I was hiding in the woods. I was remembering dad. I guess I was trying to remember dad but it was very hard to do and I felt badly. It made me cry. I couldn't remember much about dad but I did have many memories of Grandpa Perry. I felt bad about that, mom. I'm sorry that happened but I just wanted to tell you that.

"Pat, you were so young when dad died. Grandpa Perry spent a lot of time with you after that. He spent a lot of time with both you and Al," she said squeezing his hand. "You don't have to feel bad about anything. It makes sense. There's no reason to worry over that, honey. Your dad was a wonderful man. He was a gentle man who worked hard for all of us. Like you, he was in the service, too and fought bravely. You should be proud of him but don't feel you have to apologize for not remembering a lot about him. He was sick and you were only eleven when he died. Be thankful that you also had such a wonderful grandpa who loved you and took care of you," she said.

"Thanks, mom," said Pat still holding her hand. "It was only during my long isolation that I realized how important the Hathaways have been to me. I mean, like all kids, you look at your last name and figure, 'I'm an O'Brien." Then you learn over time that you're just as much part of your mom's side as you are part of your dad's. I guess young boys just think that way, huh? I think Grandpa Perry was very important to me in my life. He had a great spirit, didn't he mom?"

"Yes, he did honey. He surely did," responded Margaret, holding back her emotions. "Grandpa Perry was a great man. So was your father."

Their train switched tracks at Greybull and headed west. Next stop would be Cody. They fell silent, holding hands the rest of the way. Feeling drowsy, Maggie rested her head against Pat's arm and fell asleep while Pat focused far off at the approaching mountains and reflected on his family both past and present. After his trip, he'd be ready to marry, he thought. There would be no more wars for him after Russia.

Just then, Pat felt the train back down as they slowed into Cody. Maggie woke up and he pressed against the window looking up the track. Pat could see John and Ted standing on the edge of the platform, both men with their hands on their hips. There were others behind them but he did not recognize anyone in particular.

Everyone except Belle was gathered on the train platform in Cody ready to meet the "guest of honor" as Ellery had called his cousin.

"Mom, I see Ted and Uncle John," said Pat. "And I think that's C.C behind them," he added while squinting to get a better look.

The brakes squealed, the train lunged forward and then back again coming to a stop. Pat left his newspaper on the seat. He let Maggie step out into the aisle, then pulled himself up out of his seat using the luggage rack and stepped in front of her. Maggie glanced down quickly at the newspaper and smiled. Pat had left the news behind. It was going to be a nice visit, she thought.

"I'm glad I get to see them for the first time not needing to use my cane," said Pat.

"I'm just glad you're feeling better, Pat," Margaret responded, taking his arm.

They stepped forward then turned and made their way down onto the platform.

"Maggie!" shouted C.C., waving frantically from the other end of the platform to get her attention. Maggie was far enough away that she did not hear her sister yell.

"Gosh mom, Eda and Will are tall, aren't they," said Pat as he situated Maggie's small bag under his arm.

"Come on, Pat. It's them!" said Maggie, grabbing Pat's arm.

They stepped toward the end of the platform. Johnny Hathaway, Maggie's brother was there coming forward with a huge grin on his sun-beaten face. Pat could see his cousin Eda Belle waving frantically. She was holding her young daughter on her hip. A man that Pat guessed to be her husband, Lee Snyder, took the baby from her so Eda could run ahead.

"Oh my, Pat," said Maggie. "Look! Johnny does have a sling on his arm."

"Doesn't look like it's bothering him," responded Pat as he observed his uncle gimping ahead with joy on his face. Finally, the bulk of the family met in the center of the platform. Maggie and C.C. were the first to meet.

"Maggie, dear," said C.C. as the two sisters embraced. C.C extended herself up and gave Pat a kiss on the cheek. She began to cry.

"Pat it's so wonderful to see you again. The good Lord has brought you back to us. You look so wonderful, honey," said C.C.

"I missed you too aunt 'Cele', I'm glad to be here again," said Pat

.

Just then Pat's uncle Johnny stepped into the group, giving his nephew a hug around the neck with his good arm.

"Good to see you, boy," said Johnny. "So glad you're home."

"What happened to your arm uncle John?" asked Pat.

"Oh, it's a long story, boy," said Johnny. "Not half as much, I hear, as you went through young feller. How are you doing?"

"I'm getting along just fine, John," returned Pat.

Johnny had helped his sister C.C. and brother-in-law Ted move. While loading one of the wagons, he got his arm wrapped in the horse stirrups and was dragged some distance when the horse broke, pulling his shoulder out of place. His left arm was still in a sling. John was no longer a young man. It pained him greatly but he was recovering.

"No broken bones mind you, just a big tug from that blasted horse and the damn wagon wheel ran right over my foot, too." Pausing a second he went on. "But I didn't come down to tell you my story. I came to welcome you home, boy. It's good to see you." Just then Ted Hansen stepped up.

"Welcome home, Pat," said Ted, choking up as he put both hands aside Pat's smiling face. Then he gave his nephew a kiss on the cheek.

"Hello, Pat, you look grand," were John Hansen's words as he arrived. He too was emotional to see his nephew. After all, the entire country had seen Pat O'Brien during that past year but for the Hathaways, this was their first reunion.

"And who is this young lady?" stated Pat, looking down at a smiling young girl just under ten years old.

"I'm Martha Owens," said the long haired girl unknown to Pat. "You're tall," she said, grinning even broader than before. Ruby stood with her arm around the little girl.

"Martha lives with Sam and me," said Ruby. "Doesn't she have a wonderful smile?"

"You sure do," said Pat looking at the girl again.

Ruby explained how Martha had been abandoned with no place to go so she and Sam took her in as one of their own. Pat was touched by their meeting. The girl had a wonderful smile but Pat could see a little of the pain of abandonment in her eyes, something he remembered feeling at age eleven when Daniel died and Pat was shipped off to Wyoming a few years later.

"Come on, Martha, let's walk together," said Pat. He grabbed her hand which she readily received while looking up at him beaming with delight.

"Hi, Lieutenant," said Ellery who had shuffled up on Pat's left as he and Martha headed up the platform.

"Lieutenant? Why I haven't heard that for a while! How are you Ellery?" said Pat. "You're almost as tall as me."

"Yes, I am taller than the last time you saw me. That's what mother told me, anyway," said the young lad who was as thrilled as he could be.

Belle, Maggie's sister, was too sore to be at the train station. She was having a bad day with her rheumatism and decided to wait back at the house.

"Is Belle here?" Pat asked.

"No, she stayed back at the house," replied John Hansen. "Not a good day for her today but each day is different. She can't wait to see you, Pat."

The reunion on the platform of the entire Hathaway clan was full of emotions and some tears. To the surprise of everyone, Pat announced that he'd reserved the restaurant at the Irma Hotel.

"All of us?" shouted Ellery.

"Sure, everyone," said Pat. "Are yah hungry, boy?"

"Sure am," responded Ellery.

"Should we do this with Belle waiting at home?" asked Pat.

"That's fine, Pat," responded John. "We planned to have lunch before returning to the house."

The entire group drove to the Irma. Pat and Margaret would stay in the hotel during their visit. It was a bit crowded at C.C.'s with everyone in town. The Hathaways had a wonderful lunch. Each family member rotated seats to get some time with Pat and Maggie.

"How was it hiding for such a long time, Pat?" asked Edith.

"Well, being alone was one thing but eating those darn turnips day and night was no picnic, believe me," said Pat.

Ted Hansen came over to Pat.

"You do look good, Pat," he said. "You're a little thin but not as thin as your mom said you were. Boy, you're pretty famous now, huh boy?"
"I've met a lot of people, Ted," responded Pat.

"I read your book, Pat," Ted continued. "Seems like those Dutch were really good to you, huh?"

"Without 'um Ted I wouldn't be here," Pat related.

"Who was the guy, Pat?" he asked.

"His name was Venansius. Heck of a fellow," responded Pat. "I stayed in his house. He was close to Nijmegan, I recall."

And so it went all through lunch. Pat got as many questions as a press conference but felt no discomfort in answering any of them. He held young Eda Bell Snyder, granddaughter of C.C., for a spell. He teased her with a cookie and pulled it away as she reached for it which made all the adults laugh. The young girl was the daughter of Eda Bell Hansen, who had the same name.

Six-year-old Teddy Snyder, also Eda Bell's child, fought for time with Pat, occasionally punching Pat in the arm as young boys often do to prove their "manhood." Eda Bell protested but Pat paid no mind to the jousting. He was good with the little ones and they hung on him the whole time. Finally, after about ninety minutes, it was time to head for the house.

"Let's go, everyone," announced C.C. "I'm sure Belle's dying to see Pat and Maggie and I don't want to leave her alone too long."

Everyone headed outside and Pat paid the bill, tipping the two waiters mightily. A small crowd of onlookers had gathered in the hall peering in at the Hathaway party, hearing there was a celebrity in their midst.

[551]

"I see what you mean, Pat," said C.C. as they walked out. "You just can't get any privacy anymore can yah, hon?" Pat smiled and waved to the locals as everyone left the Irma.

The three family cars were loaded and the entire group headed towards Powell. Pat sat with his uncle John along with Willard, Ted's oldest. Willard was four years older than Pat but both remembered each other from their days in Momence. There were lots of laughs on the way to the Hansen house. Watching everything intently was young Ellery, who couldn't believe he was sitting right next to his famous cousin Lt. Pat O'Brien.

"How did you sneak around so well?" he said. "I mean, didn't you worry about getting caught while you were trying to escape?"

"Well, I sure did 'Elly," responded Pat. "Those Huns are sneaky you know. They don't' play around."

Pat and his uncle John belted a hearty laugh. Ellery was astonished by the whole thing.

The three cars stirred up a cloud of dust as they turned up the lane to the Hansen home. Belle was sitting in her chair on the porch anxiously awaiting their arrival. Pat moved directly to her, kneeling in front to give her a big hug. Margaret was right behind and bent over to give her sister a kiss. Belle cried, full of joy. It was one of her happier moments in a long time.

"I thought we'd never see you again, Pat," said Belle, looking up at her tall nephew from her chair.

"I'm sorry it took me so long to get to Powell, Belle," responded Pat. "I'm so glad I'm here at last."

The family settled on the front porch surrounding Belle who became the focus of Pat's attention for nearly two hours. He sat to her left, telling Belle of his adventures since Belgium while the family listened with amazement. As thousands had before them, Pat's own family was spellbound by his natural storytelling ability, now polished after a year of fine-tuning all across America. The youngsters held back requests for supper, not wanting to disturb the amazing stories by their "Cousin Pat".

The afternoon began to fade suddenly as the sun slipped behind Heart Mountain, casting a deep reddish-blue cast to the western sky. Belle felt fatigued and excused herself to the house where she lay down for a nap. The women gathered the children inside for a delayed supper of chicken salad and sliced apples while the men stayed on the porch, opening their share of beer bottles, changing the conversation as they often do when left alone.

"So Pat, your mother tells me you're heading for Russia?" asked Ted. "What in the world for, son?"

"Yeah, is that true, Pat?" added a curious Lee Snyder.

"Yes, that's true, Lee," responded Pat.

"After I stop in San Francisco I'm taking a ship to Yokohama. Then I make a short trip to the China port of Tianjin. From there to Peking where through some means, I'll head for the Trans-Siberian Railroad. I'll know more when I visit the British Consulate in Japan."

"But what will you do there, Pat?" asked John Hansen in a lightheaded tone. "Sounds a little dangerous, particularly going into Russia, don't yah think?"

"American railroad men from every part of the United States are there now," said Pat. "We're trying to repair the Russian railroad and get people out at the same time."

"You mean our troops?" asked John Hathaway.

"Ours, the Brits, Slavs, others and trainloads of material, too," said Pat.

"Supplies?" asked Ted.

"Supplies, tanks, armaments, trucks, troops, everything," responded Pat.

"No kidding?" John Hansen said.

"Ever since the Germans hit them hard at the beginning of the war, the Russians have been overrun by armies on all sides, some friendly, some not. Then the Bolsheviks took over and now no one knows which side anyone is on. I mean, since the Revolution the Russians have had more chaos inside their country than they ever had face-to-face with the Hun on the old Eastern Front."

[553]

"So they're still fighting, then?" asked John Hansen.

"Well, not in a traditional way, like we've seen in the West," said Pat. But a lot of the focus is along the Trans-Siberian railroad. That's the only way out and the only way in. The Czech and Slavs have controlled much of it for a time but now the Cassocks, White Army, Bolsheviks, Japanese and a dozen others are grabbing all they can before it leaves Russia."

"What a mess," said Ted.

"Sure is, Ted," responded Pat.

He tried to explain further.

"It's difficult to explain everything but the railroad across Russia from the Vladivostok to Moscow is in bad shape. Every 100 miles or so a different army is in control, some from within Russia and many from other countries. Between the Cassocks, Mongolians, Japanese, British and dozens of other counties who are there now, it's impossible for the Allies to get out. You might say I'm going in to help others get out," Pat said with a laugh. "I mean, who better than Pat O'Brien?" he said feeling a bit of the local brew. "I know trains, I know escape, and I'm used to dodging multiple armies while on the move in secret."

The other men laughed while nodding their heads in agreement and taking a sip of their cold beer.

Vladivostok was choked with troops from all over the world. Pat would avoid the congested port and approach the railroad at its midsection, from Peking north through the Gobi Desert, through the heart of Mongolia and up the center of Siberia. For Russia, the war was not over. It was just a different war. It would be Pat's last war.

The remaining week in Wyoming was full of picnics, card playing, baseball games, pictures and long hours visiting. The Hansen home was literally in the middle of nowhere but like the Prairie it gave a family vast unobtrusive space to do as they pleased.

By the fourth day, Pat felt that he had relaxed for the very first time since being home. It was therapeutic and a relief to Maggie to see him in old form. He played with the youngsters, talked at length with his uncles and had finally come home in his heart.

At dinner on Friday, he told the family that he would depart for California after the weekend.

"Let's plan a big meal for Sunday then," said CC.

"That would be grand," Belle added. "Let's plan something special, shall we ladies?

On Sunday, May 25th, a large picnic was prepared. The midday feast drifted into a lazy Sunday afternoon in the yard. The Hathaway women were busy clearing the large wooden table where the entire family had shared a final meal together. The Hansen men had created the table from long twelve-foot planks laid over homemade sawhorses. The men were sitting in wooden rockers and straight back chairs under a clump of trees on the farm property that shaded the warm sun.

On Monday, May 26th, it was time for Pat to head for San Francisco. Margaret would stay a while longer. There were tearful partings at the train station. Margaret, in particular, took a long look at her son as he kissed the others good bye. She saw how good the visit had been for him. The eyes of her sisters were flush with tears and the young kids kept pulling on Pat's arms, prompting their mothers to pull them back. Even Belle had made the trip to say good-bye. Pat gave his mother a final kiss good-bye and stepped back to turn.

"Good-bye, Hathaways," shouted Pat, catching a glimpse of his mother's eyes one last time. Pat turned back twice to wave as he made his way up the platform and then, once again as he'd done so many times before, paused at the steps, tossed a broad wave across his frame and then stepped lively up the railcar stairs.

At nearly that same moment, Lt. Col Daniel Mortimer Ottis was also boarding a train at the Chicago & Northwestern Train Station back in Rockford, Illinois. He was accompanied by the twelve doctors, twenty-one nurses, and fifty orderlies who had served in England under his command for the past year. They were making their way back to Springfield, Illinois. The group of Sangamon County medical conscripts comprised all of Unit W and had just been mustered out at Camp Grant, south of Rockford. They were done with war.

Later that afternoon, when they arrived at the Springfield Station, Sarah Ottis, Daniel's wife, was there to greet him.

"Hello, dear," said Ottis, leaning forward to kiss his wife on the cheek.

"Why Daniel, you look so drawn," responded his wife. "Didn't they feed you over there?"

[555]

Ottis grinned, hiding the sense of emptiness he felt hearing his wife's somewhat scolding tone.

"How is Gwenie," he asked. Gwendolyn was the only child between Daniel and Sarah.

"She is fine," responded Sarah. "She's grown quite a bit since you've seen her. You'll have to get to know her. It's time you get to know your daughter before she's grown and gone."

The chill of Sarah's reception cut through this genuinely warm and caring man who still felt strong effects from his time away in war's hell.

Chapter 44

Precipitous Passing

One thousand miles now separated Pat O'Brien from Agnes MacMillian. Pat leaned back in his seat and gazed out the window for about thirty minutes before falling asleep. On the backside of the Rockies he awoke refreshed and gazed out at the beautiful vistas that graced the landscape. He had two things on his mind, Agnes and his trip to Siberia. He was eager to see her but was not swooning over thoughts of a long and emotional reunion. The prospect of Russia dominated his thoughts.

For years he had followed the turmoil in the Russian state and in a matter of days he would see it for himself. The chaos there was so very inviting. For the first time since he'd hopped on the back of a motorcycle in England and flew off to France, he felt the rush of excitement that had always been a prime motivator his whole life.

As his train descended from the jagged terrain of the mountains and began to take a more direct trajectory south toward San Francisco, he relived memories of other such exhilarating moments. He recalled his first sprint to the old quarry with his buddies to swim for the first time. He pictured his earliest trips to the unknown world of the Chicago rail yards with Gus as a young boy. He remembered his arrival at Toronto amid hundreds of other young, eager, yet experienced pilots, all hungry to go to war. His first flight over the French border in search of the dreaded Hun flashed through his mind as well. And his nearly convulsive mental debate before leaping from the train in Germany was an emotion that, to this day, held the same intensity.

Had Pat's lifelong passion to grip every formidable challenge become his seduction? Was his cast in life truly to be the epitome of exception, as his mother had told him on the train? Or were his endless quests merely a deflection away from life's more enduring commitments such as order, stability and consent?

These thoughts lingered as he drew closer to Richmond and to his eventual meeting with Agnes. She was, in fact, one of those commitments he was not quite ready to take on. As his train approached the station he weighed two emotions that pulled him in opposite directions. They were real and as different as the opposing sides of the Holland fence he had once traversed. Was it time now to start his life with Agnes or did the unfinished war, as he called it, require his presence out of respect for the many he had seen die in Europe? Did he owe it to Paul and to the others at Borden, most of whom were now dead?

He was quick and deliberate as he weighed the appropriateness of his plan. He went with his gut, as he always had. He knew one thing to be true and he had little interest in rationalizing his options. His trip to Russia was foremost. There would be time for Agnes and settling down. Russia was not only his final opportunity but was clearly the final chapter of the war. He was driven to be part of it.

About the same time Pat was reflecting on his fate, Agnes was trying to comfort the baby back at Noe. Just as she was about to depart for the train station, little Carol had become terribly fussy. She'd been colicky for about a week and could not be comforted.

"Why don't you go to the station, Arlene?" said Agnes . "She's just too fussy.

"But Agnes!" pleaded Arlene. "You cannot - not be there."

"I know, Arlene, I know but I can't leave her this way," responded Agnes as baby Carol cried louder. "I'll settle her down here with a bottle and get her to sleep. By the time you return, she'll be fine. I'll meet Pat at the bakery."

Arlene nodded with a reconciled look on her face.

"The tricky thing is you have to get back before he gets to the bakery because I'd like to be there when he arrives," added Agnus.

"Ok," responded Arlene. She touched Agnes's arm in a comforting gesture then turned briskly out the door.

Pat pulled himself up and out of his seat as the train came to a final stop at the Richmond station. Preferring to greet Agnes without the aid of his cane, he inserted it into his long travel bag before stepping down onto the platform. He turned toward the terminal and looked for Agnes. He saw a woman in average clothes and no hat who was waving toward him from afar.

"Perhaps that woman is waving to someone else," he thought. "But where is Agnes?" He'd pictured her in a fashionable dress with a carousel as she had appeared in the past. But she was not there to greet him this time.

The woman waving was Arlene Stevens.

"Hello, Pat," she said as he got within range.

"Hello," responded Pat, a bit bewildered. "Where's Agnes?"

"She apologizes for not being here, Pat," said Arlene. "She's in Noe, her old neighborhood. She asked that you meet her there. She was detained and apologizes for not being here." She paused and looked at Pat for a reaction. He had listened but was already peering out and thinking ahead of the moment, as was his way.

"Can I help you get there somehow?" Arlene asked.

"No, no," said Pat while craning his neck a bit to see if there might be a cab nearby. "I'll catch a cab. I know where it is."

"Do you have bags, Pat?" asked Arlene.

Sounding and still looking a bit befuddled, he responded, "No, I mean, yes. I have bags but they are being transferred. You see, I'm due to take a ship," he paused. "Well, a ship, you know. They do that. They transfer your bags directly. It really works quite well."

"Oh yes, very convenient," said Arlene. They continued to walk toward the terminal. "I would imagine with all the traveling you've done you have these sorts of things down quite well, huh Pat?"

"I've learned a few short cuts along the way," he said, still looking ahead for sign of a taxi.

"So, Arlene," he said turning his head to look directly at Arlene, at last. "How is she? Is she ok?

"Why yes, Pat. She is fine. She's been trying to see the doctor all week. The only appointment he had was this morning in Noe. Nothing serious, mind you. She's been battling a cold and tried to get in before you arrived but the only possible time to see her doctor was this morning. She's terribly sorry, she said. She wants to meet you at the Noe Valley Bakery. She said you'd know it. Do you recall?"

"Sure, I remember," responded Pat.

Just then a cab pulled up, then a second and a third.

"Thank you Arlene," said Pat taking her hand. "It was nice of you to meet me here. I really appreciate it so much. Perhaps we'll both see you in the next few days before I leave?"

"That would be grand, Pat," she responded, trying not to show her concern over what were obviously Pat's plans for a short stay.

As Pat turned and stepped toward the cab stand, tears came to Arlene's eyes as she watched him walk away. Pat's comments about traveling probably meant that the baby would now be given away. She was sad for Agnes. They had become as close as sisters since the whole ordeal began. What did this mean for Agnes and Pat's engagement? How would Agnes react? Might she, in the end, tell him of Carol? She thought not.

Agnes was a determined young woman. She would not want to think that Pat O'Brien wanted to marry her out of responsibility for the child. Agnes had been firm about that from the beginning. Still, it was a terrible time for her while she kept her secret not only from Pat but from many others. Out of wedlock childbearing was not viewed positively by anyone. It was the primary reason she had moved to the small area of Noe. She'd been hiding her circumstances for a year now, awaiting Pat's arrival in the hope of reconciliation and marriage. In a small way, she could appreciate how he must have felt hiding for seventy-two days in Europe.

"The baby!" thought Arlene, suddenly breaking her trance. Just as she was about to bolt for the next taxi, Pat turned back and waved before stepping into his cab. Arlene waved her kerchief back at him and sported a smile so as not to look concerned. As soon as he was out of sight, Arlene ran quickly to an awaiting car.

"Hurry," she said to the driver. "I'm running late." The driver obliged and she arrived at the house in twenty minutes. As she entered, Agnes was placing Carol in her baby basket. The baby was fast asleep with a belly full of milk. Agnes turned slowly and fixed her hair as she walked toward Arlene.

"How do I look?" she asked her friend.

"You look beautiful," responded Arlene. "Now go quickly before he gets there before you do.

"Bring the baby to your place just in case we happen to come back here after lunch," Agnes said as she walked out.

Arlene had kept the cab waiting and Agnes was whisked off to the bakery ahead of Pat's arrival. Agnes was sitting at a small table in the window of the Bakery when Pat's cab pulled up. She saw him step from the cab, turn back, hand the driver a bill and give him a snappy salute before turning to look up at the marquis.

"What an exciting man he is," she thought. She took one final look in the small mirror of her compact then quickly snapped it close, placing it in her purse and hurriedly picking up a menu. She was nervous.

When Pat entered the small shop Agnes looked up and smiled.

"Hello, Agnes," he said in a soft voice.

Agnes rose and the two held an extended embrace.

"I'm sorry I could not meet you at the train, Pat," said Agnes. "I felt badly that I had to send Arlene but I could not see the doctor any other time."

"It was fine," responded Pat. "How are you feeling?"

"He's given me a treatment. I'll be fine," she said. "It's just lingered now for nearly two weeks and I didn't want to be sick when you arrived but it seems that everyone in San Francisco is sniffling."

Pat smiled at her. He thought she looked very nice and didn't appear to be sick. In fact, she was not but her nerves were stirring her stomach. She kept her gestures deliberate and speech hushed hoping to conceal her healthy vigor.

"So, tell me about your visit with the family, Pat," she said as they looked over the menus.

"It was a wonderful time, Agnes," responded Pat. I don't think I've felt that relaxed in years. They all asked about you. I hope you can meet them all soon." This gave Agnes some hope.

"And how is your aunt?" asked Agnes. "Which one is it again?"

"Aunt Belle," responded Pat. "Yes, she's having a tough time."

Agnes was having a bit of a rough time, too. But as they chatted about all that had transpired since their last meeting, both began to relax and for nearly two hours laughed and talked about everyone but themselves. Twice Pat had reached across the table to grasp her hand. More than once, Agnes fought back tears and a lump in her throat that she was convinced must have been visible. Her emotions were cascading back and forth like the tides. She tried to relax.

A few times Agnes thought she might have shown too much energy but Pat never became suspicious. She felt badly that she had not been truthful about her doctor visit. She felt worse every time she thought of baby Carol.

It was 3:30 in the afternoon. Both sipped one final cup of coffee following their long meal together.

"Can you come with me?" asked Pat.

"Come with you?" asked Agnes sounding confused. "My God," she thought, is he asking me to go to Russia with him?"

"To the hotel," said Pat.

Exhaling in relief, Agnes responded, "Why, of course, dear. I'd like to get a few things at home first. Is that ok?"

"Sure, I hear you are living back in Noe again," Pat said.

"Yes, it's nice to be in my old neighborhood again," responded Agnes. "Besides, Arlene is there and she is a great comfort to me."

There was a slight pause and then Pat said, "I'm sorry I've been away for so long, honey."

"No need to be sorry, Pat," Responded Agnes. "You have a lot of pressures on you. I understand."

And so, they departed, stopping at Agnes's modest apartment to grab a few things. Arlene had taken the baby and basket to her place as the two women had planned. Agnes had tucked away any sign of baby items. As she was packing a small bag she noticed a large container of talc on the small table near in her bedroom. Though there would be no reason for Pat to be tipped by such an item, she felt her tummy flip in fear. She had placed it there while changing Carol's diaper on the bed. She quickly gathered her thoughts, realizing that only she would connect the talc to the baby. It was a common item.

They took a cab to the St. James Hotel in Richmond where they'd meet friends the next day at the Ivy Inn. Pat checked in at the front desk as Agnes sat in a flowered chair located in the lobby.

"Jack Drummond still work here?" asked Pat, inquiring about a friendly bellman he'd come to know during his days in Richmond.

"Who, sir?" responded the young man behind the counter.

"Drummond? The bellman?" repeated Pat.

"Sorry, sir. Don't know him," he said. "He must have been before my time."

As the young clerk handed him his key, it struck Pat how young the kid looked. Like most men approaching thirty, Pat was experiencing the moment when young men notice younger men replacing them. The words "must have been before my time," echoed in Pat's head as he took the key.

In war time, the young lad would have likely been standing behind a Springfield rifle in the mud of France and not behind a hotel service counter sporting a pink-faced smile. But on this day, Pat had become personally aware of the arrival of America's next generation of youth.

"Thanks, son," he said, turning toward in the direction of the lobby.

"Thank you, sir," responded the clerk.

As they entered the room, Pat reached over and turned on the floor lamp standing just inside the door. Agnes made her way to the small table near the bed and placed her bag on it. As she turned back, Pat was standing near her and the two locked in a deep embrace. It was their first private moment together. After a series of soft whispers the two sat on the bed in full embrace, then settled back. A few hours later, they both awoke.

"Are you hungry?" asked Agnes.

"A little, you?" responded Pat.

"Rather hungry, yes," she said.

The two got dressed and made their way to the Ivy for dinner. A few regulars noticed them and came over to say hello. Though a major gathering of Pat and Agnes's friends was to occur the following night, a good number of them just happened to show up this night. It was reminiscent of the old days in Richmond. It wasn't until midnight that Pat and Agnes finally said "good night" to everyone.

As they had in the past, Pat and Agnes spent most of the night awake talking, something they had always been able to do with great ease. Eventually their conversation ceased and faded into slumber. Around four in the morning, Pat carefully lifted the blanket and sheet off them as the heat of the night had warmed the bed. He graced her left arm with slow comforting strokes as they faced each other and spoke in whispers. At one point, Pat's hand came into contact with the ring resting on her hand and he took hold of it, slowly turning the diamond under, then up again and around the circumference of her finger.

"You trying to take that thing off?" asked Agnes with humor.

"No," he said.

"So what might be your plans regarding the ring, Mr. O'Brien?" she said in a teasing tone."

"How do you mean?" responded Pat, genuinely not catching her drift.

Agnes pulled her hand back. Breaking out of a whisper and into full voice she spoke directly.

"Pat, I've been waiting for you for so long. I can't believe you don't feel the same way," she said. "Don't you *want* to get married? You speak so little of it. You're always talking about the war, your speeches, your buddies, everything except our future and when you might want to marry. I can't live in this limbo any longer. I only want to know, Pat. That's all. I just want to know."

Finally, after months of wrangling with herself, she had spoken frankly. She never considered pressing Pat when he first returned from war. And every time she thought about bringing it up, something told her to hold back. But things were different now. She had to make a decision with Pat or without him, for the sake of Carol. She was firm and serious and Pat could tell. What he did not know and could not know was that Agnes was feeling the pressure of being the mother of a fatherless child, not the pressure of a woman without a man. Pat was perplexed at first but then blamed himself.

"I'm sorry, hon," responded Pat. "I guess I just didn't think about what you've been through. I never thought about how it must have been to hear of my capture. I can't imagine how alone you must have felt when everyone believed I was dead and then suddenly I appeared again.

"I never gave up during that time, Pat," she said sincerely, feeling a little bad about her rant.

"I know that, hon," he said. "I could tell you never gave up. We're both that way."

Reaching for her hand once again, he went on.

"You know, Agnes, The horror and the memories are so strong that we come home and often don't recognize our own feelings let alone the feelings others that love us. I hate that about war. The tragic thing about war is that it leaves a mark on everyone – soldiers, their families, their loved ones - everyone."

"You're right, hon," responded Agnes. "We're all affected." Agnes reached back for his hand. He continued.

"No soldier is ever the same afterwards and the war continues inside us. Every soldier has to fight out his own ending to war inside. The chance I had to tell thousands of people all over the country about the evil Hun was part of my fight. The book was, also, I guess. But I've gained from those things, too. Some people think I've gained too much. I'm a rich man, Agnes. In some ways that's robbed me of my ending to the war. As long as there's a war on somewhere, I need to be there, until my war is over.

"I know. I know, Pat," she said wanting to comfort him. His words sunk deeply into Agnes's heart though. She knew now that Pat was not ready and he couldn't tell her when he might be ready because he didn't know.

There was more silence and then Agnes made one last point.

"It's not us, Pat. It is just what life has dealt us," she said caressing his hand. "You have to put your life back on track and if that means witnessing the ultimate end of the war for your own peace of mind or the legacy of your friends that died, then you need to do that. I know you have to. How I fit into the choices you make, I don't know. I do know we love each other, and we'll always have that. But how it weighs against everything else in our lives is not known to either of us. We will have to wait and see."

Pat fully understood his choices. He surmised that Agnes understood her choices and they would have a lot to do with his. Agnes was letting Pat go to Russia based on what was best for him. He knew she would make decisions that would be best for her. They both did this out of love for each other. It was a situation that could not be decided jointly. She could never fully understand all that weighed on him and, of course, he was completely in the dark regarding her dilemma.

"I love you, Pat O'Brien," she said.

"I love you, too, Agnes," he said. They then both fell fast asleep.

It was midday before the two awoke. Pat pulled the door closed as they stepped into the hall. He gave her a kiss and flashed his warm smile and they both went downstairs for coffee.

"Let's enjoy our last night with our friends, Pat," said Agnes.

"Yes, let's," he said sipping the last of his second cup. "They are always such a joy."

They spent the afternoon in Richmond window shopping, stopping for ice cream and walking along the bay shore. Around 5:00 they were back at the Ivy for dinner. Nearly everyone that knew them both was in attendance and it was as nice a gathering as either could remember. As was the group's practice, they all sat "mixed." Most couples were split from each other sitting in different locations at the table visiting. More than once, Pat and Agnes caught each other's eye with a smile, both having a genuinely great time but thoughtful of each other just the same.

It was nearly ten by the time things began to break up. It took some time for everyone to say good bye as they mingled out front of the Ivy.

"Don't stay away so long this time," said Jerry Solich to Agnes.

"I won't, Jerry. Good to see you," responded Agnes.

Finally, it was time to leave. They walked up the street a bit to say good-bye. They had decided at lunch that he would not see her home. Agnes felt it best to part following dinner at the Ivy. "If you see me home it may be another long night and you need to travel in the morning", she had said to him. It was the presence of the baby that made this arrangement necessary.

Agnes rested her head against Pat's chest but held back tears. They stood still and felt the presence of the other's body against their own. Their parting and the loss of her baby was just one of a million scars that befell soldiers, mothers, fathers, families, wives and couples as a result of mankind's first mechanized war. It was sad that the war and Pat's healing from it would cost all this, she thought.

A cab pulled up. Pat placed his open palms on both sides of Agnes' cheeks and gave her an emotional embrace. Holding her right hand, he opened the door of the awaiting taxi, gave her one last kiss and she entered the cab. As the driver put his car in gear, Agnes looked back at Pat. He was staring directly at her. The car jerked forward and raced away. Agnes looked forward, now holding a handkerchief tightly with both hands.

Pat stood a second watching the cab turn right at the corner and out of sight. He took a breath then stepped towards the hotel surveying his surroundings, recalling the night in Richmond with fondness.

The next day, Pat traveled to Redwood country for a day with his buddies where they camped and relived their early days. On Friday, May 30, Pat boarded the train for Seattle. It took the weekend to work through the maze of Seattle by train, then across the border to Canada and a final ferry ride to Vancouver. He spent a few days there and had a chance to relive the time spent in Vancouver on his way to Borden. On June 7th, he visited the Japanise embassy receiving signature of his passport for sail to Yokohama on the Empress of Russia. He was ready to go.

PART NINE

THE RUSSIAN CHANCE

Chapter 45

Shanghai

Pat made his way up the ramp of the SS Empress of Russia, flashed his passport and proceeded to his room located among the 285 first-class cabins. A number of people noticed him, not because they recognized the famous aviator but because of his obvious means. He sported an expensive derby hat from London and a long double-breasted Ulster coat, punctuated by a pair of Berluti shoes which he had purchased in Paris. Pat O'Brien had become a very rich man. His magnetic personality, acquired fame and now his lifestyle and wealth had placed him among rich and famous people wherever he went.

Pat's accommodations on board were of the highest class. He would travel for twelve days across the Pacific to Yokohama, Japan and stay at the Grand Hotel, located on the Bund, overlooking Yokohama Harbor. It was a hotel frequented by the likes of Rudyard Kipling, and other famous names of the day. After a few days in Japan, he would travel around the southern tip of Japan to Shanghai, China, and stay at the Astor Hotel, the first and most prestigious Western hotel in China. The Astor was often host to royalty such as Prince Alfred, son of Queen Elizabeth, during his visits.

Pat's plan was to spend a few days in Shanghai before proceeding north by ship along the coast to Tianjin, the major port city of northern China. Seventy miles inland lay Beijing, his jumping off point for a cross-country trip north, around Korea, into Russia and to the teeming city of Vladivostok. He had yet to identify his means to travel by land. But a man, who walked alone and undercover for seventy-two days behind enemy lines with no map and no resources, would find an unplanned trip through rural China, Mongolia and the Siberian territory hardly daunting.

Arriving at his private cabin, he found his trunk already in place on the valet. Pat placed his hat on the small bed, removed his coat and began to unpack his trunk.

"With so many experienced people on this ship," he said out loud, "I'm sure to find someone with an idea of how best to travel on land. I'll have to purchase the right clothing when I get to Shanghai. Hopefully I'll find something for a man of my height," he said, half-chuckling.

Once all his belongings were stored, Pat checked himself in the mirror, then stepped out of his cabin to join others on the deck. Everyone on board was eager to watch the departure. A large contingent of well-wishers also watched from shore. As Pat reached the deck level he felt the slight nudge of a tug pushing the ship free of its moorings. He moved directly to the railing where another gentleman had already taken a position to view the retreating Canadian shore. The deck was full of passengers who all leaned out to wave good-bye.

"Nice clear day for departure, wouldn't you say?" said Pat and he took hold of the railing with both hands.

"Yes, indeed," returned the passenger. "One doesn't often see a clear day leaving Vancouver."

Pat nodded in confirmation. Both men took in the view, tugs below, the flurry of stevedores pulling back rope, dock workers clearing the cargo area of the dock, hundreds of family members waving kerchiefs up and down from observation platforms and the broad rise of Vancouver slowly moving away.

"My grandfather was a dock worker," said Pat.

"Really, where in Europe?" responded the man.

"No. it was on the Ohio River and down the Mississippi, many years ago" he said. "Apparently, he spent some time in Cincinnati and New Orleans. In those days, the river was the only way to travel. My mother always said I was much like him."

"Well, no offense man, but you don't appear to be a dockworker," quipped the smiling stranger.

"No, far from it," said Pat. "It's hard work. I'm afraid I wouldn't be much help to those boys down there."

"Bad back?" asked the man.

"No, war injuries," responded Pat.

"Oh, sorry," he said, looking back at the shore. "Where'd you serve?"

"France," said Pat, pausing. "I was a pilot for the RAF."

"How'd you get injured?" asked the man still looking toward shore.

[572]

"Got shot out of the sky," said Pat, rather matter-of-factly.

+The gentlemen stood erect, freeing his hands from rail and turned.

He paused and then asked, "You're American, yet flew for the British?"

"Yes, there were a few of us back then," responded Pat. "A small, crazy few."

The man held his gaze a moment.

"Are you, O'Brien?" he asked.

Turning slowly to look at the man Pat said, "You recognize me? Have you seen me speak?"

"No, but I've seen his photo and you certainly look like him," said the man, still surprised.

Pat flashed his smile and extended his hand to the man, "Pat O'Brien, glad to meet you!"

"Glad to meet you, Lt. O'Brien. Glad to meet you, certainly," repeated the man while shaking Pat's hand vigorously. "I'm Joe Sharkey, American Associated Press in Tokyo. I'm the lead correspondent there. How fantastic to meet you. How very keen, indeed."

Pat sensed Sharkey was genuine and he didn't feel imposed, upon as he might meeting a reporter eager to ask the stock questions that he had answered so many times before. Sharkey was obviously a senior person for AP, someone who directed the efforts of others. He was a distinguished looking gentleman, older than Pat, with obvious experience, but enthusiasm nonetheless. Surely a guy like this, Pat thought, could offer advice.

"A pleasure to meet you, Mr. Sharkey," responded Pat. "Have you been home visiting?" Both men looked at the shore once again.

"Yes, in fact," said Sharkey. "My wife needed to see the family. Japan is a long way from home for her, you know."

"Well, you need trees but you also need birds," said Pat in a quiet tone gazing out at the departing shore.

"What's that, you say?" quizzed Sharkey, turning his head to look at Pat.

"Nothin'," responded Pat. "Did your wife stay?"

"No, she's aboard," said Sharkey, turning back to look ashore himself. He then spoke slowly as the two men panned the shoreline.

"Something about departures with her," said Sharkey. "You know, some people get sick rolling on the seas but that doesn't bother her. Pull away from a dock sideways though and she's a wet noodle. She'll be fine once we're out of port."

Pat thought to himself that he, too, always felt better once he left the port.

And then he said, "Well, you can't say you've left unless someone else stays behind, can you?" Pat responded, again in hush tones.

"Right," responded Sharkey, somewhat confused by Pat's response. Both men fell silent for a spell taking in the scene before them.

Joseph E. Sharkey was, in fact, someone with extensive experience in Asia. As the leading western news agency executive in the region, he was well connected within Japan and, naturally, knew many counterparts in China and Russia that kept him informed. The press was all over Russia trying to make "heads or tails" out the calamity that was occurring since the Revolution.

"Say, Pat, why don't you join me and some of my guests for dinner tonight," said Sharkey. "We have a fantastic evening planned with some very exciting folks that I'm sure would also be thrilled to meet you."

"I'd like that, thanks," said Pat, pulling out of his reflective moment in gradual fashion.

"I'm working with a number of people who are coming to Tokyo next month to plan the Japanese portion of the Aerial Derby Around the World. Some of the gentlemen at dinner are on my committee. Your thoughts would be very welcome. Have you heard about it?" asked Sharkey.

"Why sure, I've heard about it but don't know the details" responded Pat, now fully focused. "It's basically a timed global air race, correct?"

"Precisely," responded Sharkey. "And it is particularly important for the race to occur now. We have a tremendous amount of aviation capacity deployed all over the world. Suddenly, the war is over, there is no more demand, nothing to drive development going forward.

"Just the reverse of what happened at the end of the old exhibition days," confirmed Pat. "All of a sudden every plane was being produced for war use and exhibition days were over."

"Right," responded Sharkey. "So the Aero Club of America is enlisting airfields all over the world for the race. That keeps airfields open and gives the industry a little more time to transition to commercial flight. More importantly, it creates needed cooperative relationships between countries who were once sworn enemies. It's an important bridge to the future."

"What's your group doing?" asked Pat.

My Tokyo committee is recruiting Japanese airfields to complete our leg of the event. We think whoever wins will take at least six months to complete the course.

"It's a fantastic vision," said Pat.

"It really is. And after dinner, I've arranged for a few guests to hear a presentation by Robert Wilton who's traveling back to Russia. He's the New York Times correspondent in Petrograd, and is considered one of the top observers of events in Russia since the Revolution. Apparently, things got hot in recent weeks. They called him home for bit. He's a Brit, you know," said Sharkey.

"I don't know him but if he's been as far in as Petrograd then he's seen a lot," responded Pat.

"Yes, he knows as much as anyone I've met," said Sharkey. "After dinner we'll retire to the liquor parlor where he'll talk about what he's seen. Great chance to ask questions."

Pat was imagining the reporter's experience leaving Russia. The Trans-Siberian Railway was the only way in and out and the entire route was full of dangers. "I assume he must have exited via the railroad," stated Pat.

"Well, there's no other way out. I'm sure he did," responded Sharkey.

Pat couldn't believe his luck. He was going to hear, first-hand, about conditions on the ground in the middle of the Siberian chaos. Pat's mission could very well be defined on his first night aboard after a conversation with Robert Wilton. He was thrilled.

Sharkey explained the location of the dining room and asked if Pat might see himself there on his own.

"I'm sure I can find it," said Pat.

"Great. Dinner is at 7:00 p.m." Said Sharkey.

Two well-dressed maitre d's stood at the door of a private dinning room greeting Pat as he arrived. He was dressed in a fine Savile Row suit he'd purchased in Westminster on his last London visit. The two waiters bowed as Pat entered the room and inside were about six men and four ladies. All were fashionably dressed, the older men wore long "morning coats," as they were called then, and the younger men, like Pat, sported the more modern short lounge jackets. The ladies were dressed nicely, all of similar style.

There was a bar set into the wall on one end of the room, a large boardroom style table that looked as though it was set for twenty people or so, all with fine silver and china. The guests were milling about, talking and sipping various quality spirits.

As Pat entered the room Sharkey saw him immediately.

"Lieutenant!" shouted Sharkey, waving him over to his group.

Pat walked toward the group of five people or so taking a quick glance around the room, wondering if correspondent Wilton might also be present. Pat had no idea what the man looked like but Wilton was the man he wanted to meet.

"How great to see you, Pat," said Sharkey, shaking Pat's hand.

"Thanks for inviting me, Mr. Sharkey," replied Pat with a genuine smile.

Turning to his small group of friends, Sharkey announced, "Folks meet Lt Pat O'Brien. You all know of him I believe? He's on his way to Siberia."

"Greetings, lad," stated a spry looking man in his mid-60's who vigorously shook Pat's hand.

"Hello, Sir," said Pat.

"I'm Sam McClure. This is my wife Harriet. Good to meet another fine Irishman. I've read your book, Lieutenant. Quite a story. I hope we can visit sometime while on board. You know I went to school in Valparaiso, Indiana as a young man. That's not too far from your hometown is it?" said McClure.

"No, not at all," said Pat. "I've been there. I also have family in Lowell."

"That's marvelous," replied McClure.

Samuel Sidney "S.S." McClure was the founder of McClure's Magazine. He was quite successful, aggressive and known for his quick, gruff style. He was a continuous flow of ideas. He was born in Ireland and moved to America at age nine with his mother after his father was killed in an accident. One of his famous writers, Frank Doubleday, described McClure as "a cyclone in a frockcoat who was a great man but he'd kill me in a week with mere surplus of energy." McClure and his writers were among the leading progressives of the day. While he and Pat could match energy levels, their politics were on opposite sides.

Also present at dinner was Andrew Avinoff, attendant to the late Czar who had escaped to America at the height of the Lenin takeover. He was now living in San Francisco. To Pat, he was the second most important person in the room to meet after Wilton.

"Hello, Lieutenant. I'm Walter Lum from San Francisco" another man said. "I am the founder of the Chinese American Citizens Alliance." He was an Asian man of about forty years. Lum was considered the leading Chinese American civil rights advocate in the Bay Area.

"Hi, Mr. Lum," said Pat. "I worked for the Santa Fe for a number of years. Lived in Richmond.

"Ah, very nice town. Yes, I know Richmond," said Lum.

About that time the "call to dinner" bell was rung by the head waiter and guests began to find their seat.

"Come with me Pat," said Sharkey. "I know you have a keen interest in meeting Mr. Walton. He's over here with me."

"Thank you, Joe," said Pat.

Approximately eighteen people took their seats around the large mahogany table. Sitting across from Pat was T.M. Laffin, a longtime resident of Yokohama. J.M. Sherwig from International Banking Corporation in Cleveland and his wife were present. Next to the Sherwigs sat Mr. and Mrs. C.B. Leach of the Erie Railroad, also from Cleveland.

Pat was at his seat before Wilton but remained standing. Wilton was attempting to turn away from an admirer who was lagging behind with questions. Finally, she relented. Wilton turned, pulled his seat away from the table and stepped around it to sit. Still standing, Wilton turned to Pat.

"Hello, I'm Robert Wilton," he said

"Pat O'Brien, glad to meet you," said Pat. The two men took their seats.

Wilton, who was born in England, was son of a British mining engineer employed in Russia. In 1889 he joined the European staff of the New York Herald and covered Russian and German affairs. After fourteen years he moved to The Times office in Petrograd, and became known as a keen observer of events in Russia during the last years of the Czarist regime. When Lenin took over he moved to Siberia and was spending time reporting on the conditions along the Trans-Siberian Railroad.

Once everyone was seated, Sharkey clanged the side of his water glass to gain the attention of the guests. He introduced every person at the table. When he got to Pat, he referred to him as "one of the true heroes of the Allied efforts during the war," which Pat found uncomfortable. Though Pat had heard it many times before, it had been a long time since anyone had introduced him as such. Most everyone present knew of Pat's story. Those that had not were amazed just hearing Sharkey's introduction and brief summary. Pat stood when introduced and the small room bellowed with applause.

Conversations over dinner were a mix of politics, emerging styles, stories of the war and broad speculations about what the balance of power would look like in the months and years ahead. Pat had the opportunity to learn a great deal of the situation in Siberia from Wilton.

"I suggest you go directly to Vladivostok first and then travel straight west," said Wilton. The refugee movement east on the railroad is so massive now that you will want to take an alternative route back to Beijing."

"In what way?" asked Pat.

"Once you get to Omsk," replied Wilton, "There will be plenty of British there. You can negotiate a vehicle to drive you south at Irkustki through Mongolia, to Ulan Bator and directly on to Beijing. There is no reason to come back east all the way to the sea at Vladivostok. It is desert, yes, but it is manageable and much more direct.

Pat now had the best route. There would be time on the ship to learn about resources on the ground. He had not felt this energized in a long time. Aviation was such a catalyst and there was nothing like war to press action.

Following dinner, Sharkey announced that the men, "and any ladies with an interest in the mundane details of mother Russia," were welcomed to join him and Mr. Wilton in the liquor pallor to hear the details. The group moved down the hall towards the pallor. A few of the ladies joined their husbands for the presentation, while others went as a group to enjoy the opening night entertainment on board.

The presentation room was fitted with comfortable furniture, a completely stocked bar with attendant and along the long wall hung an eight-foot by three-foot map of Russia. The guests selected their preferred after-dinner drink and took their seats. Joseph Sharkey introduced Mr. Wilton again.

Wilton began with a brief overview of his personal life. Pat was surprised and impressed to learn that Wilton had served with the Russian army during the war, and was awarded the Cross of St. George. Like Pat, Wilton had fought with an army not of his native land. This, all the more, created for Pat a connection to Wilton.

Wilton began with a geographic explanation of the conditions in Russia. He stood at the map extending his right arm to the western side first.

"As you know, most of Russia's population lives here in the west," said Wilton. Extending his left arm he continued, "Far to the east is Vladivostok on the Pacific Sea. Much of what you read regarding Allied occupation is centered on this city but it is strictly a release point for the highly pressurized situation that germinates from the west. The only connection is the railroad, the longest railroad in the world. Keep in mind, seventy-five percent of the population and ninety-five percent of the Russian conflict exists west of the Urals," he said. "But the only way in or out of Western Russia today is from the east and the Trans-Siberian Railroad."

President Wilson made the important decision to press for U.S. control of the railroad. Protecting this route was critical to bringing Allied support from the east but more importantly it was an assurance the Allies could get out of Russia, including some 60,000 Czecho-Slovak troops who were promised safe passage by Wilson.

The presentation lasted for two hours. Pat and many of the other guests asked numerous questions. By the end of the night, Pat felt he had increased his understanding of the situation in Russia tenfold.

[579]

The SS Empress of Russia sailed with ease for the next twelve days. Pat met hundreds of passengers from all lots of life. He gained valuable information from people who had firsthand experience in northern China, Mongolia and western Russia. As his ship drew within a half day's distance of Yokohama, he felt the same surge of energy and excitement he felt arriving in Liverpool with the "original eighteen" two years before. He thought of them now and it brought a strong feeling of sadness over his heart, particularly for the fifteen that never returned.

Yokohama was fast becoming the biggest egress and ingress for the country of Japan. It was not until U.S. Commodore Matthew Perry demanded, at the point of a gun, that the small village open its ports to American trade in 1854 that the city became a primary port. Only seventeen miles from Tokyo, Yokohama was now a city of two million people that Pat would see for the first time within minutes.

Prior to exiting the ship, Pat said goodbye to Sharkey who offered his assistance in helping Pat discover the city and help getting his papers in order for entry into China. Sharkey was more than gracious, serving as a personal guide to such places as Japan's largest Chinatown where Pat and Lum, Sharkey, and a number of their friends ate samplings of Chinese food indigenous to central China. The trip to Shanghai would take approximately forty-two hours. There would be stops in Osaka and Nagasaki, Japan, but they would be brief.

A week later, on Thursday, June 26th, Pat stood at the base of a Yokohama long pier, waiting to show his papers. As he looked up he could see two sizable steamer ships along opposite sides of the pier. There was a bright green shelter between them, no doubt, with staged cargo. He could see the gangway extending parallel from the ship on the right, projecting behind the shelter where passengers would obviously be boarding. The ship on the left had no extensions, indicating to Pat that his ship was on the right. Four uniformed security officers were briskly walking toward him from the pier. Pat noticed a tall man in a long brown traveling coat looking back as if waiting for a fellow passenger. Six or seven rickshaws were parked neatly on the left and one was rolling toward Pat and his fellow passengers who had just formed a line. The other six broke ranks and were now wheeling toward their potential customers. The walk to the ship was about two hundred yards but Pat decided to walk.

Having cleared security, Pat took the long walk down the pier, refusing a rickshaw ride five times until he arrived behind the cargo shelter, walked up the staircase, flashed his papers one more time and traversed the gangway crossing onto his ship. A short Japanese passenger agent greeted Pat in perfect English. Pat heard him repeat the welcome in Japanese to the next passenger.

Shanghai was not simply a congested collection of temples, chop-sticks, jade, rickshaws and pajamas. In reality, it was an immense modern city of well-paved streets, skyscrapers built by Britain, France and America since the opium wars of the mid-1800.

So entrenched were these countries that trade treaties created literal sovereignties within the city called Settlements. Pat would find Shanghai to be populated by large numbers of British, some French, Americans and the Japanese.

Pat would find the relatively short trip between the many islands of Japan with stops at Osaka and Nagasaki tedious. He was very eager to get to Shanghai and the nearly two-day steamer couldn't go fast enough. Soon they would be clear of Japanese waters and sail directly for Shanghai across the East China Sea.

Pat entered the dining room of the ship on the first night. He panned the room and found a buffet-style selection of mostly Asian food with a smattering of meats and breads that were recognizable. He'd had no experience with chop sticks but did find a few wooden utensils fashioned similar to a large fork but realized they were for serving. "I'll have to learn to use these things if I'm going to eat," he said to himself. Suddenly, he flashed back to his many nights searching for turnips in the fields of Belgium. How ironic, he thought, that for a moment chopsticks seemed like a barrier to food. Pat filled his plate with chips of dark brown beef, some type of long green bean and some white spouts that looked like they might be easiest to eat with sticks. He turned and looked for a seat in the common cafeteria style dining room.

A Chinese man dress in a professional, yet Asian style suit spotted Pat and was standing next to his round table gesturing for Pat to join him. Pat nodded his head and moved toward the man.

"Welcome, won't you join me for dinner?" said the smiling man in clear English.

"Thank you very much," said Pat as he took his seat. A waiter was immediately at his side and said something in Japanese to Pat which he did not understand.

"Would you like some tea, sir?" said the Chinese man, attempting to interpret.

"Sure, tea would be fine," responded Pat.

The Chinese man spoke to the waiter in Japanese and in rather commanding terms. The waiter obviously viewed him as an important person and confirmed while backing away and offering a continuous smile and bow.

"I am Liu Feng Qi. I apologize for being so bold as to invite you to my table before introducing myself but I see you are traveling, perhaps for the first time, to China and perhaps I can be off assistance to you," said the man. "I am a Chinese businessman returning from Japan. I am quite familiar with the challenges of traveling."

"Yes, thank you Mr. Liu," responded Pat. "Do not apologize, I appreciate you offering me your table."

Pat and Liu enjoyed their dinner and Pat was able to relate his plans. Liu was very helpful and gave Pat a general idea of where things were in Shanghai. Pat had a map, another fact that he found uncanny when reflecting on his lost map during the war. Mr. Liu marked the key locations.

"How does one get around Shanghai? Are there busses?" asked Pat.

"Very few but the cost of a rickshaw within the city, once you get to your hotel, is very manageable and more efficient. Where are you staying?" asked Liu.

"I'm staying at the Astor Hotel," responded Pat.

"Oh, very prestigious, very nice also, you will like this hotel," said Liu. "It is a perfect spot for you, right on the Bund and near all the key locations in the center of Shanghai."

"I have heard of this place called 'The Bund'," responded Pat. "Is that the name of a river, or a street or what?"

"It is a particular area of Shanghai, the most famous part of Shanghai. It is the area on the west side of the Huangpo River," said the man. "It means embankment or levee. You will find others in India and Japan but there is no place as famous as The Bund in Shanghai. You will see it from you hotel. So tell me young man, why do you come to China? Are you a businessman?"

"No, I am going to Russia," said Pat.

"Russia!" exclaimed Liu. "It is very chaotic there now. No one desires to go to Russia. You are not a soldier, so why do you go?" asked the Chinaman.

"But I am a soldier," he paused. "Not formally, of course, but many from the west are going to Russia to protect our interest. Many of us are soldiers from the war. In my case, I have much experience with railroads and..."

Pat paused. He was about to say, "escape" but something stopped him. Something felt unusual about Liu and his line of questioning. He thought better than to reveal his plans. He suddenly wondered if he had confirmed too much. Was this man, who simply appeared and seemed so eager for Pat to join him for dinner, something other than what he appeared? Sure, he was Chinese, but could he be a spy? Might someone know Pat was coming or was Pat attributing too much to his own importance. Suddenly, that night in Brussels sitting at the table with two Germans flashed in his mind. He decided to error on the side of caution and direct the conversation to another topic. Liu did not press, and Pat felt there was no need for concern. Once they were finished eating, he thanked Liu for his hospitality and information. Liu bowed and then shook Pat's hand, typical of an Asian professional exposed to both cultures.

On Saturday, June 28th, the Japanese steamer slowed as it approached the pier at Shanghai. Pat was able to see the approaching city and it struck him how different Shanghai looked compared every port he had viewed in Japan. There is a keen difference between the Japanese and the Chinese. Japan is impeccable, orderly, neat and defined. China is spontaneous, scrambled, so often unplanned. Shanghai had color but it was muted. It looked mostly brown in hue. The tapestry of the two countries was quite different. Pat noticed it right away. Any westerner on Pat's ship that was seeing this same sight for the first time could feel the difference that was China.

With ship secure, Pat and his fellow passengers crossed the gangway and made their way up the pier to awaiting transportation. Here, too, rickshaw drivers were soliciting the passengers but in sporadic groups of three and four, like bees, all jabbering rapid Chinese. Experienced travelers walked past them paying no attention. Pat and others attempted to give each solicitor the courtesy of a "no thank you" either by shaking their head or actually responding in their native tongue. But the Chinese continued to "sell" all the way to the end of the pier and in that short time Pat acquired the skill of ignoring their pleas. That was China, unrelenting stimulus.

Pat secured his trunk and two men, who seemed to be freelancing off official cargo handlers, picked up his trunk and began walking toward a crush of wagons and rickshaws. Pat quickly turned toward the men and yelled, "Wait!" They did. The intensity of Pat's voice overcame what language barrier existing between Pat and the eager Chinese. Pat turned back to the official stamping his paperwork, grabbed the approved documents and quickly turned toward the two men who had resumed their trek toward the end of the pier.

Pat redirected the two men to what was clearly a top quality service and away from the drab looking collection of men with dated and repaired carts who all shouted solicitations to the two men carrying Pat's trunk. Pat gave a strong visual directive to carry the trunk in the direction of the more expensive service and the two men obliged. There were no pleas from the others rickshaw drivers, they simply turned like birds in the nest and began waving and shouting in the direction of the next business opportunity walking up the pier. The two men placed Pat's trunk on the large rickshaw. Pat handed them a tip and uttered, "thank you," as he turned to step up into the rickshaw but he wasn't sure the two were paying attention to such niceties. They took the money and fled to the next opportunity. This, too, was China.

After about forty minutes riding from the pier, Pat could see the approaching Settlement and the area Liu called "The Bund."

"I didn't expect to see this," said Pat as he viewed the long curved façade of European-style buildings that faced the Bund along the Huangpu River.

What he was seeing were buildings built by the British, French and Americans. The British and Americans had literal control over what was called the International Settlement. Within the Settlement a westerner could find accommodations, merchandise and, most importantly, fellow English-speaking westerners who could help them traverse the exotic landscape of China.

Pat's rickshaw traveled directly up Zhongshan Road from the south. On the right was the Huangpu River and on the left were the buildings build by Europeans that made up the Settlement in the area of Puxi. There was very little across the river in the Pudong section except a modest dock with small agricultural operations loading grain onto small commercial boats.

The view on Pat's left looked like any other European façade. His ride proceeded north where he could see a collection of both Chinese and Europeans enjoying the river area. Traffic was heavy and one could see dense crowds in every direction. The rickshaw crossed the bridge over the Wusong River which poured into the Huangpu River. It followed the curve to the right and arrived at the Astor. It was as grand as had been described to Pat.

Pat found the Astor full of both Asians and Westerners. Most of the Asians were employees and those from non-Asian countries their rich customers. A few well-to-do Japanese were also present. There was little sign of the military, just a few officers in uniform, perhaps returning home or en route Russia. It was hard to tell.

The whole hotel had the appearance of a ship, complete with fake portholes on the walls of each hallway. Pat stood at the counter to check in and asked the attendant about the unusual decor.

"Such an interesting hotel the Astor is," said Pat, handing the clerk his identification.

"Well, that's all due to our managing director, Captain Harry Elrington Morton," responded the clerk.

"An old sea captain then?" asked Pat.

"Yes, I believe our last three directors have been former sea captains," responded the clerk. Mr. Ezra, our owner, likes the way former military run a hotel I suppose."

"How about you?" asked Pat with a smile.

"Well, there's no confusion on what's to be done, that's for sure," responded the clerk without looking up. He looked French. "That will be sixty dollars per night, sir," said the clerk. Pat nodded in approval.

Morton was from Ireland and had been coming to Shanghai for twenty years. When he retired, owner Edward Isaac Ezra, a millionaire from Shanghai, son of a Jewish merchant, hired him. Ezra had made his fortune in the opium trade but since 1900 was heavily invested in real estate in China. These well connected aristocrats signed long-term land leases with the Chinese. Captain Morton was paid $900 a month plus board and lodging. He ran the hotel like a ship and Ezra approved.

Once Pat got checked in he prepared for dinner. Practically everyone dressed for dinner, which never was served before eight o'clock. The less expensive section of the hotel, called "steerage" like a ship, resembled an American club, because practically all of the rooms and suites were occupied by young Americans who had come out to join the consulate, commercial attaché's office, or business firms whose activities were undergoing rapid expansion. Sanitary arrangements left much to be desired. There was no modern plumbing. The bathtub consisted of a large earthenware pot about four feet high and four feet in diameter. Chinese servants were assigned to carry in an endless number of buckets of hot water to fill the tub in the morning. Pat's accommodations were much nicer and called "first class."

On July 1st, Pat walked to the Russian Embassy which was a few blocks from the hotel. He acquired permission to enter Russia but would need additional signatures at the British Consulate in Shanghai before his entry into Russia was assured. On the seventh he received approval at the Embassy. Pat looked down at his passport, it read "permit for Vladivostok and Omsk via Mukden." It was signed by the British Counsel General. Pat was finally set to enter the Russian Chaos. He smiled thinking about all the bogus papers he had used to escape Belgium. How odd to have everything in such order.

Following dinner for the next five nights, Pat mixed with the young Americans who were thrilled to meet him, having read of his war experiences at home. He also met a number of sinister-looking German, American, British, French, Italian, and Swiss arms dealers in the lobby of the Astor House that dangled fat catalogs of their wares before the eager eyes of cautious buyers. An embargo to prevent Chinese war lords from acquiring munitions had passed in the spring. This cut off most Chinese and foreign nationals from weapons as well. A huge black market business in Shanghai was thriving at the Astor.

There were weapons sellers everywhere, another byproduct of the sudden drop in demand. Pat purchased a weapon for his trip north. It was a small German-made Parabellum-Pistole which was a toggle-locked recoil-operated semi-automatic pistol, designed by Georg J. Luger in 1898. Pat knew little of what he would confront north of China. This seemed like a perfect opportunity to acquire weapon at a reasonable price.

On Friday, August 8th, Pat decided to see the real Shanghai. He had spent all of his free time in the Settlement area, The Bund, and generally where tourists usually go. He wanted to witness life as the Chinese lived it in this sprawling city of 1.5 million.

What stuck Pat immediately were the masses of people. He walked through small congested streets with bicycles and rickshaws twenty across "getting nowhere in every direction." Amid a few automobiles walked everyday Chinese. There appeared instantaneous repair shops, china sellers, and old women running crude handmade spinning wheels.

Along the river north and south of The Bund were sampans and junks all snug against the river's edge where people worked and lived. Men selling birds in bamboo cages, laborers doing back-breaking work under the ardent command of a labor boss, two men "shaving tobacco" right on the street and wild pigs being directed to boats for shipment downstream. They were sites that were stunning and very different than most any place Pat had seen in his many travels. What struck him was how hard people worked and how oblivious they were to the complex and explosive world that existed beyond their mud-walled neighborhoods. It was a humbling experience that would stay with him forever.

Pat secured a ticket for a coastal steamer that would take him to Tianjin on Monday August 11th. From there he would travel the next seventy miles to Beijing where he would catch the Peking-Mukden Line. Once at Mukden, he would take the final leg into Russia, to Vladivostok and into the calamity that existed all along the Trans-Siberian Railroad.

Chapter 46

Siberia

The trip up the coast from Shanghai to Tianjin took just short of three days. Tianjin annually handled more cargo than any other Chinese port in the north despite the fact that almost fifty miles separated the city from its port. While not the most efficient, it seemed to the Chinese that the extra layer of protection between the sea and the city was wise. China's capital of Peking, which lay eighty miles further inland from Tianjin, was afforded additional protection from seaborne invaders. China had a long tradition of protectionism. They had spent centuries building the Great Wall to prevent invasion by land.

Pat stood on the deck of his Chinese steamer as it slowed into port. It was an odd site. Compared to his arrival in Shanghai, the Tianjin port was barren, arid and absent a glittering city looking down with pride on its shipping functionalities below. He could see rail lines and hundreds of small wagons, horse drawn carts and a few mechanized vehicles pulling cargo over the horizon. An equal number could be seen returning empty for more.

"What an odd site," Pat said to himself. "Where's the town?"

Pat and a sizable number of passengers began departing the ship as the horn sounded announcing their arrival. Once on the pier, there was a gathering of baggage handlers scurrying up to the passengers like small pond fish attacking bread. It was another variation of Asian hospitality, different from Shanghai and quite a contrast to orderly Japan.

The ride into Tianjin was ninety minutes of drab scenery. Northern China is extremely dry and there is little productivity from its soil. Once in the city however, Pat found it pleasant and more manageable than Shanghai. It was less crowded and had some acceptable amenities. Pat's taxi brought him directly to the Astor House which dated from 1863. Like its namesake in Shanghai, it was the best in the city. Ulysses S. Grant had stayed there during a two-year world tour following his second term. It also housed Herbert Hoover in 1899, when he lived in Tianjin working as an engineer for the oil firm Bewick, Moreing & Co.

Like Shanghai, Tianjin had a number of European settlements called Concessions. There were three times as many foreign sectors in Tianjin than existed in Shanghai. Pat's stay in China's third largest city would be short, however. There would be little time for sightseeing.

After checking in, he returned to the lobby to find the concierge. A pleasant looking uniformed man with a flat cap greeted Pat as he stepped up.

"Can I help you, sir?" asked the concierge in clear English.

"Yes, thank you," responded Pat. "I'm an American traveling to Russia. Can you tell me how to reach the American Embassy here in Tianjin?"

"Certainly," responded the young man. "I will summon a car for you."

The concierge gestured for Pat to join him outside which he did. From the steps of the hotel the host waved in the direction of a motorized vehicle. The two walked down to street level and the concierge told the driver where to bring his guest. Pat tipped the young man who bowed and gestured until Pat took his seat.

The U.S. office was on somewhat of a side street in the American sector. Pat was surprised to see the obvious demarcations of the various Concessions he passed on the way. Signage was limited but he could easily tell by the architecture which neighborhoods mimicked Germany, Britain, France and others.

"This looks British to me," said Pat to the driver, forgetting their language barrier. The driver understood enough to respond, "Englash, Englash, yes Englash." In the German sector Pat said, "Deutschland" but the driver responded "No Deutschland." The buildings were built in the past and were clearly German in origin but since the war they had been occupied by Chinese officials. It was not uncommon for rich Chinese to move into an entire Concession when relations went sour with the guest country.

After twenty minutes, the taxi pulled up next to a four-story, ornate building painted in a classic, deep Chinese red. Pat paid his driver and proceeded up the steps. A young clerk greeted Pat immediately as he entered the lobby, which looked more like a large parlor or receiving area. There were rooms on the right and left where guests met with officials. Pat was facing a large double door in the center with guards on both sides. The young man spoke English and asked Pat the nature of his business.

"Indeed, sir," the clerk said. He held his arm out in the direction of the parlor on the left. "Wait here and I will get assistance for you."

After about five minutes a man around thirty years of age entered the room and Pat stood up.

"Hello, Mr. O'Brien," said the man, holding a small note in his left hand and extending his right. "I'm Gauss, Clarence Gauss. How can I assist you?"

Gauss was born in Washington D.C., joined the Foreign Service following college and was currently stationed at Tsinan, a city located about 250 miles south of Peking. He was in Tianjin for a few weeks attending meetings and assisting the Tianjin office with general duties. He would later go on to become Ambassador of China.

"My name is Pat O'Brien. I am heading for Siberia and wanted to make sure my paperwork was in order to enter Russia," Pat said.

"Very well, let's see what you have," said Gauss.

Both men took a seat. Gauss began flipping through Pat's credentials.

"You're British?" asked Gauss.

"No, American," responded Pat. "I carry a British passport from my days with the Royal Flying Corps. I flew for the British during the war."

"Yes, I see your stamps from France," said Gauss. "And this is clearly a British issued passport." He read in more detail, turning the book right and left to see the various stamps and signatures scattered throughout.

"Mr. O'Brien, you have a number of signatures here and they all seem proper," said Gauss. "I would highly advise, however, that you acquire an American passport. You are no longer in the RFC, correct?"

"That is correct," responded Pat. He had no illusions about his status but hearing Gauss verbalize "no longer in the RFC" compressed Pat's spirit just a bit.

"Well, Mr. O'Brien, Russia is very tricky these days," responded Gauss. "I think you reduce your risks significantly if you carry a passport from your home country."

"Can I do that here?" asked Pat.

"You can acquire one at Peking," said Gauss. "Peking is about eighty miles from here. You can take the train and be back the same day."

"That's a relief," said Pat. "I want to head north as soon as I can. Can they issue the passport on the same day?"

"I'll place a call and make sure they do so you can get on your way," responded Gauss.

"Thanks," said Pat.

"Very well," said Gauss. "I recall reading about a British pilot by your name. Yes, I believe it was O'Brien. He escaped from the Germans, I believe. I was in China at the time but I recall reading about it. Is that..."

"I am he," said Pat, interrupting the man's question.

"Good Lord!" exclaimed Gauss. "How have you been doing since the war?"

"Very well," said Pat. "I'm off to Russia for one last push. Want to see this thing through, you know."

"Indeed," reflected Gauss. "You know I find it very interesting how many soldiers I have met since the war's end who seem to linger in the memories of war. It must take some time to stop fighting mentally even after the physical combat ends."

It was obvious to Pat that Gauss was not a vet. His comments were passionless, as were those of so many non-vets Pat had heard over the last two years. Though Gauss spoke in a clinical and matter of fact way, his words were not without concern. This sparked a new reaction in Pat. Usually, unwitting comments by those who did not fight would only intensify a veteran's feelings of fraternity with fellow warriors who did. It also solidified the vet's bond to those who he had seen die or get left behind.

But for the first time, Pat envied, rather than resented, a man like Gauss who had never felt the anguish of war and, therefore, had never relived it day after day, as he had. Though there were still too few in 1919, Pat also knew veterans that had found a way to leave the war behind them. He had not. He knew that his bond with fellow vets, dead and alive, had been the generator of all he'd done since coming home. After hearing Gauss, he realized that putting the war behind him required that he allow himself to do so. Perhaps this last run in Russia would let him do just that.

"Thank you very much for your help, sir," said Pat. "I appreciate it, very much."

"You're quite welcome, Mr. O'Brien," Gauss said. "I wish you well."

Gauss walked Pat out the door and down to the curb. A driver pulled up. Pat shook hands with Gauss, opened the back door of his cab and said to the driver, "Astor Hotel, please."

Three thousand miles away in San Bruno, California, Agnes and Arlene were walking up the porch steps of George and Vesta Hughes. Agnes was carrying baby Carol and Arlene had two bags of baby clothes and other items. The day had come for Agnes to pass Carol over. Any longer would have been an additional pain for Agnes and the Hughes couple as well. Besides, Carol was growing quickly and needed to discover her new mother.

Arlene had artfully negotiated an acceptable agreement between the Hughes' and Agnes regarding the adoption. Agnes was grateful to have such a caring friend to handle the details of what was a very painful decision for her. George and Vesta were wonderful, understanding people and wanted the transition to be as painless as it possibly could be.

Arlene had hosted three meetings between everyone over the last few weeks and handled the legal paperwork required for adoption. In the end, all agreed that Agnes would be able to see the baby periodically but only the immediate family would know that Agnes was the mother of young Carol. "We can call you 'Aunt Agnes,'" said Arlene in a sweet, cute way so as not to offend Agnes. Agnes smiled though her eyes were full of sadness. After a few deep breaths she cried. Arlene and Vesta both put their arms around her and comforted her with their own tears. The care and genuine goodness of the three women was a key factor in easing the pain and most importantly providing Carol with a loving home and a bright future.

"Well, I guess it's time we go now," Agnes said, as she stood up placing her empty coffee cup on the small table. Vesta was holding Carol and also stood, bouncing slightly to keep the baby still. Her eyes were filled with tears for Agnes and tears of joy. At one point Vesta and George thought they may never have children. Today, Carol became part of their life. Agnes genuinely felt comforted to know that Carol would have such nice people as parents.

"We'll give you some time, Vesta," said Arlene. "Then when it seems like a good time, Agnes and I will come by for a first visit."

"Yes, honey, we want to give you time to get to know Carol," said Agnes, wiping tears but smiling at Vesta nonetheless. "She's a very good baby."

All embraced. Arlene and Agnes turned and passed through the front door held open by George. They stepped down the steps and walked hand-in-hand up the street.

"Thanks Arlene," said Agnes. "You're a true friend."

"They're good people, Agnes," responded Arlene.

"I know. That makes me feel good," said Agnes.

The two friends went to dinner, then Arlene walked Agnes home. Agnes spent about an hour tidying up her apartment and then went to bed about 9:00. It was a quiet night and Agnes was tired. She slowly fell asleep to the sounds of children playing tag down the street in the summer's evening heat. Agnes would take a week off work, then returned to work the following Monday. She would start a new life without Carol in her daily life. It was Saturday, August 16th.

Halfway around the world, Pat was starting his Sunday morning with breakfast. He would go to Peking today, visit the capital, and then go to the Embassy first thing Monday morning. As was his habit, he was reading through an English paper as he jammed his toast into the dried yoke of his three eggs. Naturally, he was looking for news of Russia. There was little but he did read about efforts in Europe to recoil the extensive war machine.

The roll-up of naval air stations in Europe had begun in December with the disestablishment of Porto Corsini, Italy. The Assembly and Repair Base at Eastleigh, England, was demobilized. Pat was pleased to read that the U.S. Chief of Naval Operations issued a preliminary program for postwar naval Aeroplane development. Specialized types desired were fighters, torpedo carriers and bombers for fleet use, single-engine, twin-engine and long distance patrol and bomber planes for station use, and a combination of land and seaplanes for Marine Corps use.

"My goodness," whispered Pat. "How far we have come since San Diego. It truly is astonishing."

Pat finished up his eggs, tipped the waiter, stepped out to the street and hailed a cab. He arrived at the Tianjin train station but could not read the schedule. He walked up to a uniformed officer and said, "Peking." The man in green pointed in the direction of track two.

The ride to Peking was comfortable and Pat was surprised to be riding in none other than a Pullman car, made in Chicago. The Peking-Mukden Railway ran from Tianjin to Peking stopping six times before arriving at the Qianmen Train Station, the largest train station in China. It was built in 1901 and was located just outside the city wall south of Tiananmen Square.

Pat stepped down onto the platform, exited the station and within minutes was walking across the expansive square. In front of him was the Forbidden City, long the central symbol of China. It is an impressive structure of nearly eight million square feet and 980 building structures. Though Puyi, the last Emperor of China, still lived in the Inner Court, the Outer Court had been opened to the public in 1912.

Pat walked around the square for about an hour taking in its expansive nature and watching the Chinese go about their business. There were a number of westerners present as well. Tiananmen Square was close to government buildings, hotels and essential services sought by travelers. Finally, he crossed the street, standing in front of the Forbidden City, then walked left to the corner to catch a rickshaw.

After a short ride, he arrived at The Grand Hotel. It had been recently rebuilt in 1917 and had all the amenities sought by western travelers. He checked into his room and then at the front desk to find a place to eat. There was a small restaurant in the hotel that featured basic Chinese food such as noodles, beef and sprouts.

Following lunch, Pat arranged for a tour of central Peking. He spent two hours traveling to various points within a square mile of the hotel offered by a rickshaw service. Most of the structures in the area were official buildings. But just beyond the perimeter of central Peking was cluster after cluster of walled neighborhoods comprised of clay mud huts with thatch roofs. Each neighborhood was surrounded by eight foot walls much in the style of the Forbidden City but on a smaller scale. It revealed further the protectionist nature of the Chinese. The larger streets were full of Chinese and Westerners enjoying one of the few sunny and warm days in Peking.

That evening the concierge suggested the Quanjude Restaurant on Qianmen Street, just south of the square, for dinner. Like most visitors to Peking, Pat was encouraged to enjoy Beijing's specialty, Peking duck.

The Quanjude was the most popular with Westerners. It had a large, colorful, classic Chinese façade. Two female hosts opened the double doors for Pat as he stepped out of his cab. Once seated he was greeted by a waiter who immediately poured hot water over loose tea leaves that had been pre-placed at the bottom of the cup. They immediately floated to the top. "I wonder how I drink this?" thought Pat. He let the tea sit a while then negotiated a few sips.

A small menu in Chinese was handed to Pat by a waiter who stood at the ready. Pat sat the menu down and simply said, "duck." The waiter understood. Soon bowls of rice, sauce, greens, roots and other somewhat identifiable dishes arrived. About the time he thought everything had been served, along came six, seven and eight more dishes, all different. "This is a lot different than home," chuckled Pat to himself. "And to think, all I asked for was duck."

As Pat was negotiating an oblong bean at the end of his chop sticks, a man came up to his table and said, "Pat? Pat O'Brien?"

"Yes, I'm O'Brien," responded Pat.

"I'm Burr, R.A. Burr from San Francisco," said the man. "Do you remember me?"

"Why yes, what a surprise to see someone from home here in Peking," Pat said. "Are you alone? Would you like to join me for dinner?"

"Yes, I would. I just got here and haven't ordered yet," Burr said. "Let me ask the waiter to transfer me over."

Burr was someone Pat had met first in Chicago during his Pullman days. He crossed paths with him later in San Francisco during his time with the Santa Fe. In Chicago Burr's company, the Central Coal and Coke Company attended the First International Aviation Meet when Pat was a student flyer at West Pullman. Later, Burr was in San Francisco working for the Combine Oil and Leasing Company and met Pat through Joe Cato. Burr was a sales representative for both companies and had a general interest in flying. Cato was seeking some money for his latest test project and Burr had visited him in Stockton a few times to consider it.

Pat and Burr had a long dinner and talked about all that had transpired since they first met. Naturally, Burr had followed Pat's adventures and Pat enjoyed revisiting his early days in the Bay Area. Both were impressed with each other. Pat was world famous and Burr had risen to become President of his company.

"So what are you doing in Peking?" Burr asked.

"I'm on my way to Russia," responded Pat. "I need to get a new American passport. All I have is a British passport from my war days."

"You'll need a witness for that, Pat," said Burr. "Perhaps I should go with you to help prove who you are."

"Oh my, I forgot about that," said Pat. "How lucky am I that we bumped into each other? I would really appreciate that Burr. Can you go in the morning at 8 o'clock?"

"Sure," Burr said.

The two men enjoyed their dinner and drinks well into the evening, finally departing around eleven.

The next day, Pat checked out of the hotel early and took a cab to the embassy. He met Burr there and had a new passport in about one hour.

"Thanks for the help with this Burr," said Pat, shaking his hand.

"More than happy to assist, Pat," responded Burr.

The two men promised to look each other up back in the states. Burr told Pat to be careful, to which Pat responded, "Hey, you, too."

Pat was back in Tianjin that evening. He checked out of the Astor, tagged his trunk at the train station and boarded the Train De Luxe, a first class transport of the Peking-Mukden Railroad. He was finally heading north, to Manchuria, Russia and the chaos. The track did not follow a direct route north but hugged the coast line allowing passage around the eastern end of The Great Wall where it ran to the sea. Once around this huge barrier, Pat's train cut back toward Mukden.

Pat's train pulled into the station and after affecting the transfer of his trunk to the hotel, he came out the main station door and found a distinctive Japanese flavor to the exterior, including a large number of Japanese suspended lampions lighting rows of neatly aligned jinrikishas manned by Chinese rickshaw coolies waiting to take travelers seven miles over the macadamized road to the Mukden City. Also present were droshkies, driven by fine horses and led by Russian "mafoos," horseman who managed local stables for hire. Pat opted for the more expensive and accommodating droshky. They were fine, two-wheel carts able to sit two people. The carts were attractively decorated with more than adequate and comfortable padded seats.

In less than one minute Pat had witnessed the three legged stool that was Manchuria. Russians, Chinese and, in recent days, Japanese all claimed pockets of nebulous strongholds throughout the region. Manchuria meshed the ancient people of China with a diverse mix of Russian-Siberian races and the highly interested Japanese who had always possessed a craving for the region. For the Japanese, Manchuria was strictly an expansion of its limited island homeland. Since the turn of the century, all of Manchuria contained local pockets of power from these three countries. This would continue well into the 20th Century.

The ride into town was a pleasant one with few characteristic winds, warm temperatures and an animated driver who barked continuously at his horse in thick Russian. As they approached Mukden, Pat could see it was a modern city, more Russian in flavor than Chinese, with some sizable buildings and a population of about 100,000.

Pat's droshky traveled to the center of town where it came upon an exquisite looking white five story hotel located on a roundabout that featured a spired monument at its center. A large curved drive-through occupied most of the front lawn where he was dropped off under the main entrance canopy. He paid his driver, turned, and entered the hotel lobby where his trunk was sitting on a cart, already delivered ahead of him. After settling in his room he took a seat in the restaurant off the lobby.

The menu had a good selection of western food, ample wine choices and quality spirits. Pat was hungry from his travels and ordered a sizable meal. Patrons of the eatery were a mixture of Western, Chinese and Russian. There were military officers from Japan and China, as well. After dinner, Pat sat in the lobby, conversing with an occasional westerner including a few Australian officers who had heard of Pat's exploits. He retired at about ten.

The next morning Pat was up early. His train pulled out of the Mukden station at 6:00 a.m. and headed straight north to the city of Harbin where he transferred to the Trans-Manchurian railroad and headed straight east toward Vladivostok, Russia. He had been advised to enter the city using this route as opposed to the Trans-Siberian Railroad which lay a bit farther north. "You can sneak into town a bit easier this way," the Australian Colonel had told him.

Pat was not the only person attempting to "sneak" into Vladivostok during the summer of 1919. Thousands of civilians, military, industrialists, former government officials, businessmen, railroad operators, and 60,000 crack Czech-Slavic troops were all attempting to travel five-thousand miles across the Trans-Siberian Railway to Vladivostok unnoticed. White and Red loyalists, Cossacks, thieves and disgruntled political factions seeking independence from the Russian state were all picking off men and materiel of any ilk along the way.

In order to combat this continuous sabotage there were 72,000 Japanese, 60,000 Czechoslovaks, 12,000 Poles, 9,000 Americans, 4,200 Canadians, 4,000 Romanians, 4,000 Russian auxiliaries, 2,000 Italians, 1,600 British, and 760 French all trying to save Russia from the Bolsheviks and the throng of other opportunists, many operating in Siberia. Thus far it was not working.

At Harbin, a young Canadian officer entered the train and sat in the seat opposite Pat.

"Heading to Vladivostok, are you?" said Pat, opening a conversation.

"Indeed," responded the young officer. "On my way back."

"Are you stationed there?" Pat asked.

"Yes, unfortunately," responded the man. "It's quite a mess there, what with the Japanese, U.S., Russians and us. Every warehouse is full, there's supply laying along the track for miles to the west. Ships can't get there quickly enough for me. The boiling pot is 5,000 miles west, mind you, but we get all the steam on our end."

"I'm Pat O'Brien, by the way," Pat said, extending his hand. "I trained in Toronto."

"Military?" asked the Lieutenant.

"Yes. Trained at Borden early on," responded Pat. We were part of the first batch of Canadian Flyers into France."

"Good Lord and with all that, why in God's name are you going to Vladivostok?" asked the Canadian, smiling with an inquisitive look.

"Just curious, I suppose," said Pat. "I'd like to see if I might be of assistance, you know. I guess I'm drawn to the unpredictable."

"Well, so be it," said the officer. "I'm Massey. Aiden Massey. Nice meeting you O'Brien.   I'm with the 260th Battalion, we're trying to get out and get back to Canada. You say you trained at Toronto then? Are you Canadian?"

"No, American but flew for the RFC. I was there just as Borden got started," responded Pat. "Everything was a big rush back then. The Brits were desperate then you know. I was part of the first few to fly into France. The U.S. didn't even have an air corps then."

"Oh, a pilot then," said Massey. "Don't envy you boys."

"It beat the mud on the ground though," responded Pat.

"Or the freezing sleet of Siberia," said Massey.

"So, what's it like at Vladivostok?" asked Pat. "I'm hoping to jump on the train to Omsk and see what happens."

"You're loony," said the young Canadian. "Everyone else is trying to get the hell out of there."

"But like I said…." started Pat.

"You're curious, yeah I know," interjected Massey.

The two men laughed, then Massey tried to explain what Pat would find once there.

"The city is scattered along a steep hillside. The locals are friendly and women and children moved about freely. Most of the common labor is handled by Chinese coolies. The better class of Russian people are a fine appearing race. The woman and girls are quite attractive but, of course, they don't speak English. Besides, there's a ton of uniformed men all attempting to meet them, except the Japanese, of course. They're all about their business," Massey said.

"I suppose they're looking to claim a piece of it all once everyone pulls out, then," stated Pat.

"Exactly," responded Massey. "Nobody likes the bastards, you know. We're all there to help get everyone out. They just march through the street so everyone knows they're still there. But as soon as we empty the place I have no doubt they'll stay to claim what's left, and then some."

There was a genuine distrust of the Japanese on the ground and within most Allied capital cities. While they fought for the Allied cause, no one doubted that they're primary motivation in Manchuria and eastern Siberia was expansion.

"So how far in do you think I can get?" asked Pat.

"Well, it's hard to say," responded Massey. "You see on the east end you have Vladivostok. Everyone that has given up in the west is clamoring to get there. Many of them have no plans once they do get there and the rest are stacked up waiting for another ship to arrive to get out. Going west? Well, you can get west easier but it might take you twice as long to get back."

"But what's in the west?" asked Pat.

"At the other end is Omsk," said Massey. "That's where the Trans-Siberian splits in two. One line heads north to Moscow and the other south. Omsk is just this side of the Urals. The White's, so called, capital is there and most of the Brits are too. You really don't want to go any further than Omsk. There are four or five fronts in the east, pockets of resistance everywhere and, really, no place that's safe."

"So, where are the Czechs?" asked Pat.

"They're beating a path this way," responded Massey. They held their ground at Omsk until the Brits got there but now they're getting out. They've done their duty and then some. They're a great force. Without them, the railroad would have been lost months ago. That's added to the chaos. They're strung out all along the railroad."

He went on. "Kolchak, he's the leader of the Whites. He kept the Reds out of Omsk for a long time with the help of England and the Czechs. But since April, the Reds have been taking ground. They took Ufa on June 9th and broke through the Urals the last week of June. Since then all hell has broken loose along the railroad. Everybody knows that if the Reds are past the Urals, Omsk is doomed," said Massey.

"And, of course, there's no way out except east to the Pacific coast," added Pat.

"Precisely," confirmed Massey.

Freed from the geographical constraints of the mountains, the Reds made rapid progress, capturing Chelyabinsk on July 25th and forcing the White forces to the north and south to fall back to avoid being isolated. For all practical purposes, much of the military activity along the Trans-Siberian Railway now was turning into a rescue mission of men and supplies. Though few perceived it at the time, it was likely the beginning of the end for the Whites. In Europe the end of the "war to end all wars" became official with the signing of the Treaty of Versailles on July 28th.

As soon as Pat's train pulled into the Trans-Siberian Railway station at Vladivostok eight hours later, he immediately sensed the density of a city teeming with urgency. The platform was already jammed with people cramming to board the train once it emptied. Seeing no way to leave by ship, many were intent on heading south by rail. The train came to a jolting stop and steam washed over the huddled throng waiting to get on. Fifteen men walked down both platforms shouting orders the crowd to move back and allow the passengers off. Pat stepped off the train, turned left and shuffled his way, along with the others, toward the terminal. People were literally darting through the exiting passengers and onto the train despite orders from the guards.

"Which way out?" Pat asked a ticket agent inside.

"Ya ne ponimayo, angliyskiy" responded the agent indicating he did not speak English.

"Out, out!" repeated Pat.

Somehow the Guard understood and pointed to the right. Pat got half-way across the main terminal lobby and then remembered his trunk. He circled back and was about to ask the same agent the location of bags when he saw a large number of people walking toward him with bags in hand. He walked against their flow until he came to an area with cargo and baggage stacked in random piles. Pat spent twenty-five minutes searching until he found his trunk. He pulled it from the stack and waved over one of the many baggage handlers looking for a fare. A young man loaded Pat's trunk onto his cart.

The entire entrance, walkway and street were filled with congestion. Pat managed to find an awaiting droshky. His handler lifted the trunk into the wagon. Pat tipped him and climbed in. It took nearly three minutes to pull away from the curb as a crush of people continued to walk in front, behind and around the various horse-drawn carts attempting to do business.

As Pat waited patiently for the droshky to pull out, he was amazed to see not only the number of people crammed into the street but their assorted mix. There were Chinese, Japanese, and Korean residents, many of whom lived in the Millionka, the Oriental Quarter of the city. Men in uniform from Canada, France, Britain, Poland, Romania, Japan, Italy and the United States were all present. There were Russians, Mongols and Cossacks. Among them were the officials, the rich, the tidy and the unkempt, all going about their business with no regard for the collective. It was an amazing site and an even more amazing dissonance of multiple languages.

Pat's driver finely found an opening, snapped his reigns and shouted, "Ostorozhno!" telling the few people around him to "look out." Pat's head jerked back as the horse jumped to a trot.

The droshky proceeded to the center of town and up Svetlanskaya Street, the main street, arriving at the Hotel Zolotoy Rog, the "Golden Horn hotel" in English. The four story hotel was built on a corner featuring the typical flat corner façade common in many Vladivostok buildings, and was comparable to a high quality hotel in Europe.

It was Saturday night, August 23rd. Thousands of military personnel were enjoying a weekend of relaxation. Pat made his way to the center of town to look for the Aleksander Bar which was a popular spot for officers and enlisted men from every occupying Army. When he entered, he saw a large group of British and Americans seated around a table for ten with a few open seats.

"Mind if I join you fellas?" asked Pat.

"Certainly, have a seat," said a young British Lieutenant.

"I'm O'Brien, Pat Obrien," said Pat, extending his hand.

"I'm Sid Tremblay," said the officer. "This here is Joe Clark".

"Glad to meet you both," said Pat.

"Looking for a beer, O'Brien?" asked Tremblay.

"That I am," responded Pat.

"Piva, Piva," shouted Tremblay, ordering a beer from a passing waiter.

"What are you doing in Vladivostok, O'Brien?" asked Clark. "You a reporter?"

"Do I look like a reporter?" responded Pat.

"Well, no, in fact you don't," said Clark.

"Good," said Pat laughing. He then explained his interests in taking the train west to Omsk.

"I just want to see what conditions are like," said Pat. "What's the best way to get there? Do you think I could latch on with a U.S. troop train or perhaps one of your transports?"

"Well, the Yanks aren't too eager to go anywhere," said Sid. "It's only us Brits that are really sinking our teeth into this thing. But, then again, War Minister Churchill wants to drive the Bolsheviks out altogether. If we could empty this town and all head west at the same time, we'd have Lenin in jail within a month."

Tremblay wasn't too far from the truth. A total of 120,000 Allied troops were now in Siberia. But each allied country had a different agenda which made it impossible to initiate any unified action on the ground and turn back the Bolsheviks.

"So, what's the problem?" asked Pat.

"Well, the Japs only care about the east coast. The Canadians already went home and the Czechs feel they've already done their job so they're all heading this way to board ships.

Two Americans across the table were eavesdropping on the conversation. One of them leaned in to offer advice.

"Hi, O'Brien, I'm Johnson. Clark here is right. Nobody wants to go on a train ride west because you tend to get interrupted, know what I mean?

Pat smiled, nodding his head.

Johnson went on. "Old man Graves keeps telling us that we're not to get involved in Russian affairs but every time I've gone out there to guard some supply dump or ammo stockpile, wouldn't you know it, a Cassock or Russian Red tries to take it away from us," he said humorously, gesturing overhead with both arms.

Turning to his buddy he went on to say, "Imagine that Tremblay, those bad Russians want our bullets," this time gesturing in an Italian way, off the edge of his chin. Pat and the others laughed.

[603]

"Look O'Brien," said the other American. "Oh, by the way, I'm Starkey," said the other eavesdropper.

"If you want to sneak your way out to Omsk on a site seeing tour," he said, suddenly looking at his buddy Johnson, "and mind you Hal, I have no damn idea why anyone would want to do that," He looked back in Pat's direction, "your best bet is to take a Red Cross or Medic Train. That way you can go pretty much undercover and if someone tries to steel your bandages, you can pretend you're a doctor," again the men laughed heartedly.

"Well, that's more than I knew when I walked in here," said Pat. The men each took hardy swigs of beer.

"So where you from, O'Brien?" asked Tremblay. "You sound like a Yank."

"I'm an American," responded Pat. "But I flew for the RFC."

"You're a pilot?" asked Clark.

"I used to be," said Pat. "I was shot down but survived. The war ended pretty quickly for me. That's why I'm here. I'm looking for one more kick, you know?"

"We're looking for no more kicks, yah know what I mean, O'Brien?" Clark said causing the others to wail once again. "We're ready to go home."

"I can see that," Pat said.

"Wait a minute," said Tremblay. "You're not the pilot that jumped out of a train and escaped, are you?"

"Yes, that's me," said Pat.

The table soon knew who was in the room. Tremblay introduced the men to Pat and all were amazed to see a man as famous as Pat in Vladivostok.

"Once a daredevil, always a daredevil! Right, O'Brien?" said an inebriated young officer from the 31st Regiment.

"Shut up, Jones," said Clark. "This guy's a real hero. Have some respect."

Pat enjoyed the raw exuberance of these young military men. He spent the rest of the night enjoying something he never grew tired of doing, talking military with his fellow warriors. As the night ended, Pat finally realized that he was no longer a warrior as were these young, eager chaps. The next generation was charging forward. War never truly ends, he reflected. It starts again for eager young men who are convinced that their time is the most significant in history. Seeing these young officers made Pat realize that war, with all its regret, abandonment and death would return again for another generation to fight. He had had his time. It was now time for him to find life after war.

Pat would take one more train ride before his war would end. In the morning he would seek out the Red Cross and travel across the most treacherous railroad on earth, into the jaws of a harried retreat by thousands seeking to end their war as well.

Chapter 47

The Harry Tates

The Trans-Siberian railway connected hundreds of big and small cities from one end of Russia to the other. It spanned 5,772 miles, through eight time zones and took several days to travel the entire length. Pat's target, Omsk, was 3,500 miles west of Vladivostok. He calculated it was about as far as New York to San Francisco, so he felt he had a sense of how long his trip might take.

It wasn't that simple, however. The white Czarists were still facing major pockets of resistance all over the vast terrain of Russia. Numerous splinter Armies were now engaged. With Germany "officially" done fighting Russia, Axis armies from eastern European countries who had been fighting at Germany's side were fighting with each other and picking fights with whomever they saw as the enemy, including the "allied" Russian Whites who had forced them into the fight.

Pat walked into the Red Cross headquarters at 8:00 on the morning on August 24th. It was Sunday, yet no different than any other day of the week at the Red Cross, except for the presence of Orthodox clergy picking up their assignments for the day. Priests and other men of faith visited refugees on Sundays in the many barracks in Vladivostok. They spent most of their time with abandoned and sick children who were arriving from the west each day.

A young female nurse at the reception table greeted Pat when he walked in. "Hello, can I help you?" she asked.

"Yes, good morning," said Pat. "I'm interested in speaking to the person that assigns personnel on hospital trains to the west. I understand medical staff travel continuously between here and Omsk and make stops along the way?"

"Yes, that is true. Are you a volunteer?" asked the woman.

"I can be of assistance," said Pat. "My purpose is to get a firsthand look at the conditions along the railroad and get to Omsk. I plan to meet some British military there, but I am a civilian."

"Well, we certainly have a number of volunteers that offer to help us here," she said. "I do believe you are the first to volunteer for our medical train, however. Nonetheless, I will see if the Lieutenant can help you."

"Thank you," Pat said.

Most Red Cross workers were nurses with a smaller number of doctors, numerous volunteers and military personnel assigned to help with logistics, particularly in the field where the coordination with military units was critical. Large companies assigned an officer or two to oversee their medical staff which was often Red Cross support teams attached to their units. Many Red Cross teams also worked freelance, running along the Trans-Siberian Railroad addressing military casualties and civilian suffering.

Pat waited about ten minutes and then a tall, lean American Lieutenant named Nelson arrived to greet Pat.

"Can I help you, sir?" he asked.

Pat explained his interest in traveling west on a Red Cross train and also his willingness to be of assistance in lieu of travel costs. The Lieutenant was open to the idea, expressing the need for as much help as could find. Pat would assist where he could.

"Do you have any medical experience?" asked Nelson.

"No, but I was a POW in Germany. I escaped and I walked two hundred-fifty miles to freedom," said Pat. "I learned to survive in dire circumstances. I was a pilot with the Royal Flying Corps.

"Good Lord! You're O'Brien, aren't you?" said Nelson with an astonished look on his face.

"Yes, I am sir," responded Pat.

It was not unusual for Nelson to have heard of Pat. Most Americans knew of him, even those that had spent the last four years overseas.

"O'Brien, I believe you could certainly be a resource for us," said Nelson. "It doesn't hurt to have a man of your cunning on the train. Most of our people are medical folks, non-combatants and specialists. Your presence could be helpful to us. Siberia is highly unpredictable right now."

"Thank you, Lieutenant," said Pat. "How soon can I be assigned?"

Nelson had a unit in mind that was leaving in the morning. Though they were experienced, and had some military personnel on board, they were young. Pat would be a good addition. It was understood that Pat's main purpose was to get the Omsk. He had the option to stop along the way if he desired and he could separate from the train at any point should circumstances require it. But as long as he rode the Red Cross train, he would assist like all the others.

"Should I find the need to stop prior to Omsk, are there regular Red Cross trains that would allow me to continue my trip on them?" asked Pat.

"Well, there are fewer every day but generally at least one per day. I believe you could expect to see that number for the next two weeks or so. But the situation is quite fluid and Omsk is experiencing heavy pressure from the Reds," said the fatigued officer.

Pat thanked the Lieutenant and arranged for a departure the next morning. Nelson requested he spend thirty minutes visiting one of the head nurses who would be making the trip with him. He met with a Canadian nurse volunteer who had stayed behind to work with the Americans when the Canadian force pulled out. Pat left the Red Cross around ten o'clock.

Back at the hotel, Pat determined it would be best to leave his trunk in Vladivostok and take a smaller bag of essentials. If, for some reason, conditions prevented him from returning he arranged for his trunk to be shipped to Yokohama and held there. Pat's return home, regardless of how he left Russia, would eventually go through Yokohama. He spent the rest of the day preparing for departure and purchasing some additional clothing that was more conducive to his trip. There would be no Pullman cars on the Red Cross train into Siberia.

The next day, he arrived at the train station and began looking for the Red Cross train. He had received a pass from Nelson which allowed him immediate entrance onto the platform. He saw the large train on track three and walked down to the second car where other personnel were boarding. A clerk checked Pat's name off his list and directed him toward the sleeping car where Pat settled in, awaiting departure. The car was a modified railcar with cots affixed to the floor and wooden boxes for personal belongings.

The train filled with staff and Pat introduced himself to a number of male and female volunteers, nurses and three doctors who were on board. They pulled out at 8:45 and headed due north toward Khabarovsk, five hundred miles away. Vladivostok's location is at the very bottom of a Russian-owned appendage that wraps around the eastern border of China separating it from the sea.

Before heading west, the Trans-Siberian line runs straight north to Khabarovsk then takes a direct turn west, along the northern border of China which lies a mere 19 miles from the Russian rail line.

At noon Pat, along with the others, moved to the meal car which was a passenger car modified for food service.

"Hello, is this seat taken?" said Pat to a young, attractive nurse who had just taken her seat."

"Feel free, there are no reserved seats on this train," said the woman with a smile.

"My name is Pat O'Brien. I'm going along for the ride, you might say. Hope to help out where I can." Pat said.

"I'm Florence Hoffman," said the pretty woman. "My experience is that helping out is something not of our choosing on this train. You might say we're all conscripted."

Pat laughed lightly. "Have you spent time in the west?" he asked.

"Yes, most of my time thus far has been in Omsk," she said.

"Omsk, yes, what is it like there now," asked Pat, enthusiastic to hear she had served there. "I'm heading to Omsk to meet up with the British military."

"It's horrid, and I'm afraid it's getting worse," said Hoffman.

"But Omsk is the "White Capital" is it not?" asked Pat.

"Oh yes, it is and Kolchak is there," she said, "but I don't see those folks much. The refugees are pouring into Omsk by the trainloads. We try to send as many as we can east but the volume is becoming too great."

Kolchak was the leader of the Whites. The former Czarist military officer formed a provisional government after Lenin's takeover in Moscow and Petrograd.

"Are you going to Omsk to assist?" asked Pat.

"I've been there since November," she responded. "We were ordered to leave Omsk three weeks ago."

"Are the Reds that close?" asked Pat with some surprise in his voice.

"They are not there yet but the wave of refugees tells us that they are inching closer," she said. "Mind you, we were taking care of 25,000 refugees in Omsk when I left."

"My God," said Pat.

"I've been doing some publicity work for the Red Cross in Vladivostok," said Hoffman. "I'm a journalist by trade, worked for the Honolulu Star-Bulletin for a time. My editor decided to bring fourteen volunteers to Vladivostok to assist and I signed up. I'm not going back to Omsk though, too risky there. I am heading to Irkutsk, just past Lake Baikal. I'm to look into conditions there, take notes, and return to complete a report for the Red Cross. I hope to go home by December before the winter arrives."

Hoffman was not only an attractive lady but very interesting to Pat. She was obviously fatigued from her time in Siberia but her dedication and genuine concern for the refugees was obvious. It was a side of war Pat had never experienced firsthand. As a flyer, he barely witnessed the death of those he shot from the sky, let alone the many innocent civilians forced to race ahead of advancing armies. Pat and Florence Hoffman visited well into the afternoon. She had remarkable stories of the sorry conditions developing in the wake of the civil war.

"The refugees live like animals," said Hoffman. "Barracks in Omsk are low, long buildings built of logs and old boards scraped together. They're nearly 300 feet long and 80 feet wide, and each one contains about 300 refugees. Huge stoves are placed at intervals, and each refugee has a crude little stove of his own to cook by. They never have a window or door open in winter, so there is no ventilation whatever, except what comes through the cracks of the walls. You can imagine the stench. The smell is so strong that it nearly overpowers you. There are no floors to the barracks except the earth that God put there, and a lot of extra dirt that the refugees track in."

She went on. "Everything is dirty and covered with vermin. The refugees have the filthiest habits and live like animals. They are all half sick and half starving. Practically all of them have had typhus and have never gotten well again. Half have the scurvy, and some of these are so saturated with poison in their systems that if you poke your finger into them it would make a hole. About every third one has tuberculosis, and some have a combination of all these diseases. And of course, they are all suffering from malnutrition in some form or other."

Pat was generally shocked by the situation Hoffman described. This was the true after effect of war. While Pat suffered mental anguish over his experiences and over the friends he lost, these people were living a real physical hell that would certainly lead to death, were it not for people like Florence Hoffman.

They left the food car around three and headed back to their respective coach. There were six women living in one coach. In another, John Baker, head of the refugee work in Omsk, and six Czech soldiers who acted in the capacity of caretakers. Cooks and chambermaids were in another. Pat's coach was a fourth class box car where four male refugee workers and he would make the trip. The final box car was the dining car. There were two other box cars used for storage and work rooms.

The Red Cross train arrived at Khabarousk and stopped for thirty minutes while Baker procured some additional medical supplies. Soon they were on their way again, steaming due west as the sun disappeared over the horizon and darkness took over the entire country side. The men in Pat's car were already settling into their bunks.

"Ok, gentlemen," said Goran Dragoslav. "This may be the last quiet night we have. I'm going to sleep while I can."

Pat and the others visited awhile. They were genuinely good, honest fellows and Pat enjoyed hearing of their experiences across Russia which was not unlike Florence's. The entire coach was asleep by nine that evening despite the loud clacking of the rail cars speeding toward Chitta, the next city 1,300 miles away.

Early the next morning, they stopped for engine maintenance and then continued west for another full day. Pat spent more time getting to know those on board. He revealed his past service in France. Florence, having been in the newspaper business, realized who Pat was and was as eager to hear his stories as Pat was of hers. Pat, along with two others from his coach, ate their meals with Florence and two other women, all similar in age.

Following dinner the group held their first meeting under the guidance of Mr. Baker. After covering the usual topics, he warned everyone that the night could bring interruptions. They were about to enter the area of TransBaikalia which lay just east of Lake Baikal. The route around the lake was the last portion of track constructed on the Trans-Siberian railroad. At one time, trains were ferried across the huge lake, but eventually track was connected around the southern shore. Nonetheless, there were other potential barriers in this region of the country that could delay passage beside the lake.

"We will stop just near Rukhlovo for the night and spend the day tomorrow waiting for a Czech train which is coming east while providing aide to any locals that approach us," said Baker. "This Czech train has a few wounded I'm told but mostly dysentery and infection, no typhoid however."

"I hate it when we stop through the night," Florence said to Pat. "It's too risky, particularly in Semënov territory."

TransBaikalia was utterly dominated by one man, Grigorii Semënov. He set up the first serious anti-Bolshevik forces in Siberia, and was fighting when others were merely blustering or still plotting underground. Like all other militias operating on their own, his group of fighters were unpredictable, often harassing the unsuspecting, taking what he needed, and asking questions later.

The Red Cross train pulled off to a side track at Rukhlovo where the engine could be refreshed. The remote area was lit by small light hanging from a poll next to a crude shed. There were two men that worked in the shed offering minor repairs. They also had a telegraph set up but the lines to the east barely reached Omsk due to Red saboteurs. The Red Cross train engineer finished his maintenance on the engine. Pat and the others spent some time stretching and getting some fresh air. It was a warm night, so it was decided to have dinner outside on a long makeshift table.

Following dinner, the group retired to their sleeping cars. After about two hours, just before midnight, they were roused by loud shouting and banging on the train.

"Open up! Open up, I say," came the shouts from outside Pat's sleeping car. The men jumped up right away as did Pat who also grabbed his pistol, placing it in his belt under his shirt. The women were also disturbed and the Czechs, some sleeping in their boots, grabbed rifles and made ready. The banging continued. Pat slowly pulled back the door.

"What do you want?" said Pat.

"We need supplies," said a Cossack, still sitting on his horse with men around him toting rifles."

"What do you need?" responded Pat.

A younger soldier stepped forward and spoke to Pat in broken English, "We need ether and bandages," he said. "We have injuries."

Pat turned to one of the others, "Do we have that here or in the other car?"

"The supply car in the rear," said Goran.

The soldiers were a patrol from Semёnov's army. Being anti-Red, Pat and his fellow passengers had little to fear. The Cossacks under Semёnov were more focused than many of the bands of barbarians roaming the country side who robbed people regardless of their allegiance. But Semёnov had visions of his own and his barbaric methods were gaining him a negative reputation, even with his own troops.

One month prior, the 1st TransBaikal Semёnov Regiment had killed their officers and went over to the Reds. By now, partisan attacks were full scale assaults on towns, not just isolated ambushes on easy targets. From a heady mix of anarchists, Semenov's Army, refugees and bandits were increasingly infiltrated by Bolsheviks who provided the organization and cooperation that was otherwise lacking. No one could really tell who was on what side but the Bolsheviks were masters of infiltration.

Pat took his chances and stepped down from the train car, gesturing to the six horsemen. The other men in the railcar stepped down more cautiously and followed him.

"Come with me," he said. The men walked their horses to the end of the train, followed by the leader who was still on horseback. Baxter was already standing in the door of the storage train with bottles of ether in his hand. He had overheard the conversation, told the women to stay put and got there ahead of Pat.

"Very good," said the English speaking Cossack. "Give us bandages. Also, I see you have iodine. Give us iodine, also." Baxter obliged the men. They mounted their horses, turned and left without even a wave of goodbye, galloping into the dark night.

"I say, O'Brien, you didn't even flinch," said Eric Johansen, one of the American volunteers.

"Hey, if they were coming here to kills us, they wouldn't have knocked on the door," said Pat in a light hearted tone.

The men all roared with laughter and by now the ladies had opened their car and were watching with amazement at men slapping each other on the back and bellowing over what the woman viewed as a terrorizing incident.

"But really, O'Brien," said Eric. "I froze and you acted like those guys were delivering telegrams." Again, another laugh from the horde.

Everyone returned to their bunks and the night became quiet once again. Then about two in the morning, another ruckus occurred outside, this time with rifle fire. It was a group of Russian Whites. They swung open the women's car first, roused them out of bed and shouted demands. The men, hearing the noise, were quickly out their car and ran three cars down where eight men on horseback were standing, two of them stepping from their saddle into the railcar. The women were calm, considering the frightening experience. One of the men wanted to know if the Red Cross train had his wife. All denied even seeing any women near the medical train. But the soldier was convinced that she was taken to a Red Cross train in the area. Apparently, she was an interpreter and was injured in a fall and taken away by another division of White guards.

"We have no reason to capture your wife," said Pat. "We are in the business of providing aide. We do not have room to take on additional passengers."

After some further convincing and a complete inspection of the train, they were gone. Again the Red Cross crew attempted to return to bed. It was approximately 3:30 in the morning. Few of them slept. Pat had no trouble. After two hours the sun came up and the train cars began to heat up in the morning sun. By 8:00 everyone was up and drinking coffee outside. It would be a full day treating locals and the expected military train full of Czechs.

"From now on, we will barricade the doors and insist that our callers choose daylight hours for their visits." Baxter said. He was serious but it drew a chuckle from the men.

"Maybe we should post a 'closed' sign on the side of the railcars, hey Baxter?" said Pat, eliciting another laugh from both the men and women. Baxter took it in good spirits.

If any of the Red Cross crew had known Pat as a kid or during his days in Richmond or perhaps at training camp in Toronto, they would have recognized this Pat O'Brien. He was in his element, always facing calamity with good humor. Since the day he faked a drowning at the old Momence Quarry and "scared the bejesus" out of Al, he was possessed of a natural ability to engage diversity boldly. He was born with it and it had served him well. He always had guts.

About eleven in the morning, the Czech armored train arrived from the west. Soldiers were occupying every square inch of its exterior, rifles drawn, sandbags in place, and large mounted guns on each car ready to respond to anything suspicious. The lead officer stepped down and proceeded to an awaiting Baxter. They exchanged salutes and proceeded to discuss the medical needs of soldiers on the train. About twenty men made their way off the train, about half of them were carried on stretchers. Baxter and his crew made use of the repair shed to redress wounds, apply disinfection and generally providing enough care to allow the wounded to continue on their journey.

The Czech officer thanked Baxter after about an hour of treatments, climbed aboard the train again and was off. The most important priority for the Czechs was to get to Vladivostok as quickly as possible. The Czecho-Slavs were dispersed along the Trans-Siberian line in small detachments and had considerable difficulty keeping in touch with each other. Nevertheless, their fate was favorable. They were victorious almost everywhere, thanks to their wonderful spirit and discipline.

Pat and the others washed down the shed with disinfectant. Pat was washing his hands in the work sink when Baxter stepped up to do the same.

"You know, O'Brien, you should not attempt to get to Omsk. Captain Blatnik did not have good things to say today," Baxter said.

"What did he tell you?" asked Pat.

"Well, do you recall hearing how Florence told you there were 25,000 refuges in Omsk?" he asked.

"Sure," responded Pat.

"Well, in the last two weeks 600,000 soldiers and refugees hit Omsk. At least 100,000 are refugees," Baxter said.

Good Lord," Pat responded. "That can only mean the Reds are getting close."

"Exactly," said Baxter. "I put a wire out to some of my old contacts there. I'll let you know what I hear further but I'd advise you not continue on to Omsk. You may never get out. We pulled all but 12 of our Red Cross people out of there last month. It was becoming overwhelming then. It will certainly get worse."

"Thanks, Baxter," Pat said. "Let me know what you hear."

As Pat returned to his railcar, he reflected on what he had just learned. "It makes sense," he thought to himself. "The Czechs are getting out. They were the key to keeping the Reds from coming east. Now Omsk, the White Capital is being overrun. It's clear now. The Reds will win."

Pat was correct. The beginning of the end was in play. It had actually begun in October when the Czechs declared their independence in Paris. Once the Czech Legion got word of that, the slow exodus out of Russia began for the Czechs. In the past thirty days it was becoming a torrent.

They pulled out of Rukhlovo about 5:00 pm. Everyone met for dinner in the dining car.

"What a day," said Goran.

"And night," added Pat.

The group ate heartily and enjoyed some downtime as darkness fell over Siberia. Baxter broke out the vodka and all partook enough to drown out the clacking train overnight. They were 520 miles from Chita.

At six in the morning, the train slowed for some reason. Pat was awake and the others stirred at the sound of steel wheels braking against the track. The train came to a halt. The men opened their door and looked forward. Pat could see an armored train in front of them blocking their passage but he also noticed something that surprised him. It was the fuselage of an RE8, an aircraft. He recognized it right away.

"I'll be damned," he exclaimed loudly, "it's a Harry Tate!"

"Who?" asked Eric.

"Not who, Eric, what," said Pat, taking broad steps in the direction of the aircraft. The men followed. Once he got past the Red Cross locomotive he saw four aircraft. Two were parked alongside the railway line and two well-used RE8 reconnaissance bombers, their wings strapped to their fuselages, were still positioned on flat cars which were being towed by an armored train.

"For the love of God!" Pat exclaimed. "Out here in the middle of nowhere, I can't believe it. They're Brits!"

The aircraft was armed with two Vickers machine guns, one fixed forward firing and one flexible gun in the observer's position facing the rear.

"Hello, fellas," said Pat. "You taking these Tates up?"

"As quick as we can," said a young Lieutenant named Charles Tremont. "You'd be wise to take cover. There's a platoon of Reds coming up the tracks and we aim to take them out."

Just then a second Lieutenant named Sharp walked up to Tremont, "Davies can't fly, sir. He's barely lucid. Do I go up alone then?"

"No, we'll take two up," said Tremont. "It's took risky with no tail gunner."

"But sir, you saw them. They're toting machine guns," pleaded Sharp.

Pat and the other men were standing near the pilots when suddenly Pat spoke up.

"I'll fly one Tremont," said Pat. "Let me fly yours, Sharp. You can work the back gun.

"Can't do that," said Tremont. "I can't put any of my pilots at risk."

Golan spoke up. "But he's Pat O'Brien of the Royal Flying Corps. He flew over France. You don't know him?"

"No, sorry, I don't," said Tremont. Then looking at Pat he said, "You were in the Flying Corps?"

"Yes, came to France in 1917," said Pat. "Trained at Borden in Canada."

"Well, let's go then," he said to Sharp. "Pull that third plane off. But you're flying O'Brien. Let Sharp do most of the gunning."

Pat could not believe his ears. He looked to Baxter who nodded that there was time. Sharp handed him goggles and a mask as two signalers pulled the third fuselage off the railcar, quickly affixing each wing.

Tremont debriefed the men. They would fly to the northwest, then cut back and catch the Reds from behind. Tremont would lead. They'd strafe with the first two planes then Pat and Sharp would dive after the initial attack, hoping to catch the Reds by surprise after the first assault and wipe them out.

These men were part of an undercover unit of the Royal Air Force called "Z" Flight. They specialized in mobile air attacks all along the western portion of the Trans-Siberian Railroad. The Czechs controlled things on the ground and "Z" Flight terrorized Red units all along the railroad, popping up out of nowhere to heap a barrage of lead at the unsuspecting Red Army units. They were masters at quick assembly, rapid attack and seamless return to their armored train before blitzing to the next target.

Pat stepped up into the pilot's seat, checked his controls and pulled back on his Vickers gun. His starter signaled and then flipped the prop. The engine kicked in immediately bellowing grey smoke that was carried by a stiff wind into Pat's face. The smell of fuel wafted into Pat's nostrils and brought him back to France.

All three planes were up quickly. Baxter and the others watched Pat's plane pull up in third position. As planned, Tremont led the three to the northwest and about five miles out he signaled to his far left. Pat could see a cloud of dust being stirred up by what looked to be a dozen men on horses, a supply wagon and two gun turrets being towed in the rear. They appeared to be a mile away, and the three Harry Tates were high enough not to be noticed.

Tremont signaled the second plane and signaled back to Pat to hold, flashing him an open hand four times indicating a twenty second lag before diving. Tremont rolled, followed by the second plane. They headed straight toward the convoy. Pat maintained his angle and watched as Tremont and the other swept down on the unsuspecting Reds. Pat looked back at Sharp who gave the thumbs up and Pat rolled into a dive. He was so excited he nearly threw up. For a split second he reflected on the moment and then his discipline kicked in and snapped him into focus. The plane accelerated with ease and Pat could feel the energy building as he dove. Tremont and the other pilot had taken out at least half of the unit but the gunners were squaring around to aim their Vickers to the sky.

Pat saw plane number two's rear gunner take out the first turret. Tremont looped back and took out three horses and two additional soldiers. It appeared to Pat that he was still unnoticed.

"Perfect," he shouted to himself.

Tremont's strategy was firm. As Pat drew closer to his target, he saw the rear gunner turn, hearing Pat's approaching RE8.

"Hang on, Sharp!" shouted Pat as he swooped down. Sharp could tell right away that Pat was an experienced scout. Scouts never backed off their speed in a dive. It was to their advantage to come in hard and rapid. Pat knew no other way.

Pat zeroed in on the second gun. He was close enough to see the ground spitting up his metal and then saw one of the two gunners fall to the ground. Pat took dead aim at the second gunner and just before he pulled up, his shots hit the Russian reeling him back, his head jerking violently. As Pat pulled away, he heard Sharp firing away.

Tremont's plane passed on Pat's left going in for one final kill. Pat came out of his dive and pulled up left. He saw no activity on the ground. It had been a complete massacre. The entire patrol was killed. He watched Tremont and the second plane pull left and right and rise toward Pat who was flying at about 2,000 feet. They joined up again and headed back.

Baxter and others were standing waiting the pilot's return. All had been able to see the planes dive in the distance and were glad to see all three returning.

Pat and the five men leaped from their Harry Tates after shutting down the engines quickly. Three signalers started dismantling the wings immediately.

"Good work, men," said Tremont. "Great work, O'Brien. I see you have done this before."

"Thanks, Tremont," said Pat, removing his helmet and goggles. "Thanks so much for giving me another shot at it." Pat shook the man's hand and then Sharp's. He turned and felt his throat tighten up and tears filled his eyes as he walked back toward the Red Cross train. He had one thought on his mind. "I never thought I'd get another chance. I never thought I would," he said quietly as he walked to the train feeling the emotion of the moment.

Pat's Red Cross friends all congratulated him. Golan shook his hand and the others slapped Pat on the back. The women smiled admiringly, particularly Florence who could see the unique flare in Pat that many had witnessed before.

"I'm relieved those Reds are gone. Thank God the Brits where here to clear the way," said Florence, looking up admiringly at Pat. Pat just looked down and smiled, still feeling the emotion of the moment. Only he knew why.

The train pulled out after about ten minutes and headed west. They passed the location of the ambush where fifteen Red Russians lie dead, heating up in the morning sun. Pat stood in the door of his railcar as they passed, staring at the results of their efforts. He held his view until he could no longer see the bodies of men and horses strewn over the arid landscape.

Baxter's crew was again breathing easy knowing the Red platoon was eliminated at the hands of Pat and British flyers. But Florence Hoffman, who had spent more time west than the others, knew that the real evil in TransBaikalia was Grigorii Semënov. Semënov's criminal empire operated from Lake Baikal to Khabarovsk and the Red Cross train was entering Chita, the center of his power.

Semënov was the supreme military commander of the Cossacks in his region. He flourished without much interference from the White administration in Omsk and Vladivostok. His elite inner circle included some of the toughest Cossacks in Russia, a number of beautiful mistresses, and a collection of thieves, scoundrels and sadists. Many of his "officers" were of German and Austrian origin, from the Baltics and escaped war prisoners set free amid the chaos of the war's end in Eastern Europe.

An American officer once described Semënov and his crew as "bloodthirsty as a pirate crew. Yet Semënov cavorted with Chita's "high society," gold traders, rich merchants, generals and bon vivants of local salons.

Baxter had no intention of stopping at Chita for fear his train would be commandeered by Semënov's mob. He met with the entire crew just before they entered the city. He told them he would not stop unless halted forcibly. All doors and windows in box cars were to be kept closed and secured. It was his hope that they would appear to be transferring without staff and pass through Chita without incident.

The population of Chita in 1900 was 12,000 but exploded to 73,000 when the railroad was developed. On the day Baxter's Red Cross train entered the huge rail yard and made its way slowly past numerous check points, throngs of refugees and military pressed against Semënov's guards hoping to gain access on the next train heading east. There were over 150,000 people in Chita that day but Baxter, Pat and the others passed through unharmed. By noon, they were fifty miles past Chita and passed through Ulan Ude later that afternoon. Ulan Ude, normally with a population of 22,000 people was swollen with 60,000.

That evening the Red Cross train pulled into the only marble train station in the world at the town of Slyudyankaf. The small town sat at the bottom tip of Lake Baikal where the Trans-Siberian Railroad turned sharply north, up the west side of the lake for fifty miles before heading due west to Omsk. It was a stopping point for every train on the Trans-Siberian line due to the fact that it was the southernmost point on the railroad.

Travelers weary of the long journey found Slyudyankaf a logical jumping off point. It was near Russia's southern border and directly in line with Urga, the largest city in Mongolia. From there, one could reach Beijing in two days, some 850 miles away.

When they reached the station, Baxter and Pat met three British officers who had just arrived from Omsk. They confirmed the worst case scenario. According to the Brits, there were hundreds of people living in the railroad yard at Omsk. The British, French, all kinds of Russian and Czech generals were trapped, attempting to escape east to Vladivostok. The White government was falling apart. Starvation, sickness, and typhoid smothered overcrowded streets filled with refugees choking in a dying city.

Omsk was not in the cards for Pat. From a distance, Florence notice Baxter and Pat talking with the officers and knew that Pat would be leaving the group. She felt bad that he was leaving but understood that it was his logical move. Florence would travel one more stop to Irkutsk, which was her destination. She would eventually return to Vladivostok and on a long delayed journey home, away from sickness and the death of a nation. She would spring from its hapless grasp and depart Russia on December 12th.

Pat said good bye to the entire Red Cross crew. They had made a strong impression on him. Their war was very different than his. It was through this group of selfless volunteers that he realized the true impact of war, its impact on the millions of people that did not seek it, that found no glory in it and, all too often, unlike he, did not survive it.

"Take care of yourself, Pat," said Florence looking up into his eyes. They were clasping hands and were genuinely sad to be parting. Their good bye was not as two lovers might be, but of two people both erased again by war's insistent evaporation. Another case of life's many moments, swept away by war. Both knew that they would never see each other again.

He reached up and placed his hand aside her cheek and said, "Be careful, Florence. God's speed getting home."

Pat stood watching his friends walk toward the platform once again to return to the hell that was Russia. Nearly on cue, she looked back one final time and waved. He waved back, this time not with the familiar broad sweep across his frame, as he had so many times before, but unwillingly, slightly and with great remorse.

His adventure in Russia was finished. It was time to go home.

Chapter 48

The Bypass

Pat exited the station and stepped onto the street. He looked in both directions. Slyudyankaf was a mere village, not a robust city with accommodations like Chita. He walked toward what appeared to be a small inn. Perhaps he might find something to eat and discover a route to Urga, the largest city in Mongolia.

The entrance to the tavern contained and unusually steep step, nearly a foot high. He anchored his two hands inside the door frame and pulled himself up. The tavern was filled mostly with men enjoying food and drink. They all turned and looked at him in a curious way.

"I am looking for a room," he said to a stout man wearing an apron behind the bar. The man said something in Russian and waved over an older gentleman who was seated at the end of the bar and appeared to be the owner.

"How may I help you?" he asked.

Pat explained his needs and the man nodded, inviting him to follow. They entered an adjoining room where the inn keeper issued Pat a room for the night. Pat paid him, grabbed his bag and walked down the hall entering the third room on the left. Inside he observed a large featherbed, wash basin with pitcher, mirror, dresser and a thick rug. It was simple but cozy and he had little trouble sleeping through the night. The bed was a particular joy after so many nights sleeping on a jolting railcar.

Pat lay in bed, thinking about his experience in Siberia and his new friends from the Red Cross. It was the type of experience that each time Pat thought of it he remembered another detail. All of Russia was like that normally but under its current duress it was a trip of endless minutiae.

The next morning the inn keeper brought Pat to a livery, located at the edge of the village. Pat secured transportation to Urga, a town two hundred miles away. The owner of the livery stable assigned his twenty-five year old son to bring Pat to Urga by utilizing a passenger wagon pulled by two horses. He assured Pat that mechanized transportation could be found at Urga. Pat secured his belongings and the two were on their way within an hour.

The route to Urga was actually to the southeast but would place Pat on the ancient Tea Road that passed through the primary northern gate of the Great Wall at Zhangjiakou City straight north of Peking. The trip to Urga was pleasant and full of tremendous landscape.

As they entered Urga around two in the afternoon, Pat noticed that Russians were less apparent than were Chinese. For years, the Russians had done a considerable amount of private trading with the Mongolians at Urga. In fact, the treaty between China and Russia following the Opium wars in the 1860's gave Russia permission to station a number of troops in the city as well. All this accounted for the significant mix of both races in the Mongolian capital.

Pat found the city remote yet modern with hotels more in line with Chita. Military and civilian vehicles mixed with horse-drawn droshkies and Chinese rickshaw wagons. His driver took him to a four-story hotel. From here he could acquire a room and contract for transportation south across the Gobi desert, through the Wall and on to Peking. Pat estimated this final leg of his journey to Peking to be approximately 850 miles, mostly on dirt roads.

"Hello, Sir," Pat said to a young man behind the check-in counter at the hotel.

The clerk spoke English and responded, "Yes, sir, how may I assist you?"

"I am told that in addition to a room, you may be able assist me with transportation to Peking," Pat said.

"Yes, there is a transport service you can charter," the man said. "In fact, it is owned by a British company and operated by the Chinese. They have a number of American vehicles which are quite reliable."

"And they will provide a driver, I assume?" Pat asked.

"They do," the man responded. He waved a second man to the counter and ordered him to bring Pat to the transport company, located three blocks away. While the driver waited, Pat ordered a room for the night, checked his bags and then went with the man to look into transportation.

"You're in luck, sir," the man said as they walked up the street. "It's the dry season. You should not get stuck in the mud as long as it does not rain."

"Thank you, let's hope it doesn't," Pat responded.

He arrived at a small garage which had three good looking machines parked at the ready. They were Allen Touring Cars made in Fostoria, Ohio. What had brought the cars to Asia was the extensive use of the Sommer four-cylinder engine, used in many military vehicles across Europe and Siberia. L.A. Sommer, like many auto manufacturers, had converted over completely to wartime production. These cars were first brought to Asia by company officers who managed the relationships with military clients. When the war was over, the men returned to the U.S. and these cars were sold to a British manufacturer invested in Mongolia who wanted access to vehicles but leased them on a regular basis.

Pat spent the afternoon purchasing some additional clothing suited for his desert trip. He spent a comfortable night in Urga, enjoyed a satisfying meal, and retired early. The next morning he and his driver named Gavriil departed at 7:00 a.m.

The Trans-Siberian Railroad, marvel of 20th Century technology, was not the first monumental pathway to cross the Eurasian continent. Pat was traveling down the Tea Road, the southernmost leg of an historic path that connected European Russia to Siberia and China. Ever since Mongolian ruler Altyn Khan sent a gift of tea to Czar Michael I in 1638; horse, mules, camels and great legions of men tramped a solid road from Moscow to Beijing, nearly 13,000 miles.

Pat and his driver were just thirty minutes into the desert when the heat of the Gobi swarmed over their faces. Pat removed his cotton shirt wearing only a thin sleeveless undergarment. The leather convertible top of the car was in place, blocking the sun. All windows were down, allowing the warm desert breeze to cut though. Pat glanced out at the beautiful morning view of the Gobi Desert. Within minutes, the wrap of forests and green landscape pealed back to reveal a vast, treeless, yellow terrain that had no boundaries except the clear division of land and sky at the far horizon.

The planned itinerary was to travel daily from 7:00 a.m. to 7:00 p.m. If they were fortunate, they would make 200 miles per day but much depended on the condition of the road which in spots amounted to nothing more than packed down sand with a series of tire ruts carved through on wet days, hardened in the dry sun most other days. It was a road more suitable for camels than cars.

As dusk arrived, they came upon people for the first time, a group of Mongol herders, living in two yurts. There was a third yurt near bye marked "guanz." This indicated food was available and, likely, housing for the night. Yurts were portable dwelling structures somewhat in the shape of a three-layer cake. They were comprised of a crown or compression wheel that formed the lip of the "eave" portion of the roof supported by roof ribs bent down where they met the lattice wall, all supported by a tension band which held everything together. These yurts, called "gers" by the Mongols, were covered with layers of fabric and sheep's wool, felt for insulation and protection from the weather.

They stopped the car and were greeted by two men, followed by a woman and three young children. In broken Russian, Pat's driver was able to inquire as to any space that might be available for an overnight stay. The elder of the group invited them to have tea. Pat found it was salted and somewhat bitter but acquired a taste as he and his driver Gavriil washed down the dryness of the day. They all sat near a cast-iron pot on a small stove which was fueled by "argal," essentially animal dung.

Gavriil and the elder Mongol agreed to a price for the cost of shelter for the night, dinner with the hosts and fresh dumplings wrapped for their trip in the morning. At dinner time they were joined by five others living in the encampment which included a younger couple with three small children. Pat spent a good portion of time playing with the young ones who were delighted by his sleight of hand tricks and his dice, which he still carried. He allowed them to toss them repeatedly on a sheep cloth after which they would all point to and count all the dots, much to the delight of their parents. Pat captured their fancy with his infectious smile as well. He had always had an instant connection with children, wherever he went.

The next morning they were off once again, into the heat of the Gobi desert. Barring any unforeseen delays, Gavriil estimated that they would be in Peking in four days. The next three days were filled with diverse and breathtaking landscapes including huge dune structures one day and thick grassy steppes the next. Camels, nomadic settlements, desert lakes, the Dundgobi Rock Towers and enormous Chinese pyramids in the southeast Gobi desert were stunning discoveries. Pat particularly enjoyed seeing the ornate Mongol saddles that adorned their many horses and the colorful clothing made by the Mongol women for their husbands and children. It was a rugged yet pleasant trip across a landscape of simple lines, clear demarcations and friendly people that lived as Mongols have for centuries.

On Wednesday, September 3rd, Pat and Gavriil saw The Great Wall for the first time and made their way toward the Daijing Gate at Zhangjiakou. They passed through the ancient portal in line with every means of transportation one could conceive of. It was noon and they were now inside China, 125 miles from Peking.

The route to Peking was filled with traffic. At four in the afternoon, the Allen car arrived at the city limits. Gavriil made his way to the center of the city arriving at the Grand Hotel where he prepared to drop off his Passenger.

"You must stay the night," Pat said to his new companion and friend.

"I return to Mongolia now," Gavriil responded.

"No, I insist," Pat said. "Have dinner with me, I will pay for your room so you can rest before you return. I would very much enjoy that."

Shocked at Pat's offer, Gavriil raised his eyebrows in disbelief and nodded his head, then broke into a broad smile. Pat instructed a hotel attendant to park the car and the two men walked into the hotel lobby and acquired their rooms.

The next morning, Pat saw Gavriil off. Though there was little language between them, a friendship had developed and Gavriil was genuinely touched by the kindness and friendliness of Pat. He was brought nearly to tears when Pat handed him a significant tip. He bowed, shook Pat's hand, bowed again and then was off.

Pat stood with his hands on his waist and watched the Allen car pull away and around the corner. He stood there a moment and drew a deep breath.

"What an amazing trip," he said to himself. The entire experience was one of finality for Pat. During the trip across the Gobi desert, he had not had one conversation in English with anyone for five days, including Gavriil. It was living, stripped of the veneer that covered the modern world, yet it did not lack tradition, formality, emotion or culture. For Pat, it was emotional bath that afforded him the chance to turn a page in his life.

Pat spent the next week visiting the many sites of Peking and surrounding areas. He'd only had two days to see Peking on his previous visit for a passport. One night he was surprised to see that one of Peking's few movie houses was showing a Charlie Chaplin film. Following dinner he took a rickshaw ride to the location and was impressed to see such a modern, elegant theatre in China. Chaplin was enormously popular throughout the world, with China among the many countries where audiences loved his films. His movies were being shown there for the first time and a large audience was on hand. He saw a few other westerners but the majority of the crowd was Chinese and every seat was filled. Chaplin's films meshed perfectly with Chinese audiences' tastes at the time, as slapstick comedy shorts were the dominant genre of China's own developing movie industry. The silent antics of Charlie Chaplin were universally understood by everyone.

The next day, he met up again with his friend Burr and they spent a few days touring the numerous relics of the old Chinese Dynasties that permeated the Peking area.

On September 11th, Pat was enjoying breakfast in the restaurant at the Grand Hotel. He was reading the English morning paper which reported on the arrival of General John Pershing and 25,000 U.S. Army veterans in New York. There was a photo on the front page of the huge ticker-tape parade for the general and the boys back from Europe. It made him miss home for the first time.

He decided he would visit Shanghai for a week and then return to Tianjin for his trip to Yokohama and home again. He spent a week visiting the many sites of Shanghai Province including numerous towns up the Yangtze River. His favorite spot was the peaceful city of Hangzhou. It lay alongside West Lake and was a popular spot for both western and Chinese tourists, alike. But on his second day there, he became restless.

He had been away from home for some time and he felt an impatience he had not experienced since before the war. It seemed his trip to Russia had closed a chapter for him. But now he had a tremendous feeling of urgency, an urgency to get on with his life, to do new things, to take risks again, to make a new mark. Though he'd experienced more than most in his short thirty years, he suddenly realized it had all been a preparation for what surely awaited him next. His health had improved dramatically in the last year. He'd grown accustomed to the occasional aches and pains that would likely never go away. He was young and had wealth. He also knew his fame could open doors that few could access.

After seeing the despair of Russia and the timeworn conditions in China, the United States invigorated him as never before. On the heels of its newly acquired power around the world and an explosion of prosperity at home, America had more promise than ever. Like his grandfather, Pat was determined to cash in.

On September 29th he departed Shanghai for Tianjin on the same small vessel he had before. He checked into the Astor where his trunk was safely secured, having arrived from Vladivostok weeks before. On the morning of October 4th, following breakfast, he was flipping through the English paper, prior to leaving for the Tianjin port.

He was shocked to read that President Wilson had suffered a stroke on September 25th and was paralyzed. On the next day he'd been hit by a heart attack. He was campaigning in the United States to win approval for the Treaty of Versailles and League of Nations. The president would have subsequent strokes that would paralyze his left side and cause significant brain damage. This also weakened his ability to get both the Treaty and League of Nations charter ratified in the Senate. There was strong evidence that Wilson's second wife, Edith was, in reality, serving as acting president since the stroke.

There was one other noteworthy news in the paper that day. The British had finally pulled out of Archangel, the northern seaport of Russia. It was the beginning of the end of their campaign to save Russia from Bolshevism.

Babe Ruth was setting new homerun records every week as post-war baseball returned to its potency with the return of young men from Europe. There was a humorous note about his friend John J. McGraw and his New York Giant baseball team. The Giants had set a record on September 28th, dispensing the Phillies six to one in fifty-one minutes, the shortest professional baseball game in history to that date.

"McGraw probably had a train to catch," quipped Pat. He knew the baseball manager and had spent time amid the social circuit of New York during his touring years. McGraw was an operator and not only managed the Giants team for owner Charles Stoneham, but was invested in a few of Stoneham's projects including the largest racetrack in Havana, Cuba.

"I've got to look him up when I get back," said Pat. "There's a lot of people I need to see."

He recalled Hesser telling him to call when he returned. There was the matter of his farm in Indiana which he wanted to sell to his brother who had returned to Momence after years in California. Before he had left the States, Pat had been approached by any number of people about investing in projects, inventions and ventures that were now popping up all over the victorious United States since the war.

He was in Yokohama on October 5th, boarding the Japanese ship Fushimi Maru bound for Seattle. At Yokohama he wired Hesser, John McGraw and his sister, Clara. He'd wait to call Agnes once he got home. Many of the passengers were Japanese and other Asians. At dinner on the first night Pat met attorney James Yeager and his family. Yeager was a Midwesterner and graduate from University of Michigan. With the U.S. still controlling major portions of the Philippines, Yeager was serving as District Attorney in the Mindanao area. Yeager and his young wife were traveling with their four young children of six years and under. Pat enjoyed their company as the couple was his age. He spent a good number of mornings entertaining one or more of the children, as well.

Most of the Americans and British on board socialized and ate with each other if for no other reason than the language barrier with the Asians. Bernard Lambert, who worked for the Hong Kong Shanghai Bank took some time to talk to Pat about his personal finances and logical ways to invest his money. His knowledge of the post-war market was highly valuable due to the fluid nature of world economies as 1920 approached. Lambert would be in New York in a month and suggested Pat look him up next time he was in town. Lambert would introduce him to some investment people that could help. Pat indicated he would contact him in about three weeks.

Finally, Pat spent most of his time visiting with Francois Quentin. Quentin was a flying engineer who knew nearly every Allied and enemy aircraft deployed in the war. He was French but spoke fluid English. Pat met him on his first day aboard at dinner. The two men hit it off quite well, talking about aircraft, aviation in general, and exchanging strong opinions about the merits of one plane verses another. Both were lifetime students of flying and their long conversations filled much of the idle time across the Pacific.

Quentin has just spent the last eight months in Vladivostok, traveling to Omsk and back a number of times. On the day before the Fushimi Maru arrived in Seattle, the two aviators were out on the deck, sitting in the afternoon sun and conversing as they had all week, enjoying one of Quentin's latest wine suggestions.

"So, Quentin," Pat inquired, "was Vladivostok a mess when you first got there or has all that just happened in the last few months?"

"Oh la' la', no, it was a mess the whole time I was there, Pat," the Frenchman responded. "You see, from the very start everyone had a different reason for being there. From Vladivostok to Omsk it has been the most ridiculous thing I have ever witnessed," he said shaking his head. "Now, with the Czechs racing to get out, it will be worse." He took a sip of wine.

Since the start of the Revolution, the Czech Legion controlled the Trans-Siberian Railroad from Omsk to Vladivostok. They were loyal supporters of the Whites but they were not railroad men. The weak rail bed was being crushed by overloaded trains, full men and armaments that ran round-the-clock. By November of 1918, the line was falling apart. If the railroad shut down it would halt every Allied initiative across Siberia. Essentially, the war in Siberia was a war along the Trans-Siberian railroad so it was a critical asset.

The Allies called on President Wilson to find someone to handle the mess. America had just spent the last fifty years covering its landscape with the most advanced rail technology in the world. The solution had to come from the United States. Europe was in ruins.

Wilson appointed John Frank Stevens to take over. Stevens was likely the only man on earth that could save the railroad. He had built the Great Northern Railway and had been appointed Chief Engineer for the Panama Canal by President Taft in 1905, completing the nearly impossible task with American technology and personal tenacity.

"Well, the Czechs were clearly scrambling to get out when I was there," Pat responded.

"Of course," Quentin said. "There is no reason for them to be there now. The Reds have clearly won. Although it will take months to gain control of Siberia, Kolchak is finished in Omsk. It is a sad state of affairs, these Russians."

Quentin took another drink of wine and then added, "The thing I worry about is who will likely replace the Czechs once they are gone."

"How do you mean?" Pat asked.

"Look here, my American friend," Quentin said leaning in. They were obviously on a Japanese ship and Francois glanced around quickly before speaking next to Pat in hushed tones.

"Think about it. The United States, they send in what…5,000 men into Siberia? 7,000 perhaps?" Quentin said.

"Yes, I would say seven to eight thousand," Pat confirmed.

"Well, the Japanese, they sent in 70,000 troops," Quentin said, "parading up and down the street, never getting too involved, just making sure everyone knows they are there. I tell you, O'Brien, they cannot be trusted. These Japanese, they are very dangerous. They want Manchuria, they are ruthless and frankly they are in Russia to…how you say it in English? 'Pick up the pieces,' yes?"

"I think you are correct," Pat said. "I do not like them. They are just like the barbarians we experienced all along the railroad only their uniforms match".

That drew a laugh from Quentin.

"It is so obvious to me they want to control this region and the south Pacific as well," Quentin said. "We French, we are not that pleased the United States is in control of the Philippines for example, but we would much rather have you there than the Japanese. They cannot be trusted."

Little did Pat know how prophetic Quentin's words were. There was general feeling among all Allied armies that the Japanese would assist only if they could strengthen their own position. Few believed they were in Russia to support the Whites. Their strategy from the beginning was to take what they could from the spoils of the civil war and let the Reds and Whites fight to the death. It mattered little to them. They wanted territory.

"But you Americans are in a very strong position now," Quentin said. "Your country is not torn to bits, as is France, and you are on the winning side. Europe will need you now. You will become the great power. You already are the most important power."

"I think you are right Quentin," Pat said. "But Europe is a mess. You will have to mend your own fences."

"What is this fences you speak about?" Quentin asked.

"Oh, nothing," Pat said, chuckling a bit. "It's an American slang. It means you repair the fence between your property and your neighbor's property. It means to reconcile."

"Perhaps you will show us how to fix this fence?" Quentin said.

"We have our own fences to fix back home," Pat said.

"Ah, yes, 'reconcilier' at home, we have this also," exclaimed the Frenchman.

Angry over the loss of their jobs held before the war, returning veterans were rioting in three dozen cities across the U.S. Their target was the Negro. Despite the fact that the Army was still segregated, over 350,000 black Americans served in the war but those that did not, approximately 500,000 black men, filled many of the jobs vacated by the over four million white soldiers who fought.

"I have read that there are riots in the streets at home," Pat said, looking out to sea. "White veterans are lynching black men. It's horrible. I don't understand this. Unlike our fathers who returned to the family farm following the Civil War, these men are returning to the factory, the job site or office to find they have been replaced. The New York Times even went so far as to blame the Bolsheviks for instigating these race riots."

"This is unique to America," Quentin said. "Yes, we have these problems with demobilization at home but we do not have the feelings toward the Negro as do you Americans. This will be a big challenge for your country."

Pat and Quentin visited until dusk. They promised to stay in touch. Quentin would return to France. His war duties were finally complete.

The next morning, October 26th, the Fushimi Maru pulled into port at Seattle, around ten. It was good to see American soil once again Pat thought. The port was teeming with as many ships as could be crammed into Elliot Bay and the sun was glistening over the entire shore, unusual for the all too frequently overcast skies of the Puget Sound.

It took a long time to get ashore. Pat became impatient with the checking and double-checking of the Japanese and then American immigration officers. The length of his trip weighed on him and he was eager to be home again.

He finally stepped down onto the pier and made his way to the baggage claim area to secure his trunk. Porters were on hand and one assisted Pat with his luggage. They walked to a row of taxis parked at street level. Pat tipped the baggage handler, stepped in and said to the driver, "Sorrento Hotel, please."

Ten minutes later, the cab arrived at the Sorrento, Seattle's first hotel and its finest. His trunk was taken by the bellman. Pat tipped the driver and entered the hotel which had an unusually low lobby ceiling for a hotel of its size. It was ornate and quite pleasant with large wooden beams extending out from a center pillar in the middle of the lobby. It reminded him of so many rooms on a ship, however. He was tired of ships. He smiled, shaking his head at the irony and stepped up to the check-in counter.

"Hello, my name is Pat O'Brien. I have a reservation," Pat said.

"Yes sir," the clerk said. He flipped through his index cards, busily made notes on the necessary paperwork, and then turned to get Pat's key.

"Do you have a long distance phone available in the hotel?" Pat asked.

"Certainly, sir," stated the uniformed clerk. "There are phones booths across the hall," he said pointing in their direction.

"Can you change a few bills for me?" Pat asked.

"Certainly," the Clerk said. "For the phone, sir?"

"Yes," Pat responded. "How much would you estimate a call to San Francisco would cost?"

"Well, we have post-pay phones so I will give you ten dollars in coins but if you need more the operator will cut in at the end of your call," the young man stated. "If you run out, she will wait for you to get more change."

Pat handed the man a ten dollar bill. Long distance calls were expensive in those days. He reached into his pocket and pulled out the number of the City of Paris Store in San Francisco.

"Here you are, sir," the clerk said, handing him a cloth bag full of coins. Pat walked over to the bank of phones.

"Hello, operator," he said. "Could you please connect me to 'Redwood 4767?"

"Which city are you calling, sir?" asked the operator

"Oh, I'm sorry ma'am," Pat responded. "San Francisco, Redwood 4767."

"Thank you," the operator said.

Pat heard a number of clicks and pops on the line as the operator connected his call. After about two minutes, the phone rang. It rang eight times, then suddenly a female voice answered.

"City of Paris Store, fifth floor employee room," said the young female voice on the other end.

"Hello, I am calling for Agnes MacMillan," Pat said. "Is she there? I mean do you know if she is working today?"

"Which department, sir?" replied the girl.
"I'm not certain, ladies department somewhere," Pat said.

"One moment sir, I will check with the floor supervisor. Can I tell them who's calling?"

"O'Brien, ma'am," Pat said. "Pat O'Brien."

"Matt Ryan?" the women said who was finding it difficult to hear Pat on the line.

Pat spoke up, "No, Pat O'Brien, ma'am. O'Brien's the name, ma'am."

"One moment, Mr. O'Brien," the young woman said.

Elise Wunder exited the staff room to look for Mr. Marshall, the supervisor. She found him reviewing procedures with a new stock boy.

"Mr. Marshal, sir," Wunder said. "There is a telephone call for Agnes MacMillan. It's long distance, sir."

"Long distance!" Marshall responded. "MacMillian you say? Check for her in the lingerie department."

"Thank you, sir," the young woman said. She was seventeen, tall and skinny with a rather gnawing high-pitched voice.

Agnes was busy placing women's corsets on a new display table in the lingerie department. Wunder saw her bending over and carefully placing a price sign at the back of the display as she approached.

"Hello, I'm looking for Agnes MacMillan," Wunder said. "Do you know her?"

"I am her, honey," Agnes said.

"There's a telephone call for you ma'am," Wunder said, "a long distance call."

"Long distance?" Agnes said. She stood upright and stepped back from the table, turned to step away with the woman and then suddenly froze in her tracks.

"Where is the call coming from, sweetie?" Agnes asked.

The young girl responded, "He didn't actually say, ma'am. He didn't actually say."

"It was a man's voice, then?" Agnes asked.

"Oh, I remember now," said the young girl. "The operator did say, 'hold one moment for a long distance call from Seattle'."

Agnes knew who it was.

"I cannot take the call right now," Agnes said. "Tell the operator I am not here today."

"But ma'am…"responded the young girl.

"Just tell them," Agnes said, interrupting the girl's plea with a smile.

Meanwhile, Pat had been waiting for a good ten minutes. He dug into his pocket to make sure he had plenty of tens to cover the call.

"Hello," Wunder said, returning to the phone. "Hello, are you there?"

"Yes, I'm here," Pat responded. "Is that you, Agnes?"

"Know sir, this is not Agnes," Wunder said. "She is not working today. She is not here."

Pat's heart sunk. "Well, do you know if she's coming in later?" Pat asked.

"I wouldn't know sir," Wunder responded. "I could go ask her supervisor."

"No, that's fine," Pat said, frustrated with complication of the whole matter. "I'll try calling this afternoon."

"Ok, sorry sir, goodbye," the young woman said. She then slowly hung up the phone while staring off to the side, wondering what just happened.

Pat called again at 3:10, then one more time at 4:00. Agnes was not available.

"I really am sorry, sir," Wunder said. "You sound like a very nice man, sir. Apparently she is not coming in today but I can check if you'd like."

"No, that's fine," Pat responded. "I've bothered you too much already. Thank you for helping me young lady."

"You're welcome, sir," Wunder said, blushing just a bit.

"That's odd," he thought. "It's Friday. Maybe she took the day off." Thinking it over quickly, he then said out loud as he walked up the stairs to his room, "But she always works Friday. Friday's are big days for her!" It confused him.

Before he went to dinner, Pat sent a few telegrams. He sent one to his sister Clara indicating he was in Seattle and safely home. In it he indicated he'd be home "in a few days". He wired Hesser, simply stating, "I'm back. Staying at the Sorrento in Seattle if you need to reach me." He then wired his old friend and manager Lee Keedick saying, "Hey chum, I'm back from Russia. At Sorrento Hotel in Seattle. Expect to be in New York in a week or two. Let's have dinner."

Pat had dinner in the hotel, alone. He thoroughly enjoyed reading nearly every single word of the Seattle Times. "It sure is good to read an American newspaper again," he thought to himself.

On page two Pat read a detailed story about the huge strike that had occurred in Seattle the previous February referred to as "Seattle General Strike of 1919." It was a five-day general work stoppage by over 65,000 workers. Dissatisfied workers in several unions struck to gain higher wages after two years of World War I wage controls. Most other local unions, including members of the American Federation of Labor and the Industrial Workers of the World, joined the walkout. Although the strike was non-violent and lasted less than a week, government officials and much of the public viewed the strike as a radical attempt to subvert US institutions.

Pat was baffled reading the final paragraph that attributed the strike to "the work of Bolsheviks and other radicals inspired by un-American ideologies."

"How strange," Pat exclaimed. "How in the world does this man think the Bolsheviks have time to mess in our affairs? Something's happening in the country. Vets are rioting in thirty cities and men are walking off the job."

He reflected on the fence building conversation with Quentin. Somehow the whole thing made little sense to Pat. "It's the Japanese we have to worry about. Not the 'indomitable Bolsheviks.' They can't even get control of their own country let alone take over ours."

Many commentators were raising such alarms. The Seattle story was one of the first concentrations of anti-Red hysteria that erupted in the U.S. following the war. It would develop into the Red Scare of 1919 and 1920. Reporters read stories of the dramatic Russian Revolution and it fueled their rationales for events at home. In fact, the labor activities around the country in 1919 were not unusual in a post-war environment. But the "Bolshevik angle" sold papers. No one was writing about the Japanese. But the veterans, who witnessed their activities from Vladivostok to Manila Bay, knew. The Japanese Navy, in particular, would be a force to be reckoned with some day.

Pat glanced down at his watch. It was nearly eight o'clock. The City of Paris Store would be closing by now. He'd try Agnes again in the morning. If he couldn't reach her he thought, perhaps he could reach Arlene. After all, Agnes just might be on vacation. Perhaps up at the Redwood territory they visited so many times before.

The next day, he called the store at 9:00 a.m. hoping he might catch Agnes before her shift. She was not available. He dialed the last number he had for Arlene.

"Hello," said a female voice on the other line.

"Hello, I'm looking for Arlene Stevens." Pat responded.

"This is Arlene," said the voice. "How can I help you?"

"Arlene, it's Pat. Pat O'Brien," Pat said sounding a little harried. "How are you?"

"Pat, hello, I'm fine," she responded a little startled. "Where are you?"

"I'm in Seattle, Arlene," Pat said. "I've just returned from Russia."

"Oh my," she said. "How was your trip?"

"Oh, fine. It was fine," Pat responded. "Listen Arlene, have you seen Agnes? I've been calling the store and she doesn't seem to be around. Have you seen her?"

"Well, yes, I saw her about a week ago," Arlene responded. "Where did you call her, at the store?"

"Yes, the woman's store," Pat said. "I've called two or three times. She's not been at work apparently and no one seems to know when she might be back in."

"Are you coming to San Francisco, Pat?" Arlene asked.

"Well, I was thinking about it, but I'd like to talk to Agnes first," Pat said.

The words, "thinking about it" gave even Arlene a chill and she was just a friend.

Arlene felt she needed to respond right way, in some way. What would Agnes want her to say? Agnes had told her that Pat had called the store. "What should I do?" were Agnes' words to her friend. It had been over five months since Pat and Agnes saw each other. Agnes had begun to get on with her life.

Work at the store was going quite well and she had recently been promoted. Less than a week earlier, she had paid her first visit to the Hughes' since giving up Carol. Carol was a boisterous happy baby and Agnes was starting to feel like the arrangement just might work fine. She was referred to as "Aunt Agnes" by Vesta so as to prepare Carol for future visits when the baby would become aware of her family.

"Pat," Arlene swallowed hard. "It's been a long time for Agnes, not hearing from you for such a long time. You have to see how it must be for her. Perhaps she needs some time right now. Perhaps you both need time."

"Time!" Pat exclaimed a little too loud than he intended. "Good Lord, I've been gone for five months, I've finished my war, I'm home now. There's been a lot of time already. I just wanted to see her. Do you know where she is? Has she spoken to you or is this your own opinion?"

"I'm sorry, Pat" I didn't mean to upset you. I..."

"I'm not upset," he said interrupting her. Calming himself he said, "I was just wondering if you'd seen her, might know where she is, that's all. I've just been trying to get ahold of her."

"Well, are you coming here?" Arlene said.

"If she is there, I will have time to come down to the Bay before I head home. I have meetings in New York in a few weeks and, of course, want to spend some time with my mother and family but yes, I have time to come to San Francisco. That's why I've been trying to reach her, that's all."

"Perhaps, if you cannot reach her, you should take time to go home, get settled in, go to your meetings and then it might be a better time," Arlene said, attempting to lead him in another direction. She really did not want to reveal Agnes' current intentions.

"But I'm here now," Pat pleaded. "Do you think you can help me locate her?"

"Well, I'm in Richmond now but my husband and I are leaving for the San Joaquin as soon as I get off work. I might not see her," she said holding up a firm façade. The story of her trip was totally erroneous.

"Well, ok. I'm sorry to have concerned you with this," Pat said. "Perhaps I'll try again before I leave for home."

He hung up the phone in complete despair. "What the hell is so hard about finding her?" he said to himself out of frustration. He walked somewhat aimlessly across the lobby toward the restaurant. For some reason that low ceiling, the crush of his phone call with Arlene, the whole idea of being in a hotel the entire day waiting to make a phone call to someone who may or may not be there, rattled him to no end.

"I can't hang around here all day, wasting a day, not knowing if she is there or not," he said loud enough for others to hear. "I've got to get out of here and get on a train home."

And with that, he hurriedly rushed over to the counter, checked out of his room, ordered a cab and was on his way to the Seattle train station with his trunk, a large bag of items he'd brought with him from Asia, and a degree of integrity still in tack as a result of his own personal encouragement.

Pat had planned to take the train south to the Bay area and then switch to the main line east to Chicago. To do so now seemed like a detour to him. He had wanted to call her from the station in Oakland. If he couldn't reach her he'd likely have another two to four hours of downtime before he could head east. Depending on the time of day, it could mean an overnight stay until the morning. Then there was his trunk, a place to stay and all this added up to a last minute decision.

"I'd like a ticket to Minneapolis, please," he told the ticket agent. Pat would take none other than John Frank Stevens' own Great Northern Railroad from Seattle directly across the northern plains to Minneapolis and from there to Chicago and home. He had made the decision to by-pass San Francisco.

PART TEN

VIRGINIA

Chapter 49

McGraw

The view across the Rockies was equally as beautiful as the southern route which Pat had usually taken in the past. The great mountains looked more like the route across Canada he'd seen in 1917.

"Good God, it's been nearly two years since Borden," Pat thought to himself. "Let's see, I think it was December of that year when I left Vancouver for Toronto."

He spent a good portion of the first afternoon thinking about his days with the Signal Corps, the move to Canada and the "Original 18" that bolted out of Borden ready for anything. Naturally, this brought him back to memories of Raney, his buddy. His sad feelings for Paul never really faded over the last two years.

Pat had a light dinner in the dining car about 8:00 p.m. and then decided to go to bed. It had been a long day. He finished off the last of his wine and looked out at the darkening view from his window.

"Well, buddy, I did what I could," he said softly, reflecting on Paul. "I hope you feel I did my best."

He retired to his bunk and slowly drifted off to sleep, holding on to those final visions from the sky over Siberia where he and a British tail gunner, punctuated the end of his war. He fell into a deep sleep.

The next day, Pat's train arrived in Minneapolis about 11:00 a.m. He had about a one hour layover and then headed south for Chicago on the Chicago, Burlington & Quincy line. He arrived at the Northwestern Train Station about 8:00 p.m. He decided he was too tired to make the final leg to Momence so he transferred his trunk to LaSalle Street station for overnight storage, grabbed his bag, and took a cab to the Palmer House.

After checking in, he walked out on Wabash Avenue and bought a Tribune from a small kid in a cap. He was really eager to read some local news. He sat in the ornate lobby of the hotel on the second floor as people came and went unnoticed.

As usual, the paper enthralled him. There was a small article marking three months since of the Red Scare riots that had gripped Chicago in the summer. The Chicago riots were among the worse claiming twenty-five black Chicagoans, fifteen white and over 500 casualties of both races. The influenza epidemic had also attacked the city. Many had already perished, by the time Pat arrived. More than 20,000 Chicagoans would die before the year was up.

"Wow, look at that," Pat said under his breath. He'd come across a photo of the Goodyear dirigible called "Wingfoot" that crashed in the middle of downtown on July 21. It had mysteriously caught fire and crashed through the skylight of the Illinois Trust and Savings Bank.

"Those damn balloons never were trustworthy," Pat thought.

Page two had a map entitled "Russian War Movements" which Pat perceived was likely three weeks behind reality. There was a photo of Parisians dancing in the street the previous June in celebration of the signing of the Treaty of Versailles.

On the local page, strikes by garbage workers and others had crippled the city over the summer. A young girl, missing since spring, turned up murdered by a predator. And "Big Bill" Thompson, mayor of Chicago was announcing his plans for 1920 after winning re-election in April. Pat had a particular distain for Thompson because of the mayor's well-known pro-German and anti-British feelings before the war. "Kaiser Bill," as some called him, had actually organized public book-burnings destroying pro-British books taken from the public schools.

Pat spent some considerable time reading financial news which had recently become of interest to him with his accumulation of moderate wealth. Since armistice, the war-levy had converted to an income tax but was not sufficient, prompting lawmakers in Washington to adopt a wide range of excise taxes. Some were paid by manufacturers, including the makers of cars, tennis rackets, firearms, cameras, hunting knives, chewing gum, candy, and cosmetics, and some were on private club dues and a host of other goods and services including ice creams sodas. He chuckled and thought of Jensen's drug store when he read of this.

Pat flipped to the sports page. In bold print across the top of the page it read, "Comiskey Denial May Not Be Enough." On October 15, Charles Comiskey, owner of the Chicago White Sox, denied that any of his players were involved in a plot to throw the 1919 World Series against Cincinnati.

The heavily favored Sox had lost the Series on October 9 and allegations of a fix began circulating around baseball almost immediately. Reporter Hugh Fullerton wrote that sources he could not yet name had evidence that gambling was a factor in the series. Without naming names, he wrote that investigators had tipped him that the money trail was extensive, not limited to south side gaming rooms or the mob-operated parlors on the north side. The money was big and its source was not Chicago.

Pat was returning to a different country than he once knew before the war. He noticed a story about a bill in congress that was expected to pass the next day, something called the Volstead Act. It would be the Eighteenth Amendment prohibiting the manufacture, sale and transportation of alcoholic beverages in the United States. He decided to go out for a nightcap.

The next morning, Pat departed on an 8:00 a.m. train south to Momence. When he arrived, Al was there with his new car. Sitting in the front seat was his sister, Clara. As the train pulled up, he could see them both hurry out of the car and run up to the platform.

"Pat!" exclaimed Clara, running up to him with a big hug. Pat kissed his sister and held her for some time before his life-long buddy walked up. Pat extended his right hand to Al still holding on to Clara. The three stepped down off the platform. A young lad wheeled Pat's trunk to the car and the three lifted it up into the back seat.

"Damn, you still have that trunk, huh?" said Al.

"Yep, dragged it all across Asia," said Pat. "Look, I've got stickers from everywhere. Shows where I've been - Japan, China, Russia, it was very reliable. I didn't take it on the long run into central Siberia though. I figured it was too attractive and would probably get stolen anyway!"

"Well, it did its job then," responded Al

Turning to Clara, Pat asked, "Where's ma?"

"She's coming, Pat," responded Clara. "She's staying with Lila in Lowell. Ben's bringing her over in about a half hour. We planned a lunch for all of us at my place.

"Sounds good, Clara," said Pat. "You still have access to a phone, right?"

"My word, Pat, everyone has a phone these days," Clara said. "Well, not everyone but certainly many more than did even last winter. But yes, I have mine."

"I also need to wire a number of people while I'm here," responded Pat.

"Yes, you can wire at the Progress office," indicated Clara. "Gosh, you just got home from Russia and you've got business cooking already?

"Why sure, you know me sis, no time to waste, you know," said Pat with a big smile.

"Today we just all want to hear about your trip," said Clara. "Promise me, now, no business today, Pat. Mother wants to hear about your trip too."

"Ok, I promise," responded Pat.

"So how was it, Pat," asked his good friend Al.

"Al, you can't believe what a mess it is there," responded Pat with passion in his voice. "I mean you saw France, sure that was bad but the battle front was at lease defined there. Hell, in Russia, there's 15, 16 as many 20 different armies all fighting with each other in every direction. Where I was all the action was up and down their big railroad."

"Is that right," responded Al. "Did you get in on anything?"

"One time, one time, Al," said Pat, now with even more exuberance. Clara turned and looked at him half surprised and half concerned.

"I spent most of my time on a Red Cross train there with some really wonderful folks, and we had our troubles with the Cossacks and others," said Pat. "But this one day we came upon a group of four Brit planes, half assemble on rail cars. They would spend each day running up and down the railroad sabotaging the Reds. They'd pull up, throw the wings on, take off and dive on some enemy up the railroad a ways, return and scurry off once again."

"So what happened?" pleaded Al.

"Well, there were about 15 Red soldiers five miles down track from us. The Brit's plan was to take up three planes and catch the Reds from behind but one of their pilots was real sick, so I pushed my way in and flew the third plane," said Pat.

"Oh, good Lord, Pat," said Clara. "You shouldn't have done that. You'll kill yourself."

Al and Pat roared with laughter.

"Well, I already did," said Pat still catching his breath.

Then turning back to Al, "So we went up in Harry Tates, you know, those two-seaters with the tail gunner facing away?"

"Yeah," urged Al

"We were the third of the three to dive, we delayed a bit from the others mind you, the dove in and took the last of the patrol out," Pat was very excited now, swishing his right arm through the air as pilots often do when telling stories of their air battles.

"Oh, you two are terrible, just like when you were kids," Clara said scolding them with a big smile on her face.

The two old friends went on back and forth until the car pulled up to Clara's place. Elmer was there. He'd just arrived from the farm in Morocco, Indiana. Elmer was now divorced and moved back from California. His brother Ivan and wife and Alma had moved to town and so Elmer was running Pat's farm.

"Pat! So good to see you," exclaimed Elmer.

The group walked up stairs to Clara's apartment. About twenty minutes later, Margaret arrived. Pat thought she might be moving a bit slower since he saw her last. She'd been under the weather but was generally doing well. The family visited through the afternoon. Ben Worley returned to Lowell after dropping off Margaret then came back again around six for dinner. He brought Lila with him who was thrilled to see Pat. Lila had rested most of the afternoon, feeling particularly touched by her rheumatism that day. Her spirits picked up greatly seeing Pat.

Dinner extended into the evening. Al stayed the whole time and a few other family friends popped in. The Worley's and Margaret headed back and Pat and Elmer stayed at Clara's. After Clara turned in, the men went to a local tavern in town to enjoy what they determined could be the last beer of their life, what with prohibition being passed that day.

"Oh, hell, we don't have to worry about that," said Al. "There's a still in every corner of that Marsh out there. If Momence men really need a shot of booze, there won't be any trouble finding it here."

The next morning, Clara was off to shop about 10:00 a.m. Elmer had headed back and Pat was alone in the apartment and figured it would be a good time to try Agnes, one more time.

"San Francisco Redwood 4767," Pat said to the operator. "Yes, ma'am, California."

More pops and clicks and then the phone rang. A female voice answered,

"City of Paris Store, 5th Floor employee room," was the familiar response.

"Calling for Agnes MacMillian," said Pat.

"Sure, one moment," said the voice, this time the person that answered was not the young girl.

Agnes was in the employee room no more than three feet from the phone.

"Here you are kid, it's for you," said Hazel Grummund, handing Agnes the phone. Agnes was hurriedly checking in for the day. She didn't think twice and grabbed the receiver.

"Hello," Agnes said.

"Agnes, is that you?" it's Pat.

"Pat," said Agnes, stunned.

"I'm so glad I reached you," replied Pat. "Did Arlene tell you I called?"

"I've not seen her," replied Agnes. "I think she and her husband when on vacation."

"I wanted to see you," said Pat. "But no one at the store could locate you. Have you been on vacation?" Even that sounded stupid to Pat as soon as the words came out of his mouth. "I mean, did you work Friday?"

"Where are you, Pat," said Agnes.

"Well, I'm home," Pat replied haltingly. "I'm back from Russia."

"Yes?" Agnes replied with no anticipation of where the conversation would go next.

"How's work?" said Pat, another stupid question he thought.

"Work's fine," said Agnes. Now determined to move the conversation along she continued. "Are you in San Francisco?"

"No," said Pat. "I'm back in Chicago. Well, Momence actually. I'm here, at home, visiting family."

Agnes did not respond. There was silence. Pat continued.

"I didn't want to stop unless I knew you were there," I was rather hung up in Seattle so I figured, well, I'll get home, get things settled and then get back out to the Bay area after checking in at home."

"Yes?" said Agnes, again intentionally at a loss for words.

"I've got meetings in New York in about two weeks and then Washington, then I'll likely be out your way and we can spend some time together," said Pat.

"Pat, look," said Agnes, but not in an angry tone. "You've been gone a long time. You've got other plans on the east coast." She paused. "I mean, Pat, I do love you, but I just don't think our relationship can work. We're on such opposite polls in our lives. You have things you must do, and I have...I have things...I have to go on with my life, too. Even if two people love each other, sometimes circumstances just don't allow them to be together for more than a short time. This happens all the time. It happened to many of my girlfriends all through the war. It certainly has happened to us. I think we should both go our separate ways, Pat."

She was angry with herself for talking too long and saying too much. Of course, mentioning Carol never rose in her consciousness. That was off the table a long time ago. Barring a plea from Pat to "please take him back" with language that convinced her, Pat understood why she had not reacted the way he'd hoped. There was no way it could work, if she didn't want it to.

Agnes had already decided weeks back. She had to move on.

"You want to move on, then?" said Pat in a low tone.

"I think it's the only way at this point," replied Agnes, feeling strong again.

[651]

"Well, ok Agnes," replied Pat. "I'm just a bit surprised. But, ok. I understand. I love you, Agnes," he said weakly.

Agnes held. No response gave Pat a clear message but, in fact, Agnes was in tears on the other line. She loved him, too, but there was no way to make it work. Pat interpreted it as one might expect. She was done with him, he thought.

"Good bye, Agnes," said Pat.

"Good bye, Pat" said Agnes in a slightly raised tone.

As they had done once before, they both hung up the phone at the same time, very slowly.

Pat walked over to the sink and drew a glass of water. He stared out of the kitchen window. "That didn't work so well, did it?" he said, clearly talking to himself.

Thoughts ran through his head in rapid succession.

"There must be some other guy involved. I wonder if she's sick or something and can't tell me. Didn't we leave each other before Russia on good terms? I thought she agreed that my going to Russia was something I had to do. She didn't seem that urgent then. What happened to change her mind? Why didn't she try to reach me if something changed while I was gone?

He took another sip of water then went on. Oh, that was stupid. How in the hell was she supposed to reach me? I wonder if I just was gone too long. I really don't think she had another boyfriend. But she could have. I mean, she's not a wall-flower. She goes after what she wants. I mean she really did see my need to pursue one more campaign in Russia. She got that. I guess I never thought enough about what she might want."

He reached down and filled his glass again, took a sip then froze, continuing his conversation with himself.

"Let's see, when did I leave? It was in the middle of summer, right? It's what now, October? October…" We'll really it's almost November. Wait a minute, let's see, I last saw her, when? It was actually end of May, wasn't it? That's one, two, three… nearly five months. That is a long time. Now that I think about it, it was a long time. Who knows what could have happened? Well, if we're meant to be then, perhaps it will happen someday. She's a wonderful gal. I just know I've got to be ready or it wouldn't work out anyway. It would be foolish to go back to San Francisco and settle in to life as everyone does. And at my age? I'm not even thirty yet. It wouldn't work. She wouldn't be happy that way. I'd be wanting to do things. I mean, what the hell would I do? Go back to working on the Santa Fe? No, that's not for me."

He set down his glass. He turned on the water, grabbed the bar of soap and aggressively washed his hands. He recalled how difficult it was to wash his hands in Russia. Reaching for a towel he dried them with a similar amount of aggression talking out loud as he did.

"Man, I've got to get moving," Pat said. "I've been away too long. If I don't get active again, tons of opportunities are going to pass me by. I feel so behind. The country is so charged up right now. Every day, I read something new. I've never seen the U.S. so hungry for anything that is new. If there's something out there to be had, I'll find it. I'll start tomorrow.

"What's that, Pat?" said Clara who had just walked in carrying a bag of groceries. Pat hadn't heard her come up the stairs. He was thoroughly wrapped up in his thoughts.

"Oh, nothing, Clara, said Pat. "You got more of those?"

"Yes, be a dear and get the other bag," said Clara. "Be careful I bought a cake. I don't want you to drop it!"

"Yes, ma'am!" he said exiting the kitchen with a big salute.

It's one thing to turn a page and Pat had finally done that in Russia. It is another thing to then launch oneself unfettered into an unknown and undeveloped future. Most people flounder during these life transitions. They dream hopelessly of how things were, when unchanged routine provided complacency and ease. It is the minority who press hard into the winds of change with elation and genuine excitement. Still others, very few, drag the wind with them and take all of us to uncharted realities. Thus were the few who dreamt man could fly and of this lot came Pat O'Brien, through no choice of his own, easily seen by all who knew him and equally unexplainable.

Pat would spend a mere fifteen days in Momence. He had ample time with family and friends, including a stop at Jensen's with his buddy Al. Just for kicks, Pat suggested they order an ice cream soda. Sure enough, as he expected, no tax was collected. Apparently, word had not reached Momence.

"When you leaving?" asked Al.

"I'm heading for New York on the 13th. I figured it would be nice to be here for Armistice Day on the 11th.

"Yeah, that would be nice to have you here," said Al. "There's going to be a parade and many of us who served would love to have you march with us!"

"Sure," said Pat. "Naturally, I'd be there."

"Funniest thing," Al continued. "They're planning a two minute suspension of business beginning at 11:00 a.m. on that day. President Wilson declared it. Hell, if we're having a parade in Momence, nobody's going to be open any way."

The two friends got a healthy laugh out of that.

On November 8, Pat and Elmer helped their brother Ivan and his wife Alma move into 376 6th Street in Momence. Alma was expecting at the time. Ivan had been working the farm but now with the baby, it made more sense for them to live in town.

At 11:00 a.m. on November 13, one month before Pat's 29th Birthday, he boarded the train for New York City. He'd been in communications with his buddy Hesser who had his photography studio there, John McGraw who asked him to come out to "talk about some things," and Lee Keedick who he planned to have dinner with that evening. He also was able to set an appointment with the banker Bernard Lambert, whom he had met on the ship home and had promised to arrange a meeting for Pat with some key investment people.

"Thanks for everything, Clara," he told his sister.

"We always enjoy seeing you, Pat," responded Clara. "Particularly mother. Now don't stay away so long this time."

"I won't. I'll be back before you know it," replied Pat and he gave his sister a kiss.

At the same time Pat's train was pulling out of Momence, Charles Stoneham, owner of the New York Giant baseball team was holding a luncheon meeting on the 11th floor of the Astor Hotel with his team's management personnel. They were discussing the upcoming baseball winter meetings which were scheduled in New York December 9. Stoneham had just purchased the team from John T. Bush for an astounding $1 million dollars, the biggest price paid for a team to date. His ownership partner was none other than Giants Manager, John McGraw.

Stoneham and McGraw already had a history together. They were both avid gamblers, operated various establishments around New York and Baltimore and had direct ties to the New York mob scene including the most famous Arnold "The Brain" Rothstein. It was Rothstein who served as middleman for Stoneham's purchase of the Giants. An intense gambler himself, Rothstein was considered the dean of the Jewish mob in New York for a time.

Pat new McGraw well. The two had met during Pat's speaking days and were introduced by Lee Keedick. Recognizing the fame, guts and "potential" in Pat, McGraw had sought him out first in 1918. Since that time, the two men had dinner together every time Pat came to New York. Often, Keedick joined them.

"Don't let me hear that you've come to town and didn't look me up, O'Brien," he once said to Pat. Pat enjoyed his company and his intensity. He was one of the rare matches to Pat's wit and guts. He admired him for that. Both commanded the attention of anyone who met them and were both famous. It's fair to say a bit of a healthy rivalry existed between them.

But they had a lot in common, too. Both were Irish. McGraw's father, like Pat's, fought in the Civil War and also worked on the railroad. Pat often told the baseball manager about railroad work and it gave McGraw some idea about a father he hardly knew. That was the other similarity between the two. Both were separated from their fathers at young ages. Pat was age 11, McGraw, 12. There was one difference. Daniel O'Brien died leaving Pat to fend for himself. McGraw was removed from his father's home after being severely beaten during one of the elder McGraw's drunken binges. This, along with his tough New York upbringing was what made McGraw a bit more edgy than Pat.

Mary Goddard, a widowed neighbor, raised McGraw along with her two sons. Pat had Grandpa Hathaway and the Hansens once he moved to Wyoming. McGraw's early passion was the baseball. For Pat, life revolved around the aeroplane. They played different games but possessed the same passion.

At 16 years old, Johnny McGraw entered professional baseball. He had little of the physical stature of Pat. He stood barely 5'7" and weighed little more than 100 lbs., but that didn't stop him from becoming a star. In 1890, the year Pat was born, one of McGraw's teammates, former National Leaguer Al Lawson organized a winter tour in Cuba. McGraw went along and played shortstop for the "American All-Stars."

McGraw's fiery personality made him fascinating to contemporaries outside sports. Gamblers, show-business people, and politicians were drawn to him. He'd ventured into Vaudeville for 15 weeks in 1912, appearing with such acts as "Odiva the Goldfish Lady." He still maintained interest in the theatre and had some investments in the entertainment world of New York as a result of this early experience. Again, similar experiences to Pat's

But the future Hall of Famer was a baseball man at his core. As the Giants manager, he administered harsh tongue-lashings to his players and frequently fought with umpires. He was ejected from 118 contests during his career, far more than any other manager. Arlie Latham, former player and later part of Giants operations, once said of him "McGraw eats gunpowder every morning for breakfast and washes it down with warm blood."

As his celebrity grew, McGraw became increasingly involved in various, often questionable, off-field activities, most notably gambling and other enterprises associated with the underworld of New York. For a while McGraw owned a famous poolroom in Manhattan with Rothstein. Thus, it was gambling that brought McGraw, Stoneham and Rothstein together.

As Pat's train sped east toward New York he looked again at the telegram McGraw had sent to him. He read again the sentence containing the words, "talk about some things." Pat knew how McGraw was. He was a straight talker. Something had to be cooking for McGraw to use such vague words.

"Well, maybe it's just something he couldn't put in a telegram," Pat thought to himself.

That "something" was about to get underway. At 12:30, Stoneham, owner of the Giants, cut into everyone's desert and began the important business of the afternoon.

"Alright, let's get started here," said the bellicose Stoneham. "You ready, Mac?" he said to his manager McGraw."

"Sure, let's go," replied McGraw.

Like all men involved in big things, Stoneham seldom had unimportant meetings. Meetings were, after all, highly unproductive. But they were necessary, not to plan but to convince. Men like Stoneham decided more than they planned. McGraw was no different. Thus meetings such as these were designed to put people in a room and convince them of the plan. The big decisions were made by only a few, not in big meetings but in small parlors with drinks and closed doors.

Such was the nature of this meeting. Stoneham had laid things out with McGraw three days before. Assisting in taking notes and offering occasional advice was Ben Short, one of Stoneham's personal attorneys. Today's meeting was actually four meetings held in the same location, back-to-back with different people. Only those that needed to hear each topic needed to be there. At no time would there be anyone present that didn't need to be. And most certainly, only those that needed "convincing" would be invited. That's how men with big ideas keep things close.

There were four meetings planned. First, meeting "A" was about the upcoming winter meetings. It was strictly about baseball. Therefore, present were Stoneham, McGraw, player-coach Christy "Matty" Mathewson and Larry "Laughing Larry" Doyle, the second base captain who had the full trust of manager McGraw. The men discussed players, prospects and various proposals expected at the December meeting, including rule proposals, some of which McGraw found ridiculous. As a player, McGraw had used every trick he could to curtail opposing offences including tripping base runners. "McGraw used every low and contemptible method that his erratic brain could conceive to win a play by a dirty trick," wrote one reporter.

Meeting "A" was finished. McGraw dismissed his men and in came two attorneys. Ben Short was the team's attorney and the second was Morgan Frumber who specialized in legal contracts.

"Hi, men," said McGraw to the two.

Stoneham greeted them also and they set their briefcases on the table, pulling out a number of papers. Just then there was a knock at the door.

"Yeah!" said McGraw.

A hotel steward, who had been standing outside the door, opened it, allowing a man in. It was Ban Johnson, Founder and President of the American League.

"Hello, Ban," said Stoneham.

"Ban, how are you?" added McGraw extending his hand.

All five took their seats and meeting number two began. The American League was in a complicated state following the 1919 season. The Yankees, Boston and Chicago White Sox dominated the league and it threatened to destroy it. Cleveland, Detroit, Washington, Philadelphia and the St. Louis Browns still struggled. In the case of Johnson, these were the teams he had brought into the group to actually form the "junior division."
Johnson began the conversation.

"Now, as you know the Yankees currently play in your stadium at the Polo Grounds," said Johnson. "They're the number two team in New York, but they continue to draw respectfully."

"Yes, that is true," said Stoneham.

"Well, there's talk," said Johnson. "Just talk, mind you, but I have it on very good authority that Boston is about to sell the young kid Ruth to the Yanks."

"So," said McGraw shrugging his shoulders. "So, somebodies getting traded, big deal."

"Hey, don't kid yourself, Mac," responded Johnson. "This kid is going to turn baseball upside down. Nobody hits like Ruth."

"So, what do you want us to do about it," inserted Stoneham.

Well, I've got the Yankees, Boston Red Sox and Chicago White Sox on one side," Johnson explained, and the other five clubs that I brought in, on the other. I'm trying to build a league here, for Christ's sake. The big three, including my old buddy Comiskey, fight with me on everything I propose." His voice rose exposing the desperate nature of the current situation. Stoneham saw it as a weakness.

"What do you want me to do about it," responded Stoneham.

"Look, if the Yankees sign Ruth, they become more competitive and they'll outdraw the Giants," he said adding, "And you're renting to them."

"That's Bull," replied McGraw in his usual style.

"No, wait, John," said Stoneham to his partner. "Let's hear him out."

Johnson had formed the American League out of a minor league organization. Though he had more teams supporting him, the powerful New York, Boston and Chicago teams controlled his league. Their talent and influence usually swayed two of Johnson's five to vote against him. He needed to weaken one of the big three.

"Look, Chuck, you're in the National League," said Ban. "Your concern is to protect your gate in New York. If Ruth comes, you become second fiddle to the Yankees in your own stadium and they're not even in your league. I've got a plan that will guarantee that won't happen and help me at that same time with my situation."

"Ok, cough it up. What's your idea?" backed McGraw, always the urgent one.

"Evict the Yankees," replied Johnson. "They'll be without a stadium and that will give me all I need to force a sale to a more pliable owner, someone I can control."

Stoneham and McGraw were impressed with Johnson's strategy, though they kept it to themselves. They told Johnson, they'd think about it. McGraw offered Johnson a drink but Johnson declined. This was a big meeting for him but only half as serious as his next one planned by "The Brain."

Johnson would take the afternoon train back to Chicago and visit with his old friend, now adversary, Charles Comiskey of the White Sox. The game-fixing gambling rumors that seeped out of the 1919 World Series were not going away. Johnson thought only he knew how real the rumors were. He was wrong. Another man walking up the staircase of the Astor hotel to talk to Giants ownership knew, for a fact, that it was real.

A knock came at the meeting room door. Again, the steward opened the door and in walked, Arnold Rothstein.

Walking towards his associates, the smartly dress money-man was removing his gloves, one figure at a time.

"So, how did your afternoon of meetings go, gentleman?" he said placing his belongs on the seat to his right.

"Oh, you know, baseball business," said McGraw. "This ain't fair, that ain't fair, trade this one, buy that one. Very boring stuff."

Stoneham and Rothstein laughed as the three men took their seats. Meeting number three had begun. The group was getting smaller. It was apparent to these three professional schemers that the real meetings were about to begin.

Stoneham had a close business relationship with Arnold Rothstein, a notorious organized crime boss who ran numerous gambling operations. Rothstein brokered Stoneham's purchase of the New York Giants baseball team earlier in the year. He also co-owned a billiard parlor with McGraw. These three had their hands in everything but clearly, Rothstein was "the guy." He sat at the top of the three-man financial pyramid.

"Let's talk about Havana first," said Rothstein.

"First?" said McGraw. "Is there a second topic?"

"Well, yes, there is," replied Rothstein, "But let's talk about Cuba."

"Well, I agree with you Arnie," said Stoneham. "This whole prohibition thing, while sure it's a blow to our current operations, it does open up tremendous opportunity for us in Cuba.

"I agree," replied Rothstein. "What we have to do now is get to the people that we know have the means, the interest and the time to go down to Cuba. What's the status on your properties there?"

"We're fully on track to open on Thanksgiving day," reported Stoneham. "John's going...when are you going down, John?" he said turning to him.

"I'm supposed to leave on the 19th," said McGraw.

"Good, that's good," so you'll be able to give us a report then?" asked Rothstein.

"Sure," responded McGraw. "But what I hear is that the track is looking good." McGraw and Stoneham were now owners of Oriental Park, the largest race track in Cuba.

"And the hotel?" inquired Rothstein.

"Same time," responded Stoneham. "All that's looking good."

"Excellent gentlemen, excellent," responded Rothstein. "It looks like we can make a lot of money on that island."

Rothstein was generally pleased. With his backing, McGraw and Stoneham now owned the largest race track in Havana, the most elegant hotel and a number of clubs. They were part of a huge movement by American investors, many of them part of the undercover world that flocked to Cuba after the war. Much of this was the result of prohibition which would curtail the operations in the U.S. significantly despite the large number of speakeasies and private clubs offering alcohol. Those customers were limited to people willing to take the risk and capable of paying the price.

"Now, what we need to do is to get the right push behind the whole thing," said Rothstein. "You need to get to your newspaper people, travel groups, social organizations and the elite with money and create a hunger for Havana."

"Hey, I like that," said McGraw. "Hungry for Havana!"

The three men laughed and all took a sip of their wine.

"And get the right type of people down there, "said Stoneham. "Get the right girls there, the right class of folks and bring the celebrities. I mean McGraw you know everyone. Trigger your New York crowd, get the athletes there, you know, stock it with the rich and the famous. Hell, even just the famous will do. If they're famous enough, we'll make them rich."

Again, another laugh from the group.

"For example, said Rothstein, you've got entertainers you know, charlatans, officers from the war, war heroes. Who's that guy that jumped out of a plane, O'Reilly or something?"

"Ha!" laughed McGraw. "He didn't jump out of plane. He was shot down in a plane. He jumped out of a train." He repeated this a few times, the whole group feeling rather light at this point.

Ok, plane, train," said Rothstein, "it sounds the same."

"O'Brien," said McGraw. "The fellow's name is O'Brien."

"Yes, him," said Stoneham. "Get people like that to Cuba and we'll promote the hell out of it and it will bring respectable people with money if, for no other reason, to see and be seen by the rich, famous and beautiful."

"I'm all for it," added Rothstein. "So get things moving. We stand to make a lot of money in that little country."

"In fact, O'Briens' due to arrive," pausing to look at his watch, "hell in about half an hour. We'll be having lunch tomorrow."

"Great, now let's talk about the last thing," Rothstein's tone lowered. The fourth meeting had begun. "This whole White Sox mess, hey?" he said. "I know you've heard about it, right?"

"Sure, we've heard about it," responded Stoneham.

"Hell yes, we heard about it," added McGraw with irony in his voice. "The whole league knows it's out there."

"Well, fine," said Rothstein. "So now listen, boys. We've done a lot of business together and I've backed you very significantly, would you say?"

"Sure Arnold," said Charles. "You know we know that, and we appreciate it."

"Well, what I'm going to tell you, you must hold in complete confidence," said Rothstein. "Few, no, I'd say nobody knows this but some suspect it, and a few government types believe they can prove it."

"So what is it, Roth?" said the impatient McGraw. "Cough it up, man."

Rothstein looked at him a little perturbed but went on. "Well, it's all true. The players, they threw games. I funded the whole damn thing. Meanwhile, with the amount of money I had on the Reds, I made a fortune."

"Jesus, Mary and Joseph," said McGraw.

"And Abraham, mind you," added Rothstein, which got a chuckle from the group.

Rothstein went on. "It may go nowhere. It could impact a lot of people and frankly, I don't know what the effect will be. You fellows just need to lay low and thank your lucky stars that you're not involved. It could even affect our investments in Cuba. If the government proves deal-making, they'll ban everyone associated with it. The only people that will be able to do business around baseball will be the boys hawking programs and selling peanuts."

McGraw and Stoneham were shocked by this information. Not that they were naive and thought gambling never occurred. They were shocked when Rothstein told them. Both McGraw and Stoneham knew immediately that it put them in a very tight box. Two baseball owners now knew what everyone in baseball would soon be clamoring to find out.

"Damn it, Roth!" shouted Stoneham. "Why drag us in to this" He was visibly shaken. "We're baseball owners, for Christ's sake. We can't know this information. You're asking us to keep our mouth shut and this thing could be in court and everyone in baseball could be put on the stand. You know how these government lawyers are. Damn it, Roth!"

"First of all, Chuck," said Rothstein. He always called him "Chuck" when pressuring his business partner. "You don't have to lecture me about how government lawyers act. I think I've had a few on my tail in my time, ok?" Stoneham looked away. "Secondly, I'm not worried about you two spilling the beans. I think you know where your money comes from and I know I can count on you two to keep your mouth shut. I've invested enough in both of you to insure it."

They got this. Rothstein had just turned the tables on them, and knew what he was doing the whole time. Rothstein knew they wouldn't go running to the league after he told them because he'd call in his loans to them. And every day that went by meant that McGraw and Stoneham were more "in" than "out" and that meant Rothstein had more control of them.

Stoneham thought of Comiskey right away. They were good buddies going back to Comiskey's Cincinnati days, but of late he and Comiskey were arch enemies. Still, Charles knew what this could mean. It could not only ruin the White Sox, it could destroy baseball. He also knew his hands were tied.

The men discussed things for another half hour or so, and then shook hands promising absolute confidentiality.

"Now boys, get some nice respectable, good looking people to Havana." Rothstein ordered. "Don't worry about publicity. I'll get the newspapers down there. We need a nice respectable image right now."

Rothstein exited the room still confident that things would work out fine. Stoneham and McGraw were not as certain.

After the war, the lines between gamblers and ballplayers became blurred. Some players were big bettors and some gamblers were former big league players. Most teams had at least one player on the roster willing to help tip a game for a little money. Baseball in 1919, was in the stranglehold of gamblers, and had been for some time. It was a cesspool of men willing to risk all to grab the huge opportunity to become very, very rich.

It was into this shifting quagmire that Pat O'Brien entered as he stepped off the train in New York City, on Friday, November 14th. His train came to a jolting stop and he walked up the platform entering Grand Central Station. He immediately went to a large bank of telephones and called McGraw at the number he'd given him.

"Hello, John," it's Pat. "I just arrived."

"Pat O'Brien," responded McGraw. "Your timing is impeccable, my friend.

Chapter 50

Whirlwind

After making arrangements to meet McGraw the next day for lunch, Pat headed for the dining room to have dinner with Lee Keedick. Most of the time when Pat came to New York, he had dinner with Lee on the first night in town. They were good friends and Lee always had his ear to the ground. He always knew the very latest that was going on in the city. New York opportunities popped up every minute.

"Pat, over here," came a voice as Pat entered the dining room at the Astor Hotel. Lee Keedick had already secured a table along the wall. He rose from his seat, placing his napkin behind him and stepped forward to greet his friend.

"How are you, Pat, said Keedick.

"Great, I'm starving," replied Pat. The two shook hands grabbing each other's forearms, as two close friends often do. They took their seats, Keedick gesturing in a gentlemanly way towards Pat's chair.

"You look great, Pat," said Keedick. "Russia must have been good to you."

"Hardly," said Pat. "I think my sisters cooking the last two weeks brought me back to life, though."

Keedick laughed and then asked. "How is it there? Russia, I mean."

"Let's just say I'm glad to be home safely," replied Pat. "It's still really a mess, even now, a whole year after the end of the war."

"Well, you know, I read things in the paper and hits hard to tell what it's really like," said Keedick.

Before Pat could answer a waiter came forward.

"Can I get you two gentlemen a drink?" said a sharp looking man in tuxedo.

"Pat?" asked Keedick, gesturing toward his friend.

"I'll have a soda water with a lime twist," responded Pat.

"I'll have white wine," Keedick added.

The waiter returned with drinks. Pat and Keedick ordered and then poured headlong into conversation.

Pat talked about Russia, China and the Gobi desert for about fifteen minutes. Keedick found it interesting and ask a number of questions.

"So, now what, Pat," asked Keedick. "What are you doing in town?"

"I hope to look up a few friends and do some business," said Pat. "I met a fellow on the ship home who's going to help me with my investments. I also have a presentation in Washington on the 21st so I have much to do. I'd like to see "Hess" while I'm here. I hear he's doing quite well. Have you seen him?

"Yes, I see him here and there. He was working for First National Pictures," replied Keedick. "They are really kicking Paramount in the behind right now. Hesser told me that they eclipsed over 4,000 theatres last month."

"My God, the film business is so much bigger than the old Vaudeville days, huh, Lee?" said Pat.

"It's astounding," said Lee. "I mean the work we used to do to produce live shows! When I think of all the miles I traveled just to make sure the show worked. Hell, now once you've got it in reels, all you have to do is make sure you get your money."

"How much of your business is in film, Lee," asked Pat.

"You know not a lot but guys call me all the time because I have relationships, you know," he said. "I know people. I mean, they call me looking for help with some theatre boss that won't let them in or ask me to have dinner with a big time operator that I may know from the old days, just to grease the deal. It's easy work. I show up, have dinner, talk nice to an old friend and as we get up to leave after two hours I whisper in his ear that he ought to do the deal. Then I'm off and a check comes in the mail."

Pat was grinning through the whole rant. He'd forgotten how fun Lee was.

"You know, Pat, you should look at the movies," said Keedick.

"Ah, heck, I don't know," responded Pat. "I know some folks in that business and they tell me it's long hours, lots of waiting, lots of early mornings. I don't know if I want to work that hard.

"There's tremendous money in it Pat," said Keedick. "You're a built in draw, good looking. You perfect for the screen."

"I'm not sure if anyone knows who I am anymore, do they?" asked Pat in a lighthearted way.

"Are you kidding?" responded. "Listen Pat, you don't have to think too hard over all this. It's like those old-timers who used sit around debating whether or not the automobile could ever replace the buggy. Meanwhile, thousands of cars are rolling off the assembly line in Detroit and cities start banning horse traffic in the center of town. There's just some industries that are unstoppable. I tell you there's lots of room to make lots of money in the movie business and you've already got a leg up on the most of them. You're a known quantity."

"Perhaps," said Pat. "Sounds like Hess is getting known in that business too, huh?"

"He's also a very hot commodity right now," replied Keedick. "He's just opened his private studio in Manhattan in addition to the work he's doing for National. He's really a talented guy. I remember the first time I met him. I saw him at a dinner and we got to talking and your name came up. I was really surprised to learn how well you knew each other."

Sure, he and I go back to California even before the Signal Corps," said Pat. "He did some shows for me too, mostly toward the end. Hess can do about anything."

"There's a lot of pressure on the business here in New York to move to Hollywood. Hesser told me that one week after he signed his lease for his studio in Manhattan, he had four calls," said Keedick. "I have no doubt that Hesser will leave sooner than later. And why not, the weather is perfect, there's tons of money flowing out there, beautiful women all trying to hit the jackpot and new studios going up every day."

Hesser was, in fact, an up and coming photographer who would eventually move to Hollywood and become one of the top glamour photographers of the silent era and someone who's work collectors eventually sought out as works of art. His clients would include stars such as Jean Harlow, Mary Pickford, Lilian Gish, Clare Bow and others.

"I'm seeing him this week, too," said Pat. "Perhaps we'll talk about this."

"Here you are gentlemen," said the waiter as he placed a beef and potato dish under Pat and as pasta clam dish to Keedick.

[667]

"Could we see the wine list, please?" asked Keedick.

The two men had a warm and long visit, parting around 10:00 p.m. They shook hands in the lobby. Keedick departed and Pat took the elevator to his room.

The next day, Pat was up late enjoyed reading the New York Times in the lobby while he waited for McGraw who was coming for lunch. The New York Giants manager arrived about ten to noon and the two old friends took a table in the Astor Restaurant.

"I can't believe you survived, again," said McGraw joking with his friend. Only an Irishman like you could crash an Aeroplane twice and then spend two months in the middle of the Russian revolution and make it home without a scratch."

"I'm a fortunate "Mic," ain't I, Johnny," Pat replied in an Irish brogue that cracked up McGraw.

Pat was enjoying his lunch with McGraw. It was good to see old friends and engage in conversation that moved, cut hard and was full of the other guy "stepping all over the last three words of your sentence." This was New York. Fast, furious and full of chatter, everybody on the take and money flowing in quicker than people like McGraw could bank it.

"So, Pat, you need to come to Havana with us," said McGraw after reviewing all his latest ventures in Cuba. "We need people like you to seed the place, know what I mean?"

"Seed it, huh?" replied Pat.

"Well, you know," said McGraw. "If people see the likes of Pat O'Brien in our hotel, hanging around the race track and all that, well, they'll figure 'why ain't I there.' Know what I mean?"

"Sure, I guess," said Pat, taking another bite of his lunch. "If you think it helps you. Who am I to argue with a few days in the sun?"

"Few days," replied McGraw. "Hell, we'd like you down there a few weeks, a number of times per year, Pat."

"Boy, things must be slow, Mac," replied Pat.

"Ah, shut-up," he said in good fun. Then he went on.

[668]

"No, really, Pat. We open the Oriental Race Track and the refurbished Hotel Plaza on Thanksgiving day," McGraw said. "It would be great to have you down there with us, photos and all that. Then we'll publicize it all over the country and bam! Everybody comes to Havana. Hey, we need your pretty face, that's all."

Pat laughed and McGraw did too, chewing a big piece of beef at that same time. Then pointing his fork at Pat he said, "And you ought to consider kicking in some money on this project, Pat."

"So that's it, huh, Mac," said Pat with a smile. "You want my money, huh?"

"Hey, O'Brien, do you really think we need your money with a guy like money-bags Rothstein backing us up? Huh?" said McGraw, this time opening up is palms and leaning back in an "Italian way."

"Yeah, yeah, I know," said Pat taking another bite. "I appreciate that. I'm taking a look at where to put my money now so I'll put that on the list."

"Oh," he said in an "excuse me" tone, "Big time money guy now, huh?"

"I do all right for a washed up British pilot," responded Pat. "So when are you going?"

"I leave Wednesday," McGraw replied.

"Next Wednesday?" said Pat, somewhat startled.

"Sure," replied McGraw.

"I can't possibly go that soon, Mac," Pat said. "I just got in town and I've got a lot of business to do. Hell, that's only four days away. Besides, I have to do a presentation in Washington on Friday. There's no way I can go next week."

"Ok," responded McGraw, "so you can't do the track opening. How about after the winter meetings? I'll be back for those on December 8 here in New York, then should head back to Havana around, say, the 13th or 14th"

"My birthday," replied Pat. "My birthday is on the 13th."

"See, perfect," McGraw said. "We'll celebrate your birthday. How old you gonna' be?"

"Twenty-nine," replied Pat.

"Twenty-nine, holy crap if I was only that age once again, McGraw lamented. "When I was your age, I was digging up ground balls in dusty old ballparks. Look at you, you're famous, single, good looking, a war hero and you've got money."

Pat turned a deaf ear to McGraw's comments and then said, "So if we leave around the 14th, how long will we stay."

"Well, we'll let that determine itself," responded McGraw. "Let's talk about it when I get back. You agreed to go then?"

"Sure, sounds like fun," said Pat.

The two really enjoyed their time together. It was always a contest regarding who possessed the largest quantity of Blarney. Other times they intentionally talked "past" each other avoiding a response.

"Hey, how about we go to the gym this afternoon, huh?" said McGraw.

"The gym?" asked Pat.

"Yeah, Lou Stillman's new place. Dempsey's working out there this afternoon. Rothstein set me up to go watch him spar a few rounds," said McGraw.

"Hell, yes," said Pat. "Jack Dempsey. That would be marvelous. What time?"

"I'll have cab pick you up at the hotel, say, about 3:00 o'clock. He's starting at 3:30," responded McGraw.

"Perfect," Pat said. "I'll be there."

"Three o'clock then," McGraw added.

"Great," replied Pat. And the two men shook hands.

McGraw went back to his table and laid a big tip down. He looked over his shoulder and saw Pat exiting out the front door. Just then Stoneham walked in from the interior hall way opposite the lobby, he walked up to McGraw, chewing on a tooth pick.

"How'd it go?" asked Stoneham.

"Good, good," replied McGraw in a quiet voice still looking back at the front door. "He'll be good."

There were many household names in the United States in late 1919. Certainly, Pat was one. But the war heroes were fading in the psyche of the American public. Athletes, movie actors, mob bosses and others, many of them vets, captured the minds of everyday Americans and certainly the press.

Few had the stature of Jack Dempsey ever since his surprise victory over Jess Willard on the fourth of July, 1919. Ruth was big and about to get bigger once traded to the Yankees but even at the peak of his career he'd make about $70,000 a year. Dempsey would make a staggering $300,000 for his 1921 defense against Frenchman and light heavyweight champion Georges Carpentier at Boyle's Thirty Acres in Jersey City, N.J.

The big sports stars emerging on the American scene were Dempsey, Ruth, Red Grange of the Bears, pro tennis player Bill Tilden and golf legend Bobby Jones. The golden age of sports was about to begin. It seemed like every other sports star was also dating a "Hollywood actress," including Dempsey.

If one believed every story written by sports and social page journalists in the country in 1919, there must have been a million fledgling Hollywood actresses on the arms of big strong athletes in every city in America. But mostly Los Angeles and New York.

McGraw pulled up sharply at three o'clock and Pat slipped into the back seat. They traveled twenty minutes to Harlem and pulled up in front of Stillman's Gym on 125th street.

"You got change?" asked McGraw.

"What, for the cab?" asked Pat.

"No, I've got the cab, Pat," replied McGraw. "Nobody gets into Stillman's without paying twenty-five cents. Not even the stars. More than one world champion or celebrity has been embarrassed at the door because they didn't have a quarter. Hey, with Stillman it's 'no money, no entrance' He doesn't care who you are."

They stepped out of the car. McGraw paid the driver. Pat looked up at the sign over the storefront building. It read, "Marshall Stillman Athletic Club." It had opened earlier in the year and was operated by Louis Ingber. Ingber was often called "Mr. Stillman" by the clientele and he never corrected them. Years later he'd change his name to match what everyone called him anyway.

The gym was a dark, smoky place, hot, emitting a combination of odors the general public would, thankfully, never experience. There were twenty or more rough-housing types with bashed noses in groups of two or three surrounding their young hopeful as he shadow boxed, awaiting his turn.

Pat and McGraw made their way through the thick crowd and stood along the wall. There were men of all assorted types, some with Irish lids on their heads and other more formal looking gents that appeared to have money. Many of them were holding folded up newsprint which they would regularly check, marking something with their pencils when a strong punch landed in the ring. The Irish lads just pointed and winced, often cheering for one of their own trying to make it big in the boxing game.

"Hi, McGraw," said middle-aged man passing Pat and the baseball manager.

Thirty seconds later, two men came. "Hey, Mac, you gonna' manager next year?"

"Yeah, yeah, sure," said McGraw. "Those scraps can't even run the bases in the right direction unless I'm there to point for 'um."

That got a hardy laugh from the two men. Pat smiled and looked back up into the ring.

It was obvious that everyone knew McGraw. He felt right at home in their surroundings, too. Pat and John stood watching one round after another as "new meat" was tossed into the ring. There was a parade of arrivals looking for a place to stand and watch Dempsey. As they walk by in the din they shouted at McGraw, "hey, Mac" or "How 'bout next year, Mac," and one guy stopped, looked at McGraw up close to his face and barked, "What gives? You managing the Giants next year or ain't yah." Without batting an eye, McGraw shouted back, "Get the hell out of my face, ya bum!"

Finally, Dempsey arrived and a cheer went up followed by boos for the stooge who was to spar with him. The fight went a surprising three rounds and the noise, cheers, boos and general mayhem was such that Pat couldn't' decide whether to watch the fight or watch the crowd. He felt like a "kid from Momence" away from home in this place but he enjoyed the intensity. To Pat it was a condensed battle scene limited by ropes and controlled by a referee. War had no such limitations.

Three hundred miles south in Washington D.C. another group of people, much more serene than the tobacco chewing mob at Stillman's Gym were gathering at Cora Rigby's Christian Science Monitor office about to plan a battle of their own. They were made up of one-hundred percent women, all journalists determined to get a "real assignment" from their editors. There were women journalist in 1919 in Washington but they were limited to the social pages and never covered political, business or, God forbid, crime stories.

Rigby was a correspondent for the Monitor and a leader among female journalist. The group had come together to form the Women's National Press Club. They were mostly young, under thirty. The number of experienced female reporters in the newspaper business was limited. The War and the recent passing of the nineteenth amendment five months earlier had put some extra zip in the careers of women in journalism and many other fields. The amendment gave women the right to vote.

Women's-based organizations in Washington increasingly featured speakers from the political, military or the business world. It had afforded Rigby and others a chance to make small inroads into more serious topics by covering the woman's luncheon and inserting significant commentary regarding the lecturer's points.

"Is this seat taken?" said a young pretty woman to an older fellow journalist already in place.

"No, certainly, have a seat my dear," said the woman.

"Thank you so very much," said the women and she took her seat.

The elder glanced out of the corner of her eye and noticed the young girl was quite attractive, dressed well and had crossed her right leg over her left, hands folded in her lap, revealing a very stylish "Russian boot" as it was called. It was very popular with the young girls at the time. The longer boot worked well in winter as an offset to the much shorter hemlines which were creeping up daily since the war.

"My, that's a very stylish boot," said the woman. "Where did you get it?"

"Los Angeles", replied the young woman, "Their quite new and popular. Why anyone in California would need one, heaven knows. But they are a marvelous solution to the snow and cold here on the East Coast."

"Indeed," replied the elder. "I just love the big heal, very stylish, quiet stylish."

The young woman smiled and crossed her opposite leg. It turned her away from the older woman a bit, perhaps not intentionally but nevertheless, it did turn her back toward the women and it was noticed. Just then another young lady arrived.

"There you are, Virginia," she said. "I found you. I tell you the congestion in this city is almost unbearable. You'd think they'd ban animals from city streets altogether, wouldn't you?" She was speaking very rapidly, out of breath. Placing her belongings on her chair, fussing with her dress, the young woman finally sat, plopping down next to Virginia, turning immediately toward her as she went on.

"So my taxi pulls around the corner, and wouldn't you know it, he pulls up right alongside a line of three buggies with horses and my only exit out of his cab is to step out into the street right behind the arse of a horse. Good Lord, I'm glad I didn't disturb the poor thing. I mean can you imagine, allowing horse and buggy in the capital of this country, on paved streets in 1919. I mean, it's almost 1920."

In the middle of the women's rampage, Virginia had turned and twinkled a broad smile at the elder woman so as to excuse her talkative friend, then turned back giggling at the entertainment that had just taken a seat to her right.

"Elise, you do get worked up about things don't you," said Virginia smiling and dabbing at tears induced by humor.

Well, don't you think it's absurd Virginia," said Elsie. "In this day and age! My holy Gabriel."

"Sounds like you had quiet an ordeal, young lady," said the mature woman leaning over to look around Virginia. "Now my husband says it's the cars disturbing the horses, so I supposed it depends on your point of view."

Looking back and forth between Elise and the older woman, Virginia enjoyed the distraction. Then the elder woman redirected her gaze a Virginia.

"I'm Gerda Schumacher," said the woman extending her hand to Virginia.

"Hello, ma'am," responded Virginia. "I'm Virginia Allen."

"Are you a reporter, dear?" as Schumacher.

"I'm a freelance writer, said Virginia. "I write for a few papers in Washington, social events, meetings, things like that."

"Don't we all," responded Gerda leaning back in her chair, exasperated. "When was the last time you heard a female reporter covering a congressional hearing, mind you?"

Elise jumped in.

"That's another thing," said Elise. "It doesn't surprise me that a town with horses can barely bring itself to acknowledge women's rights... how long has it bee...five months since suffrage?" Checking her powder in small mirror, dabbing aggressively, she went on "Men just don't understand us women, I tell you."

Virginia and Gerda again nodded to each other in agreement but with a simultaneous grin that acknowledged the humor of the gushing of Elise.

Virginia Allen was technically no longer Mrs. Allen at all. Her maiden name was Livingston and she had married in her young twenties to a Charles Allen of Alexandria, Virginia. But as oft young marriages go, it did not last. Virginia Elizabeth Livingston maintained her ex-husband's name for business purposes. It was the one thing she cherished after her short-lived marriage. Her new last named sounded good in the newspaper business. She also thought it sounded good for the stage. She once said, "Livingston sounds like I'm the wife of a banker or something, how boorish!"

She was, in fact, a stunning young woman with brains, wit, charm and a sensuous way about her that usually melted the hearts of young men just seeing her enter a room. Her father had money and she felt very little pressure to hurriedly find work to "make ends meet." There was plenty of financial support at home and she'd won a significant prize in her divorce from young Mr. Allen, as well, he being from the well-to-do, also.

Her charm often gave her access to men, normally reserved when facing reporters. They would lean in and whisper to her, "I don't usually tell people this but…." Virginia's ability to entice others to divulge even their most cherished opinions was increasingly noticed in journalistic circles around Washington. She stood out among the "young girls" who routinely pounced on instantaneous moments with the famous that occurred daily in Washington D.C.

She had another passion, however, not found in Washington DC. The lure of movie stardom and the excesses of the beautiful crowd in southern California had caught her fancy right after her divorce. Naturally, her beauty got the attention of most casting directors. But to date she had not landed much more than bit parts. Tramping around Los Angeles, looking for acting opportunities was not her idea of a good time. Most of what she desired she'd been provided with throughout her life thus far.

So, in between acting opportunities she'd come home to Washington and made use of life's conveniences provided by her parents. She regularly attended social events and luncheon meetings where she could mix with the rich and powerful. Her journalistic colleagues all sought the same access. It was their lifeblood. If one wanted to hear of the latest gossip, one needed to be "in the mix." The difference with Virginia, despite her natural talent to inquire and write, was her motivation. Essentially, she viewed her press credentials as merely access to important, powerful and wealthy people, who could open doors for her in film.

And so why spend time in Washington? Why not Los Angeles or New York? Having grown up around Washington, she intuitively understood that people with power had influence. In her mind the "hungry bottom feeders" scrambling from one audition to the next in the dusty lots of Hollywood or the congested streets of New York, were working bottom up. Virginia was a top-down theorist, very much attributable to her upbringing.

After the ninety minutes of discussion and formal actions, the female journalist in the room that day ratified the Woman's National Press Club. Following a stirring speech by the newly elected president, the ladies mixed for another hour. Finally, Virginia was bored. Elise had an appointment

"I'm getting hungry," said Virginia. "These long meetings bore me. Would you like to have lunch?"

"I can't," said Elise. "I've got an assignment. I'm so excited!"

"Wonderful, hon, where are you going?" asked Virginia

"I'm covering an exhibition at the Metro Museum of Art," responded Elise. "I love those assignments."

"Sounds like fun," responded Virginia who kissed her friend on the cheek. "Enjoy yourself."

"I will, Ginnie, I will," responded Elise continuing her constant exuberance and youthful overbearance. Elise ran off and Virginia said good-bye, one more time, to the elder woman she'd met upon arrival. After waving to a few other friends across the room she turned briskly and headed out.

"Have fun, indeed," thought Virginia. She found assignments such as Elise's mundane and repetitive. Fortunately for her, she could afford the luxury of refusing such work by politely saying "no." Elise could not. She had to eat.

As Virginia exited the building and stepped down the marble steps to the sidewalk, she heard someone call her name.

"Virginia, I'm over here!" yelled a young Navy pilot in full uniform holding open the cab door for her to enter. It was her brother, Hugh Livingston.

Livingston was a 2nd Luitenant and Naval Pilot. There were few American pilots compared to the British and French. There were even fewer Naval pilots. Livingston was part of a new wave of aviators. They had little connection to the old Signal Corps roots and were part of the push to bring airpower to the sea.

All through 1919, the Army was still engaged in a huge draw down of troops from Europe. The Navy had a somewhat different agenda. For the Navy and the Marine Corps the next apparent opponent seemed to be Imperial Japan. Beginning almost the day after Armistice they began thinking, war-gaming, and developing plans on the tactical, operational, strategic, and logistic problems that might arise in a conflict in the Pacific. For the Army the vision and innovation of armored divisions in combat in Europe would come much later.

"Hi, sweetie," said Virginia, giving her brother a kiss on the cheek. She stepped in, slid over, followed by Hugh who pulled the door shut. The cabby had turned and saw Virginia entering his cab. He then turned back, raising he eyebrows in admiration of Virginia then said, "Where to, folks?"

"Occidental, please," said Hugh to the driver.

The Occidental Grill was Virginia's favorite. Located near the White House at 1475 Pennsylvania Avenue it assured all those lucky enough to get a table a glimpse of cabinet members, senators, sports heroes, literary greats and celebrities. It was "made to order" for the upstart Virginia Allen.

It was at the Occidental where Virginia had charmed D.W. Griffin, the most significant movie producer in California. Originally from New York, he shot the very first film ever in California and was considered the dean of film producers along with Adolph Zukor, Herman Casler and others. Though he was impressed with Virginia's guts, obvious charm, and good looks, he'd said to her, "The movie business is a business and my success has not been by taking a chance on unknowns. You might be better advised to start with a small studio and work your way up."

That word "work" jumped out at Virginia again. "I just need to find the right contact that is interested in me," she'd once told her brother. "If they take a look at me and then tell me to get more experience, then maybe I'm not as beautiful as they say I am."

"If you were not my sister, I swear I'd fall in love with you myself," Hugh had always responded.

"Oh, shush with such talk, Hugh. You're so cavalier," was her oft response.

Hugh and Virginia took their seats and scanned the menu. After they ordered, Hugh took a sip of club soda, situated his silver and napkin and appeared nervous to his sister.

"What is it, Hugh," said Virginia. "You're so antsy!"

"No, I'm not," said Hugh nearly out of breath. "Ok, I am a little excited today. I'm going to meet Rickenbacker, Eddie Rickenbacker."

"How'd you arrange that?" said Virginia.

"There's a presentation scheduled next Friday for Navy pilots in the DC area.

"What's the occasion? With the war over does it matter?" asked Virginia.

"To the Navy it does," Hugh replied. "You see, sis, the Aeronautical School at the Naval Air Station in Pensacola just opened November 1. It was a pretty paltry start. There's one Marine and four Navy officers enrolled."

"Oh my," replied Virginia. "

He went on. "The Chief of Naval Operations has ordered all new pilots in D.C. attend this panel presentation next week. They're sending around certain veteran pilots to talk to us new fellows and get us charged up about the new Navy flying program. They're going to talk about their war experience and Rickenbacker is leading the panel. It's going to be tremendous. I can hardly wait."

"So, who else is presenting?" asked Virginia.

Hugh went on to explain further. Five very well-known pilots would be present. Leading the group would be Eddie Rickenbacker who was still in service and considered the most important surviving pilot of the Great War. Canada's William "Billie" Bishop with 72 kills during the war would also speak. Second, behind Bishop with 60 Hun downings, was Ray Collishaw, another Canadian pilot who also flew for the RAF. Francis Gillet, twenty kills in Europe, was an American who flew for Canada in the early days of the war was also scheduled. Finally, Lt. Pat O'Brien, American born pilot who'd flown for the British with a fantastic story that all of America knew.

"Oh, Hugh, you must get me into that presentation," said Virginia. "I'd love to submit a story to the Post. Not only that, I'm sure, if nothing else, Rickenbacker and O'Brien will be of great interest to the civilian crowd. Is it just for military folks or can others attend?"

"Well, I'm not sure," replied Hugh. "I'll try to find out and see what I can do to get you in, sis" said Hugh.

Back in New York the following morning, Pat was awakening to a significant headache. After spending most of the afternoon with McGraw at Stillman's gym, the two had gone "out on the town," frequenting the many hot spots where McGraw was well known. They met up with a few Giants players as well and Pat did not return to the Astor Hotel until 1:00 a.m. At 1:00 p.m. his phone rang.

"O'Brien!" said the phone on the other end. It was Hess.

"Yes, this is Pat," he responded.

"My God, man, you sound terrible," replied Hesser.

"Sorry, Hess," Pat said. "I had a long night. That damn McGraw did me in once again."

"You going to come by today?" asked Hesser.

"Oh, yeah," responded Pat running his fingers through his hair. "What time is it?"

"One o'clock," Hesser replied. "What time can you be ready? I'll pick you up."

"Give me an hour, Hess," Pat replied.

"Ok, see you in an hour," Hesser confirmed and the two hung up.

At 2:00 p.m. Pat walked gingerly down the stairs of the Astor and out the door. There was Hesser, right on time, standing by a cab at the ready.

"Hess, how in the hell are you?" asked Pat as the two men embraced locked in a big bear hug for a flash.

"It's good to see you, O'Brien," replied Hesser. "Come on let's get in."

The two longtime friends climbed inside the back seat.

"Where we going, Hess?" Pat asked.

"Coney Island, my friend," replied Hess. "We're going to Stauch's."

"Outstanding!" replied Pat as the cab spun off.

Their cab took a quick jog over to 7th avenue and turned south. Pat was still a little queasy from his long night. It was the middle of the afternoon but that mattered little on the streets of New York. It was a particularly congested route down 7th avenue.

"It'll take us a while," said Hess. "But there's plenty to see. When I have to get through town, I just sit back and enjoy the sites."

"I'm in no hurry," replied Pat. "After my day yesterday a slow relaxing drive is more than welcomed."

"What did you do that made yesterday so bad?" asked Hesser.

"Oh, I had lunch with McGraw," replied Pat. "Then we went to a gym up in Harlem and watched boxing for a while. Have you ever seen Stillman's Gym.?"

"Oh, hell no," replied Hesser. "I know of it but don't usually frequent those places. What got you to go there?"

"Hey, it was fun," Pat replied. "But there are a bunch of characters up that way. We saw Dempsey spar. McGraw, he took me there."

"Ah, that makes sense," replied Hesser elevating his voice a bit. "You gotta' watch out for those gambling types, you know, Pat."

"Yeah, I know. They're fun but they do dabble a bit in the macabre," Pat replied.

"They dabble in a lot of crime, too," said Hesser.

"Yah think so?" asked Pat, sounding just a little naive to his buddy.

"Are you kidding?" replied Hesser. "McGraw is a baseball man, I know that. But he and his buddy Stoneham? They're all tied up with the Jewish mob in New York, you know Rothstein and that bunch."

"Well, I guess so," said Pat. "I know one thing, John flashes around a lot of cash."

"Yeah, and that isn't from his baseball salary, I can guarantee you that," replied Hesser.

After about twenty-five minutes down 7th Avenue, their cab took at left at 32nd street at Penn station. Pat was quite familiar with this neighborhood having arrived from Chicago many times terminated at the Penn. They headed east to Broadway and took a right, heading south again. They soon passed Madison Square Park and through the elite neighborhood of brownstone row houses and mansions that graced the area.

"Teddy Roosevelt was born right there," Hesser said pointing to a large mansion on the right.

Winston Churchill's American mother was also born in the neighborhood which had a number of hotels where everyone from Mark Twain to President Grant had stayed. They crossed 23rd street past the Metropolitan Life Insurance Building which was the 2nd tallest structure in New York. They took a right at 3rd Avenue through the East side and straight south through Chinatown and across the Brooklyn Bridge. From there they traveled another twenty minutes through Brooklyn, West Brighton and finally arrived at Coney Island.

Stauch's was a huge restaurant, dance hall and bathhouse on the Bowery. It was unusual in that it was built of stone after suffering a few fires over the years. Pat and Hesser got out of their cab. Hesser paid the driver and Pat surveyed the unique façade that was Coney Island. Most patrons of Coney Island were middle class at the time as the subway and elevated station there was still under construction. When completed in 1920 it would draw thousands, often times a million working class New Yorkers to the cool beach during summer's sweltering months.

The two had a long and enjoyable lunch. It was a real change of pace for Pat. Hesser was educated, had class and appreciated the refined things of life. Not so with McGraw and the bunch he'd encountered the day before.

Hesser talked about his plans for a studio. While he continued to do promotional work for the film company, he was getting more and more requests for photographs by some of the up and coming stars in the business. He saw a lucrative market in this work. It would eventually draw him to Hollywood where we would become a photograph of artistic reputation. When desert arrived, Hesser mentioned something he'd almost forgotten.

"Hey, Pat," he said. "I had this call from a woman that said she knew you."

"Oh yeah, who's that," Pat replied.

"Well, I don't recall at the moment," said Hesser. "She lived in New York or Washington. No, I recall now she lives here but frequents Washington. I think she was formerly married to an officer, medical officer I believe. What was her name?" he said taking another spoonful of ice cream. There was a pause. Then it came to him.

"Ottis, yes, Ottis was her name," do you know her?

"Ottis?" Pat said, "No, not off hand. Let's see, Ottis." He paused a short second. "Nope, don't think so. Hell, I've seen so many people in my travels. I think I've forgot more than I remember.

"Well, she sure sounded like she knew you," said Hess.

The two men ate a few more scoops of ice cream and then Pat inquired further.

"What did the woman want?" asked Pat.

"Something about a movie," replied Hesser. "Yeah, she said she knew you from Chicago. Apparently, heard you speak or something. She's some big muckety-muck with a group of officer's wives in Washington.

"Nope," Pat said, finishing off his ice cream, tossing his spoon into the empty dish with a clink.

"I remember now," said Hesser. "Her name was Sarah Ottis. Yes, that's right, Ottis."

Suddenly, Pat pictured exactly who she was. The lobby at Orchestra Hall in Chicago flashed through his mind and that night in Decatur when she'd commandeered Pat and his brother to meet a bunch of people from Springfield.

"Dammit, yeah, I know who she is," said Pat. "How did she reach you and why? I mean, how did she know we knew each other?"

"I don't know," said Hesser. "Apparently, she'd heard of my work and knew my military background. Who knows, maybe she read a story about us being old chums or something."

"Well, I don't recall being that friendly to her," said Pat. "You know how it is Hess. These gals all come up like they know you, wanting to get close to somebody famous. It goes on all the time."

"Does it, now?" said Hesser with a humorous tone in his voice. He was the "roly-poly type not necessarily stunning but captivating to the ladies once they saw his eye for photography. He was charming and women loved him once they got to know him and saw the magic he could work with his camera. Women would often say, "I look twenty years younger," when seeing his photos. It endeared him to many.

They spent the rest of the day together, talking about old times in California, the war, prospects now that the war was over. Pat had a great day with Hesser. It stabilized him from the chaos of McGraw and his buddies. Hesser and Pat went back longer than most of Pat's war buddies. They laughed until tears welled up in their eyes over the hapless aircraft they once tried to build back in California.

When they were finished, Hesser dropped Pat off at the Astor. The two men slapped each other on the back, and held a firm lasting handshake until saying good-bye.

Meanwhile, the phone at the Livingston house in Washington D.C. was ringing. Virginia Allen hurried to the kitchen and lifted the receiver.

"Hello, Livingston residence," she said in a sweet and pleasant tone."

"Sis, it's Hugh," said her brother on the other line. "I found out about the presentation next week,"

"Yes?" replied Virginia.

"You can go," said Hugh with enthusiasm in his voice. "Anybody can go. I guess it's going to be quite an affair. I thought it might be tough to keep the general public away. It could be the last time people can see the likes of these famous war heroes in one room."

"Marvelous, honey," said Virginia. "Will you be able to pick me up?"

"No, I can't," said Hugh. "I'll be tied down assisting with a small reception beforehand that the Admiral is hosting for the panel. Can you take a cab?"

Sure, hon," said Virginia. "It's next Friday, right?"

"Yes," replied Hugh.

"What time?" Virginia asked.

"Seven p.m." Hugh replied.

"Wonderful, see you then," said his sister.

"Ok, sis," replied Hugh. "Love you, sis." And they both hung up the phone.

The next day, Monday, Pat has a two hour meeting with Bernard Lambert of the Hong Kong Bank. For a banker, Lambert enjoyed the folky and authentic. As a treat for Pat, he arrange for them to have lunch at McSorley's Old Ale House, one of the oldest Irish taverns in New York. It was located in the East Village of Manhattan and was for "Men Only." The place featured old artwork, newspaper headlines on the wall, sawdust floors, and Irish immigrant waiters with a Brogue as thick as a peat bog.

There are also wishbones hanging above the bar. They were hung there by boys going off to the war two years previous to be removed when they returned. Pat looked up from his menu and glanced at forty or fifty above the bar. Nearly half of the wishbones remained unbroken from those that never came back.

.

On the wall above table a sign read, "Be Good or Be Gone." Still another hanging from the ceiling announced, "Good Ale, Raw Onions and No Ladies."

"Only the goofy Irish," Pat said out loud looking down at his menu.

"What's that you say, O'Brien?" asked Lambert looking up from his."

"Awe, nothing Lambert, replied Pat. "You're French. You wouldn't understand."

Just then Lambert's friend entered the bar and he waved him over. His name was Drew Huntington. Lambert knew him from Shanghai. Huntington was charged with doing the groundwork for J.P. Morgan who planned to open a Shanghai office in 1920. He introduced him to Pat and the three men discussed some of Pat's options. In the end, Huntington advised Pat to invest some of his money in bonds. Pat had about $50,000 in cash currently sitting in banks in New York, Chicago and San Francisco. Revenues from "*Outwitting the Hun*," totaled over $20,000 at this point and to date, he'd not touched that money. He also had about $25,000 in liberty bonds and more cash in the Parrish bank in Momence. After about two hours, Pat thanked Lambert for introducing him to Huntington. Pat and Lambert bid him farewell and then had one more drink before making their way back to the Astor hotel.

On November 19th, John McGraw left for Havana. He'd placed a call to Pat from the train station indicated he'd see him when he got back. The next day, Pat received a telegram from Clara, whom he'd called to let her know where he was staying while in New York.

Pat's brother Ivan and his wife had just had a baby girl. They named her Patricia and all was fine. She also indicated that they were settling into their new house nicely and that Elmer was looking forward to a good planting season on the Morocco farm this spring.

Pat boarded the train to Washington at 5:00 p.m. the next day. When he got to Washington, he took a cab immediately to the Willard hotel on 1401 Pennsylvania Ave NW, not three blocks from the White House. It was an exquisite hotel. One of the finest in Washington. He checked in and proceeded to one of the numerous ballrooms where the reception for the panel members was to occur.

The room was half full as only special guests had been invited to the reception. When Pat entered a young officer recognized him and escorted him to meet the others. Pat was a little nervous in the company of such notables but he also did not go unnoticed. He was not the only panel member not in uniform which made him feel more comfortable.

"Ah, O'Brien," said Rickenbacker shaking Pat's hand. Quite a war you had, young man. Congratulations on your miraculous return. I've read your book. Quite amazing."

"Thank you, sir," replied Pat. He felt better after that. Rickenbacker made him feel welcomed.

Pat met the famous Billie Bishop who also knew of Pat's book. They talked about Borden a bit and the Canadian Corps. Pat felt at home with Bishop. Francis Gillet came up and shook Pat's hand. "I'm happy to see I'm not the only man out of uniform tonight," he said. "Then again, being that we are both Americans who flew for the Canadians, we'd probably just confuse the hell out of everyone anyway. How are you, O'Brien?"

"Great," replied Pat.

Gillet introduced Pat to Collishaw and the panel mixed near the podium stage with invited guests. After about forty-five minutes, the group was asked to retire to a small anti-room attached to the ballroom while the remaining guests for the evening were allowed in. The room soon filled to the brim with dignitaries from the military and civilian life fortunate to have acquired a ticket. The press was heavily represented including Virginia Allen who took as seat toward the rear of the hall.

A group of Yeoman reservists stationed in D.C. and another group of officers' wives were showing people their seats. Typically, female Yeoman reservists performed clerical duties such as typing, stenography, bookkeeping, accounting, inventory control, and telephone operation. They also volunteered for special events. Wives of current and former officers also volunteered with official events around Washington. It was a way to stay in touch and support the military as boys continued to come home well into 1919.

Once the crowd settled in, the MC for the evening, Josephus Daniels, Secretary of the Navy, stepped to the microphone and introduced the panel who entered the ball room from the anti-room one by one. All received tremendous applause.

Standing at the back of the room, surveying the crowd and smiling at the joy of being present was Sarah Jane Ottis, estranged wife of Lieutenant Colonel Daniel Mortimer Ottis of Springfield, Illinois.

Chapter 51

The Swarm

As Secretary of the Navy, Daniels thanked the esteemed panel for their presentation. The overflow crowd in the Willard Ballroom rose to its feet in an ovation that roared to the ceiling. It was reminiscent of Pat's days in 1918 when the fever of war still flowed through the veins of nearly every American. Pat and the other four stood before the audience thanking them and nodding their heads in acknowledgement. The Navy couldn't have asked for a more dynamic presentation.

Pat did well. Early on, the presentation was dominated by Rickenbacker which was a surprise to few. He used the opportunity to promote the Naval Aviation program. He shared just a few stories of his own from the war. This disappointed some who wanted to hear more firsthand about his marvelous record. Billie Bishop was dynamic and passionate. His presentations in the U.S. since the end of the war in support of military aviation had been big influences on Congress and the general public. Tonight was no exception. Gillet and Collishaw came off more as tacticians than motivators but their stories were powerful. All were impressive in their own right.

It was Pat that, most would say, stirred the passion in the audience that night. There was no one on the podium, even Rickenbacker, with Pat's ability to tell a story, stir an audience or motivate the young flyers. He'd done this many times before. Pat was a professional speaker at this point who knew from experience how to capture an audience through the art of storytelling. When he spoke the room froze with attentiveness. It held its breath, just as it had at Carnegie Hall, the Majestic in Kankakee, Emerson Hall at Harvard, Hearst Theatre at Berkeley, the Murat in Indianapolis, the Coliseum in Dallas and in dozens of Chautauqua tents across the Midwest.

From a theatrical point of view, there was no doubt in the mind of Virginia Allen who "stole the show." Naturally, she noticed his youthful and debonair demeanor when he entered the room. But when he spoke, her pencil froze in her hand and she was taken in. Her position in the room was some distance from the front stage but he impressed her significantly.
As stirred as she was by her attraction to him as a man, she had not dismissed his obvious advantage. He fit perfectly into her "top down" strategy. She had to meet him. There was a huge crush at the stage after the presentation as nearly everyone in the hall attempted to speak to the presenters one-on-one. Virginia wasn't certain she could even get close enough to get his attention.

"Hello, ma'am," said Virginia to a woman wearing a committee ribbon. "I see you are part of committee for tonight's event. I'm Virginia Allen writing for the Washington Post."

"Hello, Miss. Allen," said the woman. "Yes, I'm on the committee but I'm just a volunteer. We're here with a group of officer's wives assisting with the event. How can I help you?"

"Do you know if they plan an additional press conference following the event," she asked.

"I don't know but I believe one already occurred prior to the reception," replied the woman. "I'd be glad to check for you."

The volunteer walked to a yeoman reservist who had been handling the press through the night. She confirmed that no further press conference was plan. The volunteer returned to Virginia.

"Sorry, Ms. Allen, they did have a short press conference in the hotel suite of the Secretary of War, prior to the event," Sarah said.

"Oh, drat, we never hear about the private press conferences," said Virginia. "Well, I had really hoped to meet Lieutenant O'Brien but there's such a throng up there, I'll never get to him." Again, a little effort affronted her nature. She looked at her watch and gasped.

"I know him," said the woman.

"You do?" responded Virginia.

"Why, yes, I've known him for years." Reaching out her hand she introduced herself. "I'm Sarah Ottis. I'm originally from Illinois where Lieutenant O'Brien is from. Perhaps I can speak to him and see if he will be in town a few days to afford you a chance to interview him."

"That would be grand, Mrs. Ottis. Mrs., I assume?" said Virginia continuing to shake Sarah's hand.

"Well, not for long, mind you," replied Sarah raising the pitch of her voice. Then placing her left hand on Virginia's shoulder, she leaned into her and said softly. "January 11."

"Ma'am?" replied Virginia not understanding the comment.

"January 11, that's the day of my court hearing," said Sarah. "After that I'll be as free as a bird!"

"Oh, divorce," replied Virginia. "I've had the unsavory experience. It's much better once you get through it all."

In fact, Sarah Ottis had been "free as a bird" for some time. Her husband, Dr. Daniel Ottis had returned to his practice in Springfield, Illinois after the war. But like many men who returned, Dr. Ottis was not quite the same man. His wife, however, was unchanged.

Prior to his departure for Europe in May of 1918, Dr. Ottis had spent one year intensely building his medical unit and did not return from the war for a full year after that. Sarah had been coming and going as she pleased, traveling extensively to New York, Washington, Chicago, Los Angeles and anywhere she desired. During 1918, she had practically shadowed Pat to hear him speak. Sometimes she would make a point to say "hello" at receptions. Other times she would simply sit in the audience and watch him take control over hundreds in the hall. She understood his powerful nature. Pat only saw her a few times. He was generally unaware of her presence with the exception of Chicago and the encounter in Sullivan, Illinois.

Like many officers' wives Sarah volunteered during the war. She worked at bond rallies, wrapped bandages for the Red Cross, helped with receptions and volunteered for attractive events as she had this night in Washington D.C. She knew Pat was on the panel. She'd read it in one of the many war-time magazines to which she subscribed.

Virginia looked forlornly at the large crowd around the stage all attempting to meet the speakers personally.

"Gosh, it will be an hour before I get close enough to meeting anyone," Virginia said. "It's been such a long day. I wonder if Mr. O'Brien will be in town a day or two. I'd really like to talk to him."

"Look, sweetie," said Sarah. "I've got an idea. I'll be in town a few more days. I can talk to Pat and see when he plans to depart. If there's a way, perhaps you can obtain an exclusive interview with him. Do you have a business card? Can you be reached locally?"

"I do have a card, Virginia said. "Let me write my parents number on the back. I reside with them when I'm not in Los Angeles. Will you really call me? I mean will you, for certain?"

"Why, of course, dear," replied Sarah. "I promise I'll talk to Pat and call you. I can't guarantee he'll be here long, of course, but I will find out for you."

"Oh, thank you so much Mrs. Ottis," responded Virginia. "I really appreciate you helping me. If I can get this interview it will impress my editor. He's so hard to please."

Virginia really cared little about impressing her editor. Oh sure, perhaps it would get her a plum assignment here or there but she really had little trouble getting to the events she desired. The social circle was perfect for her. Pat was someone with a name, an image and connections that just might get her where she wanted to be, back on the silver screen. She'd had a few bit parts here and there but nothing substantial. To Virginia, Pat was perfect. He was a known war hero, strong presenter on stage and a look that rivaled anyone in Hollywood. She could surely get into a producer's office by offering to introduce them to the famous Pat O'Brien.

Virginia thanked Sarah again and left for home. Forty-five minutes passed and Sarah was finally able to get to Pat.

"Lieutenant O'Brien, how are you?" asked Sarah extending her two hands and an overdone smile.

"Hello, ma'am," Pat said, "Sarah… Ottis right?" He'd spoken her first name and she added her voice to his when he pronounced her last name, slowing him down with emphasis. They both laughed nervously. Pat would not have recalled her were it not for Hesser mentioning the call he received from a woman named Ottis.

"It's so wonderful to see you here in Washington," she said. "I haven't seen you for some time."

"Yes, I've been in Russia," replied Pat.

"I know. I know," said Sarah, again with exaggerated warmth. "I spoke with your good friend Edwin Hesser. Such a wonderful man, talented, too. I hear he is considered one of the most talented photographers in the movie business. And he tells me he's known you for some time."

"He has," replied Pat.

"Look, Lieutenant, the reason I called Mr. Hesser was to get a message to you," Sarah said. "I brought your name up with some friends of mine in Washington last September. I assume you've heard about the formation of the American Legion?"

"I have," Pat replied.

"These men were officers from the war. A few knew my husband. They were in Washington to address a Congressional committee about receiving their charter. Our group of volunteers hosted a reception for them," explained Sarah. "Actually, it was right here at the Willard.

"Ok," replied Pat, listening a bit now.

"Well, naturally, we socialized with the men and talked about their plans," she said. "They told me about the goals and projects they'd like to support. By the way, they just finished their first convention in Minneapolis; let's see, five days ago. I received call from one of the men, just yesterday, wondering if I had any luck."

"How so?" asked Pat.

"We were talking about one of their interests, a film," said Sarah.

"A film, you mean a movie?" asked Pat.

"Sure," responded Sarah. "They want to sponsor a film about the Japanese."

"Is that right, the Japa…" said Pat drawn in a bit more.

"Sure," she said interrupting him. "Of course they know nothing about the movie business, so I said to them, 'I could probably put you in touch with someone in the movie business.' You see, my daughter is married to a young man in Hollywood. She was married to him but then I made her get a divorce. I mean the boy was only 18. But he's a fresh face, apparently he can act and, well, she fell for him. He's from Chicago. So anyway, Just as these Legion men were getting ready to leave, it struck me."

"What?" Pat asked.

She went on. "I said to Mr. Wood, just before they left, "Look Erik, I know who you should put in that movie of yours. Then he said 'who?' and I said 'Pat O'Brien!' I told him you were perfect, well known, well spoken, good looking. He rather agreed. I think they want someone that can draw an audience."

"How are they involved again?" asked Pat.

"They're willing to put up some money," responded Sarah. "They seem to have strong feelings about the Japanese."

"I can understand that," Pat said. "The Japanese didn't impress me while I was in Russia. None of our allies trust them. I do believe they have an agenda in Asia. Listen Mrs. Ottis, I'll talk to my friend Hesser, see what he says. If he agrees, then you can tell someone to contact me if they haven't selected someone already."

"That's grand," replied Sarah. "How can I reach you?"

"Well, I'm traveling now so the best thing is to call either Hesser or call the New York Giants office and leave a message for McGraw, their manager. I'll be with him quite a bit in the next few weeks. From there, who knows?"

Pat shook her hand and left the ballroom. He wondered whether or not any of what Sarah Ottis said was real or if she was just creating something on her own. "Oh, well," he thought. "Hesser will know what to do. He knows these people. At least she can't find me directly. If it doesn't smell right, Hess will intercept for me."

Pat was hungry but he decided to get into some more comfortable clothes and then come down for dinner. Most of the dining rooms required a tie but he wanted to get out of his shoes. They were new and bothered his feet. Pat had a quiet dinner alone that night.

The next morning the phone was ringing at the Livingston estate.

"Hello, Livingston's," said Virginia.

"Virginia Dear," said Sarah Ottis. "I have great news. I spoke with Lieutenant O'Brien. He's open to it."

"An interview?" asked Virginia

"Interview?" Sarah paused. "Oh, no dear, doing a film. I asked him about doing a film."

"You didn't ask if he'd meet with me?" replied Virginia.

"Sure, in a way, don't you see," assured Sarah. "Were I to ask him straight away of course he would say no. This way a meeting is arranged, a second perhaps and you can be brought in, my dear. Not as a reporter, mind you, perhaps as my assistant, let's say. Yes, that would work wonderfully. I arrange for Mr. O'Brien to meet some film people, you're along with me and not only do you get more than an interview, you meet some film people, as well."

Sarah Ottis had few contacts in the film business but Virginia didn't know that. Sarah had a way, however, of inserting herself into advantageous situations and then seeking a solution after she committed. In her mind, Virginia's request gave her a reason to approach Pat, as if she was strictly a messenger. In really, she had totally forgotten Virginia's request once she got to Pat and he received her willingly. Always able to think on her feet, she concocted a strategy to explain her omission. Virginia bought it.

Sarah figured she'd go back to Hesser. But before that, she needed to reach Colonel E. Lester Jones. Jones had been selected to lead the first Legion post in Washington and had just returned from Minneapolis where the organization had been formalized. Sarah met had him, along with others on the committee, when they visited Congress seeking their official charter back in September.

In Europe, frustration ran rampant among U.S. troops following Armistice. American soldiers were more than ready to leave the mundane, muddy and morbid European battlefield and be home once again. They read about booming times, cities all across America that were modernizing, and carefree young adults, many their age, enjoying the first postwar euphoria of the 20th Century. Troop draw down after war is always slow. But the mounds of paperwork and sluggish processing had become unbearable for the two million soldiers in Europe waiting for a ship home.

By the spring of 1919, morale had plummeted within American ranks still in Europe. The Bolshevik uprisings taking place in Russia, Finland, Germany and Hungary were not lost on the minds of U.S. Army brass, either. Something needed to be done to improve conditions for the American soldier still trapped in Europe, waiting to go home.

The situation in Europe concerned Lt. Colonel Theodore Roosevelt, Jr., eldest son of the 26th President. In January, he discussed the situation with National Guard officer George A. White, a former newspaper editor with the Portland Oregonian. Roosevelt's idea was to form a new servicemen's organization for all members of the American Expeditionary Force overseas and the soldiers who had already made it home.

The early involvement of George White was significant. Being from Oregon, he not only understood the general fear of the Bolshevik movement within the United States, but he also understood the secondary concern that permeated the west coast, concern about Japanese ambition.

Roosevelt, with the approval and directive of General Pershing himself, led the first caucus for European-based American soldiers at the YMCA in Paris on February 5, 1919. Following a second caucus in St. Louis and the Founding Convention held in Minneapolis in early November, the first Legion Post was established and named for General John G. Pershing, located in Washington D.C. The focus in Europe was keeping the troops happy and affecting a more rapid exit home. On the U.S. side early founders were concerned about assimilating the veteran to American life after the war, holding firm on Veteran's benefits, establishing posts around the country, and forming a political voice that would represent the interests of all American Vets in Washington.

After talking with Virginia, Sarah placed a call to her contact with the American Legion, Colonel Jones. She was surprised when he picked up the phone directly.

"Hello, Colonel Jones, is this you?" asked Sarah.

"Yes, this is he," responded Jones. "How may I help you?"

"Oh Colonel, I'm surprised, well not surprised but pleased it is you," responded Sarah. "This is Mrs. Daniel Ottis calling. You may recall my husband headed Unit W in the war? I spoke with you and the other officers in September when you received the American Legion charter. Do you recall?"

"Yes, I do recall," responded Jones.

"Well, I had a question for you Colonel," Sarah said. "I remember you discussing the committee's plans for the American Legion. You mentioned sponsoring a film about the Japanese issue. I was wondering. Is your group still considering this?"

"Ah, yes," replied Jones, "it was discussed in Minneapolis. I know that Adjutant General White is quite high on the idea. He's from Oregon of course and this sounded important to the folks on the west coast."

"Good, that's very good, Colonel," responded Sarah. "I hate to bother you with such details Colonel but has anyone on your staff or within the American Legion been put in charge of seeing this through?"

"If my memory serves, I believe we put the Los Angeles post in charge of speaking to the Hollywood people about this," Jones said. These would be the people on the ground taking first steps. I believe the officer's name is Taylor Duncan. He was at our convention and if I remember correctly, he seemed to have a lot contacts in the movie business and was part of the Los Angeles group.

"Wonderful!" exclaimed Sarah. She couldn't believe her ears. Colonel Jones gave her much more than she anticipated. She had assurance that the Legion still had interest and she had a contact. All she had to do was confirm if Duncan had spoken with any film people yet and then use Hesser to bring Pat's name to the fore.

"Thank you very much, Colonel," Sarah said, quite literally ready to bust at the seams. "You've been a tremendous help."

"You're quite welcome, Mrs. Ottis, said the Colonel. "Contact my office here in Washington and I'm sure they can provide you with contact information for Duncan. How is Colonel Ottis these days? I must say, I have never met your husband but know of his great work in Liverpool during the war. Such a difficult plague he had to deal with there. He did tremendous work in the war."

"Yes, he's fine," she said jolted a bit by the question.

"You wish him well, will you?" replied Jones. "He's a good man."

"I certainly will, Colonel" replied Sarah. "I most certainly will."

Sarah hung up the phone a bit dizzy from that last conversation. "Lord help me," she thought to herself. "It hadn't crossed my mind but I might face a bit of a handicap not being able to use Daniel's name after January. Well, until my divorce is final, I need to make use of it. Everything needs to happen before January 11th."

Sarah was a manipulator, a virtuoso, in fact. She had some strong desire to be someone other than who she was, to be something more than what she was, to be somewhere else other than where she was, and be considered indispensable to anyone she met. She was a driven woman in pursuit of a happiness that she surely had in presence of Daniel Mortimer Ottis. But for some reason, she never seemed happy living with the highly admired man who failed to possess the same thirst for attention as did she.

Pat returned to New York on Sunday evening, November 23. He checked back into the Astor Hotel and when he got to his room, the phone was ringing.

"Hello," said Pat.

"Pat, it's Hess," was the voice on the other line.

"Yeah, Hess, how are you," replied Pat.

"Hey, that woman called me again." Hesser said.

"Who's that?" asked Pat.

"You know, that Ottis woman," replied Hesser.

"Oh, yeah, her," said Pat. "What does she want?"

"Well, she wants to meet with us," replied Hesser. "She lives in New York and wants to have lunch." Pausing he continued. "Tuesday."

"She probably wants to talk about that movie stuff, right?" asked Pat.

"Oh, you know about that, huh?' Hesser asked.

"Yeah, she tackled me in Washington, Hess," Pat said.

"Well, you want to meet with her?" asked Hesser.

"I don't care. Does she have anything?" asked Pat.

"Apparently she's talking to some American Legion guy and a local vet in Los Angeles who's supposed to be putting the project together."

"Yeah, Japanese deal, right?" Pat replied.

"Right," said Hesser.

"It can't hurt to have lunch with her," confirmed Pat. "Go ahead and set it up if you want. Let's see what she says."

"Ok, let's do it in the hotel," replied Hesser. "We don't want to spend the whole afternoon on a fishing trip."

"I agree," Pat said. "Talk to you tomorrow."

[697]

"Right," said Hesser, "I'll call you in the morning."

The next day, Hesser called while Pat was having breakfast down stairs. As Pat was finishing up his last cup of coffee, a bellman stepped over and handed him a note. It read:

"All set. Delmonico's on Fifth Street, tomorrow at noon. Be downstairs at 11:30." Hesser also left a phone number.

"Thank you," Pat said to the bellman who was standing dutifully at attention for a reply, and a tip. "Call Mr. Hesser at this number and let him know that I have received his message." Pat handed the boy a tip who clicked his heals and went off.

Pat spent the day as a tourist. He'd been to New York many times and had spent leisure hours between speeches just walking around Manhattan. He returned to the hotel about 5:00 p.m. He felt like he'd been on a roller coaster ever since he'd hit town. He was tired. When Pat got tired it usually only lasted a day and he knew when to take a day off. Before riding the elevator upstairs, he walked over to a bank of phones in the lobby. He reached into his pocket and pulled out a phone number he'd written on a small piece of paper.

"Hudson 3747, please," he said to the operator.

"Hello," said the voice on the other end.

"Weems! You dog!" said Pat. "It's O'Brien."

"O'Brien!" said the man on the other line. "How did you find me? Where are you?"

"I'm in New York Hess gave me your number," Pat replied

"Where you staying?" asked Weems.

"I'm at the Astor," responded Pat.

"Pat, come out to our show," responded Weems. "I'm doing a review with Harry Delf and Ralph Herz at Keith's"

"My God, Weems you're still playing Keith's," said Pat.

"It's not so bad," said Weems. "I mean Herz and Delf, you don't get much better than those two. Why don't you come out?"

[698]

"Not tonight, Walter," responded Pat. "I've got to get some sleep. I just got back from Washington. Before that McGraw kicked my backside all over Manhattan."

"Those guys?" said Weems laughing. "They are relentless. So when, Pat? When can we get together?"

"I assume you're off next Monday night," replied Pat. "How about next Monday?"

"Let's do it," agreed Weems. "Why don't I show up at the Astor at seven o'clock and we'll start with dinner."

"Perfect," Pat said. "I'll see you in a week. Great talking to you Walter,"

"Crazy, man," Weems said. "See you next Monday."

Pat had become good friends with Weems at the end of 1918 when Pat was speaking on the Vaudeville Circuit. Though he disliked those final days on the road, he enjoyed the many "show-biz" people he met in New York. Weems spoke fondly of the time he visited Momence with Pat. Weems was a real pro. He'd done classical Vaudeville including "Black Face" through most of 1918. He was a talented singer, dancer and musician, playing the tuba in his act, turning the mundane into a comedic skit that highlighted his show. Everyone on and off Broadway knew Weems. Hesser knew him well. Both Weems and Hesser had dabbled in some movie making in Hollywood. Weems acted in a film written by Hesser in 1917 and was casted, as usual, in a comedic role full of slapstick.

Pat got a good night's sleep and was up early reading the paper the next morning over three eggs and a steak. At 11:30 he went out to look for Hesser.

"Morning, Pat," said Hesser as he pulled up in a cab, swinging open the door.

"Hi, Ed," responded Pat.

Hesser went over the likely scenario of the Ottis meeting.

"We'll let her talk, react slowly and see if she's really got something," said Hesser. "If she does, you'll be able to tell. I'll start asking probing questions and give you a signal. If that happens then feel free to ask what you wish. Just don't commit. If the whole thing sounds like bull, we'll probably both pick that up."

[699]

"Sounds good to me, Hess," responded Pat.

Ten minutes into the luncheon meeting, Hess gave Pat a positive signal. Sarah had learned that Paul Hurst had agreed to do the film and the American Legion was prepared to put up $150,000. Hurst was an established actor and director in Hollywood. Hesser knew Hurst from his time in Los Angeles.

"I'll be happy to call Paul and recommend Pat for the film," Hesser said to Sarah.

"Wonderful!" she replied.

Pat was indifferent but thought it would be fun. He'd never acted before but both Hesser and Ottis were confident he'd be a natural. Sarah thanked the two men and asked Hesser to call her as soon as he spoke with Hurst. He promised he'd call Hurst in the morning.

"Perhaps if Mr. Hurst has interest he can come to New York and meet with us," said Sarah.

"Let's see what he says first," replied Hesser.

Ottis left leaving Pat and Hesser alone at the table.

"I notice she said 'us'," stated Hesser.

"You noticed that, huh?" replied Pat with a grin.

"The woman is pushy," stated Hesser. "I don't need her to put a movie deal together."

"Well, to be fair, she did bring it to us," replied Pat.

"Yeah, but I don't trust her," answered Hesser.

On Friday of that week, Hesser reached Hurst.

"Hi Paul, it's Ed Hesser in New York," he said.

"Ed, how are things," replied Hurst.

"Quite well. I keep getting muscled by producers to move to Los Angeles," replied Hesser.

"You should," Hurst stated. "It's mad out here. There's more work than we can handle. We need talented people like you."

"Yeah and New York goes dry, I suppose?" Hesser said with humor in his voice. Hurst laughed.

"Say, Paul, I'm told you might have gotten approached by the new veteran's group about doing a film, is that true?" asked Hesser.

"Yeah. Those guys have some money. They're pretty serious," replied Hurst.

"What's it about?" asked Hesser.

"Well, they want something that convinces audiences that the Japanese have their sites on American soil," explained Hurst.

"What do you think?" asked Hesser.

"What? About the project or the Japanese?" asked Hurst?

"Yeah, the Japanese," replied Hesser.

"Hell, I don't know," replied Hurst. "Who the hell cares, the money is there, that's for sure. If they want a convincing film, I can make it for them."

"What's your idea?" asked Hesser.

"Well, I thought we'd do a standard cowboy film," replied Hurst. "You know, young good looking cowboy, beautiful young girl. The hero goes off to war. The Japanese edge their way in, try to take over the ranch while our war hero is off to war, hassle the women and just when the bad guy is about to cut our sweet young heroine's throat, our hero marches in, back from the war, and saves the day!"

Hesser belted out a hardy laugh. "Nobody knows how to make that work better than you, Hurst" said Hesser still laughing.

"Listen, Paul," said Hesser, finally catching his breath. "I think I've got a hero for you."

"Who's that?" asked Paul.

"You've heard of him, I think," replied Hesser. "I've known him since my Signal Corps days. Pat O'Brien, the war hero."

"The pilot that escaped, right?" asked Hurst.

"Yes, him. I've known him for years," responded Hesser.

"Can he act?" asked Hurst.

"Hell, I don't know," replied Hesser. "But I'll tell you he can speak, that's for sure. I've seen him in action. He made more money than William Jennings Bryant in 1918. Talked all over the country."

"Hey, so did Woodrow Wilson, but I'd never put him in a film," replied Hurst, again causing Hesser to laugh.

"Ok, I'll give you that. But no, this guy's got looks, personality, great eyes and an infectious smile," said Hesser. "Not only that, Paul, the whole damn country knows who he is. He's perfect."

"I don't want him too perfect. My wife Hedda is playing the lead female role," said Hurst jokingly.

"Well, I can't help you with that, pal," replied Hesser.

Hurst agreed and expressed a willingness to come to New York to meet Pat. Hesser would get back to him on a date, either prior to the holidays or right after the first of the year. Paul was pleased. He had a money commitment, a lead male and lead female. His wife was Hedda Nova, a soulful brunette actress from the Ukraine. She became an early star for the pioneering Vitagraph Company, appearing in such melodramas as The Changing Woman in 1918 and the serial The Woman in Red that same year. Nova's popularity was fleeting, however, and at this point she was starring in cheap Westerns and other low-budget genre films. Paul thought a national hit such as the American Legion anti-Japanese film, could revise her career.

Hurst asked one more question.

"You want to write it, Hess?" he asked.

"Now you know I can't right cowboy scripts," replied Hesser.

"Ok, I just wanted to ask you first, Hurst replied.

"Thanks, Paul. I'll talk to you soon," ended Hess and the two men hung up.

Hurst would sign Seymour Zeliff to write the script. Zeliff had been acting in films since 1915, one of the early legends to come to Hollywood. He was a New Jersey boy but became acclimated to California and was fond of playing cowboys. This would be his first screenplay which he eagerly took on when Paul called giving him his chance. Hurst would contract Cinema Craft and Motion Pictures Producing Company of America to produce the film, two small production companies one of which he owned.
Hesser called Pat the next morning.

"Welcome to the movie business, O'Brien, he said.

"Ok, what did you do behind my back, Hess," said Pat.

"I talked to Paul Hurst in Hollywood. He's on board with the whole plan," said Hesser. "He's met with the American Legion guys and says they've got a good purse behind the whole thing, over $150,000."

"Holy shit," said Pat.

"Exactly," replied Hesser. "Look Pat, he wants to come to New York next week and meet you. Are you in town all next week?"

"Sure, I'm here," said Pat. "McGraw comes back from Cuba on Friday but other than that, I'm open all week. Oh, wait, I'm having dinner with Walter Weems Monday night. Why don't you join us?"

"Weems, sounds great. Let's do that," replied Hesser. "Just let me know. In the meantime, I'll get back to Hurst and see when he can be here. Naturally, it will take him a while to travel to New York. My guess is likely Wednesday or Thursday. He seems ready to get moving on the whole thing."

"Ok, let's talk tomorrow," said Pat. "But plan on dinner with Weems Monday, ok?"

"Sure thing," replied Hesser. "Talk to you tomorrow."

Hesser wired Paul Hurst. The two exchanged telegrams and in a phone call on November 30 confirmed a meeting in New York for Wednesday, December 3. Hesser left a message at the hotel for Pat. It read, "All set for Wednesday with Hurst. We'll talk details Monday over dinner."

Paul enjoyed a quite November weekend in New York. On Sunday morning, he went to church at John Street Methodist Church in south Manhattan. The church was the oldest Methodist congregation in all of America, founded in 1766. It was a reflective time for him. He could feel a new chapter opening for himself, perhaps. "God only knows where I'll go next," he thought to himself as he sat listening to the choir sing the hymn "Lord, I'm Coming Home," Written in 1892 by William J. Kirkpatrick. As his thoughts drifted elsewhere the lyric suddenly seeped into his consciousness.

I've wandered far away from God:
Now I'm coming home;
The paths of sin too long I've trod:
Lord, I'm coming home.

Coming home, Coming home,
Nevermore to roam;
Open wide Thine arms of love:
Lord, I'm coming home.

On Monday, Hesser arrived at the Astor to pick up Pat and Walter Weems.

"Where we going?" asked Pat.

"I say we do Italian tonight," said Weems. "Driver, Pete's Tavern on 18th Street, please."

Hesser and Pat looked at each other and shrugged in acceptance. They rode down Broadway then left a few blocks arriving at 18th and Irving. All three got out and Pat paid the driver. Pete's Tavern had been around since 1864 and was a favorite of Walter's. It had just the right mix of lore and cuisine that he sought. William Sydney Porter, known by his pen name, O. Henry, wrote his classic "Gift of the Magi" here in 1904 while sitting in his favorite booth near the door. A sign hung over their intricately carved bar that read, "The bar that O. Henry made famous."

Pat and his friends took a seat in one of the dark wooden booths, complete with lamp post-like fixture that lit their table. They all three ordered the "house ale" which was standard operating procedure for regulars at Pete's. "Ok, Hurst is coming in Thursday, Pat," stated Hesser.

"That will work fine," responded Pat. "McGraw is due to arrive Friday and I'm sure he'll want to tell me all about his time in Cuba. Their grand opening was last Thursday, on Thanksgiving."

Right then, Pat realized that Thanksgiving had passed and he totally missed it. He'd not called Clara or sent a wire, or anything. "Holy Hell," he thought. "I've got to call Clara, first chance I get."

"Wait a minute fellows," said Weems, "McGraw, Hurst, who we talking about. Not Paul Hurst is it?"

"Sure," said Hesser, "Didn't Pat tell you? He's going to be in the movies."

"Fantastic!" shouted Weems, as the whole bar looked toward their booth. "How marvelous, and you didn't tell me, Pat?"

"I haven't seen you until today," replied Pat who then took a deep swig of his beer.

Hesser then went on to explain the whole arrangement, who was already planned to write and produce the film and other details he knew. He and Weems told Pat what to expect from Hurst and discussed legal matters. Hesser told Pat that he would call his friend in Pittsburgh after the Hurst meeting.

"We'll call Myron Selznick in Pittsburgh," said Hesser. "He can advise us on price but we need to wait until we meet with Hurst.

"You're such a big help to me, Ed," said Pat. "You can do about anything can't you."

"That, he can," exclaimed Weems, "That, he can." He took a solid swig of his ale.

In the early years of the film industry, there was a constant series of mergers and acquisitions among studios as individual moguls jockeyed for position. In 1917, Selznick merged with Adolph Zukor's Famous Players Pictures, creating Select Pictures, later reorganized as the Selznick Film Co. He eventually bought out Zukor and merged the two companies into Selznick-Select, then acquired World Pictures' film exchanges, which he renamed Republic Distributing Corps. He knew the business side of the motion picture business as few did in 1919. His brother was David O. Selznick who was just learning the business.

Dinner went on 'till midnight. The three friends covered nearly every topic from aviation, to Vaudeville, the Great War, women, Russia, China, the movies and sports. As they stood to leave, Pat asked Hesser a question.

"You gonna call the woman?"

Hess looked up at him while placing his tip on the table. "You mean Ottis?" he said.

"Yes," replied Pat.

"I supposed I should," replied Hesser. "I see you're making her my job, huh?"

"Hey, I'm the star now. You need to be my manager. Managers make phone calls for their stars, right?" Pat said in a jokingly manner. "Besides Hess, the women love you, you know that, Hess."

"You're an ass, you know that, O'Brien?" replied Hess.

"Private 1st Class!" stated Pat as he went to attention and flashed a British salute.

The next morning Hess called Sarah. She was animate about being at the Hurst meeting.

"After all," she said, "I brought the whole deal to your attention."

Hesser relented and promised to let her know of the time and location as soon as he knew.

The following day, Pat got a call from McGraw's office. The lady on the phone indicated that the Giants Manager planned to be back in New York on Friday for the winter meetings.

"He'd like to call you, Mr. O'Brien. Might there be a time when you'll be in your room and he can call you from Havana?"

"Well, I'm here now," replied Pat. "I can take his call until 2:00 p.m. when I must leave for a meeting.

"I will have him call you shortly, ok?" said the woman.

"Sure, I'll wait by the phone," replied Pat sitting back down on the edge of the bed.

The woman hung up and Pat lay back on his bed fully dressed for the day but now detained. He crossed his legs and fell asleep until the phone rang about twenty minutes later.

"Hello," said Pat somewhat groggy from his cat nap.

"One moment for Mr. McGraw, please," said the voice on the other end.

"Pat? It's John," said McGraw sounding some distance away.

"Hi John," replied Pat. "How are things in Cuba?"

"Tremendous," McGraw said with enthusiasm. "We're making all kinds of money down here. I can't wait to get you to Havana."

"Sounds great, John" replied Pat. With the flurry of activity the last few days, he'd almost forgotten about John's talk of Havana with him going there and all.

"Listen, Pat, I'll be home Friday," said McGraw. "I've got those damn baseball meetings then I'm heading right back to Havana and I want you to come back with me."

"When do you plan to return?" asked Pat.

"We'll be done in five days with our meetings. I'll want to get right back so no more than a week," replied McGraw. "You and I should plan on leaving New York on the twelfth, a week from Friday.

Pat's head was spinning. How could he pick up and go to Cuba in eight days. Hurst was due in the next day. There'd be meetings, perhaps another trip to Washington in case the Legion wanted to sign off. What if Hurst needs him to go to California? When would he they actually start shooting. How could he possibly go?

"John, some things have developed here," said Pat. "I don't know if I can get away to Havana just now."

"What the hell are you talking about, O'Brien?" barked McGraw. "We talked all about this. You were going to come down, stay at the hotel, gamble a little, hang around the race track. I told you we need some pretty faces down there. We need Americans with money. With people like you around it will be an additional draw. I told you Pat, it's all on us."

Pat explained the whole situation, the movie deal, Hurst arriving, Sarah Ottis. McGraw was quiet on the other line.

"Look, Pat, I've got a tremendous idea," replied McGraw. "Let's bring the whole damn crowd down. What better way to put the deal together then in the beautiful climate of Cuba. You, Hess, Hurst, the woman, anyone from Hollywood or New York that needs to be there. Hell, bring the whole American Legion for all I care. The more the merrier."

"I can't speak for everyone else but I'll bring it up to Hesser," replied Pat.

"Bring it up!" he said raising his voice. "Don't just bring it up. Call Hesser now and ask him. I can call you back later today. No better yet, give me his number. I'll call him."

"Well, listen, John," said Pat, firmly. "At least give me time to alert the guy. For heaven's sake I don't want to spring this whole thing on him cold."

"You're right, you call him first," said McGraw lowering his tone. "I'll wait a few hours then give him a call."

The two men hung up. Pat called Hesser and explained the whole deal. To his surprise Hesser was not against it. He told Pat to give him time to call Hurst, which he did. Hurst was also positive. "A week in Cuba sounds like fun," he said. "There's little on Hedda's or my schedule now that we're contracted for this project."

McGraw called Hesser about 3:30 in the afternoon and repeated the whole scenario.

"We're good on this end, John," Hesser told him. "Hurst will likely bring some folks as will I. There may be some people from Washington, too.

"Absolutely perfect," shouted McGraw distorting the signal in the telephone. "I'll be back in New York tomorrow. That will give us time to work out the details."

"Great, John," replied Hesser. "See you when you get back."

Hesser called Pat. "It's on Pat. We're all going to Cuba. Don't know when but McGraw will be back tomorrow and we'll put it all together."

"Hurst, too?" asked Pat.

"Yeah, he's all for it," replied Hesser.

"Ok, then, sounds like it's coming together," Pat said. "I'll talk to you tomorrow, ok?"

"Sure," said Hesser.

"Better call that woman, Hess," reminded Pat.

"Oh yeah, forgot about her," Hesser replied. "Thanks for the reminder, pal."

Hesser called Sarah Ottis. She could not have been more exuberant. She was thrilled to hear the news. Hesser told her he'd get back to her with details once McGraw and he met.

"It's absolutely marvelous," she said. "Talk to you soon," her voice lilting up as before.

"Indeed, Sarah," replied Hesser.

As soon as Hesser hung up, Sarah Ottis tapped on the receiver rapidly to signal the operator. The operator came on the line.

"Would you like to make a call, ma'am?" she asked.

"Yes, give me Jefferson 4450 in Washington DC," said Sarah.

"Hello, Livingston residence," said Virginia on the other end. Sarah recognized her voice.

"Virginia, my dear," said Sarah. "How would you like to go to Havana, Cuba with none other than Lieutenant Pat O'Brien?"

Chapter 52

Havana

John McGraw arrived in New York City on Friday, December 5 at 10:00 a.m. Edwin Hesser, Sarah Ottis, Lee Keedick, and Pat were sitting in the lobby of the Astor Hotel awaiting his arrival. Pat had asked Lee to participate as a personal favor to him. Though he and Hesser were close, Pat felt more confident having Keedick there. Hesser was more on the creative side. Keedick was an entertainment business manager. Hesser had put Pat in touch with Selznick in Pittsburgh that morning. Selznick advised they not commit to a dollar amount for Pat until they heard the entire scheme, budget and offer which would be made by Hurst.

John McGraw entered the lobby of the Astor and everyone moved to the restaurant. McGraw offered use of his Havana hotel at no cost. He asked that Hesser simply send him how many rooms would be needed and he'd set it up. Meeting rooms would also be available.

It was decided to leave in one week on Friday, December 12. That would get them to Key West on Sunday. It was agreed to depart for Havana the following Monday.

"Friday, the 13th," commented Pat.

"Pilots, always superstitious," said Hesser, which drew a chuckle from everyone.

"No, it's my birthday," replied Pat.

"That makes it even more special!" said Hesser. "How old?"

"I'll be 29," replied Pat.

"Just a child," added Keedick.

McGraw would be in baseball meetings all week. Pat would make a short trip to Annapolis, Maryland. He'd been asked to meet with a small group of the Navy Pilots who'd heard his speech the previous week but requested additional time with Pat. He had agreed.

Sarah mentioned she'd be bringing a personal assistant with her to Cuba. Hesser invited Keedick to join them. Lee indicated he could not come down until after the holiday but agreed he'd join them for a few days.

"I've got too many shows running in December," Keedick said.

At 9:00 a.m., Monday, December 8, Pat took a train to Baltimore. Two smartly uniformed Navy pilots were standing next to a 1919 Dole Aero-Eight Tour Sedan. The two officers were Lt. Michael J. Howling and Lt. Hugh Livingston. Pat walked up to the two men and shook their hands.

Hugh Livingston was one of the new breed of Naval Pilots, men who graduated from Annapolis and would form the backbone of the new Navy Air program.

Hugh opened the back door on the driver's side. Pat could see there was a female sitting on the other side of the back seat. He could not see the woman's face, just her dress which covered her knees, revealing white hose and a pair of stylish shoes.

"Sir, my sister is with us," said Hugh. "She is a journalist and is covering our event this afternoon. I hope you don't mind if she accompanies us to the Academy. Do you mind if she interviews you?"

"Not at all, Lieutenant," said Pat, glancing inside the car again at the woman's legs. "I enjoy giving interviews," as he quickly glanced inside and back at Hugh.

"Lieutenant, this is my sister Virginia," Hugh said extending his arm into the car. Then leaning down to look in he stated, "Virginia, Lieutenant O'Brien."

Pat lowered his frame and climbed into the back seat. Once settled he sat square and turned to the woman.

"Hello," he said.

"Hello, Mr. O'Brien," said Virginia. "I'm Virginia Allen. Thank you for agreeing to visit with me."

"Glad to meet you," said Pat extending his hand which Virginia clasped delicately bowing her head slightly.

Pat, like most men, found her quite beautiful. She had a confident demeanor yet delivered in waves of feminism that disarmed even the most calculating male. Pat notice how stylish she dressed in the latest modern style.

[711]

Virginia asked a number of questions and was effective. Both were easily charmed by each other. By the time the car arrived at the Academy, the two were bellowing in a lighthearted manner as if old friends. At one point, their laughter even caused the two young Lieutenants to look at each other with raised eyebrows.

The presentation was intimate, twenty-eight top pilots, all graduates of the Academy. Pat made a short statement but as was his usual approach with fellow soldiers, he let the men ask any questions they wished. In less than ten minutes a repartee hung thick over the group of pilots. Pat had once again drawn in his audience, each pilot imagining a one-on-one conversation was occurring.

Virginia noticed his ability to communicate above all other qualities. His stories and descriptions about dog fights included hand gestures that intrigued each pilot in the room. He talked about Europe, the French and British Air Force and, of course the Deutsche Luftstreitkräfte or German Air Force.

The presentation was over about 4:00. The men hung around Pat for another half hour with "just one more question." When finished, Hugh drove Pat and his sister back to Baltimore. Pat insisted Virginia sit in the front seat with her brother. He sat in the back. Virginia talked most of the time, turned ninety degrees with her arm draped across the back of the front seat which Pat also found attractive.

When they reached Baltimore, Pat asked Hugh where he was based.

"I'm actually at home at this time. I'm to be transferred to Pensacola in a week so I'm currently on leave," said Hugh.

"Let me buy you two dinner," said Pat. "I'm staying the night and would enjoy the company."

Hugh looked to his sister, "Sis?" he asked.

"Sure, sounds like fun," said Virginia.

Pat took them to Marconi's Restaurant which had just opened. The night was a mix of personal histories, the new contemporary fashions, people of note, and the future. Pat enjoyed talking about "normal stuff" and not about his war.

After two hours, Hugh dismissed himself. The conversation between Pat and Virginia suddenly narrowed to flirts, teasing, personal desires and gleeful conjecture about what the night might bring.

Clearly, the flicker of the candlelight was not the only flare illuminating the corner table in Marconi's that night. Pat and Virginia left after three hours and decided to walk south toward the Light Street Pier on the Inner Harbor. It was a mild night for December yet chilly enough that Pat offered his arm to Virginia who willingly wrapped both hands through, snuggling closely as they walked into a light breeze. It had been a very long time since Pat had experienced a private conversation about personal thoughts with anyone, let alone a beautiful woman.

At midnight, Pat hailed a cab and made the short trip to the Belvidere Hotel on Charles Street. They both exited the cab and stood chatting near a streetlamp illuminating the walkway.

"I think it best if I arranged a car for you," said Pat, facing her and holding her two hands.

"I don't disagree with you nor would I disagree should you suggest something different," Virginia said, leaning toward him.

Pat lowered his arms and wrapped them around her as if to hold off the evening chill.

After about a minute, he let go and said hastily with a smile, "I'll get a driver."

Then just as quickly, he turned his head slightly and kissed her lightly on her red lips. He turned and stepped over to the doorman leaving Virginia standing in disbelief if for no other reason than the suddenness of his move. Her arms held still, wrists arched down as if still holding his. Pat came back to her quickly.

"They're getting you a comfortable car, Virginia," Pat said. Then he looked at her perplexed stare and her arms up in what appeared like a begging position. "You look like a hungry puppy."

Virginia cracked up and smacked him on his arm. They both laughed then faded into a genuine hug that moved gently into a long kiss and full embrace.

[713]

Pat heard a cab pull up, released his hold on Virginia and taking her hand, escorted her to the curb. He opened the door. She passed in front of him and before stepping down turned kissed him quickly on the cheek.

"I had fun, Pat," she said.

"I did, too," Pat replied.

Virginia slid into the back seat and the cab pulled away.

The next morning Sarah Ottis dialed up the Livingston home. Hugh answered the phone.

"She's sleeping," Hugh told Sarah. "She had a long day, yesterday."

"Ok, I will try her later," responded Ottis.

Pat was up, in usual form, downing three eggs, a steak cooked rare, and reading the Baltimore American, one of the oldest newspapers in the U.S. He caught a story about McGraw on the sports page. There was speculation that John was considering leaving the Giants. He denied it vehemently. Stoneham and McGraw, though business partners, did have their differences, mostly over business. The strain on their relationship seemed to be over operations in Havana and not baseball. McGraw knew baseball. Stoneham new that. Pat passed it off as typical baseball gossip, designed to sell papers.

He did notice a much smaller story at the bottom of the page. It read, "Possible Rothstein link to Series Fix." It was a one paragraph highlight but what caught Pat's eye was the last sentence which read, "Rothstein is known to have business relations with Giants owner Stoneham and its manager John McGraw."

Pat looked up from his newspaper and stared across the dining room. A few more suspected dots were appearing in the puzzled world of John McGraw but Pat was not quite ready yet to draw lines between them.

Suddenly, Pat thought of Virginia, the upcoming trip and the prospects of Hollywood. "This should be fun," he thought. "I don't leave 'till Friday. I think I'll stay in Baltimore."

And, with that, he rose suddenly, dropped money on the table and stepped quickly out of the dining room. He moved to the phone bank in the lobby and called Virginia.

"Hello, Livingston's," said Hugh picking up the phone again.

"Hi, Hugh," said Pat. "How are you this fine morning?"

"I'm very good, Pat," replied Hugh. "How are you?"

"If I was any better, I'd have to be you," replied Pat soliciting a laugh from Hugh.

"Well, you're sure full of vigor this morning," stated Hugh, "and after a fairly late night, as well."

"I see you're keeping track of your sister again," said Pat still humoring the young Lieutenant. "Is she there?

"I'll check. She was still sleeping last time I looked," replied Hugh.

Just then Virginia made her way down the large staircase which descended to the main floor. She was still tying off her gown.

"It's for you, sis," said Hugh handing her the phone.

"Hello?" said Virginia in a high pitched voice.

"Good morning," said Pat on the other line.

Turning to sit on the phone bench she looked up at her attentive brother who was standing square, hands on his hips as if at the ready. She brushed him away with her free hand, embarrassing him a bit for eavesdropping. He turned and went into the kitchen.

"Hello? Are you there?" asked Pat

"Sorry, Pat. Yes, I'm here," she said. "How are you this morning?"

"I'm full of vigor, young lady," said Pat

"My, aren't you," replied Virginia. "Don't you ever tire?"

"Now why would I be fatigued this morning," said Pat. "I had a very casual and free evening with a beautiful young lady, a small amount of wine, food, conversation and," saying this with emphasis, "I even behaved myself."

"Indeed you did, Lieutenant," replied Virginia

[715]

"Virginia," said Pat lowering his tone. "I've decided to stay a few more days, have some fun, you and me. What do you think?"

"I'd like that," replied Virginia now holding the phone closer in a more caressing way.

"How soon can you get downtown," asked Pat. "I want to do a whole lot of things today."

"Well, I supposed within an hour or so," replied Virginia.

"Wonderful," Pat said. "Oh, and Virginia, why don't you bring your things and stay downtown? I'm not trying to suggest anything inappropriate mind you but I could get you a room at the hotel and then you'd not have to take such a long trip home and back. We'd have more time together."

"I'd like that, Pat," replied Virginia. "Give me two hours, then. I'll be there by eleven."

"Marvelous, I'll see you then, in the lobby. No, I'll look for you out front," he said.

"Ok, Pat, see you in a bit," said Virginia and then she hung the receiver on its base, holding for a moment thinking, "Pat knows nothing of my relationship with Sarah. He has no idea I am to see him in Havana." She gasped. "How on earth can I explain this? He'll surely suspect I have ulterior motives." She paused again. "Well, it is true, I did have motives. But after last night, I shan't need such motivations to be with him, should I? But for heaven's sake, how will I explain myself?"

She quickly bolted up the stairs, thinking all the way up how she might make things work.

They spent all of Tuesday together. They had dinner then saw "The Miracle Man" staring Lon Chaney at the 1500 seat Empire Theatre on Fayette Street that night. After the show, the taxied to Fells Point and found a small Irish Pub overlooking the Harbor, where they mixed intimate conversation with hand clapping, Irish fiddling music performed by "straight-overs" as Pat called them. Virginia thoroughly enjoyed the flavor of the place and the obvious zest for life Pat demonstrated, tune after tune. He could hardly stay in his seat as one familiar chorus after another beckoned his Celtic heritage. It was a far cry from the preferred demeanor that the stuffy English Livingstons beckoned. They seldom tapped their foot to even a fine Mozart quartet.

During a pause in the night's entertainment, Pat leaned over to ask Virginia a question.

"Virginia dear, I'm heading to Havana, Cuba Friday with some friends," said Pat. "There are some people interested in putting me in a film, people from Hollywood. My good, close friend Edwin Hesser is coming along with some nice folks from New York. I'd like you to go with me."

"How long will you be gone?" she asked, trying not to burst with obvious joy at the 'gift' she'd just received.

"We don't really know," replied Pat. "I'm sure the business portion of the trip will be short of a week but we really have all the time in the world. The whole affair is being put up by John McGraw's group. They own the hotel, a race track and casino. We could be there a month. But I would really love for you to go with me."

"I think it would be marvelous, Pat," responded Virginia.

"Tremendous!" exclaimed Pat. "Waiter, another ale please."

Just then the fiddle kicked in, followed by tin whistle and pan. The whole house broke into a regular downbeat of force not unlike the days of Martin O'Brien in Ohio and generations of Irish going back in time all over Ireland.

On Wednesday evening, they took a midnight cruise on the "Louise" along with 400 other diners. Dancing extended for two hours past dinner. Thursday morning, they had breakfast together downtown. Virginia needed to get some things together for the trip. Pat told her he'd make all the arrangements for her ticket. He'd leave her ticket in Key West since it would be difficult to meet up arriving on different railroads. Pat kissed her good-bye and departed in a cab for the train station about 10:00 a.m. She stood waving until he was out of sight. Standing in the very same spot he'd first kissed her a few evenings before. She leapt off her feet with a bright shrill of joy in her voice.

"What luck!" she exclaimed and the hailed a cab for home.

When Pat returned to New York he remembered to cable his sister. He told her he was heading to Cuba. He apologized for not communicating on Thanksgiving. "It's been a whirlwind of activity for me," he wrote. He also mentioned, "There's an opportunity for me in Hollywood. Will inform you after Havana meetings. Send my love to mother, can't say if I'll be home for Christmas. Your loving brother, Pat."

[717]

Pat, Hesser, Weems and McGraw all boarded the train for Florida on the morning of Pat's birthday, December 13. For breakfast, McGraw ordered champagne and they all toasted Pat's birthday as their express train sped south along the Atlantic coast.

Edwin Hesser was important to the trip in that he had Pat's best interest in mind and understood more of the varied components of film making than many. Weems was along just because he was a good time. Pat wanted him there and McGraw knew he'd attract some attention in the hotel and casino which would also draw the press. Weems was the quintessential "party in any room."

Virginia, Sarah and her daughter Gwendolyn were boarding a similar train in Washington. "The trip will do you good," Sarah had said to her daughter who was recently divorced. "Besides, now that our fair maiden is preoccupied with a Lieutenant O'Brien I will need your help." Virginia looked up from her newspaper and smiled at Sarah who was not looking back.

Never shy about enjoying the Caribbean Sun at the expense of someone else, the Los Angeles crowd departed southern California on Thursday. Heading the group was director Paul Hurst, his wife Hedda Nova, leading lady, along with Seymour Zeliff who would not only act in the film but was the script writer. The script was in outline form at this point. Zeliff liked to "get a feeling" for the lead hero which, he felt, would develop certain elements of the plot. Critical to the meeting was the look, demeanor and interplay of Ms. Nova and Pat. Hurst understood that in order to make a film that was believable there had to be a genuine chemistry between the hero and leading lady. This he could find out in Havana.

There were others. James Dayton was hired by Hurst to do scenery and properties. He was an active set designer at the time and had a reputation for developing realistic visions achieved inexpensively due to his understanding of camera work. Paul felt he would be critical to the film. Dayton also could get a feel for the film by meeting the two leads. In addition, much of the script would be developed while in Havana. This trip afforded him the time to literally look over the shoulder of Zeliff as he developed the storyline, supplementing visually as the film's content evolved.

Overseeing the entire production would be Charles Hickman. As production supervisor he was vital to any discussions in Havana that needed "checking" from a practicality point of view. Hurst had also convinced Charles Hansen Towne, Hollywood columnist, to come along, "at least for the first week." Paul had requested he attend so he'd have a reference point to promote the film. Finally, Taylor Duncan, war veteran and head of the Hollywood American Legion, was on board. After all, a good portion of the cost was being funded by the Legion. He was thrilled to be invited along as a guest of Paul's.

As it turned out, none of these groups passed through Key West at the same time. First to arrive was Pat and the New York group. Pat had not brought his passport to New York having no plans to travel overseas at the time. He applied for a new one when he arrived in Florida. John McGraw signed and witnessed it. They would take the rather short ferry ride to Havana on the P. & O. Steamship Line. The ticket office was literally on the beach in Key West.

Pat's steamship left on Monday, December 15. It arrived in Havana two hours later. Pat and his friends sat in comfortable wicker chairs on the narrow deck all the way to Havana, along with dozens of other well-to-do travelers. They were all heading for the hot spot of the American rich in the 1920's. Surely, a major attraction was the free-flowing alcohol, which was becoming increasingly scarce since prohibition in the States. But it was Cuba itself, the music, language, people, beautiful women, pencil thin mustached Latin men, dancing, and round-the-clock entertainment that was intoxicating the "Victors of the Great War," as 1920 arrived.

The next day, the London Gazette listed their regular official notice of honored soldiers, sailors and airmen declared notable enough to receive accolades from the King. At the top of the page it read, "Supplement to the London Gazette, 16 December, 1919. At the top of the right column appeared the following post:

"War Office, Whitehall, S.W. 1, 16th December, 1919
His Majesty the KING has been pleased to approve of the undermentioned rewards being
confirmed on Officers and other ranks of the Royal Air Force in recognition of the
gallantry in escaping from captivity whilst Prisoners of War:"

First, was a list of ten men receiving a bar to their Military Cross. The next list indicated those "Awarded the Military Cross." The tenth name on the list was "2nd Lieutenant Patrick Alva O'Brien."

The name "Patrick" was ironic in that Pat's first name was actually Alva. His baptized name was "Alva F. O'Brien." As is common among families, the nickname of "Pat" was the only name he was ever called. During his touring years, he made it a routine to check with MC's beforehand who regularly would introduce him as "Patrick" out of respect. Indeed, the respectful British would find it bad form to shorten what they believed was his given name. But it was not "Patrick."

Pat stepped foot on Cuban soil on December 15 ready to embark on a new project, film making. Film was arguably the most significant record of mankind's achievements ever created. It was capable of extending individual legends well into the future. Ironically, as Pat took his first steps into the enchanting world of moving pictures, evidence of his true legacy was being recorded on newsprint in the English speaking capital of the world, for subsequent generations to witness, should they choose to. Pat would be unaware of his recognition for many weeks. He had just arrived in the center of the most festive location on the planet and the real world was nowhere to be found.

A car ordered by McGraw was standing by for Pat and the New York group when they landed. Pat looked around in every direction thinking he might see Virginia at the dock, also. There were over twenty-five ferry boats and small ships unloading. People were streaming onto shore. Havana was jammed with Americans being welcomed by colorfully dressed young men and women who continuously smiled. If they spoke English, a heavy Spanish accent flavored every word. The weather was hot. New arrivals, including Pat, with their shoes, dark clothes and city garb would soon give way to the simple white slacks and shirts that allowed tropical air to cool the torso.

The group checked in to the Plaza Hotel, a breathtakingly beautiful white marble structure with Roman style columns that ran the entire block of the front entrance. It featured exquisite rooms, a large lobby and ballrooms throughout. Rothstein, Stoneham and McGraw were operating what was considered the most lavish and beautiful hotel in the Caribbean.

Wealthy Americans were discovering Havana and turning it into their winter playground with country clubs, a national racetrack, casinos, yacht clubs, golf courses and for those seeking a tropic summer home, the Havana suburbs were filling-in fast with large estates. The timing for McGraw and his friends couldn't have been better.

By 5:00 p.m. everyone involved in the film had arrived. Lee Keedick was notably absent but would come after the holidays. Dinner was scheduled for 7:00 p.m. Everyone would be there as guests of John McGraw who made it a practice of welcoming his large groups of customers on the first day.

"I want to welcome all my friends from New York and my new friends from Washington and Los Angeles," said McGraw. "Please do not hesitate if there is anything I can do for you during your stay here. Call on me personally."

Looking at Pat he went on.

"Now I know you have much business to take care of while you are here in Havana, correct?" He was nodding around the table then looked back at Pat and said, "Correct, Pat, there's work to be done, right?" Pat and the others smiled all confirming.

"But tonight... tonight is all fun. No work tonight!" exclaimed McGraw. He then pronounced, "None of my guests are permitted to work on their first night in Havana. Tonight we celebrate your being here with food, plenty of drinks and a night you will always remember! Salud! Salud! Salud!"

The entire table, all smiles and laughing, rose from their seats toasting across the table and walking around to everyone clinking each other's glass. As they did so, twelve waiters in white coats entered the room with food held high overhead as the private dining room was staged for a five-course meal.

"Salud, Lieutenant," said Sarah Ottis finally making her way around to his location.

"Salud, Sarah," replied Pat in a friendly but less bombastic tone than she had used.

"This is my daughter, Lieutenant," Sarah said introducing her. "This is Gwendolyn. Gwendolyn, this is Lieutenant O'Brien."

Pat flashed the young girl his patented smile and, of course, she melted.

"Good evening, Mr. O'Brien," said the voice from behind.

"Good evening, young lady," replied Pat. "And what might be your name, may I ask?"

"I am Virginia Allen from the Livingston estate in Washington," she said going along with the joke. "You look quite nice in your white tropical slacks and shirt, I must say."

The group continued to circle the table and meet everyone.

"Hello, Lieutenant," said an attractive brunette. "Apparently, you and I are going to star in this picture. I must say you are a very handsome man. That eases my mind. It is much easier to act like you love someone when he looks like someone you'd like to love," she said this with genuine humor laughing pleasantly. Though it wasn't quite what Pat expected, he found her comment fun and in good humor. Right behind her was another man who was also laughing at the conversation. It was Paul Hurst, a big, muscular man who looked like he'd played a number of westerns, which he had.

"Hello, Lieutenant," said Hurst, "Paul Hurst. Please to meet you. I am a great admirer of your amazing service and escape during the war. Looking around to his wife he said, "This is my insatiable wife, Hedda. Gorgeous isn't she?"

"Indeed," said Pat.

"I look forward to our project Pat," returned Hurst. "You've got a great look and you're tall. That's good."

"So must be the ways of Hollywood," Pat thought. "Being a midwest boy, I'm just not used to all this 'forward' talk, I guess."

Dinner was marvelous lasting two and a half hours and drinks flowed like Pat had never seen. Before they departed for the club, McGraw gave them a little orientation.

"Havana is a wonderful place and the people are nice but stay in the tourism sector while you are here. There are American areas, as well but don't look for them yourselves." he said. "Our people can take you anywhere you'd like to be. There's no reason to go exploring. It will only get you lost, or in trouble or robbed or all three." He laughed at his own comment. The guests did, too, but with a ring of nervousness in their voices. "But seriously," he continued. "Enjoy your stay but play it safe."

A white canopied open air shuttle was awaiting them just outside the hotel. Many people were watching as they exiting the hotel en mas. It was obvious to other Americans present and certainly the locals that these people were VIP's. Sarah and her daughter were impressed with the special care they were receiving. As they stepped down to the street to board the shuttle, Pat noticed how Sarah was watching the Cubans who were watching her. Rather typical, he thought, of someone who had suddenly found themselves among the special folks and couldn't resist looking at the envious, gawking bystanders.

The race track was stunning. The group was an exclusive guest of McGraw at the new Cuba-American Jockey and Auto Club which was not yet open to the public. McGraw and his managers were letting invited guests serve as a warm up for the newly hired wait staff. The Club was connected to the race track and was pristine. Pat, Virginia and the others enjoyed betting on races until 11:30 p.m. Then the whole group was off to the Casino.

The first night in Havana was an absolute success. It was the perfect way to start the week which would be full of business discussions, marketing, talent contracts, technical requirements, and production scheduling. Everyone got to know each other on a personal basis and no one ended the day disappointed, except for Sarah Ottis.

She found herself somewhat of a "fifth wheel" around Hurst, Hesser, Pat, Hedda Nova and production supervisor, Charles Hanson Towne. Sarah really brought nothing to the table but she didn't sense that. Was she not the cog in the entire wheel that had brought Pat and Hurst together? Apparently not. It stuck in her craw for nearly two weeks. Virginia also felt a bit on the outside, to a lesser degree. At least she no longer needed Sarah's match-making skills to win the admiration of a Pat O'Brien. Those were assured days earlier in Baltimore.

Affections between the young couple were expanding each day. Whether it was the warm tropical environment laced with passionate Conga music, carefree afternoons on the beach or the limitless supply of Bacardi rum on silver trays held by attentive waiters, Pat's interest in Virginia and hers in him was being stoked at a rapid pace. Perhaps the sudden let down by Agnes or the relief Pat felt with his war finally removed, was the cause of his lowered guard. Either way, the crescendo of their attraction to each other and the genuine good time they were having led to a stunning announcement on Christmas Day with the whole group present. Pat and Virginia would be married on January 1, New Year's Day, 1920.

"Congratulations, young man" said John McGraw giving him a solid and forceful handshake.

"I'm so excited for you both," were the words of Hedda Nova, who'd come to enjoy Virginia on the trip.

"I hope you like California, Virginia," were Paul Hurst's giddy words. "Remember, I have a signed contract in my back pocket that says, "Pat O'Brien is mine beginning June 1, 1920.

On Thursday afternoon at 2:00 p.m. Pat O'Brien and Virginia Livingston Allen were married on the veranda of the Plaza Hotel, in Havana, Cuba before all their new friends. Again a throng of Cuban onlookers paused to watch the wedding from the street as Sarah Ottis continued to look at them, watching her.

The grand entrance into the 1920's was so significant to everyone in Havana that day, indeed, to Americans everywhere. Pat's entourage celebrated both a wedding and the arrival of modern times all week. Lee Keedick arrived on January 9th as Sarah Ottis and her daughter departed that same day. Sarah would be finalizing her divorce to Dr. Ottis on the 11th back in Springfield, Illinois. She wanted to stop in New York first.

If there ever was an example of one exiting early with a tail between her legs, it was Sarah. But she would be back. She was relentless and her desire for notoriety superseded any shortcomings in life, whether they'd be a reduction of influence or the absence of a husband.

The couple isolated themselves from everyone for about four days and then joined in once again in the daily activities. As per Rothstein's plan, the press was all over the hotel digging up juicy stories to appeal to the rich back home who had yet to consider Cuba as their getaway. The publicity campaign was working.

The Chicago Daily Tribune ran a story written January 13 by a reporter brought to Havana by Rothstein's men. The headline read,

"Tourists flock to Havana For Winter Racing. Liquor, Open Town, Add to City's Attraction."

In a highlighted boxed below the headline was the following:

"President C.A. Stoneham and Manager J.J. McGraw bought a controlling interest in the Havana race track last fall. Martin Nathanson of this city, formerly secretary at Harlem, is racing secretary."

The Harlem Track referred to was located in the Chicago suburbs and was run by two notorious gamblers named George Hankins and John Condon. Chicago was becoming a significant mob town and Illinois had more tracks than any state in the country until racing was shut down by the legislature in 1905. The loss of racing in Illinois drove a number of trainers, jockeys and gamblers to Havana.

The Daily Tribune story went on.

"The E.A. Cudahy Jrs, are here for a few days. Charles E. Brown Jr. of Lake Forest came in today. Lieutenant Pat O'Brien, of war fame and Illinois birth, is a favorite around the Hotel Plaza."

These were not mob thugs, they were respectable people and Rothstein's team made sure it was noted, particularly in the Chicago press where the White Sox trial would take place later in the year.

Still other papers reported in their social columns about Pat's marriage to Virginia. Though it had been a whole year since Pat had toured, and two years since his incredible escape, he still commanded newspaper attention. A Kansas City newspaper headlined,

"Cupid His Good Angel, Lieutenant Pat O'Brien, former R.A.F. flier wins Another Victory, Pretty Washington Girl Surrendered to Daring Air Fighter After Heavy bombardment of Candy and Flowers."

It would be later in the year before Agnes MacMillian would pause stunningly, reading a wire story in the San Francisco Chronicle about Pat and Virginia, complete with a photo of the new wife.

Clara had purchased a Chicago Daily Tribune at Jensen's and read the article about Pat mixed up with mob figures in Havana and was deeply concerned.

"I hope my little brother knows what he is playing with down there," she told Al Fontaine.

"Yeah, fire," he responded.

The Chicago story had no mention of Virginia and no one at home knew about Pat's new wife as late as January 19th.

McGraw officially opened up the elegant Cuba-American Jock and Auto Club to the public on the 19th amid a minor scandal that also hit the papers. Pat had witnessed a verbal argument between Charles Stoneham and McGraw that literally came to fisticuffs in the Hotel Plaza. There was cursing and allegations that, had the two men been of right mind, they would not have said. Pat heard the whole thing and it scared him enough that he finally concluded that his association with McGraw needed to come to an end. He had already witnessed many of Rothstein's thugs throughout the hotel, track and casino that never smiled and carried "heat."

Pat had a long talk with his wife the night of the McGraw-Stoneham battle. "Honey, we need to go home," Pat said to his wife. "This place it getting to me."

"I agree, Pat," replied Virginia. "This past week has been full of chaos and there's so many people here now. Why the other day, McGraw passed me in the lobby with a determined look on his face, looking angry. I said hello to him and he didn't even respond."

"I know, honey," Pat said. "We don't need all this. I'm eager to get home and get our life organized. Don't forget, we need to move to California," he said, half not believing it himself.

They agreed that Pat would see her back to Washington and then head to Momence while she stayed behind to prepare for the move. She would disconnect from all of her newspaper contacts, affect a move from her parent's home and join him, perhaps in Momence but more likely Los Angeles. After taking care of some business in Illinois, Pat would head for Los Angeles to find a place for them to live. Production was due to begin June 1 and there was a lot to do.

One thing Pat wanted to do was to sell the farm in Indiana. He'd talk to Elmer who needed to get established again. Besides, with the condition of Lila, his mother may someday need to move in with Elmer. She no longer had a place in town and Clara's apartment above the store, which she still lived in since selling the store, was too difficult for Margaret. The stairs made it hard for her to even visit.

The next morning Pat was up early getting ready for departure. He met Virginia downstairs for breakfast in the main dining room. In between bites he was saying "good-bye" to everyone he'd met involved in the film and dozens of others who were genuinely thrilled to have met him.

He'd spent a number of evenings on the veranda with William Vanderbilt, Jr. who reveled in the discussion of Aeroplanes and engines with Pat. Vanderbilt was an avid race car hobbyist. He was, of course, heir to the Vanderbilt dynasty and one of the richest men in America. His wife became extremely infatuated with Pat when she met him one night at one of McGraw's many cocktail parties. Her first name was Alva and she and Pat had many a laugh over their common names. The rest of the time she insisted he sit with them when all were casually enjoying a pre-dinner drink or nightcap. Virginia was astounded at the whole thing. She knew she'd meet people as Pat's wife, but the Vanderbilts!

Before Pat and Virginia left for home that day, they took a ride out to the home of Mr. and Mrs. Robert McCunsey who lived on Moreno Cerro Drive in Havana. The McCunsey's were Americans and Mrs. McCunsey was from Momence. Pat had known her as Flossie Lewis. She was the daughter of Emory Lewis, old neighbors of the O'Briens. Flossie had lost her four-year old daughter to diphtheria. The poor thing was only sick five days with a sore throat then took on the disease and died in twenty-four hours. They spent about an hour comforting the McCunsey's for which they were grateful. Pat always had a soft spot for kids and it crushed him to see young children die. The memory of his little brother, Forest, never left him.

Pat and Virginia boarded the steamship at 1:00 p.m. and were in Key West by 3:00. They transferred to the train station and headed north to Washington. The couple spent the night at the Willard as man and wife. Pat promised his new bride a real honeymoon, just as soon as things were in place in southern California.

The next day at noon, Virginia saw Pat off at the train station. She was overwhelmed with sadness at his departure. He held her in his arms for some time as she sobbed. He felt very badly and hated to see her so upset.

"It's just that everything happened so quickly, then we rush out of Havana, we're here one night and you leaving and I don't know where to start," she sighed.

"I know, Virginia," replied Pat, wiping her tears with his handkerchief. "Just think about California, our new home and a new life we can begin. And remember, you've got work to do, too. We've got a picture to make. It will be a very exciting time, I promise." Hurst had offered Virginia a part in the picture as a "wedding present." She was thrilled to no end.

"I know, honey," she replied. "It's just that I feel so lost right now."

"I will call you as soon as I am home," Pat said. "Keep your chin up, kid."

"I will," she replied.

And with that he turned, looking back once and arrived at the bottom of the steps leading into his car. He turned, with a huge smile and gave his new wife that classic, broad, optimistic, exuberant wave across his long frame and then bounded up the steps.

PART ELEVEN

SHADOWS

Chapter 53

Hollywood

Pat's train pulled into Union Station in Chicago the next morning at 9:00 a.m. He'd had a comfortable night's sleep on the B & O train from Washington, sleeping on yet another Pullman sleeping car. It was a crisp morning in Chicago. He had his bags transferred to the LaSalle Street station and decided to walk there since he had ninety minutes before the train headed south to Momence.

The walk gave him time to reflect on his days in Chicago when he was younger. He walked east on Jackson, crossing the Chicago River which was "steaming" against the twenty degree air. When he got to Clark Street he decided take a detour and walk all the way to Michigan Avenue to see the lake. There was only one time each week when the streets of Chicago emptied. That was Sunday morning. At Dearborn he paused to let a lone milk wagon pass but for the most part there was little activity in the Loop. Standing on the curb he looked left and right down the cavernous street with its fifteen story buildings all stacked one against the other. The street was still dark with shadows as the sun had not yet edged over to top of Dearborn's skyscrapers. At State Street he could hear wisp brooms in the hands of negro men brushing off the late night frivolity from the sidewalks.

Passing the final façade on Jackson Street, he stepped out onto wide open Michigan Avenue where the bright sun splashed across his face. He paused, raising his hand to his brow to lessen the glare and gaze out at Grant Park. He was thinking about the day a Herring-Curtiss biplane flew right over his head, bucking a 25 mph wind and landed on the beach in front of him during the 1911 International Aviation Meet. He could hear the words of young Jimmy Ward that day saying to him, "Watch it, fella," as Ward brushed past Pat while pulling up his helmet strap and climbing aboard the first Curtiss-Pusher Pat had ever seen. As he looked out toward the Lake he remembered the dozen Pathfinders that raced that day, the G2 Caudron which was little more than a kite and the great aviator Lincoln Beachey who piloted a Curtiss biplane and later shook Pat's hand after the meet.

"To think that was only eight years ago," Pat said allowed, lowering his hand from his forehead. "My, so much has happened in this country since then.

Pat walked south down Michigan Avenue for one block, then headed west on Van Buren to the train station. He checked to make sure that his bags were secure and then boarded the train to Momence.

Clara was at the Momence station to greet him. She stepped up onto the platform, kissed him on the cheek and they rode back to her apartment. After climbing up the steep stairs, Pat dropped his bags and took a seat at the kitchen table. Clara poured him a cup of coffee.

"I read the Chicago paper about your escapades in Havana," she said to her younger brother. "Sounded like a real rampage down there."

"Oh, it was," Pat said. "I had a good time but after a while it just got to be too much."

There was a pause and then Pat continued.

"So, was mom upset about my getting married and all?" Pat asked.

"She's coming over tomorrow. Ask her yourself," Clara replied.

"That doesn't sound good," Pat said, putting down his coffee.

"No, she's fine Pat," Clara replied. "I didn't mean it that way. I just don't see her as much now that she's living in Lowell. That's all."

"That's a relief," Pat said, lifting his cup.

"So, what's she like Pat?" Clara asked.

"She's very modern, smart and knows what she wants," he replied. "She's also quite beautiful. We seemed to hit it off so quickly. Our conversations just seemed so natural. I was drying up not having someone I could talk to about real personal stuff, you know?"

"How is all that personal stuff? How is it going?" Clara asked.

"Russia was good for me," Pat said. "It cleared my head. I had to put the war behind me. I guess when I returned and Agnes had lost interest in going any further there was Virginia who was new, fresh and excited about life. It just felt natural.

"But three weeks, Pat" Clara said. "That's hardly a "howdy do."

"I know sis, but wait till you meet her," Pat said. "You'll like her. As I look back, the years since San Diego chewed me up just a bit. I'm still strong of course and my physical health is good but after a while one just needs to sit and do nothing. Know what I mean?"

"Sure, honey," his sister replied. "Say, why don't you go out to the river and fish a while. I'm sure Al wouldn't mind going as well. Or go by yourself. It could do you some good."

"I really can't, sis," Pat replied. "I've got so much to get done. You say mom's coming in tomorrow, right? She'll probably want to go to church. I'll go with her. Then maybe I can borrow a car and take her back. I want to go to the farm and talk to Elmer."

"He'll be here tomorrow, too, Pat," Clara said.

"Good, that will go fine then," Pat said. "I want to ask Elmer if he'll buy my farm. There's no sense in me owning it now. I think I'll be in California for some time."

Pat opened his pocket calendar thinking through all he had to do by June 1st.

"Let's see, if Virginia and I start working on the film June 1st, then I'm certainly going to want to be settled and in a house by May 1st, don't you think?" he asked.

"I would think so," Clara replied, checking the yokes.

"That means securing a place by April so we can get everything moved, plus time to buy furniture and settle into Los Angeles," he said, thinking out loud. "We really need to take possession in April."

Pat laid out a game plan, conferring with his sister on each point. Clara was always the one he relied on for guidance on such matters. Perhaps as a result of running a shoe store with her husband all those years gave her an ability to be decisive. Either way she was a quick decision maker and was usually right. Margaret always said that Pat would be best in a fight and Clara would be best in a business deal. By the time Pat and his sister had finished, he had a long list of things to do.

On Sunday morning, Elmer came into town and visited with Pat.

Margaret arrived Sunday and everyone went to church together. After services Pat took the whole family out to lunch at the hotel. Elmer came in early that morning and talked about the farm with Pat. Ben and Lila were even there. Lila, who continued to suffer from her chronic rheumatism, was feeling good that day so she made the trip from Lowell. Ivan and Alma brought little Patricia to church and to lunch. She was a perfect baby all day. Merwin was the only O'Brien absent. He lived in California at the time. The lunch lasted two hours and was full of hearty laughter about growing up.

Pat had good conversation with Margaret who was generally pleased about his marriage and was eager to meet Virginia. She was excited about his movie opportunity, too. Later in the afternoon, after thinking it over, Elmer agreed to purchase the farm for $17,100. Pat indicated that he and Virginia would visit Momence in May to sign over the deed and meet everyone.

On Monday, January 26th, Pat sent a telegram to Virginia which read:

"Leaving Momence for California on Monday the 2nd of February to find our dream house. Will be there until I find the perfect home for us. Think we should move some time after April 1. Hope things are coming together on your end. Will call before I leave Monday."

Pat arrived in Los Angeles on February 5th around 10:00 a.m. and checked into the Alexandria Hotel. Paul Hurst requested that Pat stay in the hotel since it was at the center of the theatre and movie communities in Southern California. "We'll be having a lot of meetings there in the beginning," he'd said to Pat when they were in Havana together.

The Alexandria was the location where powerful producers, talent directors and stars met to conduct business and often celebrate successes. It was the only place to be if you were in the movie business. Charlie Chaplin, Mary Pickford, D.W. Griffin and Douglas Fairbanks had used the dining room earlier in the year to announce the formation of their independent movie company, United Artists. Big-Band leader Paul Whiteman got his start in show business playing piano in the bar. It was, according to Chaplin, the "swankiest hotel in town."

After settling in his room, Pat came down to the dining room around 11:45. He was going to meet an old buddy of his, Virgil Moore. Moore was with him in San Diego during the Signal Corps days and had recently gone to work for Lockheed after the war. Being a former Signal Corps man, he flew for the U.S. in France. Pat had not seen him since their days together at North Island.

"Pat O'Brien, you dirty dog," Moore said as he stepped up to Pat's table. Pat was looking at the menu and didn't see him enter the room.

"Virgil Moore, how great to see you again!" Pat said. "You look tremendous. How did you know I was in town?"

"Believe it or not, Hess called me," Virgil said. "He called, I guess, while you were in Cuba and told me you were coming to Los Angeles. He told me where you were staying. Yesterday I received a wire from him indicating you'd be in today. I told him not to tell you I was in town. I wanted to surprise you."

"You sure as hell did!" Pat said. "That Hess, I always forget, he knows everybody all the way back to my early days. He's a great friend."

The two flyers ordered lunch, beer and locked in to a catch-up session covering nearly four years. Moore had as stellar a war career as anyone and fought very near where Pat did though they never knew it since they flew for different countries. Pat talked about all his adventures since the escape and learned that Moore was actually in the audience at Berkeley when Pat spoke but it was so crowded that Moore couldn't get to Pat.

Moore gave Pat some suggestions on where to live in Los Angeles. He was surprised when Pat mentioned the dollar level he could afford for monthly rent. Moore recommended an area just northwest of Hollywood near Glendale. He knew a real estate person in town and gave Pat his name and address. After a three hour lunch, they parted and agreed to see each other later that week. Pat was happy to have an old friend available to help him get acclimated.

"I'll give you a call again in a few days," Moore said. Hesser had told Moore to "keep an eye on Pat for me. He's in unchartered waters."

Pat spent the next three weeks looking at houses. He purchased a house at 2314 North Commonwealth in north Los Angeles. It was an impressive home with over 2,300 square feet. It had been built in 1918. He wired Virginia right away and told her "step one" was complete.

On Monday morning, March 1st, he went to an appointment to see Doctor Walter Seager. Pat had asked Virgil about someone he might see for his ongoing ailments from the war. Since returning to the States from Cuba, Pat's leg was particularly uncomfortable and he had not been able to see a doctor regularly since before Russia. He could tell he was a bit beat up from his days on the Siberian Train. He also felt mentally tired. Clara had noticed it, too, when she had suggested he take the afternoon off and fish. The sudden turning of his head when he heard loud noises had returned and a general twitchiness had started to return to his hands since Russia.

"He's a good medical doctor but understands the other stuff, too," Virgil had told him. "He's done wonders for me. I was a nervous wreck when I got back."

It was only with someone like Virgil that Pat could talk about the post-war issues. All vets had them but most ignored their feelings or suffered in silence. Virgil was a big help to Pat in this regard.

Pat called Virginia at noon.

"Hello," Virginia said in an energetic voice.

"Hi, Honey, it's Pat. How are things going?"

"Oh, good," Virginia replied. She sounded upbeat and that made Pat feel optimistic. "You know that table I told you about last week?"
"Sure," Pat replied.

"It was so expensive, as you know," she said. "But today the store owner called me and really wants to get rid of it and he dropped the price in half!"

"Wow, that's a heck of deal," Pat replied. "So, what did you tell him?"

"Of course, I told him I wanted to talk to you first. I mean, I think the price is great and everything, but good Lord, I've not even seen the house, I don't know if it will look good in our dining room or fit or anything," she stated, all a twitter.

"I'm ready on this end," Pat said. "I'm more than ready. When do you think you'll depart?"

"Hugh has been a big help, Pat," Virginia replied. "He's had a few of his buddies packing things all weekend. So he thinks tomorrow and then we'll be ready to leave Wednesday."

"Oh, that's fantastic," Pat replied. "Let's see. That should get you here by Friday, right?"

"I think so," Virginia replied. "Hugh's taken care of the tickets and all that and he's even handled the whole cargo arrangements, which I know absolutely nothing about. I'm so glad he's here."

"Me, too," Pat said.

"I've been very busy so it's helped the time go by fast but I really miss you, Pat," Virginia said.

"Me, too, honey," he said. "I really can't wait to show you the house. It's perfect for us."

I'm so excited," Virginia said. "So, can I tell the man at the store to go ahead then?"

"Sure, honey," Pat replied, "whatever you like."

They had a few more things to say and expressed again how lonely they both were. Pat was so happy to hear her excited again. It had been a long month and a half away from Virginia. There were pre-production meetings scattered throughout May so this would at least get her in Los Angeles before April.

"See you soon, Pat," Virginia said.

"You, too," was Pat's response.

They both hung up at the same time.

"So how was he?" asked Sarah Ottis.

"Oh, he was good, very good," she said. "He's ready. We're going Wednesday."

Pat was not aware that one of the most involved people in organizing Virginia's move was Sarah Ottis. She was a big help to Virginia but she had literally "set up camp" in Washington since their arrival back from Cuba. Certainly Virginia needed help, but it was the way Sarah assumed her role that grated on Virginia from time to time. Still, she valued the counsel.

Essentially, Virginia didn't know how to tell her no and, in fact, she did need the help. Virginia's mother was no longer alive and so it was comforting to have an older woman around. Gwendolyn was also with her mother but irritated Virginia a little with her incessant questions and minimal help. "She's more a burden than anything," Virginia had told her brother.

"You stay in touch with me now," were the words Sarah Ottis said as she saw Virginia off on Wednesday. Hugh kissed his sister good-bye and Virginia was quite emotional leaving him behind. She kissed her father and was off to California.

Pat and Virginia spent all of March and April setting up house. They were making a few friends in the neighborhood and both actually felt like a typical married couple for the first time. Pat saw Doctor Seager every two weeks and was feeling calmer with each session. Exercises the doctor gave him were also easing the discomfort in his legs.

On May 12th the young couple boarded a train for Chicago to pay their first visit to Momence as man and wife. Like all new brides, Virginia was a bit nervous but everything Pat had told her about his family, the little town of Momence and the Midwest in general seemed wonderful. They arrived in Chicago on the 14th by midmorning. Pat had the opportunity to show Virginia the city including the lake front, pointing out where he'd witnessed his first air show at Grant Park.

Elmer and Margaret were at the train station to meet Pat and wife when they arrived in Momence. Unfortunately, Clara had taken ill, spent time in Wesley Hospital in Chicago and was recovering in Lowell at Lila's home.

"Clara hopes to be here by Tuesday," Elmer told Virginia as they stepped down from the train platform. "She's made great progress."

"Poor thing", Virginia replied. "Pat's told me so much about her. I'm anxious to meet her."

The family had walked to the station from Clara's. Margaret was having a particularly good day. She and Virginia walked together and got to know each other while Elmer and Pat paired up behind them. Pat alternated his attention between conversations with Elmer and quick glances forward to see how things were going with Virginia and her mother. He smiled seeing his mother laugh at one of Virginia's comments, grabbing her arm with both hands as if old friends.

"So this is the famous Jensen's Drug Store I've heard all about," Virginia stated as they walked past the already iconic façade.

"Oh, yes," Margaret replied. "And Pat never misses the chance to partake with Al when he's home, he's always with his friend Al."

Virginia turned around and asked Pat, "Will we see Al while we're here, Pat?"

"Only if he gets out of bed in time," Pat replied with a grin that also made Elmer laugh.

"Al is not at all like Pat," Margaret said to Virginia, now arm-in-arm with her daughter-in-law. "Pat's always been so rambunctious and Al has a much more relaxed approach. Virginia smiled down at her mother-in-law, drawn in by her Irish charm.

They arrived at Clara's apartment stairs. Virginia assisted Margaret up the eighteen steps. There was cake on the table, some soft drinks and coffee.

Virginia was enchanted by the town, its beautiful river, the character of brick store fronts and busy shops teeming with energetic people. Everyone was struck by the beauty of Virginia.

Clara arrived on Tuesday as hoped. She watched closely as any sister would, assessing the character of her new sister-in-law, how she and her younger brother seemed to be together. Generally, she was pleased.

Pat and Virginia spent the week in Momence. While Clara's apartment was a far shake from the Livingston mansion in Washington and the Central Hotel where Pat and Virginia stayed, Virginia hardly noticed. She was taken in by the charm of the little City of Momence and the warmth of the O'Brien clan.

On May 25th, Pat and Virginia signed the lease to the Morocco farm to Elmer. Virginia proudly signed it "Elizabeth V. O'Brien" dropping the "Allen" and Livingston from her name, which played well back in Washington D.C. After signing she turned to Pat and said, "my first official signature as your wife," to which Pat replied, "and probably not the last."

Two days later, Pat and Virginia traveled to Lowell with Clara to visit Lila. She'd been quite ill as of late, her rheumatism causing pain through most day and nights. Virginia immediately saw the good nature of Margaret's eldest daughter. They visited the entire day and then headed back to Momence. Pat and Virginia were to leave the next day.

Clara, Margaret and Elmer saw them off the next morning. As it was time to leave, Pat bent over and picked up two bags. He felt no pain in his leg which pleased him. Standing erect again he said, "Time to go," and looking up he saw Virginia and Margaret in a warm embrace. His mother was looking over Virginia's shoulder as they hugged, watching Pat retrieve his bags. She gave him a big wink.

They were back in Los Angeles on Sunday.

"Welcome to Hollywood!" Pat exclaimed to his wife as their car pulled up in front of the house.

The term "Hollywood" was just recently being associated with the film industry. Geographically, it was located in the northwest quadrant of Los Angeles. Pat's new home was on its eastern edge. Though the American film industry started in New York and New Jersey, filmmakers were moving to California. Paul Hurst, on the other hand, was from California and not part of the migrating Broadway crowd.

On June 4th, Hurst and his wife Hedda took Pat and Virginia to dinner. He often met with his leading players before rehearsals and production. He viewed them essentially as the captains of his team. He wanted them to understand how he worked and wanted their support, particularly when things got difficult. In film-making, "things" always got complicated at some point. Their waiter brought over drinks and took orders. Paul opened the discussion.

"You know, Pat, most people in America see Hollywood as a place where dreams come true," Hurst said. "The images we create have very little to do with how day-to-day work goes in the film business. Unless you're Charlie Chaplin or Mary Pickford, life on the set is pretty much drudgery. Our job is to make a film that transports audiences to other worlds. But making films is an expensive proposition. That means we have to work as a team. It takes cooperation between numerous individuals."

Pat nodded, stirring his drink.

Hurst continued. "The other part of the business is that the people who fund us like to be around us while we work. It's a real pain in the backside but it's part of the whole deal. They're going to want to talk to you Pat, sometimes on a daily basis. Now Hickman will keep them occupied as best he can with detailed accounts of what's going on but you're the star of the movie. You're the one thing they can identify with. This other stuff that I do is all magic to them. They just like to be around celebrities and part of your job is to make them feel important."

Virginia smiled at Paul. Hedda was watching Pat for his reaction.

"Not like I've never experienced people who want to get to me," Pat replied in good humor. Paul agreed and stated it was one thing he was looking forward to. He'd had his fill of primadonnas who didn't want to be bothered with such things. He knew Pat understood how to charm people. That would keep them away from Paul.

"So what I'm saying is there are two pieces to this business, the creative people and the business people," Hurst said. "You're going to be involved with both – because you're the star. My job is to produce a great film. I'm sure the American Legion guys and our production company people will be around, too. Your job will include playing to me, and playing to these two disparate interests at the same time."

"Thanks, Paul," Pat replied. "That's good advice."

Dinner was pleasant and a nice chemistry was developing between Paul, Hedda, Pat and Virginia. Though Virginia's part was less than Pat's, Paul knew she would be important in support of his male lead.

"One more thing I want to say, Pat," Paul said. "I've never worked with you before. We've had good times in Havana and I know of your reputation but we've never worked on a film together and this is your first film. All I'm saying is to take my lead, be patient but if you have questions or don't understand something, just ask me."

"Thanks Paul. I will," Pat replied.

On Monday, June 7th, work began. The entire company met in a large barn-like studio where many of the interior shots would be filmed. Pat was stunned at the number of people needed to make a simple film. There was a large cast. Pat had just met the main characters but an additional twenty people were on hand as "extras." He met the location manager and the creative director who doubled as the set designer. The prop manager had a team of six. There were costume people, hair and make-up, camera operators, grippers, and four or five production assistants with stacks of papers as well as pencils placed behind their ears.

Pat leaned over to his wife and whispered, "It takes more people to make a picture than Ford uses to make a car."

"It's quite impressive, isn't it ,Pat?" Virginia replied.

Once the general meeting was over, the leads moved to a small room of the studio to read scripts. An acting coach was there guiding the actors through the script. He made notes that would lead to edits as the story became audible. Seymour Zeliff was on hand throughout which was convenient. He was able make changes in his script. The script contained mostly plot descriptions and scenes with blocking instructions, all subject to Hurst's "eye" once shooting began.

The title of the film was "Shadows of the West." Pat played Jim Kern, the lead. Hedda was Mary with Virginia playing a character named Lucy Norton. Zeliff played Frank Akuri and Ben Corbette played Jim's pal. The plot was a basic one, hero off to the war, leaves girl behind who is accosted while alone and nearly meets her fate until, low and behold, the hero returns in the nick of time. It was a plot as old as storytelling itself.

Hurst spoke to the cast prior to their reading of the script and described the film in the following manner:

"A California cowpuncher, Jim Kern and his pal enlist in the war against Germany." Turning to Pat he said, "Good so far, Pat?"

"Got it, Paul" Pat replied. Everyone in the room laughed.

Hurst went on. "Ok, shortly after they enlist, the audience meets Frank Akuri who has pledged to colonize the United States for his homeland, Japan. While Jim and other white males are fighting in France, Akuri forces Jim's sweetheart Mary to sell her ranch, as she is not able to run it because the only men left, the Japanese, have pledged not to work for the whites. With the ranch, Akuri begins his colony."

"Oh, my," Virginia exclaimed. That too got a hearty laugh from the cast.

He continued. "Mary counters by organizing her society women friends to appeal to Congress against the 'yellow menace.' When it seems that his plans will be thwarted, Akuri issues orders for the death of Mary and her friends but Jim and his pal return and rescue them. Akuri then kidnaps Mary and takes her to his apartment, but with the help of Akuri's wronged Japanese lover, Jim learns of her whereabouts."

Muffled giggling at this washed through the group.

"And so," Paul stated, "He organizes a posse of American Legion locals and recues Mary just as Akuri is about to murder her."

That did it. They all burst forth with laugher. Even this group of thespians laughed at the absurdity of the tale.

"The American Legion, no less," Pat roared.

"And Congress, too!" Zeliff roared, fully understanding the farcical nature of the plot, having written it himself.

"Hey, ladies and gentlemen," Hurst said, also laughing. "This is the stuff that sells."

And so went opening day on the set. Script work lasted for the full week and Pat was working ten hours a day. Virginia, who had a lesser part, was often at home by herself awaiting the next call or sitting in the warm sun on heavy production days waiting hours on end to speak her lines.

For the first two weeks of production, Pat barely saw his wife. She felt abandoned. Having dinner together even became a challenge. Hurst required a late-day sun often to film some shots which held Pat on location until dusk. By June 18th Pat and Virginia were strangers in the same house.

"I surely didn't expect never to see you again when I left my home and traveled all the way out here to this big house where I sit all day by myself," Virginia said.

"I don't like it any more than you do, honey," Pat replied. "But we're committed to do this and Paul says we should finish by fall. Just be patient, will you?"

The brevity of their courtship was tested slightly in June with all the demands of the film and the uprooting Virginia was feeling since her arrival. Pat took advantage of his first day off in nearly three weeks by meeting with a businessman who wanted to talk to him about a new project.

On Sunday, June 30th an article appeared in the Los Angeles Times. The headline read, "Pat O'Brien is on Auto Row." It went on to say, "Hedding-O'Brien Motor Co. to Handle the Allen" and "Famous Aviator Has Wild List of Experiences" and finally "Tests Out Machine Under Most Trying Circumstances."

S.A. Hedding, formerly of Minneapolis, had been in the automobile business for ten years. He was a sales manager for several large distributors in Minneapolis and had just purchased an existing Allen dealership in Los Angeles that had been struggling to sell cars. Hedding, a master salesperson and entrepreneur, had read an account of Pat's adventures in Asia and Russia and his eyes almost popped out when the story mentioned how Pat, the most famous war hero in the eyes of most Americans, had actually driven an Allen car across the Gobi Desert.

"Could my luck be any greater!" Hedding shouted when he read the story. He immediately looked up Pat in Los Angeles and the two men met a number of times at the Alexandria while Pat was still looking for a house. Upon Pat and Virginia's return from Momence, Pat signed the deal.

Pat came home from shooting on Monday and entered the house.

"How could you!" Virginia shouted, holding the newspaper in her hand and then slamming it down on the kitchen table.

"What?" Pat replied. "What's wrong?"

"This auto business. You and this Hedding fellow," Virginia said angrily.

"Don't you like the car business, honey?" Pat replied, half humorously to defuse whatever was ailing Virginia. He set his copy of the script on the countertop.

"No, it's not that," Virginia said. "How much money did you invest?"

"Oh, around five grand," Pat said. "Not much."

"Not much!" Virginia replied, crossing her arms.

"It's a good investment," Pat said. "I rode in that car. It's one of the best cars built today."

"It's not the car, Pat," Virginia retorted. "You didn't even discuss it with me."

"Well, I didn't think I had to," Pat said, walking toward her. Besides, I used some of the money I earned from selling the farm."

"The farm?" Virginia replied. "If I recall, that deed had my signature on it also, Mr. O'Brien."

"Look Virginia, I've made a lot of money in these short two years, I've visited with good financial advisors and this is the type of equity they've encouraged me to invest in, new industries on the rise. It's fine."

"I just think going forward, we need to discuss these things," Virginia said. "After all, we're married now and everything you do affects me."

"And vice-versa," Pat replied, a little put out.

The two exchanged a few additional but light volleys then agreed it would be best to go out for dinner. It took some of the sting off the whole argument and by the end of the night Pat's ability to not return anger in Virginia's direction, plus his conviction that the deal was good eased the tension between them. But Pat got a new insight into the make-up of Virginia. He reflected on her upbringing verses his as all couples do when fights occur. Were they from the same cloth? Was she going to be a wife that sought to dabble in all of his affairs? He wasn't sure. For now he was just glad things had calmed down and Virginia was smiling again over their final glass of wine.

Filming extended deep into July. Hurst announced that they would pause for two weeks after the final shooting on Friday, July 30th. He and the editing team would do "first cuts" and then more shooting would occur starting on Monday, August 16th.

"Good news," Pat thought. "I'm ready for a rest. This will give me time to visit Detroit and take Virginia on a little vacation. She needs some time away."

Hedding and Pat had talked about visiting Detroit and Bucyrus, Ohio where the Allen Car was made. Pat came home after the last day of shooting and announced to Virginia that they had two weeks off and he was finally able to give her that honeymoon trip she'd not had. "Of course, I do have to visit places for business," he said. Virginia was excited which eased Pat's worries about her demeanor over the past few weeks. The strain of making *Shadows of the West* had clearly put a strain on their relationship. It also did not help that Virginia, possessing not only a bit part but a hankering for the movies, worked only one day a week while Pat worked five and often six days per week.

Pat and Virginia had an enjoyable trip up through San Francisco where they spent one full day and saw only a few of Pat's old friends. No word had gotten back to Agnes that he was in town since Arlene's husband will ill and did not meet Pat and Virginia along with the others, who numbered around six. They took the train east and stopped in Wyoming, meeting the Hathaway clan. They were back in Chicago and then onto Cleveland and the Allen Factory in Ohio. Then they would go back to Detroit before heading southwest again through Oklahoma and eventually Southern California. It was a wonderful trip that relaxed them both and seemed to calm the tensions that had developed between them in recent weeks.

Shooting resumed Monday morning, August 16th at 5:00 a.m. The next two weeks of "fixes" seemed more grueling than the entire month of July which was more free-wheeling and broad. Now, after first stage edits, Hurst was crafting with a fine line. Takes got increasingly more repetitive and cast and crew were feeling the heat of the August sun as well. Then the roof caved in.

A strike by thirty-one of the Chinese and Korean extras who were playing the Japanese bit parts hit the production. It was rumored that people of Japanese descent in California who had caught wind of the nature of the film influenced their Asian brothers to walk off the set.

In addition, in early October T.F. Booker, an investor in the film, filed suit against Cinema Craft, Inc., charging that he was about to be defrauded of $100,000, representing one-third of the interest in the picture. He asked for an accounting of funds and that a receiver be appointed. Further, he stated that he had entered into a contract with Seymour Zeliff and his wife Caroline Clark, who was also working on the film, to collaborate in the preparation of the script for *Shadows of the West*.

There was more. Booker had provided Zeliff and Miss Clark with the "necessities of life" pending completion of the picture. He asserted that Zeliff and Clark had formed a corporation with the intention of evading paying him his one-third of the proceeds from the picture. Hurst was furious when he heard this. Zeliff had done this on his own. In order to eat, he essentially got Booker to provide him and his wife with income while he wrote the script, offering up profits from a picture he clearly did not own.

More trouble was besieging the project. On Monday, September 27th, an organized press conference held by Japanese-Americans living in Southern California announced an organized movement to prevent the showing of the picture on the grounds that it would intensify racial hatred and violate public policy.

As if that wasn't enough, Dr. Carl Patton, pastor of the First Congregational Church of Los Angeles, announced he planned to bring the matter to the attention of the Congressional Pastors' Union, at its next Monday night meeting and ask that the organization go on record as opposing exhibition of the picture.

Dr. Patton was quoted in the Los Angeles Times on September 28th that he had "little or no sympathy with the anti-Japanese sentiment and that his view is shared by a number of other ministers and church-going people in Los Angeles. He further stated that he believes the Congressional Pastors' group will recommend that the picture not be shown in Los Angeles."

"Oh, brother," Pat said as he read the times in the taxi on the way back home. He could not believe it. "No wonder Hurst had been asking all week if I had interest investing in the film. My God, what the hell have I gotten myself into?"

He could hardly make it up the short walk to the house in anticipation of all this becoming known to Virginia. When he walked in, she greeted him with a kiss. She didn't know, he thought.

"Honey, I told Hurst I'd invest $5,000 in the film," Pat said, clearly despondent. "Now I know why he asked. Look at this." He plopped the Times down next to her on the couch. It was open to the headline reading. "Anti-Jap Film has Hard Luck, Strike Delay Cinema Dram meant for Campaign, Now Lawsuit Blocks Release Showing Asian Peril, Propaganda Movement Afoot to Prevent Showing."

There was an anti-alien landowner's bill on the ballot in the November 2nd elections. The proposition would ban all Japanese from purchasing land in California. The American Legion and backers of the film intended on exhibiting the picture for a month prior to the vote. Clearly, that, too, was in jeopardy now.

Virginia broke down. She was unable to be comforted by Pat. She didn't scream at him or give him any overt indication he was to blame for the situation but clearly she was seeing her one big opportunity collapsing and she nearly passed out thinking of the rapid whirlwind that had brought her to Havana, rushed her into to marrying Pat so quickly and uprooted her. Pat could see on her face how overwhelmed she was.

"Don't worry, Virginia," Pat said. It will all work out.

"Oh, you foolish Irish optimist!" she screamed. "Don't you see how this is going to ruin us! Damn it, Pat. Must you always paint a pretty picture on everything?" She was delirious.

"But this is not the end of the world, Virginia. Get a hold of yourself."

No calamity, not even the potential loss of money or a tarnished image concerned Pat. He'd experienced the very bottom. This was not the bottom. "Steeling turnips out of a poor Belgian's garden in the middle of the night," he thought. "That's the bottom."

Virginia had never experience such a low point in life as Pat had.

Later in the evening, after no supper, Pat was downstairs making notes on the latest sales report form the Allen dealership. Sales were up but only slightly. He could hear Virginia talking on the phone upstairs. He could not make out what she was saying but he didn't care. "Let her ease herself off this cliff," he thought. "There's nothing I can do for her."

Upstairs with the door half ajar, Virginia was speaking softly into the phone.

"Sure, yes, as soon as possible," she said. "I can't do this alone. I'll go mad. Oh, please come as soon as you can. I fear I shall lose my mind."

"I'll be there as soon as I can, dear," said the voice on the other end. "Gwendolyn and I will pack our things and be on the next train to Los Angeles."

It was Sarah Ottis. She was coming to live with the O'Briens.

Chapter 54

Alexandria Hotel

Pat had a full day on Wednesday, September 29th. There were meetings nearly all day to deal with the issues facing the film. He called Virginia to tell her he would stay downtown that night.

"We're all going out for dinner with the Legion folks," he told Virginia. "It will be a long meeting. We're going to figure out a plan to gain support from the politicians before they get involved. If we can get them on our side, then we can deal with the others. I'll be home tomorrow at the end of the day, unless something comes up.

"Alright, Pat," Virginia replied. "Call me if there is a change."

Both knew that a coolingoff period was probably wise. They also knew that the next few days would be critical for the movie. All the hard work of the entire cast and crew would be wasted if outsiders prevented the film from showing. The American Legion took a risk, too, along with a handful of other investors which now included Pat. Hurst had talked to him again about investing. The film would needed additional funds for marketing now that unbudgeted legal costs were kicking in. Pat wrote out a check for $5,000 and gave it to Paul. "I hope we're not throwing money down a well," Pat told him. "Don't worry, Pat. We'll put all this to bed," Paul replied. "Keep your chin up."

First there was the matter of Zeliff and the suite against Cinema Craft by T.F. Booker. Hurst and his attorney had a private lunch with Booker on Thursday, September 30th. Hurst showed himself to be a keen negotiator.

"Look, Mr. Booker," Hurst said, "think about the situation logically. First of all, you now know that Zeliff signed that agreement totally on his own, without any knowledge on our part. I don't intend to show indifference to your situation sir but that was and still is your matter. You're a businessman. You know securing any loan made to anyone is your responsibility, Mr. Booker."

"I don't disagree with that Mr. Hurst," Booker replied. "But if the film is distributed and you make buckets of money, I'm still not guaranteed a dime from Zeliff if what you tell me is true."

"But that's no reason to sue him or us, at least not now," Hurst replied. Pat lost his poker face for a second, waiting to hear Paul's rationale for this statement.

"You mean to tell me 100,000 is no reason to sue?" Booker yelled, astonished at such commentary.

"I didn't say 'no reason to sue,' I said 'no reason to sue now,'" Hurst explained.

"How do you mean?" Booker asked.

"My only point is that if you sue us now, then the film never gets released and you have no chance of recouping your money. I'm in the same boat. I'm really angry at Mr. Zeliff, too, but I can't fire the man now. He wrote the film and if I was to fire him just because I was angry then the film doesn't get released and none of us earn a dime."

Booker looked squarely into Hurst's eyes, then flashed a look at Pat who had his poker face back on.

"All right," he said. "I won't take an action now. Just get this damn thing released so we can all get some money back."

"Exactly what I've been saying, Booker," Hurst replied.

The matter was put to rest for the time being. Though Booker added that he'd "like to shoot Zeliff in the back," Hurst was confident he'd put the T.F. Booker matter to rest for now.

"Ok Pat, fix number one is done," Hurst said to his admiring friend.

"What about the preachers?" Pat asked.

"That's where you come in, Mr. O'Brien," Paul replied.

"The hell you say!" Pat replied, a bit shocked.

"Look Pat," Hurst replied, "you're one of the few wholesome types to have associated with this picture. They might be convinced to back off if you talk to them."

It was arranged for Pat to attend the Monday Night meeting of the Congressional Pastors' Union. Paul contacted Dr. Patton and it was all arranged. The meeting was scheduled for 5:00 over dinner.

"You talk to the preachers, Pat and I'll get the meeting set up with the politicians the same night at 7:00. We'll knock them both out of the ring."

"I hope you're right," Pat replied.

"We've got to be right or we're all out to sea," Paul said.

Pat rode home feeling more upbeat. "We might beat this thing," he thought to himself. He was part owner of the film now with his cash contribution but that was not the issue that weighed on his mind. He did not want the film to fail and he felt strong about the threat of the Japanese. He'd witnessed it firsthand.

Pat's taxi pulled up in front of the house. He paid the driver and walked up to the house with a bit more zip in his step. "Yes," he said allowed. "Things are looking up."

He entered the house and a young woman was standing right inside the door, frozen at his sudden arrival. Pointing to her, Pat also froze, trying to remember where he'd seen that face before.

"You're…. that..," Pat tried to remember her name.

"Hi, Mr. O'Brien," the girl said. "I'm Gwendolyn. Do you remember me?"

"Ottis, Gwendolyn Ottis," Pat said nodding his head and speaking slowly. "What are you doing here?"

"We're visiting," replied the chipper young girl. Then in a questioning way she put her finger aside her cheekbone and said, "Or is it, living here? Visiting? Living?" She said, looking up at Pat with a big smile. "Well, either way, we're here."

"We?" Pat asked.

"Me and mother," Gwendolyn replied.

"I see," Pat said, still a little confused. "Where is your mother now?"

"She's in the kitchen stirring the pot of soup with Virginia," the girl replied.

Walking slowing past Gwendolyn and toward the kitchen Pat whispered, "I'll bet she is. I just bet she is." He entered the kitchen and there was Virginia setting the table and Sarah was hovering over the stove.

"Pat," Virginia exclaimed, somewhat startled. "You're home."

"Yes, I see we have guests," Pat replied, setting his newspaper on the counter.

"Yes, dear, I invited Sarah to visit us," Virginia replied.

"Hello, Sarah," Pat said to his new house guest.

"Hello, Pat," Sarah replied, still stirring at the stove with her back to him.

Pat looked at Virginia, raised his eyes brows and snapped his head in the direction of the dining room. He headed out of the kitchen. Virginia followed letting the door close behind her. Gwendolyn passed them in the opposite direction and entered the kitchen. She then turned and put her ear against the door to listen.

"What is that woman doing here?" Pat said in a whisper to his wife.

"I invited her to stay with us for a while," Virginia replied.

"A while, you asked her to stay a while?" Pat said, raising his whisper but still remaining inaudible to the kitchen.

"Look, Pat, you're gone all day working film business," she responded. "With the shoot over I'm not involved anymore. I've got no one to talk to all day. For God's sake, Pat, you can't expect me to me to stay locked up in this house all day while you're out wheeling and dealing with our friends and I'm stuck here."

"You don't have to be stuck anywhere," Pat replied. "You've got all the money you need. There's plenty you can do. Hurst and I are trying to save this film. I don't like it any more than you do. My God, Virginia, grow up. These are things that happen in business. I have an important part in saving our picture. I need to be in these meetings."

He paused, looking out the window. Then he continued in a calmer voice.

"How long is she going to be here?" Pat asked.

"I don't know", Virginia replied. "As long as I need her."

"Well, I don't need two wives. And I sure as hell don't need a jabbering teenage divorcee' in my house all day looking for something to do!"

"Pat, she'll be a big help to me," Virginia replied. "It's not like two wives. Think of it more like your mother-in-law, here to help."

Pat was not pleased with the arrangement but this comment did ease some of the ire from his mood. "Well, she doesn't have a mother," he thought. "And she's not the first bride to ask older women to visit and help out."

"Alright dear," Pat said in a softer tone. "But I won't have the women sticking her nose in our business. I hope she's taken the back room."

"She did," Virginia said, looking down. Changing the subject as he stepped toward the kitchen she added, "We've made soup. It's ready now."

On Monday the meeting with the ministers went pretty well. Pat was introduced by Dr. Patton as, "the world famous war hero we've all heard about." The preachers were thrilled to meet him and after introducing Pat, Patton said, "Lieutenant, I know we're here to talk about our concerns over the film, but I wonder if you might be so kind to talk a bit about your experiences. I know many of us have read your book and are thrilled to meet you in person."

It had been a while since Pat delivered his standard speech on the war. He'd done it so many times it was second nature to him and he could still muster up the suspense and excitement he'd created all over the country in 1918. As he spun his tale, the religious men in the room were as captivated as a bunch of barefoot kids in Kansas. The presentation went for forty-five minutes with questions and amazed reactions.

Pat commented about the film after his war presentation and simply stated, "I would ask for your understanding gentlemen and that you allow the film to be seen. It's a western and it's meant for entertainment. The plot does use the Japanese as a ploy but only to suggest that people be cautions and think seriously about what could happen, not what will happen. Keep in mind, this film is highly financed by veterans who used their own money. I don't think these fine men intended to create a stir among our citizens. They are simply making a statement that Americans should be cautious. It's just their opinion. You may have a different view but having the freedom to one's own opinion is exactly what these vets fought for in the first place. Is it not?"

The presentation worked. A few in the room cautioned the ministers to be fair and wait to see how the film was received. Pat had calmed their concern and appealed to their reason, fairness and patriotism. Paul Hurst had made the right move sending Pat to speak. No formal action was taken to block the film by the ministers.

Two hours later, Pat entered the Philharmonic Auditorium on 5th Street in Los Angeles. Hurst had secured the theatre for a preview of the film to be presented to elected officials in attendance. Like the ministers, they had constituencies that could impact their jobs. Anger the voters and one could easily be removed.

The theatre was the largest venue west of Chicago and had a design that was highly influenced by the Sullivan Auditorium Theatre in that city. Though one hundred politicians were in attendance, Hurst used the massive 950-seat theatre so as to minimize the perception of a large gathering. A few press were present.

Hurst was toward the end of his opening comment, checking his watch periodically as he spoke. Pat's overenthusiastic crowd at the minister's meeting had caused him to run late. When Pat walked in he saw Paul gesture to the back of the hall and heard him say, "Here he is now!"

The one hundred men rose to their feet in applause, welcoming the war hero into their presence. Paul had promised an appearance by Pat and these normally jaded officials, used to seeing Chaplin, Keaton, Valentino, Greta Garbo, and others, were thrilled to meet someone who'd proven himself in war. After all, most of these men were veterans and were certainly patriots. They were in a more precarious spot than the preachers. They needed to please constituents and at the same time not alienate veterans who supported the film.

There were many questions but in the end, Hurst and Pat had eased the tensions about the film. Following the meeting, the movie was shown. All seemed more caught up in the titillating drama and the fact that they were watching it with the actual hero of the picture in the room. It didn't hurt that the twinkling-eyed Hedda Nova also dropped in at the end. Few left concerned about the movie's strong inference. The entertaining elements of the film, at tribute to Hurst's fine work, overshadowed the message that Japanese were about to invade the west coast.

Sarah Ottis had decided that the best solution to Virginia's woes was to have parties. It began with a celebration over the film's announced release the next day. On October 3rd, the Los Angeles Times ran a feature story, complete with a photo of the heroine, announcing that the film would open on Saturday night.

"Propaganda photoplay to show at Auditorium"

"Despite many alleged attempts to block its production, and a whispering campaign against it, *Shadows of the West*, anti-Japanese film drama, which promises startling disclosures of Oriental conditions in California, will be shown at the Philharmonic Auditorium this week, it is announced.

"Aside from the serious significance of the drama, there is a delightful romance of the West to which an all-star cast gives interpretation. Scenically, *Shadows of the West* is said to be an artistic production."

"Hedda Nova, Yvette Mitchell and Virginia Dale are among the feminine stars of the cast. While Lieutenant Pat O'Brien, Ben Corbett and Seymour Zeliff take the leading male roles." Virginia had adopted the stage name, "Virginia Dale."

The initial reviews were in and at least from an artistic point of view, it was hailed. The movie was comprised of eight reels, a good sized movie in those days. Hurst introduced the film on opening night. Pat, too, offered welcoming remarks to a full house of supporters and distractors who all packed inside the Philharmonic on October 8th. The entire lead cast was also on hand.

Many of the ministers, politicians, veterans and, indeed, a few Japanese-Americans attended the first showing. Uncertain of what reaction the film would bring, the few Japanese that did attend sat in obscure upper level boxes and exited quickly once it concluded.

Virginia and Sarah planned an elaborate party at the Alexandria on October 15th for the cast and the crew. In addition, Sarah told Virginia to invite anyone she'd met in Hollywood and anyone she'd like to meet. On the invitation, the official host was listed as "Pat and Virginia O'Brien."

Fresh from the lavishness of John McGraw's Havana sensations, Sarah Ottis was not to be undone. She planned the whole event. The finest wine, the personal attention of Alexandria's head chef and an elaborate cake that may have cost more than the two-inch prime rib were mere minimums to the woman from Springfield, run amuck in Hollywood with an empty check book. Virginia's job was to finance the affair or, more truthfully, sign checks enabling Pat O'Brien to finance the event. Pat was told of the affair when Hurst thanked him for the invitation. He was upset but said nothing.

On Monday following the bash, Pat visited his friend Virgil Moore at his offices in the I.E. Hellman Building located on Main Street. Moore had become the one person in Los Angeles that Pat felt he could fully trust. Virgil suggested Pat talk to both his wife and Ottis and tell them that if money was to be spent, outside the ordinary day-to-day expenses of running a household, that Pat be told.

The next day, Pat paid a visit to Dr. Seager. He had a good session from his point of view but Seager felt he played the role of a sounding board. He had little to suggest to Pat regarding the management of his personal finances or the two women who seemed to be spending his money at will.

After the huge bash at the hotel, parties continued almost weekly and now they occurred in Pat's home. During the week, when Pat was out of the house, midday luncheons took place regularly as Sarah and Virginia built a very strong entourage of women from the movies, the military and the elite country club crowd. By the end of October, the two women had made a noticeable dent in Pat's bank account.

There were other ventures draining Pat of cash. The Allen auto business was struggling. Unknown to Pat, company officials back in Ohio had already discussed a strategy to close its retail operations around the country. Their strategy was to convert the automobile manufacturing facilities and focus on the very lucrative engine product. Their growth, as a result of huge sales to the military during war, convinced owners that profits could best be realized by limiting their efforts to motors. The problem for Allen was their network of dealers across the country holding large amounts of inventory had to be either sold or liquidated.

The Hedding-O'Brien Motor Car Company was one of six newly established dealerships created to consolidate inventory from other smaller dealers and sell off inventory. Being the sales manager for several large distributors in Minneapolis, C.A. Hedding was asked by Allen Car to find local investors for the new dealerships. If he found an investor Hedding would have no risk. If cars sold, he'd make money. If they didn't, Hedding's separate agreement with Allen Car assured he would be made whole. Pat would lose his entire investment should cars fail to sell. Hedding would get inventory equal to his investment. By November 1st, it was evident that the dealership was not succeeding.

Pat and Virgil went to dinner on Friday, November 5th.

"The woman is killing me, Virgil," Pat said to his old flying buddy.

"Your wife?" Virgil asked.

"Well, she's not helping. But I tell you it's that damned Ottis woman who's driving all this. Virginia is like a kid. She lets Sarah talk her into anything.

"Toss the woman out," Virgil said. "You've got no responsibility for this hag and her daughter. Just give her a deadline and tell her to get the hell out."

"It's not that easy, Virgil," Pat said.

"Wait a minute. Is this the same Pat O'Brien that faced down a German Guard behind enemy lines and stood firm in the presence of Cassocks in the middle of Siberia?" Virgil said, seriously confused by the hold Sarah Ottis had on his friend.

"It's not that, Virgil," Pat replied. "It's Virginia. She's so dependent on this woman. If I toss Ottis out, I've got a whole new set of issues facing me. The damn woman practically needs a nanny, Virgil."

The next morning Pat was up at 6:00 a.m. The women were still asleep. He'd had a restless night. The pressure of the film, the auto business going under, the draining of his resources and the unstable condition of his short marriage were starting to wear on him. He was standing in the kitchen looking out the window, drinking coffee as he often had in Clara's apartment. The weather was warm and birds could be heard hunting down their breakfast, tree to tree.

Two thousand miles away, Clara Clegg was washing a single dish, fork, knife, cup and saucer, having just finished her breakfast. It was 8:00 a.m. in Momence. Illinois was bracing for one of those early morning sleet storms that announce the onslaught of an impending winter for the Midwest. Clara had lived alone since the death of her husband and the departure of her son Jack for flight school in California following college. With the worsening condition of Lila, Margaret had been in Lowell for some time.

Pat noticed a large bird circling over his yard. He leaned in to watch it dive behind the neighbor's trees and soar up again in flight smoother than any plane he'd flown his entire life. The American bald eagle had one of the most recognizable flying patterns that Pat had first seen as a kid while exploring the marsh. It was the same flight Daniel had watched, hypnotized, as he rode into Momence following the Civil War. It made Pat think of home. He turned his head left and squinted to see the calendar hanging on the wall. Thanksgiving was on the 25th this year. He'd not forgotten to call home this time.

Pat missed the normalcy of Momence very much. Hollywood was full of vultures. Birds of opportunity that rarely attacked healthy prey but had a high interest in anything that was about to die. They were birds who would take advantage of a good natured war hero who, like the birds, loved to fly. A knock came at the door.

"Who could that be this early in the morning?" Pat wondered as he turned toward the front room.

"Hello," Pat said, opening the door.

"Hello, sir," responded a young man with a note.

"What do you want?" Pat asked.

"Here, sir," the lad said, handing Pat the note.

Pat opened the envelope and began to read the hand-written note inside. It read:

"Pat, sorry to bother you so early. Come downtown as soon as you can this morning. We've got issues with the film again."

It was signed by Paul Hurst.

"One moment, young man," Pat said as he reached for a nickel on the end table, handing it to the messenger.

Virginia was pouring a cup of coffee in the kitchen. She's heard the knock at the door.

"Who was that this time of the morning, honey?" Virginia asked.

"Just a messenger, Virginia. I need to go downtown this morning. Something's going on regarding the film."

"What is it?" Virginia asked.

"I don't know," Pat responded. "Paul just said to come right away."

Pat shaved, put on a tie and greeted the cab in front of his house at 6:45. He was in Hurst's office by 7:15.

When he arrived, Hickman was already there. He and Hurst were in full discussion. Zeliff was there too, script in hand. Hickman was making a lot of notes. Paul looked like he'd been up all night.

"Oh, hi Pat, come on in, sit down," Hurst said.

Pat took a seat near Hurst's desk while the three men continued their work. They were discussing scenes, lines, technical elements.

"That transition may take some additional shooting," Hickman said, shaking his head.

"No, Chuck," Paul said. "We just take page thirty-seven and blend it straight to page fifty."

"Oh, yes," Hickman replied. "I see that. That will work."

Also present was the person who was to be Paul's film editor. Hickman's number two man was confirming conversations between Hickman and the director Hurst. He'd listen and say, "We can do that. We can do that," while nodding his head.

The whole scene reminded Pat of the time he'd walked in on his father, uncle and grandfather cleaning a boatload of fish they'd caught up river, east of Momence. Pat was ten at the time. He never forgot the rapid and graceful art of the knife. Daniel, Uncle Jeff and Grandpa Hathaway could clean more fish in ten minutes than anyone he'd ever seen. The glistening blade dangerously sliced away scales from the smallmouth. The three men never watched their hands as they tore away the unnecessary parts of each fish. They then carved a master's cut. A filet was tossed in the bucket of water five paces away. They never missed but a few fish would land on the rim and Pat would walk over and tip it in with his foot.

"What gives, Paul?" he asked.

"They're shutting the film down," Paul responded, looking up for the first time.

"Who?" Pat asked.

"The government," Hurst said. "I was paid a visit last night and they handed me papers to cease and desist. What the local politicians and preachers couldn't shut down, the government just has."

Negotiations on sensitive issues between the United States and Japanese Governments were at a critical stage. American negotiators were attempting to shape an agreement with Japan that could perhaps give more assurance of post-war stability in the Pacific.

Newly elected President Warren G. Harding wanted assurances that the Empire of Japan understood that expansion in the Pacific meant an intrusion on U.S. interests. A number of Congressmen from the west coast, who were not at the advanced viewing in Los Angeles weeks before, had brought the film to the attention of the State Department. *Shadows of the West* was now bigger than a group of concerned ministers or the alderman from the City of Los Angeles made it out to be.

There was a meeting scheduled for 11:00 a.m. Paul reviewed the plan. Hickman and his editing staff would propose cuts in the movie, taking out the more sensitive parts that portrayed the Japanese so negatively. In the end, it would reduce the film from eight reels to five. Hurst would propose this to the State Department people at the meeting. He hoped the edits would allow the film to be shown.

They were joined at the meeting by a few American Legion folks who were there simply to observe the carnage. No one, not even the Legion, had a voice in this matter. The men from Washington pretty much told Hurst and his men that the film was done. Pat sank in his chair. Hurst proposed the new format with the edits that he and Hickman had made.

"We really don't care whether your film plays or not Mr. Hurst," said one of the officials.

"I know that," Hurst replied. "I'm just trying to salvage a way to recoup our money."

In the end the edits were agreed upon, pending a review of the final version by the officials. The meeting ended at 11:30. Hurst, Pat and the others went to lunch. They were all exhausted from the last twenty-four hours.

"You need to tell Virginia," Hurst said to Pat as they finished lunch.

"Yes, I will," Pat replied. "I'm not looking forward to it but I will."

Unfortunately for Virginia, nearly every significant part she had in the film had been cut by the demands of the government men. Her name would be removed from all credits.

Pat dreaded the ride home. All the way he rehearsed over and over in his mind how he would tell her. He hadn't felt this nervous since the night he struggled with Huyliger in Brussels, attempting to recover his passport. He decided to just state the situation candidly and be upfront without reservation. That was usually his way.

"Honey, I've got some bad news" Pat said to her when he got home. "Paul, Hickman, Zeliff and the others met with some men from the State Department today. They've ordered the film shut down immediately. It's too sensitive for Japanese-American relations according to the government. We had to comply but we saved something. Paul and Chuck proposed cuts to the intense anti-Japanese portions of the film. They accepted our proposal so a new version of the film will be released."

"My Lord," she said, sitting down on the couch in despair. "What in God's name is going to happen to me next?"

Virginia could only see the impact on her. It was then that Pat realized his wife of eleven months was a spoiled brat. He bit his tongue.

"There's more, Virginia," he said, withholding the "Honey" pet-name this time.
"More?" Virginia relied, now exasperated.

"Nearly all your parts existed in the Japanese scenes. They've all been cut," Pat said without emotion. "Your name is being pulled from the marquis."

She screamed in agony. Pat calmly walked over and placed his paperwork on the veranda. Sarah, hearing Virginia's yell, rushed into the living room.

"What is it dear?" she said, looking at Virginia and then at Pat who paid no attention to her entrance.

"They've pulled the film. The government says we can't show the Japanese parts. Nearly all my parts have been cut and they're cutting me from the bill."

"You bastard…"Sarah shouted in Pat's direction. He was not paying attention.

"No, Sarah," Virginia yelled, interrupting her.

Pat was removing his tie, indifferent to the machinations of his wife or the outrage of Sarah Ottis.

[761]

"It's not his fault," Virginia pleaded. "It's not his fault!"

"Or so you say, Virginia," Sarah scolded. Then looking at Pat and speaking to Virginia she added, "Do you think it's an accident that all the parts cut in the film just happen to be your scene? Well, you'll never convince me of that."

Pat ignored her again. He retired to the guest room, lay down, said a prayer and then fell fast asleep.

Gwendolyn, who had overheard her mother shouting at Pat, came out of the kitchen to help console Virginia. They decided to put on coats and take a walk in the neighborhood. Pat didn't even hear them leave. He was exhausted.

The day before Thanksgiving, Pat called his sister. He told her to wish everyone the best and that he missed them all and loved them very much. He then asked Clara another question.

"Clara, I need your help," Pat said.

"What is it, honey? Are you in trouble?" she asked.

"No, no, nothing like that," Pat replied.

"Are you sick?" she inquired.

"No. Now listen, my dear sister," Pat replied.

He explained how life had been the last two months. He reviewed his bad luck with the Auto business and the constant harassment regarding the film. Finally, he admitted something that Clara's intuition was suspecting.

"Things are not going well between me and Virginia," he said.

Clara had no knowledge of Sarah until Pat explained the situation. She was shocked that the woman had been there so long.

"She needs to move out," Clara stated. "Pat, that's just not normal. I don't care what you say regarding Virginia and her dependency on Sarah. There's no room for an unrelated second woman and her adult daughter in the same house with a married couple."

Pat was a bit embarrassed of his current situation. Clara always spoke with such clarity and Pat obviously needed clear thinking at this time.

It was agreed between them that Clara would come to California to help Pat.

"For all I know," Pat said, "I may be the one moving out. If I can't get the woman to leave, I may have to leave."

"You just stay put, sweetie," Clara replied. "I'll leave here in a week. That should get me to Los Angeles by December 6th. I'll wire you the details."

"Ok, sis," Pat said. "I love you."

"I love you, too, Pat," she replied. "Don't worry, I'll be there soon."

There was only one person living at 2314 North Commonwealth that knew how tough life could get. Only Pat had the make-up to persevere in the face of continuous setback. After determining that "nothing could get worse" it always did. Only he could get up one more time and march on. Virginia had barely experienced a setback her entire life, until now.

Unfortunately, that "one worse thing" arrived in the form a notice delivered to the house by Los Angeles County on Friday, November 26th, the day after Thanksgiving. Pat and his wife were being ordered out of the house in three days. Not only had Virginia and Sarah drained a good portion of his money on parties, clothes and the luxuries of life, they'd failed to pay any bills. The landlord had sent them an eviction notice.

Pat was furious. He went into a rage unlike any he'd ever contemplated. He had more anger in his heart than the time he was tormented by the surgeon in that German Field Hospital the day after being shot out of the sky over Belgium. He was so mad that he scared Sarah Ottis for the first time. He spoke his piece and stormed out of the house.

After walking two blocks he stopped at a local store and asked if he could use their phone. He called Virgil and asked if he'd meet with him. Virgil agreed. He then called a taxi and twenty minutes later he was sitting with his friend in his office.

Pat was pretty down. Virgil did everything he could to pick him up. It bothered him to see Pat so low. When you know someone as the most optimistic person in the world and you've seen them overcome life's obstacles time and time again, you count on them to always be there. Virgil and everyone that ever knew Pat had become accustomed to Pat always being there.

Virgil knew what he had to do. He had to support his friend. Virgil picked up the phone and called a man he knew that had various properties around Los Angeles. There was a house at 201 North Rampart. It was half the size of the Pat's current home but it was available and had plenty of room.

On Sunday, Pat, Virgil, a few members of the "Shadows" crew and the three women in Pat's house moved to the Rampart Street. Since both houses were furnished, the move was limited to personal belongings. Pat spent the first week of December working from Virgil's office, Hurst's office and the Alexandria. He'd leave early in the morning and arrive home just in time to sleep. The women came and went but no one made much contact all week.

On Sunday, December 6th, Clara arrived at the Los Angeles train station about noon. Pat got her a room near his home. They spent a lot of time together in between Pat's meetings. Pat slept at his house certain nights but slept on the couch at Clara's when it was convenient. Virgil met with Clara as well. The first week Clara was in town calmed Pat down. On Thursday, December 9th, he kept his appointment in the morning with Dr. Seager. Seager was pleased with Pat's relaxed demeanor.

Pat stopped at the house while on his way to pick up Clara for lunch. When he walked in, Virginia, Sarah and Gwedolyn were all making notes on a large piece of paper which seemed to contain a list of names.

"Good morning," Pat said to the three. They all answered the same simultaneously.

As Pat headed toward his bedroom, Sarah spoke up.

"Oh, Pat," she said, "I hope you're planning on being there a bit early on Monday. It would be nice for you to join us in welcoming our guests."

"What's Monday?" Pat asked.

Sarah turned quickly to Virginia.

"You didn't tell him?" she asked with astonishment.

"He hasn't been around," Virginia replied.

"Your party, Pat," Sarah said. "I'm sorry you weren't told. We're planning a thirtieth birthday party for you at the Alexandria."

Pat could feel the heat rushing to his head. He'd reached his limits with Sarah Ottis.

"Get the hell out!" he shouted at her, throwing his paperwork on the floor. "You blood sucking old hag. Get your things and get out of my house! I'll not have you around anymore, planning things behind my back and spending my money. Get out!"

Pat had moved close to her and had to do everything he could in his power not to strike the woman.

"But we..." Virginia began.

"Shut up, Virginia!" Pat yelled. "Stop placating this woman."

Gwedolyn made a quick exit to the back room. Pat turned again to Sarah.

"I'm giving you ten minutes to get out," Pat yelled, still in a rage. "No, make that five minutes. Take just what you can carry. Virginia will get your other things to you but you will leave now."

Sarah rose and scurried to the back room to grab her purse and a few overnight items. Gwendolyn sat huddled in the corner of the room. Her mother was so terrified she did not even acknowledge her daughter's presence in the room. In less than two minutes Sarah was out of the room and then Gwendolyn heard her mother scream in the living room while Pat yelled. Sarah had stopped on her way out to plead with Pat who then proceeded to grab the fireplace shovel from the rack nearby and raise it overhead. Sarah screamed and went running from the house.

Pat put the shovel back slowly and walked to the kitchen to draw a glass of water. Gwendolyn had entered the living room and was standing with Virginia looking out the window to watch Sarah's exit down the street. Pat took a full drink of water then feared that Sarah Ottis, capable of just about anything, might be more dangerous "on the loose."

He walked slowly into the living room.

"Go after her," he said quietly.

"What's that?" Virginia said, turning back to look at Pat.

"Go back and get her," Pat said. "I'll leave. She's got nowhere to go. She may do something foolish."

Pat went back to his room to get a few things and the two women went after Sarah to bring her back. As he passed the veranda, he noticed some mail in a pile addressed to him. He picked it up as he walked out of the house. He went down the street two blocks and hailed a cab. As the cab rolled toward downtown, Pat opened up the first envelope. It was a formal looking letter and he noticed the mark of England at the top. It was from the British consuliate in San Francisco. It confirmed the presentation of Pat's Military Cross in San Francisco for Saturday evening, December 18th at 7:00 p.m.

Pat had received notice of the award back in October. As was the practice of the King, he preferred for all such recognitions to be given strictly in person by a British official. It had taken some time to arrange for Pat's presentation. He was, of course, one of the few Americans to have ever received such an honor as a result of exceptional service to the British Crown.

Pat picked up his sister and they went to have lunch at a small place up the street from her apartment.

"I think I'll go up a few days early, perhaps meet some old friends," Pat told her after showing her the letter.

"It's really amazing, Pat," Clara said. "And it's just so incredible, is it not? Imagine what father would have thought were he here."

"Sometimes I don't believe the whole thing myself," Pat said.

They both started in on lunch and then Clara asked Pat if he planned to attend the "big affair" on Monday.

"I suppose," he said. "I need to make an appearance obviously since it's a birthday party for me."

"Just get through this and the holidays, then you can figure out what might be next," his sister advised.

"Sure, that makes sense," Pat replied. "This whole month has worn me out."

"I understand," Clara said.

They finished their lunch and then Clara took Pat shopping. She wanted him looking smart for his trip to San Francisco. They bought an entire wardrobe including suit, tie with matching kerchief, shirt, and shoes.

Pat woke up on Monday morning, December 13th at around 8:00 a.m. It was his birthday. He was now thirty years old. He'd decided to spend the night in his house since Sarah, Virginia and Gwendolyn had spent the night at the Alexandria so as to be up early that morning to begin organizing the party. Pat enjoyed being home alone for a change.

He spent the day with Clara, Virgil, Hurst and a few others from the film. They took Pat to lunch for his birthday. He enjoyed the time with his friends and Clara got to know Hurst and the others.

Pat and Clara arrived at the Alexandria around 7:00 that night. Pat had on his new clothes and Clara had purchased a new dress for the occasion. As they ascended up the stairs to the ballroom Clara asked her brother a question.

"After all you've been through with these women," she began, "Why do you think they've gone through all this for your birthday? I find it very odd."

"Not really," Pat replied. "You need to understand that the party is really for them, not for me. With Virginia out of the picture now and certainly out of the limelight, they needed my birthday as a draw to get the huge crowd you'll see here tonight. That's really all it is."

For the first time, Clara understood the natures of Virginia and her friend Sarah Ottis.

On Thursday evening, Pat was in Richmond visiting with old friends. He'd taken the early train north, spent some time visiting during the afternoon and then had dinner with a dozen or so that night. Naturally, he did not look up Agnes, nor had she heard about his visit. He thought of her a number of times during that day. He regretted that he was strapped with such a bad marriage in light of his wonderful time with Agnes MacMillan. When he left the Ivy that night he said goodbye to some and indicated to others who were going to attend the presentation that he'd see them the next night.

Pat entered his room at the Ivy in around 10:00 a.m. Before he fell asleep, he decided to head back to Los Angeles in the morning. Determined to get things right with Virginia one way or another he calculated he had plenty of time to talk to her on Friday and make it back for the award presentation Saturday night. Perhaps she'd even return to San Francisco for the presentation. Sarah would have to leave but he still felt that Virginia and he could work things out if they were left alone.

He arrived in Los Angeles on Friday at around 11:00 a.m. When he got to the house the women were not home. He read the paper. He called Virgil who was not in and then called Hurst to hear the latest about the film. Its status was still up in the air. Finally, he reached Virgil around 3:00 p.m.

"Can I come by?" Pat asked.

"Sure, come on over," Virgil replied.

Pat appeared a little disoriented when he first walked into Moore's office at about 5:00 p.m.

"I've been trying to find my wife," Pat said. "I came home from San Francisco to see if we could possibly reconcile all of our differences and agree to a date when Sarah would leave."

"That's a good idea," Virgil replied. "Getting rid of Sarah is clearly step one. You say you can't find her?"

"Right, I've waited at home for a few hours and there has been no sign of her yet," Pat replied.

"What about her hair dresser or doctor, anything like that?" Virgil asked.

"Well, she did say she had a doctor's appointment this week," Pat replied.

He gave Virgil the name of Virginia's doctor and Virgil was able to find his number. Pat called and the attendant indicated she was in with the doctor.

"Great," Pat said, hanging up the phone. "She's there."

Pat thanked Virgil and took a cab to the doctor's address. When he got there she was already gone. He called the house. Gwendolyn answered.

"Where did they go?" Pat asked.

"They were going to go to lunch, shop awhile and then Virginia had a doctor's appointment," said the young girl.

"Yeah, ok," Pat replied hurriedly. "I've got all that. What else?"

"I heard Virginia talking about also going to the bank," Gwendolyn said.

"What about the bank?" Pat asked.

"I don't know, they just said they were going to the bank to make some transfers, that's all. I haven't seen them for two days. They left with some other people, perhaps they had a luncheon today."

"Thanks, Gwendolyn," Pat said. He hung up the phone.

He was back in Virgil's office at 5:00

"Look, Virgil, these people are trying to rob me blind," Pat said in desperation.

"What people?" Virgil asked. "Are you talking about your wife and that woman?"

"Sure, them, could be others," Pat said, clearly in a panic. "There's just too much money gone. Two women can't spend that much. There's got to be others stealing from me. I'm beside myself trying to put a finger on the whole thing. But it's obvious. Something is terribly wrong here."

"Have you talked to Clara?" Virgil asked.

"Not yet. I didn't want to worry her until I knew something specific," Pat said.

"They're at the Alexandria according to the daughter," Pat said. "I guess as soon as I left town they hightailed it over there and haven't been home a day or two. What I need to do is get a room there and then talk to Virginia. If I can get her separated from the other goons we can talk and maybe I can save my marriage. It may be too late to recover all my money. I have a feeling that it's gone."

Pat called the hotel from Virgil's phone. He secured a room for the night.

Pat went to dinner with his sister first. They talked about things for a while. Pat told her all he knew. They talked about what might happen if he ended up divorcing Virginia or staying with her. They talked about Agnes and about home. Clara stressed to him that he was only thirty years old and that there was so much more ahead of him.

Pat felt a little better but was still anxious about the situation. He entered the hotel at about 9:00 p.m. and checked in. He'd asked to be put on the same floor as Virginia. As it turned out, he was placed two rooms down. He called their room continuously until midnight. He called down to the desk. They had no information on either of them. Pat checked the lobby and restaurants and generally walked the hotel off and on for two hours, thinking he may catch them sitting in a restaurant or at the bar or in a ballroom. There was nothing. He'd passed by the hotel desk so many times that at one point the hotel manager asked him, "Are you sure we can't help you, sir?"

Sometime after midnight, Pat attempted another call to Virginia's room. This time she was there. She and Sarah had returned from a night out.

"Can I see you?" Pat asked.

"I don't feel that well," Virginia replied. "I need to rest."

"I'd just like to see you, alone," Pat repeated. "I'd like to see if we can't talk through the situation. I think if we start over, just you and me, things will work out.

"I can't, Pat. I'm tired. I'm going to bed," she said before hanging up the phone.

About thirty minutes later, a room service boy was delivering two glass bottles of mineral water to room 619. He left the tray at the door and walked back to the other end of the hallway and passed room 612. As he did, he heard a loud gunshot from the room. It startled him but he knew very well it was a gun. He quickly ran to the elevator but at the last minute decided to take the stairs. He was thinking, perhaps erroneously, that any gunman that might try to escape quickly would take the elevator.

The young man flew down six flights of stairs to the main lobby. Out of breath, sweating and pale he rushed up to the front desk.

"A gun went off in room 612," he said to the night manager.

"Are you sure it was a gun?" the manager asked. "You're sure you didn't hear a champagne cork or some other sound?"

The boy looked his manager directly in the eye and said, "It was a gun."

The boy's face convinced the manager he was telling the truth. He looked terrified. Robert Kirk, the night manager, picked up the phone and dialed his security office. The night watchman picked up the phone on the other end.

"There's been a shooting on the 6th floor. Can you look into it?" Kirk asked.

"Of course," the security guard replied.

"Oh, and Truman, bring some additional people with you," Kirk said. "We don't have any information about how many people might be up there with guns."

Truman Epstein made a call to two other security guards and placed a phone call to his contact at the police headquarters down the street.

About fifteen minutes later, three security guards, two officers and the hotel manager made their way up the stairs to the 6th floor. They stood outside room 612, guns drawn, while the manager opened the door with his master key. The manager slowly opened the door.

Inside was Pat O'Brien, sitting in a chair with a bullet through his head.

He was dead.

Chapter 55

Last Train Home

Officer James Fergusson stepped into the room and looked around. He took a peek behind the door as hotel manager Robert Kirk stood still and held onto the doorknob. Fergusson then stepped carefully to the right and looked into the bathroom. There was no one. He turned, took a quick glance at Pat, then passed Kirk and exited the room.

"Alright, close the door," Fergusson said. "Kruger, you stay here and guard the door. No one goes in or out." Turning to the hotel manager he said, "Go ahead and lock it now. Is there a phone I can use downstairs?"

"Of course," Kirk replied. "Come with me."

"Oh, Mr. Kirk," Fergusson said, "I need you to stay with me continuously for the time being. I'll need you once the team arrives from downtown. Also, let's get some of your guards at the stairwells to keep anyone from coming up and also to keep anyone on the 6th floor from leaving."

Just then a door down the hall opened slightly and man stuck his head out to look. Fergusson took a few steps toward him. "It's alright, sir," he said. "Stay in your room until we announce an all clear."

That was enough for the old man. He quickly closed the door. Then behind Fergusson a few doors down another door opened. A woman was stepping toward the group tying off her gown.

"What is it?" she asked.

Fergusson stepped toward her holding up his hand. "Back in your room ma'am," he said. "You need to stay in your room just a little while longer."

The woman stopped and turned back but glanced over her shoulder as she returned to her room. It was Sarah.

In thirty minutes, the floor was full of police and two detectives from the Los Angeles Police department were upstairs entering Pat's room. Neither Detective Williams nor Captain Charles Moffati had note pads open. They inspected the scene without speaking to each other. Pat was slouched in the seat and shot through the head.

There was an army pistol "to his side," as would later be reported. Moffati inspected items on the dresser. No personal items, just a folded up newspaper that looked as though it had already been read. Then he saw a note, a handwritten note on blank paper. He picked it up and started reading.

"Only a coward would do what I am doing, but I guess I am one."

The note went on but Moffati didn't continue reading. He glanced at a few words then looked up at Detective Williams.

"Looks like a suicide note, detective," he said.

Williams walked over. "Yeah, looks like it here, too." He took the note from Moffati and started reading, then stopped and turned back to Moffati who had stepped towards Pat's body.

"Have they cleared the floor yet?" he asked.

"No, Officer Fergusson has the area secured," Moffati replied. "Everyone who was here when he arrived is still in their rooms."

"Good," Williams replied. "We're going to need a list of guests for the sixth floor. Tell the hotel manager."

"Will do," Moffati replied as he stepped into the hall and found Kirk and Fergusson who were standing at the ready. He spoke to them.

"Captain Moffati," he said to Kirk, extending his hand.

"Captain," Kirk said, nodding his head.

"Do we know who this man is?" Moffati asked.

"Yes, I do," Kirk replied. "I double checked the rooming list just to confirm but I knew who it was." He choked up a bit trying to make his last words audible.

"Sir?" Moffati said, soliciting an answer.

"He's been here many times," Kirk replied. "I spoke to him a number of times just this evening. He seemed to be looking for someone."

"I apologize, Mr. Kirk," Moffati said, interrupting Kirk's story. "But who is the man?"

"He's Lieutenant Pat O'Brien, the famous aviator, sir," Kirk replied.

"The O'Brien that escaped the Hun during the war?" Moffati asked.

"Yes, that's him," Kirk replied.

The captain pulled out a pad of paper from his back pocket and a pencil from inside his jacket.

"Look, Mr. Kirk," he advised. "You're going to have a ton of people trying to get into your hotel shortly. Press mostly. No doubt someone from your staff has already tipped a newspaper that there's been a shooting. But when word gets out who he is you'll have a deluge. I suggest you let us take it from here and you focus your efforts on controlling the activity in and around your hotel. I will speak to everyone housed on this floor before I let them leave. I will need someone from your staff up here right away so we can release the guests to another floor or out the hotel if they are departing. But I want that to occur in a controlled way. Last thing you need is twenty or more people floating around your lobby telling stories of what happened on the sixth floor."

"I agree," Kirk said. "I agree."

Kirk shook the Captain's hand and headed downstairs.

Moffati had ordered what was now four other officers to inspect rooms and talk to hotel guests. Did anyone see anything? Did they hear gunshots? What time did they hear the shots? Did they hear any running following the gun shots? Was there just one gunshot? Did anyone on the floor know the man?

Just then a young officer stepped up to Moffati who was giving orders to two other men.

"Sir," the young policemen said. "I've found some people that know the victim. Three women in a room down the hall."

"Ok, let's go," Moffati said.

He entered the large suite to see Sarah Ottis standing, talking to another officer. Gwendolyn was sitting off to the side looking rather scared and Virginia was lying prostrate on the bed in the other room. Moffati and the other officer took a statement from Ottis. They requested to see the lady in the other room.

"She's the wife," Sarah said. "She's overwhelmed by the news. Do you really need to speak to her?"

Moffati looked at Sarah with a stunned look on his face and said, "Yes, I need to talk to her and now." The charming Mrs. Ottis had even managed to irritate a cop in less than two minutes.

When they entered the room, Virginia was face down on the bed, obviously shaken. She had little to add to the officer's information but he did ask her one question.

"You're the wife, Mrs. O'Brien," Moffati said. "Did you stay in the room with your husband tonight or were you in this room?" It confused him.

"We had an argument and I came here to get away from him," Virginia said. "He checked in after us. He wanted to discuss our differences but I was too upset and told him "no." At that point she turned her face back into the pillow.

Moffati and his team spoke to everyone on the floor and the guests were released one by one.

"Alright, call Breese," Moffati said to his assistant. Breese was one of the funeral home operators in the area. They did a lot of homicide work for the department. It was approximately 6:00 a.m. at this point. The sun was up and by the looks of things in the main lobby of the hotel, the story was leaking out.

Pat O'Brien, famous aviator, shot himself in his hotel room at the Alexandria hotel. There were now fifteen squad cars outside the hotel and a half-dozen newspaper reporters all searching for answers. Someone had said "suicide" to a reporter and that story was being passed from one reporter to the next in the first hour before any statement was made by the police.

At 7:00 a.m., two police officers pulled up to Clara's apartment building. Sarah Ottis had said to one of the officers, "There's a sister. She's in town."

"Could you come with us, ma'am?" said the officer at the door after informing Clara that her brother was dead. "We'll need you to confirm his identity."

"Give me a few moments," Clara replied, displaying calm in front of the officer.

"We'll wait outside," replied the officer.

Clara went into that shocked phase where the body and the spirit blend as one and ached in a way that is only felt when grief is as severe as this was. Her crying was not audible. She just went through the motions of getting dressed, washing the night's sleep from her face and putting on a little makeup. All of this was done through heavy tears, gasps for breath and an overwhelming heaving of her chest as the body made attempts to purge the horror that possessed her grieving soul.

She was grateful she was there in Los Angeles. She was also horrified that she was there, where she would face the heavy burden of bringing her brother home for the last time. It was a morning of hell for Clara Clegg.

She exited her first floor apartment and road with the officers to the police station. On the way, she was able to relate as much information as she knew about Pat's whereabouts during the last twenty-four hours. She asked that she be taken somewhere to wire her brother Buck who was in San Francisco with her son Jack. Jack had just earned his wings, like his uncle had three years before. "He'll be so sad," Clara thought fighting back tears as she turned to look out the window of the squad car, biting her lower lip.

They arrived at the police station near the Alexandria to await word that the body had been transferred to the funeral home where Clara would make the necessary identification. The police officer had told Clara on the way that, "The last place you want to be ma'am is at the hotel. The best thing is to wait until they bring your brother to the funeral home. It will be more comfortable there."

Like anyone who loses a loved one, Clara wanted to "be where Pat is." It's a natural desire to want this, part of the letting go process and instinctive as any of life's driving emotions. But, as is also common, her mind would toss back and forth between the raw emotions that cascade inside and the fortunate order of the mind that brings reason in times of crisis.

She sat in a room at the police station awaiting word that she could wire her family. The face of every O'Brien, every Hathaway and every friend of her family back home washed through her mind as she sat feeling terribly alone knowing what she knew while others who loved Pat did not.

Back at the hotel, the hearse pulled away from loading area in the rear of the hotel with Pat's body. The press was crushing the hotel lobby now and one reporter for Associated Press had just phoned in the first story to his editor.

"Lieut. Pat O'Brien of the Royal Flying Corps, author of the famous war book, Outwitting the Hun, who made a remarkable escape from a German prison, committed suicide last night at the Alexandria by shooting himself in the forehead. The act followed an unsuccessful attempt to effect reconciliation with his wife, from whom he was separated."

Next came the entire context of the note left behind, purported to have been written by Pat.

"Only a coward would do what I am doing, but I guess I am one. With all my war record I am just like the rest of the people in this world – a little bit of clay. And to you, my sweet little wife, I go thinking of you. And my dear, sweet mother, my sisters and brothers. And may the just God that answered my prayers in those seventy-two days that I spent making my escape once more answer them."

"And bring trouble, sickness, disgrace and more bad luck than anyone else in this world has ever had, and curse forever that awful woman [two words here could not be recognized] that has broken up my home and taken you from me. The woman that stood in my home and gave [more words blurred]. She caused this life of mine that a few minutes ago was happy, to go on that sweet adventure of death. Please send what you find back to my dear mother in Momence, Ill."

"To the five armies I have been in, the birds, the animals I love so well, to my friends, to all the world of adventure – I say good-bye." Signed, "Pat O'Brien."

Margaret was served a telegram in Lowell at 11:00 a.m. Her grief and shock was overwhelming and she spent the first two hours lying on her bed in a state of disbelief and mourning as only a loving mother could. News spread through Momence as quickly as it had the day everyone heard of Pat's escape in 1917. Life stopped in Momence on December 18th, 1920.

Buck arrived in Los Angeles with Jack Clegg late that day, engulfed with grief over the news. Clara was never so glad to see her brother and Jack cried in Clara's arms for a full hour.

By noon Chicago time, the story had raced all over the country. Hundreds of newspapers in every city and town across the United States were preparing front page stories about the fallen hero. The suicide note was reprinted by nearly every newspaper in the country, having been first released by the Associated Press. The notion that Pat died of his own hand was pervasive in the early hours of his death.

The Los Angeles Times quoted Detective Williams as saying, "He immediately shot and killed himself." Their story also stated that Pat shot himself, "in the forehead." They also misreported his age as 29.

[777]

The New York Times, in their lead story, quoted the coroner's office and District Attorney as saying, "The aviator was shot through, the bullet passing out and piercing the wall near the ceiling. The angle at which the bullet struck the wall, officials say, is proof conclusive that no one but O'Brien himself could have fired the shot."

The Chicago Heights Star, like most newspapers in the country, led with the story, "Famous Lieutenant in World War Ends Life in Los Angeles Hotel".

"Suicide" was the word nearly all Americans uttered after asking their friends, "Did you hear Pat O'Brien died?"

The Momence Reporter stated, "While there is more or less mystery connected with the tragedy, the note found in his room seems to be the most reliable information which is as yet available." The local paper repeated the Associated Press story that Pat was "shot in the forehead."

But confusion and doubt persisted within the O'Brien family and among the citizens of Momence. Furthermore, no inquest was ordered by the Los Angeles police. When Clara asked the day after Pat died, the hotel doctor told her, "No inquest was needed."

Then the Oakland Tribune report quoted Captain Moffati as saying, "O'Brien was shot through the head, a revolver being found in his right hand." It hardly seemed plausible that a man sitting in a chair could kill himself with a revolver and still be gripping the gun in his hand. Moffati had first described the location of the gun as being "at his side." Never was there a mention of the gun being on the floor where most professionals who'd investigated such events felt it should be.

The most striking comment came from the undertaker who interned the body. In his official report, he indicated that the bullet did not enter through the forehead or the mouth but, in fact, the temple. He further stated some very significant information. There were "no powder burns near the wound." That would indicate that the bullet was not fired by Pat but had to have been shot by someone else.

Also, he felt that the gun must have been planted in Pat's hand after it was shot because there were "no powder burns on the victim's hand or fingers." In a direct contrast to official reports out of Los Angeles the undertaker made one closing comment.

"There is no possible way that Pat O'Brien shot himself," he said.

Virgil Moore and Clara organized a press conference demanding a second inquiry into Pat's death. A member of the British Secret Service was also present. He'd offered his professional assistance in the matter. Clara was most convincing in her statement. She contended that Pat did not commit suicide but was murdered. She intimated the group around Sarah Ottis though she never mentioned her by name. Virgil Moore was not as reserved.

"There have been some stories printed about this whole thing and all from those are not friendly to Pat. I only want to say a few things on his side. It's a short story about the coming of Mrs. Sarah Ottis. She had met Pat in Chicago years back. Mrs. Ottis liked a lot of wild parties and seemed to have a lot of influence over Mrs. O'Brien. I was out there many a night and it was always a wild time. Things got so bad that Pat asked Mrs. Ottis to get an apartment for herself, but she refused."

Virgil pointed how much money Pat had when he came to Los Angeles and how Pat was forced to move to a small home less than three weeks ago since Sarah and Virginia had spent so much.

"I saw Pat the day he died at 5:00 p.m. when he came to my office and said the gang had got all his money and had now stolen his wife. He said they were staying at the Alexandria and he was going over there to get a few things straightened. I didn't think anything very serious would happen and did not learn of the tragedy until I saw the headlines in the morning paper. I beat it to the hotel as fast as I could," Moore said. "Finally I got upstairs to the room where the women were. All three were in bed yet when I got there. They told me the same story they told you."

Buck had trouble with the three women, also. Thought he tried many times to speak with Virginia about Pat, his belongings, his money and his state of mind toward the end, Virginia wouldn't see him and never did.

The story as Virginia saw it was never told by her but by Sarah Ottis who claimed the young woman was too distraught and could not face the press. Sarah Ottis was literally the spokesperson for Virginia during the first few days following the incident. But then again, it was her name that was being bandied about in the press. If Pat had written that suicide note, it was he that pointed the finger directly at Sarah Ottis. She was not shy in defending her reputation.

Sarah Ottis spoke with reporters on day three in the lobby of the hotel.

"Mrs. O'Brien told me that she felt her husband had been mentally unbalanced and that he had planned to kill her had she responded to his telephonic request for her to meet him," Sarah said. Regarding the things said about her in the note left behind at the scene, Sarah responded, "I can only attribute his statements to his mental condition."

To the American public, the circumstances surrounding Pat's death were as unlikely as had been his escape from Germany. All over the country people made points about one unlikely scenario after another. How could a man who feared nothing in war be so intimidated by an opportunistic woman like Sarah? How could Pat O'Brien, the optimistic icon of the age suddenly fall to the lowest depths of despair? And where had all his money gone in such a short time?

Where indeed was Pat's money? Pat's brother Buck was astonished to find nothing of value anywhere. Even Pat's personal belongings, which Virgil had confirmed Pat had taken with him to the hotel that day, had been removed before detectives arrived.

Three days after Sarah Ottis attempted to restore her reputation, Virginia had gotten up enough nerve to talk to the press, all in the defense of Sarah. When she gave the interview she was still in the same room at the hotel. She spoke to reporters, lying on a cot.

"I was in mortal fear of Pat and I was afraid to live with him for fear he would take my life," she stated. "That is why I dreaded to go to his room when he telephoned that he wanted to talk to me. Mrs. Ottis was just a friend to us, more like a mother than anything else and I don't know what I would have done if she had not comforted me in my terrible distress. She was not to blame and I feel I must contradict this awful statement left by my husband."

Hardly a statement of remorse for her dead husband was expressed. She showed little genuine grief in the presence of reporters who seemed suspicious enough to keep speculation about Pat's death in the papers for weeks.

Then Virginia made an unusual statement of "fact" that countered what nearly everyone seemed to know was true. She reflected on her marriage with Pat saying, "Mr. O'Brien and I were married at Chicago. We came to Los Angeles in June and he and I both worked in motion pictures. As time went on he became subject to terrible fits of temper. He often struck me. Mrs. Ottis who had known both of us for several years came from Chicago two months ago to visit us."

Few women would forget the location of their wedding and "several years" hardly described the chance meeting Virginia had with Sarah one year previously. Few could picture Pat O'Brien as a wife beater.

Finally, Sarah, ever the name-dropper, had the last word. "I've known Lieutenant O'Brien for three years. I met him in Chicago while working with General Pershing's sister-in-law Mrs. Jessie Pershing at a war booth. I became very friendly with him and never had a quarrel with him. I accompanied Mrs. O'Brien to this hotel at her request. I always advised Mrs. O'Brien to return to her husband if she wanted to."

It was a classic diversion. To the reporters, nothing felt truthful about their statements. The problem was the only person that could counter such claims was lying in the morgue at Breese Brothers Funeral home twelve blocks away.

Finally, the people of Momence had their reasons for doubting the story of Sarah, Virginia and officials of the Los Angeles Police Department. In the story published on Christmas Eve, 1920 in the Momence Press Reporter, evidence was presented that showed Pat was likely killed. People hardly believed that Pat would take his life after going through all that he done to save it during his thrilling escape from the Germans.

There was speculation in town that he could have been murdered by the Chinese. During Pat's trip through China, he'd managed to get hold of two Buda images which he took from temples. It was common knowledge that two agents from Chicago followed him around all over the country in an effort to get them back. One agent was seen in Momence at the time the statues were being displayed in Burdick's Drug Store.

The other common thought Momence citizens had was that Pat's role and personal investment in *Shadows of the West* could have easily exposed him to Japanese agents seeking retaliation.

But in the end, the overwhelming body of evidence that cause people to doubt the "suicide theory" was simply the way Pat lived his life. One old-timer in Momence put it best when he said, "It just don't add up."

On Tuesday, December 23rd, Jack and Clara Clegg arrived in Momence on the train with Pat's body on board. Pat had taken his final train ride home, to the home he always loved.

Just as they'd done nearly three years before when Pat returned from the war, a good portion of Momence and Margaret O'Brien came out to the train station to welcome their favorite son home. There was no band, grand speeches or a street parade. As the casket was taken from the train, Margaret was overwhelmed and fell back against her son, Elmer. Christmas was in two days. It was be the saddest Christmas in the history of the O'Brien family. It was a sad Christmas for the entire town.

On Monday, December 27th, the funeral for Pat was held at the Methodist Church at 10:00 a.m. The Momence Press Reporter would describe the event in historical terms.

Even with all its infamous characters of the past, its hundreds of war vets going back one hundred years, and the good souls that held the old border town together in tough times, "Never before," began the front page story, "in the history of this city has such showers of sympathy, love and esteem been bestowed upon one of its citizens."

Though Pat O'Brien was mourned all over the world it was in this small city in northeast Illinois that felt the heaviest blow. Every man, woman and child in Momence knew Pat O'Brien, the newspaper said. And those that knew him since the days that he was a "bare-footed boy here," stood with "bowed heads and sad hearts while the final chapter in that life was brought to an end."

The funeral was so massive that even the City of Momence, which knew what big events were, needed more time. The ceremony itself started later than planned since Captain Brandt, who was leading representatives of the British and Canadian armies to town, arrived an hour late. It was eleven o'clock before the procession left home and headed toward the church. It was led by about fifty veterans, followed by seventy-five Masons. The hearse bearing the body was surrounded by active pallbearers, honorary pallbearers and the Knight Templar escort of honor. Next followed relatives and friends in automobiles. Nearly one-hundred cars trailed the casket.

Long before the procession arrived at the church, nearly every seat was taken with just enough reserved for family and those making the long walk north to the church. It was one of the largest gatherings in its history.

Mr. and Mrs. I.E. Hardy, Miss Mabel Sergeant and Will Ward provided the music of their quartet. Miss Sergeant sang "Face to Face" by Grant Colfax Tullarin, which was one of Pat's favorites. Reverend Wilson called upon Captain Brandt of the British Army, who paid tribute to Pat. The Reverend then followed with an inspirational sermon that comforted all those in attendance.

At the close of the service a very large number accompanied the remains to the cemetery north of town, up a long hill that overlooks Momence. The Masonic order conducted impressive services there and as the newspaper reported, "notwithstanding the bitter cold, none of the services were omitted and never were they more solemnly conducted." An extensive array of flowers adorned the house, church and grave from people all over the United States. It was a site few would forget.

Pallbearers were men with last names indigenous to Momence from its earliest days. They were all Shriners and most had been in attendance that night Pat first shared his most intimate feelings about war with men he trusted. F.M. Nichols, Mr. Burtt, Chuck Astle, Ed Green, C.L. Tabler, C.F. Schronts, Gaylord Hess and Mr. Basford were all there.

Elmer, Perry, Ivan and Clarence O'Brien were there. Buck had been detained in Los Angeles still handling matters and he missed his brother's funeral. Lila was too ill to attend from Lowell.

In the back of the church sat Al Fontaine. He couldn't bring himself to sit too close. He spent the whole time scanning the backs of everyone before him, looking at the casket only once. He counted the men, then the women, then the children. He named all those he recognized from behind. It was his way of distracting the deep ache that gripped his entire body. After Pat's family, he was probably more pained than anyone else present that day.

It was a sad, serene and melancholy scene in Momence that day. Like any town, it had its good and bad days, its model citizens and its bums. It had been a town built on optimism since the first settlers replaced the Pottawatomie, long removed by a long forgotten treaty.

But on this day, this sad and disappointing day, the little City of Momence took a body blow to its midsection. No matter how wonderful things would get in the future, the heart of Momence would always ache and feel a vulnerability to the new modern world that could reach in and grab one of their own, toss him to the ends of the earth and send him back to rest in an unmarked grave.

EPILOGUE

"Show me a hero and I'll write you a tragedy" - F. Scott Fitzgerald

It snowed for two days following the burial of Pat O'Brien, covering his final resting place with ten inches of soft, gentle snow. A nearly continuous caravan of cars, buggies and toboggans full of kids could be seen making the quarter-mile trip north up the hill to stop and just look at the grave site from the road. The death of Pat hung over the City of Momence for some time. Margaret spent many days staring out at the snow covered barren fields outside Lila's home in Lowell.

Buck came home two weeks after the funeral to see his family and pay his last respects to his brother. He'd spent time in Los Angeles talking to people, looking for Pat's belongings and his money. He did not find much, though he was successful on one count. Chief Lyle Pendergast of the Los Angeles Police department ordered a second inquiry into the circumstances surrounding Pat's death. The report came back unchanged: "Death by suicide."

In those days, the taking of one's own life was a human tragedy that people set in a private place. The pain and experience for loved ones was no different than it is today. But it was considered a very private affair, despite the many newspaper articles that appeared all over the country for weeks about Pat's demise. But in Momence, like in most small towns, it was something that folks agreed to "let be." Sympathy was the only feeling Momence felt for Margaret and the family. Intrigue is what stimulated the rest of the world to buy newspapers telling of his death.

On the first warm day of spring, Clara and Margaret made the trip up the hill for the first time since the funeral. They put fresh yellow flowers at the foot of Daniel O'Brien's marker. It was a sizeable stone, four feet in height, quite visible from the road. You could still tell where Pat had been buried, aside his father's stone. The ground still rose a bit and had not yet settled. It was, at the time, the only indication of Pat's burial site as the family had little money to place a marker on his grave. Clara planted a few flowers near Pat's grave, as well. It saddened her that soon the grass would grow and only a few would know that Pat was there.

Clara and her mother knelt, patting down the last bit of dirt around Pat's flowers. Clara speculated that perhaps, someday, the family could get a marker for Pat. Margaret said to her "for now, we'll just let it be." That phrase again. No marker was placed.

As it always does, life continued for the O'Briens after Pat. His brothers had children and they had children and the O'Brien name extended in time. Like all families, they continued to experience the joys and pains of life. Most could be found scattered throughout a day's drive of Momence.

Lila finally succumbed to her rheumatism in 1924. She'd never had children of her own but raised Elmer's child Marie after Elmer divorced. She died in her home in Lowell. The 1930 Census showed Clara, Ivan and Clarence all living in Momence. Clara lived alone. Margaret moved back to Momence following Lila's death. Elmer and his second wife Elizabeth continued to farm. Ivan was a shoe repairman in town, Clarence a painter. Brother Perry still lived and worked in Gary, Indiana, Buck in California.

On March 13th, 1925, The Air Force Association of Canada received a letter from Margaret. In it she asked about the "whereabouts of my son." At first the clerk reading the letter felt pity for whoever wrote the note. He, along with most Canadians, knew Pat's story as well. But he surmised that Margaret's intent was to locate Pat's records, not Pat himself. She'd gone on to ask if there might be any remaining benefits for her in lieu of Pat's service to the Crown. There were not.

Life did not get easier as the Great Depression approached. Indeed, by the fall of 1929, Margaret began to experience the common ailments of body and mind. Sometimes she would get confused about routine matters of living but generally stayed "sharp" in her late years.

Nine years had passed since Pat's death and Momence was again experiencing hard times. The boom years of the twenties had crashed in one day on October 29th, two months before Christmas. The O'Brien's experienced their ninth Christmas without Pat. Winter was again scattering a layer of protective snow over his grave. Many of the kids in the playground at Central School no longer knew who Pat O'Brien was. But teachers still told his story.

On January 4th, 1930, Margaret O'Brien received an unusual letter addressed to her son. It was a shock to receive such a note after all this time. It brought her back to earlier and happier times. The letter read as follows:

Nijmegen, Holland, December 21st

My Dear Mr. Pat O'Brien,

In the first place many thanks for your kind lines and your photo which you sent me once. Do you remember it? I must ask you to kindly excuse my tardy reply. Do you remember me? It is now about thirteen years ago since I met you near the Belgian frontier in the village of Maarheese, that night you stayed with us and the next day I accompanied you towards Cindhoven, there we said "goodbye."

Afterwards I received your letter in which you told me your vicissitudes.

Where have you been? Some month ago I read in the paper that a Mr. Pat O'Brien set a new record with a flying machine. Are you this Mr. O'Brien? In that case, my cordial congratulations on your success.

You should do me a great please to write me once. Meanwhile, I have become religious and I am doing very well.

Yours Affectionately,

Brother Venansius
Anson C. uns
Graafrcheweg 274
Nijmegen, Holland

Margaret folded the letter in half and placed it back in the envelope. What winter's light was drifting into her kitchen window was blurred by the tears in her eyes. She smiled, somehow comforted that a religious man might be thinking of her son on this day. There were many days filled with such strong memories. To think that someone out there did not know Pat was gone was sad to her but also uplifting.

Another summer arrived. Margaret and Clara kept yellow flowers in bloom at the foot of Daniel's stone and just to the right smaller patch where Pat was buried.

Margaret Hathaway O'Brien passed away on October 8th, 1930, no doubt from what was considered "old age" back then. She was fifty-five. She spent nearly all of her days, following the death of her son, volunteering for and attending the Methodist Church. It was the center of her late life.

On November 5th, 1943, Clara O'Brien Clegg died penniless in the Soldier's Widows' Home in Wilmington, Illinois. It was home to aging widows, mothers and daughters of the veterans of the Mexican and Civil Wars. Daniel O'Brien's service in the war earned her rights to their care. At the time of Clara's passing, residents included 55 Civil War daughters, 15 Civil War widows, 13 Spanish-American War widows, 10 World War I mothers and 2 World War I widows, and a waiting list of 63.

A year and six months after Clara's death, thousands of Allied troops stormed the beaches of Normandy, France on June 6th, 1944. They were about to complete the job left unfinished by the soldiers of Pat's day.

On July 15th, a young Sergeant named Rex Rowe from Momence arrived in France with the 112th infantry. He battled in France, the Ardennes and the Rhineland. It was in the Rhineland where he was captured by the Germans and spent 193 days in prison. Freed by the Russian Army on January 30th, 1945, Rex walked across Poland to seek passage on a U.S. troop ship. He was without identification and was refused permission to board. A British ship granted him permission at Odessa, Russia where he was shipped to Naples, Italy. Here he boarded a U.S. vessel on March 30th, arriving in Boston on April 9th. He then took a train to Fort Sheridan near Chicago. Unable to find further transport, he hitchhiked the final seventy-five miles to Momence, Illinois.

Rex spent the rest of his days in Momence and was elected mayor many times over. As a boy, he'd always heard the stories of Pat O'Brien but Rex's long walk across Europe gave him an even greater appreciation for the achievements of Pat.

As Rex drew closer to the end of his life, he was determined to see through one final accomplishment. It had been eighty-six years since Pat was buried north of Momence, Still, no marker adorned his grave. Neither the family, nor Rex nor anyone else could find a record of Pat's service in the United States Army. There was evidence of his service to Britain in the Royal Flying Corp but no proof he'd served in the Army Signal Corp. Rex was convinced that Pat had served under the U.S. Flag and he wanted Pat's grave to be marked as a United States Veteran. He knew without proof, a U.S. military marker would not be permitted.

Rex solicited the help of friend Marcia Tedford who was an active citizen of Momence. The two pursued official military records at the archives located in St. Louis, Missouri. Weeks later, Rex received a reply from the National Personnel Records Center, St. Louis, Missouri. It stated that all records of U.S. Signal Corps enlistees for 1916, and other years, had been destroyed in a fire in 1973.

In fact, all records of personnel discharged November 1, 1912 to January 1, 1960 were lost. No duplicate records or micro-film existed. Pat's service under the U.S. flag could not be found, an additional irony added to his mysterious end. The U.S. Army would not approve an official United States Army brass marker for Lt. Alva F. "Pat" O'Brien.

The Momence group decided to reference Pat's British military service on the marker. Ten anonymous donations were given to Rex Rowe to affect the purchase of a military bronze marker. Much to Rex Rowe's disappointment, the marker would only reference Pat's service to Britain. It was ordered and word spread among a close-knit group of friends and family that a marker would finally be placed. It would read as follows:

Lt. Patrick O'Brien
December 13, 1890 - December 17, 1920
Royal Air Force
WWI Pow

The marker arrived in the summer of 2007. With so little evidence available at the time, Pat's grave marker created more questions than final answers. Pat was never called Patrick. "Pat" was his nickname. The British, however, had referred to him as "Patrick" in some of their official documents. Furthermore, Pat actually died around 3:00 a.m. early on the morning of December 18, not the 17th. Finally, Pat served in the Royal Flying Corps which was merged with the Royal Naval Air Service on April 1, 1918 forming the Royal Air Force ten days after Pat resigned his commission as 2nd Lieutenant of the Royal Flying Corp. Fitting that the mystery of Pat O'Brien would continue on his grave marker. But at the time locals knew much less about these facts until this book.

Evidence of Pat's service under the U.S. Flag did eventually come forward in the form of a voter registration list from San Diego found online while doing the research for this book. About halfway down the list, appearing with dozens of other soldiers of the Army Signal Corps at North Island was the name Pat O'Brien. It was proof enough to this author and my research partner, Marcia Tedford that he'd served. It was also confirmation that he was present at the very beginnings of U.S. Military Aviation. But in 2007, this evidence was not known.

Once the marker arrived, Momence citizens came forward. Bill Cotter, the local funeral director who was a veteran and the founder of the Momence Honor Guard, suggested a memorial dedication service be held. His high school honor guard was comprised of selected students who performed various memorial events. Cotter's knowledge of ceremonial protocol assured Pat would be accorded proper military rites.

A bag piper was secured to perform. Dr. Brian Olofsson, an amateur pilot, would fly his vintage bi-plane over the ceremony at the appropriate time. The Honorable Andrew Seaton, consul-general from the British Consulate in Chicago, would present the British flag to the surviving family members of O'Brien. And the Momence VFW Post 7535 agreed to host a reception at their hall following the ceremony.

On Tuesday, July 31st, 2007, a group of Momence residents and members of the O'Brien family gathered to commemorate the life, service and death of Alva F. "Pat" O'Brien. There were over one-hundred people in attendance. The program opened with a prayer delivered by Reverend Michael Frazier of the Calvary Baptist Church. Mary Bock of Steger, Illinois performed "Amazing Grace" on her bag pipe following the prayer.

Bill Cotter then made some introductory remarks, welcomed those in attendance and highlighted the significance of the life of Pat O'Brien. The British Flag was presented by the honorable Andrew Seaton, Consul-General of the British Consulate in Chicago, to Jack O'Brien oldest living member of the O'Brien family at the time. Military Rites were then accorded by the Momence Honor Guard.

As the sound of rifle fire drifted away it lingered still in the silence of everyone present. In the distance could be heard a vintage aircraft, one of the many that Pat loved so much, that grew louder and closer before fading again to be heard no more. Rex Row had seen it through and now the young warrior from the Great War he admired so much had finally been properly laid to rest.

This author was not present that day. But had I been, I know I would have turned my head to the south and gazed down the hill towards town, to the southeast where the marsh still lies. I would have looked for that soaring eagle with the hope that I'd see it for myself. But my guess is the sky would be clear of that majestic bird, never to return again.

And the likelihood we'd ever see one like him again would be rare indeed.

Rex Rowe

December 30, 1921 – June 17, 2009

Marcia Tedford & Kevin McNulty, Sr.

In 2007, two events took place that laid the groundwork for the project, *Lt. Pat O'Brian*. A handful of people from Momence, Illinois, inspired by the strong leadership of former Mayor Rex Rowe, decided to do the right thing.

Each year, a smaller number of Momence citizens knew the story of Pat O'Brien. No one, in fact, knew the whole story. Not even Pat's relatives. As a result of these loyal few and members of the O'Brien family, a proper marker and ceremony was realized through the efforts of these patriots. As has been detailed in this book, there were key people in town that made it happen. None more so than Marcia who saw that things got done.

Also, that year, after years writing for business and serving as publisher got two business magazines, I decided to try my hand at writing a book. It was a simple picture book about the history of my home town, Momence. It put me back in touch with the town I left forty-five years ago.

Our partnership to find Pat was a labor of love. Six years and thousands of emails later, Lt. Pat O'Brien's story can now be told.

Besides, anyone that knows Marcia, knows you just don't say "no" Marcia Tedford!

OTHER BOOKS BY KEVIN MCNULTY, SR.

"Around Momence" by Kevin McNulty, Sr.
Copyright © 2007 Kevin McNulty, Sr.
Published by Arcadia Publishing
Charleston SC, Chicago IL, Portsmouth NH, San Francisco, CA
ISBN   978-07358-57289

"Outwitting the Hun" by Lt. Pat O'Brien.
Originally written and published in 1918 ~ Republished 2013
Copyright © 2013 KMC PUBLISHING COMPANY
Reprint includes added details and notes written by Kevin McNulty, Sr. that
Pat was unable to write in the first print during the war years.
ISBN- 978-0-9897965-0-7

"The Barns of Kankakee County" by Kevin McNulty, Sr.
Copyright © 2014 KMC PUBLISHING COMPANY
All Photography is property of Kevin McNulty, Sr.
ISBN-10: 0989796515
ISBN-13: 978-0-9897965-1-4

"Finding Pat O'Brien" by Kevin McNulty, Sr.
Copyright © 2014 KMC PUBLISHING COMPANY
All rights reserved.
ISBN-10: 0989796523
ISBN-13: 978-0-9897965-2
(3rd Edition, January 2015)

Made in the USA
Middletown, DE
23 December 2014